THE GEORGE FISHER BAKER
NON-RESIDENT LECTURESHIP IN CHEMISTRY
AT CORNELL UNIVERSITY

THE NATURE
OF THE CHEMICAL BOND

BY

LINUS PAULING

THE GEORGE FISHER BAKER
NON-RESIDENT LECTURESHIP IN CHEMISTRY
AT CORNELL UNIVERSITY

THE NATURE
OF THE CHEMICAL BOND

AND THE STRUCTURE OF MOLECULES
AND CRYSTALS

An Introduction to Modern Structural Chemistry

BY

LINUS PAULING

*Professor of Chemistry in the
California Institute of Technology*

SECOND EDITION

ITHACA, NEW YORK
CORNELL UNIVERSITY PRESS
LONDON: HUMPHREY MILFORD
OXFORD UNIVERSITY PRESS
1948

PRINTED IN THE UNITED STATES OF AMERICA

THE COLLEGIATE PRESS, MENASHA, WISCONSIN

TO

GILBERT NEWTON LEWIS

433

PREFACE TO THE SECOND EDITION

The progress made in the field of modern structural chemistry during the past year has consisted in the main in the determination of the structures of a number of especially interesting molecules and crystals. I have been glad to have the opportunity provided by the exhaustion of the first edition of this book to revise it by the inclusion of references to these researches and of discussion of the new structures. A few corrections have been made, and the argument in some places has been expanded in an effort to improve the clarity of its presentation. Two new sections have been added, dealing with restricted rotation about single bonds (Sec. 14d) and the conditions for equivalence or non-equivalence of bonds (Sec. 22a).

I have again to thank many friends for their advice and assistance; I am grateful especially for their aid to Dr. E. W. Hughes, Research Fellow in Chemistry in the California Institute of Technology, and to Mr. W. S. Schaefer of the Cornell University Press.

LINUS PAULING.

Pasadena, California
February 28, 1940.

N

For a long time I have been planning to write a book on the structure of molecules and crystals and the nature of the chemical bond. With the development of the theory of quantum mechanics and its application to chemical problems it became evident that a decision would have to be made regarding the extent to which the mathematical methods of the theory would be incorporated in this book. I formed the opinion that, even though much of the recent progress in structural chemistry has been due to quantum mechanics, it should be possible to describe the new developments in a thorough-going and satisfactory manner without the use of advanced mathematics. A small part only of the body of contributions of quantum mechanics to chemistry has been purely quantum-mechanical in character; only in a few cases, for example, have results of direct chemical interest been obtained by the accurate solution of the Schrödinger wave equation. The advances which have been made have been in the main the result of essentially chemical arguments—the assumption of a simple postulate, which is then tested by empirical comparison with available chemical information, and used in the prediction of new phenomena. The principal contribution of quantum mechanics to chemistry has been the suggestion of new ideas, such as the resonance of molecules among several electronic structures with an accompanying increase in stability.

The ideas involved in modern structural chemistry are no more difficult and require for their understanding no more, or little more, mathematical preparation than the familiar concepts of chemistry. Some of them may seem strange at first, but with practice there can be developed an extended chemical intuition which permits the new concepts to be used just as confidently as the older ones of the valence bond, the tetrahedral carbon atom, etc., which form the basis of classical structural chemistry.

The foundation of the modern theory of valence was laid by G. N. Lewis in his 1916 paper.[1] The theory was extended in his

[1] G. N. Lewis, *J.A.C.S.* **38**, 762 (1916).

book "Valence and the Structure of Atoms and Molecules" (Chemical Catalog Co., New York, 1923), in N. V. Sidgwick's volumes "The Electronic Theory of Valency" (Oxford University Press, 1927) and "The Covalent Link in Chemistry" (Cornell University Press, 1933), and in numerous publications by Irving Langmuir, W. M. Latimer, W. H. Rodebush, M. L. Huggins, W. A. Noyes, A. Lapworth, Robert Robinson, C. K. Ingold, and many other investigators. The detailed discussion in the following chapters is based to a large extent on seven papers with the general title "The Nature of the Chemical Bond," published between 1931 and 1933 in the *Journal of the American Chemical Society* and the *Journal of Chemical Physics*, and on other papers by my collaborators and myself.

I have felt that in writing on this complex subject my primary duty should be to present the theory of the chemical bond (from my point of view) in as straightforward a way as possible, relegating the historical development of the subject to a secondary place. Many references are included to early work in this field; the papers on the electronic theory of valence published during the last twenty years are so numerous, however, and often represent such small differences of opinion as to make the discussion of all of them unnecessary and even undesirable.

The opportunity and incentive to prepare this work for publication have been provided by my tenure of the George Fisher Baker Non-resident Professorship of Chemistry at Cornell University during the Fall Semester of 1937–38. I wish to express my sincere thanks to Professor Papish and his colleagues in the Department of Chemistry of the University for their kindness in extending to me the invitation to present the Baker Lectures and in making available the facilities of the Baker Laboratory of Chemistry during my period of residence in Ithaca. I am grateful for advice and assistance in the preparation of the manuscript to many friends, including Dr. E. W. Hughes, Dr. C. D. Coryell, Dr. H. D. Springall, Dr. G. Schwarzenbach, Dr. J. H. Sturdivant, Dr. G. C. Hampson, Mr. P. A. Shaffer, Jr., Dr. E. R. Buchman, Dr. S. Weinbaum, Dr. Fred Stitt, Dr. J. Sherman, and Dr. F. J. Ewing. My wife joins me in expressing our appreciation to the young men of the Telluride House at Cornell University, who were our hosts during our stay in Ithaca.

LINUS PAULING.

Gates and Crellin Laboratories of Chemistry,
California Institute of Technology, Pasadena, California.
June, 1938.

CONTENTS

xi

CHAPTER III

THE DIRECTED COVALENT BOND. BOND STRENGTHS
AND BOND ANGLES. THE MAGNETIC CRITERION
FOR BOND TYPE

CHAPTER IV

THE RESONANCE OF MOLECULES AMONG SEVERAL
VALENCE-BOND STRUCTURES

CHAPTER VIII

THE ONE-ELECTRON BOND AND THE THREE-ELECTRON BOND

CHAPTER IX

THE HYDROGEN BOND

CHAPTER X

THE SIZES OF IONS AND THE STRUCTURE OF IONIC CRYSTALS

CHAPTER XI

THE METALLIC BOND

Chapter XII

A SUMMARIZING DISCUSSION OF RESONANCE AND ITS SIGNIFICANCE FOR CHEMISTRY

THE NATURE OF THE CHEMICAL BOND

CHAPTER I

RESONANCE AND THE CHEMICAL BOND

1. THE DEVELOPMENT OF THE THEORY OF VALENCE

The study of the structure of molecules was originally carried on by chemists using methods of investigation which were essentially chemical in nature, relating to the chemical composition of substances, the existence of isomers, the nature of the chemical reactions in which a substance takes part, and so on. From the consideration of facts of this nature Frankland, Kekulé, and Couper were led nearly a century ago to formulate the theory of valence and to write the first structural formulas for molecules, van't Hoff and le Bel were led to bring classical organic stereochemistry into its final form by their brilliant postulate of the tetrahedral orientation of the four valences of the carbon atom, and Werner was led to his development of the theory of the stereochemistry of complex inorganic substances.

Modern structural chemistry differs from classical structural chemistry with respect to the detailed picture of molecules and crystals which it presents. By various physical methods, including the study of the structure of crystals by the diffraction of x-rays and of gas molecules by the diffraction of electron waves, the measurement of electric and magnetic dipole moments, the interpretation of band spectra and Raman spectra, and the determination of entropy values, a great amount of information has been obtained regarding the atomic configurations of molecules and crystals and even their electronic structures; a discussion of valence and the chemical bond now must take into account this information as well as the facts of chemistry.

In the nineteenth century the valence bond was represented by a line drawn between the symbols of two chemical elements,

1

which expressed in a concise way many chemical facts, but which had only qualitative significance with regard to molecular structure. The nature of the bond was completely unknown. Following the discovery of the electron numerous attempts were made to develop an electronic theory of the chemical bond. These culminated in the work of G. N. Lewis, who in his 1916 paper,[1] which forms the basis of the modern electronic theory of valence, discussed not only the formation of ions by the completion of stable shells of electrons[2] but also the formation of a chemical bond, now called the covalent bond, by the sharing of two electrons between two atoms.[3] Lewis further emphasized the importance of the phenomena of the pairing of unshared as well as of shared electrons and of the stability of the group of eight electrons (shared or unshared) about the lighter atoms. These ideas were then further developed by many investigators; the work of Irving Langmuir[4] was especially valuable in showing the great extent to which the facts of chemistry could be coordinated and clarified by the application of the new ideas. Many of the features of the detailed theory which is discussed in this book were suggested in the papers of Langmuir and others written in the decade following 1916, or in the book "Valence and the Structure of Atoms and Molecules" written by Lewis in 1923.

All of these early studies, however, contained, in addition to suggestions which have since been incorporated into the present theory, many others which have been discarded. The refinement of the electronic theory of valence into its present form has been due almost entirely to the development of the theory of quantum mechanics, which has not only provided a method for the calculation of the properties of simple molecules, leading to the complete elucidation of the phenomena involved in the formation of a covalent bond between two atoms and dispersing the veil of mystery which had shrouded the bond during the decades since its existence was first assumed, but has also introduced into chemical theory a new concept, that of *resonance*, which, if not

[1] G. N. Lewis, "The Atom and the Molecule," *J.A.C.S.* **38**, 762 (1916).

[2] This was treated independently at about the same time by W. Kossel, *Ann. d. Phys.* **49**, 229 (1916).

[3] Earlier attempts to develop a theory of valence involving the sharing of electrons by atoms were made by W. Ramsay, J. J. Thomson, J. Stark, A. L. Parson, and others.

[4] I. Langmuir, *J.A.C.S.* **41**, 868, 1543 (1919).

entirely unanticipated in its applications to chemistry, nevertheless had not before been clearly recognized and understood.

In the following sections of this chapter there are given, after
an introductory survey of the types of chemical bonds, discussions of the concept of resonance, the nature of the one-electron
bond and the electron-pair bond, and the formal rules given by
quantum mechanics for the formation of covalent bonds.

2. TYPES OF CHEMICAL BONDS

It is convenient to consider three general extreme types of
chemical bonds: *electrostatic bonds, covalent bonds,* and *metallic
bonds.* This classification is not a rigorous one; for although the
bonds of each extreme type have well-defined properties, the
transition from one extreme type to another may be gradual,
permitting the existence of bonds of intermediate type (see Chap.
II and later chapters).

2a. The Chemical Bond Defined.—We shall say that there is a
chemical bond between two atoms or groups of atoms in case
that the forces acting between them are such as to lead to the
formation of an aggregate with sufficient stability to make it convenient for the chemist to consider it as an independent molecular
species.

With this definition we accept in the category of chemical
bonds not only the directed valence bond of the organic chemist
but also, for example, the bonds between sodium cations and
chlorine anions in the sodium chloride crystal, those between the
aluminum ion and the six surrounding water molecules in the
hydrated aluminum ion in solution or in crystals, and even the
weak bond which holds together the two O_2 molecules in O_4.
In general we do not consider the weak van der Waals forces
between molecules as leading to chemical bond formation; but in
exceptional cases, such as that of the O_4 molecule mentioned
above, it may happen that these forces are strong enough to make
it convenient to describe the corresponding intermolecular interaction as bond formation.

2b. The Ionic Bond and Other Electrostatic Bonds.—In case
that there can be assigned to each of two atoms or groups of
atoms a definite electronic structure, essentially independent of
the presence of the other atom or group, such that electrostatic
interactions are set up which lead to strong attraction and the

formation of a chemical bond, we say that the bond is an *electrostatic bond*.

The most important of these is the *ionic bond*, resulting from the Coulomb attraction of the excess electric charges of oppositely charged ions. The atoms of metallic elements lose their outer electrons easily, whereas those of non-metallic elements tend to add additional electrons; in this way stable cations and anions

Fig. 2-1.—The atomic arrangement in the sodium chloride crystal. (This figure is from the paper by W. Barlow, *Z. Krist.* 29, 433 (1898), referred to in Section 47.)

may be formed, which may retain their electronic structures essentially as they approach one another to form a stable molecule or crystal. In the sodium chloride crystal, with the atomic arrangement shown in Figure 2-1, there exist no discrete NaCl molecules. The crystal is instead composed of sodium cations, Na^+, and chlorine anions, Cl^-, each of which is strongly attracted to and held by the six oppositely-charged ions which surround it octahedrally. We describe the interactions in this crystal by saying that each ion forms ionic bonds with its six neighbors, these bonds combining all of the ions in the crystal into one giant molecule. A detailed treatment of ionic crystals is given in Chapter X.

In $[Fe(H_2O)_6]^{+++}$, $[Ni(H_2O)_6]^{++}$, $[Ni(NH_3)_4]^{++}$, and many other complexes the bonds between the central ion and the surrounding molecules result in large part from the electrostatic attraction of the excess charge of the central ion for the permanent electric dipoles of the molecules.[1] Electrostatic bonds of this type may be called *ion-dipole bonds*. Electrostatic bonds might also result from the attraction of an ion for the induced dipole of a polarizable molecule or from the mutual interaction of the permanent electric dipoles of two molecules.

2c. The Covalent Bond.[2]—Following Lewis, we interpret the ordinary valence bond, as in the formulas

$$H-H, \quad Cl-Cl, \quad H-Cl, \quad H-\overset{\displaystyle H}{\underset{\displaystyle H}{C}}-H, \quad etc.,$$

as involving the sharing of a pair of electrons by the two bonded atoms, and write corresponding electronic structures, such as

$$H:H, \quad :\overset{..}{\underset{..}{Cl}}:\overset{..}{\underset{..}{Cl}}:, \quad H:\overset{..}{\underset{..}{Cl}}:, \quad H:\overset{\displaystyle H}{\underset{\displaystyle \overset{..}{H}}{\overset{..}{C}}}:H, \quad etc.$$

In these Lewis electronic formulas the symbol of the element represents the *kernel* of the atom, consisting of the nucleus and the inner electrons, but not those in the valence shell, which are shown by dots. A pair of electrons held jointly by two atoms is considered for some purposes to do double duty, and to be effective in completing a stable electronic configuration for each atom. It is seen that in methane the carbon atom, with its two inner

---

[1] I. Langmuir, *J.A.C.S.* **41**, 868 (1919), especially pp. 930–1.

[2] The convenient name *covalent bond*, which we shall often use in this book in place of the more cumbersome expression "shared-electron-pair bond" or "electron-pair bond," was introduced by Langmuir (*J.A.C.S.* **41**, 868 (1919)). Lewis prefers to include under the name "chemical bond" a more restricted class of interatomic interactions than that given by our definition in Sec. 2a. (" . . . the chemical bond is at all times and in all molecules merely a pair of electrons held jointly by two atoms." Lewis, "Valence," p. 78).

electrons and its outer shell of eight shared electrons, has assumed the stable ten-electron configuration of neon, and that each of the other atoms in the structures shown has achieved a noble-gas configuration.

A double bond and a triple bond between two atoms can be represented respectively by four and six shared electrons, as in the following examples:

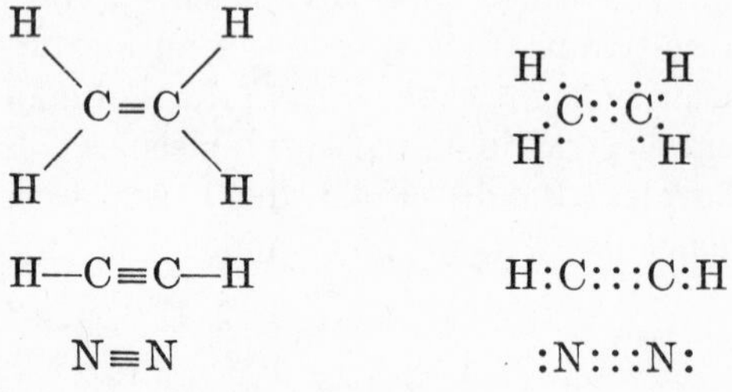

$$
\begin{array}{ccc}
\text{H} & & \text{H} \\
\diagdown & & \diagup \\
& \text{C} = \text{C} & \\
\diagup & & \diagdown \\
\text{H} & & \text{H}
\end{array}
\qquad
\begin{array}{ccc}
\text{H} & & \text{H} \\
& :\!\overset{\cdot}{\text{C}}::\overset{\cdot}{\text{C}}\! & \\
\text{H} & & \text{H}
\end{array}
$$

$$\text{H}\!-\!\text{C}\!\equiv\!\text{C}\!-\!\text{H} \qquad\qquad \text{H}:\text{C}:::\text{C}:\text{H}$$

$$\text{N}\!\equiv\!\text{N} \qquad\qquad\qquad :\text{N}:::\text{N}:$$

Electronic structures such as $:\!\overset{\cdot\cdot}{\text{N}}\!:\!\overset{\cdot\cdot}{\text{N}}\!:$, corresponding less closely to the classical valence-bond formulas, have also been proposed. The quantum-mechanical considerations described in Section 6 indicate that these structures are not to be preferred to those which assign four and six electrons to the double bond and triple bond, respectively.

In order that the nitrogen atom in trimethylamine oxide, $(CH_3)_3NO$, might be assigned the neon structure with a completed octet of valence electrons, Lewis wrote for it the electronic structure

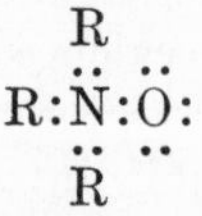

$$
\begin{array}{c}
\text{R} \\
\overset{\cdot\cdot}{\text{R}}\!:\!\overset{\cdot\cdot}{\text{N}}\!:\!\overset{\cdot\cdot}{\text{O}}\!: \\
\text{R}
\end{array}
\qquad \text{(with R = CH}_3\text{),}
$$

in which the nitrogen atom forms four single covalent bonds and the oxygen atom one. If it be assumed that the electrons of a shared pair are divided between the two atoms which they connect, it is found on counting electrons for this formula that the nitrogen atom has an electric charge of $+1$ (in units equal in magnitude to the electronic charge, with changed sign), and the oxygen atom a charge of -1. We shall call these charges, calculated with use of an electronic structure by dividing shared electrons equally between the bonded atoms, the *formal charges* of the atoms for the corresponding structure, and we shall often represent them by signs near the symbols of the atoms, as in the following examples:

$$
\text{Trimethylamine oxide,} \qquad
\begin{array}{c}
\text{R} \\
\overset{..}{\text{R}}\!\overset{+}{:}\!\overset{..}{\text{N}}\!\overset{-}{:}\!\overset{..}{\text{O}}\!: \\
\text{R}
\end{array}
$$

$$
\text{Sulfate ion,} \qquad
\left[
\begin{array}{c}
:\overset{..}{\text{O}}\overset{-}{:} \\
-\!:\overset{..}{\text{O}}:\!\overset{..}{\underset{..}{\text{S}}}\!\overset{++}{}:\overset{..}{\text{O}}\overset{-}{:} \\
:\overset{..}{\text{O}}: \\
\overset{..}{}\overset{-}{}
\end{array}
\right]^{- -}
$$

$$
\text{Ammonium ion,} \qquad
\left[
\begin{array}{c}
\text{H} \\
\text{H}\!:\!\overset{..}{\overset{+}{\text{N}}}\!:\!\text{H} \\
\overset{..}{\text{H}}
\end{array}
\right]^{+}
$$

These formal charges are, as indicated by their name, to be considered as conventional in significance; they do not show in general the actual distribution of electric charges among the atoms in a molecule or complex ion. Thus in the ammonium ion the unit positive charge of the complex is not to be considered as residing exclusively on the nitrogen atom; as a consequence of the partial ionic character of the N—H bonds, discussed in the following chapter, part of the excess positive charge can be considered to be transferred to each of the hydrogen atoms.

We see from the electronic formula which we have just written that the bond between nitrogen and oxygen in trimethylamine oxide may be considered as a sort of double bond, consisting of one single covalent bond and one ionic bond of unit strength. A bond of this type has sometimes been called[1] a "semi-polar double bond." The name "co-ordinate link" has also been used,[2] together with a special symbol, →, to indicate the transfer of electric charge from one atom to another. Electronic formulas have also been used in which the presumable original attachment of electrons to one atom or another is indicated by the use of different symbols (dots and crosses) for different electrons. We

[1] T. M. Lowry, *Trans. Faraday Soc.* 18, 285 (1923); *J. Chem. Soc.* 1923, 822.

[2] Sidgwick, "Electronic Theory of Valency."

shall not find it convenient to make use of these names or of these symbols.

In a few molecules there occur covalent bonds involving one electron or three electrons, instead of a shared pair. These *one-electron* and *three-electron bonds* are discussed in Section 4 and Chapter VIII.

2d. The Metallic Bond.—The most striking characteristic of the bond which holds atoms together in a metallic aggregate is the mobility of the bonding electrons, which gives rise to the high electrical and thermal conductivity of metals. A brief discussion of the metallic bond and its relation to the covalent bond is given in Chapter XI.

3. THE CONCEPT OF RESONANCE[1]

There is one fundamental principle of quantum mechanics which finds expression in most of the chemical applications of the theory to problems dealing with the normal states of molecules. This is the principle which underlies the concept of *resonance*.

A structure for a system is represented in quantum mechanics by a wave function, usually called ψ, a function of the coordinates which in classical theory would be used (with their conjugate momenta) in describing the system. The methods for finding the wave function for a system in a particular state are described in treatises on quantum mechanics. In our discussion of the nature of the chemical bond we shall restrict our interest in the main to the normal states of molecules. The stationary quantum states of a molecule or other system are states which are characterized by definite values of the total energy of the system. These states are designated by a quantum number, represented by the letter n, say, or by a set of two or more quantum numbers, each of which can assume any one of certain integral values.

[1] In preparing this non-mathematical discussion of a phenomenon which is essentially quantum-mechanical in nature I have introduced concepts and principles which are based on the theory of quantum mechanics whenever they are necessary for the argument, without attempting to place the discussion on a postulatory basis or to make the development of the argument logically complete.

The discussion in this book may be complemented by that in "Introduction to Quantum Mechanics, with Applications to Chemistry," Linus Pauling and E. Bright Wilson, Jr., McGraw-Hill Book Company, Inc., New York and London, 1935, to which later reference will be made under the title "Introduction to Quantum Mechanics."

The system in the nth stationary quantum state has the definite energy value W_n and is represented by the wave function ψ_n. Predictions can be made regarding the behavior of the system known to be in the nth quantum state with use of the wave function. These predictions, which relate to the expected results of experiments to be carried out on the system, are in general not unique, but instead statistical in nature. For example, it is not possible to make a definite prediction of the position of the electron (relative to the nucleus) in a normal hydrogen atom; instead, a corresponding probability distribution function can be found (Sec. 4a).

The stationary quantum state which has the lowest value of the total energy of the system (corresponding to maximum stability) is called the normal state. The quantum numbers are usually assigned values 1 or 0 for this state.

Let ψ_0 be the correct wave function for the normal state of the system under discussion. The fundamental principle of quantum mechanics in which we are interested states that *the energy value W_0 calculated by the equations of quantum mechanics with use of the correct wave function ψ_0 for the normal state of the system is less than that calculated with any other wave function ψ which might be proposed;*[1] in consequence, *the actual structure of the normal state of a system is that one, of all conceivable structures, which gives the system the maximum stability.*

Now let us consider two structures, I and II, which might reasonably or conceivably represent the normal state of the system under consideration. The methods of the theory are such that the more general function

$$\psi = a\psi_I + b\psi_{II}, \tag{3-1}$$

formed by multiplying ψ_I and ψ_{II} by arbitrary numerical coefficients[2] and adding, is also a possible wave function for the system. By calculating the energy corresponding to ψ as a function of the ratio b/a, the value of b/a which gives the energy its minimum value can be found. The corresponding wave function is then the best approximation to that for the normal state of the system which can be constructed in this way. If the best value

---

[1] For a detailed discussion of this principle see "Introduction to Quantum Mechanics," Sec. 26, "The Variation Method."

[2] Only the ratio b/a is significant, the nature of the function ψ not being changed by multiplication by a constant.

of b/a turns out to be very small, then the best wave function ψ will be essentially equal to ψ_I, and the normal state will be represented more closely by structure I than by any other structure of those considered. It may well happen, however, that the best value of b/a is neither very small nor very large (in which latter case the best ψ would differ little from ψ_{II}), but is of the order of magnitude of unity. In this case the best wave function ψ would be formed in part from ψ_I and in part from ψ_{II}, and the normal state of the system would be described correspondingly as involving both structure I and structure II. It has become conventional to speak of such a system as *resonating* between structures I and II.

The structure of such a system is not, however, exactly intermediate in character between structures I and II, because as a consequence of the resonance it is stabilized by a certain amount of energy, the *resonance energy*. The best value of b/a is that which gives the total energy of the system its minimum value, this value lying below that for either ψ_I or ψ_{II} by a certain amount which depends on the magnitude of the interaction between structures I and II and on their energy difference (see Sec. 4c). It is this extra stability of the system, relative to structure I or structure II (whichever is the more stable), that is called the resonance energy.[1]

The structures considered in the discussion of the normal state of a system need not be restricted in number to two. In general a wave function

$$\psi = a\psi_I + b\psi_{II} + c\psi_{III} + d\psi_{IV} + \cdots \qquad (3\text{-}2)$$

may be formed by linear combination of the wave functions $\psi_I, \psi_{II}, \psi_{III}, \psi_{IV}, \cdots$ corresponding to the structures I, II, III, IV, $\cdots$ which suggest themselves for consideration. In this wave function the best relative values of the numerical coefficients $a, b, c, d, \cdots$ are to be found by minimizing the energy.

The concept of resonance was introduced into quantum mechanics by Heisenberg[2] in connection with the discussion of the

---

[1] Because the resonating system does not have a structure intermediate between those involved in the resonance, but instead a structure which is further changed by the resonance stabilization, I prefer not to use the word "mesomerism," suggested by Ingold, for the resonance phenomenon.

[2] W. Heisenberg, *Z. f. Phys.* **39**, 499 (1926).

quantum states of the helium atom. He pointed out that a quantum-mechanical treatment somewhat analogous to the classical treatment of a system of resonating coupled harmonic oscillators can be applied to many systems. The resonance phenomenon of classical mechanics is observed, for example, for a system of two tuning forks with the same characteristic frequency of oscillation attached to a common base. When one fork is struck, it gradually ceases to oscillate, transferring its energy to the other, which begins its oscillation; the process is then reversed and the energy resonates back and forth between the two forks until it is dissipated by frictional and other losses. The same phenomenon is shown by two similar pendulums connected by a weak spring. The qualitative analogy between this classical resonance phenomenon and the quantum-mechanical resonance phenomenon described in the first part of this section is obvious; the analogy does not provide a simple non-mathematical explanation of a most important feature of quantum-mechanical resonance in its chemical applications, that of stabilization of the system by the resonance energy, however, and we shall accordingly not pursue it further. The student of chemistry is, I believe, able to develop a reliable and useful intuitive understanding of the concept of resonance by the study of its applications to various problems as described throughout this book.

It must be pointed out that there is an element of arbitrariness in the use of the concept of resonance, introduced by the choice of the initial structures I, II, III, IV, etc. as the basis for discussion of the normal state of a system. It is found, however, that for many systems certain structures suggest themselves strongly as most appropriate for this purpose, and that great progress can be made in the discussion of complex systems such as molecules by using the structures of related simpler systems as a starting point. A striking example of this is given by the most important chemical application of resonance which has been discovered, that of the resonance of a molecule among several valence-bond structures: it is found that there are many substances whose properties cannot be accounted for by means of a single electronic structure of the valence-bond type, but which can be fitted into the scheme of classical valence theory by the consideration of resonance among two or more such structures.

The convenience and value of the concept of resonance in discussing the problems of chemistry are so great as to make the disadvantage of the element of arbitrariness of little significance. This element occurs in the classical resonance phenomenon also— it is arbitrary to discuss the behavior of a system of pendulums with connecting springs in terms of the motion of independent pendulums, since the motion can be described in a way which is mathematically simpler by use of the normal coordinates of the system—but the convenience and usefulness of the concept have nevertheless caused it to be widely applied.

4. THE HYDROGEN MOLECULE-ION AND THE ONE-ELECTRON BOND

In this section we make the first chemical application of the idea of resonance in connection with the structure of the simplest of all molecules, the hydrogen molecule-ion, H_2^+, and the simplest of all chemical bonds, the one-electron bond, which involves one electron shared by two atoms.

4a. The Normal Hydrogen Atom.—According to the Bohr theory the electron in the normal hydrogen atom moved about the nucleus in a circular orbit with radius $a_0 = 0.529$ Å and the constant speed $v_0 = 2.182 \times 10^8$ cm/sec. The quantum-mechanical picture is similar but less definite. The wave function ψ_{1s} which represents the orbital motion of the electron in this atom, shown in Figure 4-1, is large in magnitude only within a region close to the nucleus; beyond 1 or 2 Å it falls off rapidly to zero. The square of ψ represents the *probability distribution function* for the position of the electron, such that $\psi^2 dV$ is the probability that the electron be in the volume element dV, and $4\pi r^2 \psi^2 dr$ is the probability that it be between the distances r and $r + dr$ from the nucleus. It is seen from the figure that this last function has its maximum value at $r = a_0$. The most probable distance of the electron from the nucleus is thus just the Bohr radius a_0; the electron is, however, not restricted to this one distance. The speed of the electron also is not constant, but can be represented by a distribution function, such that the root-mean-square speed has just the Bohr value v_0. We can accordingly describe the normal hydrogen atom by saying that the electron moves in and out about the nucleus, remaining usually within a distance of about 0.5 Å, with a speed which is variable but is of the order of magnitude of v_0.   Over a period of time long enough to permit many cycles of motion of the electron the atom can be described as consisting of the nucleus surrounded by a spherically-symmetrical ball of negative electricity (the electron

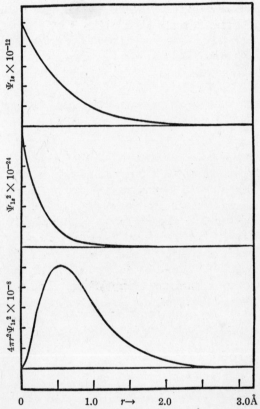

FIG. 4-1.—The wave function ψ_{1s}, its square, and the radial probability distribution function $4\pi r^2\psi^2_{1s}$ for the normal hydrogen atom.

blurred by a time-exposure of its rapid motion), as indicated in Figure 4-2.

4b. The Hydrogen Molecule-ion.—The structure of the hydrogen molecule-ion, H_2^+, as of any molecule, is discussed theoretically by first considering the motion of the electron (or of all the electrons in case that there are several) in the field of the atomic nuclei considered to be fixed in a definite configuration.   The electronic energy of the molecule is thus obtained as a function of the configuration. The configuration for the normal state of the molecule is that corresponding to the minimum value of this energy function, and giving the molecule the maximum stability.

For the hydrogen molecule-ion our problem is to evaluate the energy as a function of the distance r_{AB} between the two nuclei

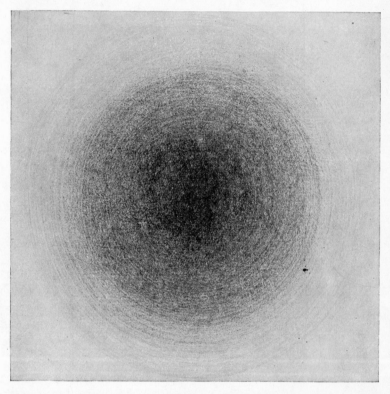

Fig. 4-2.—A drawing illustrating the decrease in electron density with increasing distance from the nucleus in the normal hydrogen atom.

A and B. For large values of r_{AB} the system in its normal state consists of a normal hydrogen atom (the electron and nucleus A, say) and a hydrogen ion (nucleus B), which interact with one another only weakly. If we assume the same structure $H + H^+$ to hold as the nuclei approach one another, it is found on calculation that the interaction energy has the form shown by the dashed curve in Figure 4-3, with no minimum. From this calculation we would say that a hydrogen atom and a hydrogen ion repel one another, rather than attracting one another to form a stable molecule-ion.

However, the structure assumed is too simple to represent the system satisfactorily. We have assumed that the electron forms a normal hydrogen atom with nucleus A:

Structure I: $H_A \cdot$ H_B^+

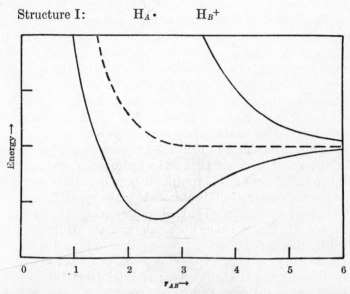

FIG. 4-3.—Curves showing the energy of interaction of a hydrogen atom and a proton. The lower curve corresponds to the formation of a hydrogen molecule-ion in its stable normal state. The scale for the internuclear distance r_{AB} is based on the unit $a_0 = 0.529$ Å.

The structure in which the electron forms a normal hydrogen atom with nucleus B, which then interacts with nucleus A, is just as stable a structure as the first:

Structure II: H_A^+ $\cdot H_B$;

and we must consider the possibility of resonance between these two structures. These structures are equivalent, and correspond separately to exactly the same energy; the principles of quantum mechanics require that in such a case *the two structures make equal contributions to the normal state of the system.* On repetition of the calculation of the energy curve with use of the corresponding wave function, formed by adding the wave functions for structures I and II, the lower full curve shown in Figure 4-3 is obtained.[1] This curve has a pronounced minimum at about $r_{AB} = 1.06$ Å, showing that *as a result of the resonance of the electron between the two nuclei a stable one-electron bond is formed,* the energy of the bond being about 50 kcal./mole. The way in which this extra stability and the consequent formation of a bond result from the combination of the two structures I and II cannot be simply explained; it is the result of the quantum-mechanical resonance phenomenon. The bond can be described as owing its stability to the resonance of the electron back and forth between the two nuclei, with a resonance frequency equal to the resonance energy, 50 kcal./mole, divided by Planck's constant h. This frequency for the normal molecule-ion is 7×10^{14} sec.$^{-1}$, which is about one-fifth as great as the frequency of orbital motion about the nucleus of the electron in the normal hydrogen atom.

(The upper full curve in Figure 4-3 represents another way in which a normal hydrogen atom and a hydrogen ion can interact. The two structures I and II contribute equally to this curve also, the resonance energy in this case making the system less stable rather than more stable. The chances are equal that a hydrogen atom and a hydrogen ion on approach repel one another as indicated by this curve or attract one another to form the normal molecule-ion.)

In this discussion another type of interaction between the hydrogen atom and ion has been neglected; to wit, the deformation (polarization) of the atom in the electric field of the ion. This has been considered by Dickinson,[2] who has shown that it contributes an additional 10 kcal./mole to the energy of the bond. We may accordingly say that of the total energy of the one-electron bond in H_2^+, 61 kcal./mole, about 80 per cent, 50 kcal./mole, is due to the resonance of the electron between the two nuclei, and the remainder is due to deformation.

Very accurate calculations[3] have led to the value

$$D_0(H_2^+) = 60.95 \pm 0.10 \text{ kcal./mole}$$

[1] L. Pauling, *Chem. Rev.* 5, 173 (1928); B. N. Finkelstein and G. E. Horowitz, *Z. f. Phys.* 48, 118 (1928).

[2] B. N. Dickinson, *J. Chem. Phys.* 1, 317 (1933).

[3] Ø. Burrau, *Det Kgl. Danske Vid. Selskab.* 7, 1 (1927); E. A. Hylleraas, *Z. f. Phys.* 71, 739 (1931); G. Jaffé, *ibid.* 87, 535 (1934).

for the energy of formation of the normal hydrogen molecule-ion from a hydrogen atom and a hydrogen ion. This is in agreement with the experimental value, which is less accurately known. The calculated values of the equilibrium internuclear distance, 1.06 Å, and the vibrational frequency, 2250 cm^{-1}, also agree with the experimental values to within the accuracy of their calculation and experimental determination.

The electron distribution function for the molecule-ion is shown in Figure 4-4. It is seen that the electron remains for most of the time in the small region just between the nuclei,

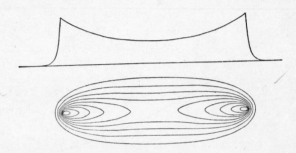

Fig. 4-4.—The electron distribution function for the hydrogen molecule ion (from Burrau, *loc. cit.*). The upper curve shows the value of the function along the line through the two nuclei, and the lower figure shows contour lines, increasing from 0.1 for the outermost to 1 at the nuclei.

only rarely getting on the far side of one of them; and we may feel that the presence of the electron between the two nuclei, where it can draw them together, provides some explanation of the stability of the bond. The electron distribution function is very concentrated relative to that for the hydrogen atom, the volume within the outermost contour surface shown (with one-tenth the maximum value) being only one-sixth as great as for the atom.

For convenience we may represent the one-electron bond by a dot midway between the symbols of the bonded atoms, the hydrogen molecule-ion then having the structural formula $(H \cdot H)^+$.

4c. The Conditions for the Formation of a One-electron Bond.—The magnitude of the resonance energy of the one-electron bond in the hydrogen molecule-ion, 50 kcal./mole, is determined by the amount of interaction of the two structures I and II ($H \cdot H^+$ and $H^+ \cdot H$) as calculated by the methods of

quantum mechanics.   Because the two structures correspond to
the same energy, the interaction energy is completely manifested
as resonance energy; there is complete resonance.   If, however,
the two nuclei A and B were unlike, so that the two structures

I: A·   B$^+$

and   II: A$^+$ ·B

corresponded to different energy values, the conditions for complete resonance would not be satisfied.   The more stable of the

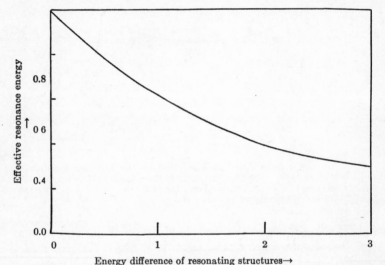

FIG. 4-5.—Curve showing the effective resonance energy as a function of the
energy difference of two resonating structures, both measured relative to the interaction energy of the two structures (the "resonance integral").

two structures (structure I, say) would contribute more to the
normal state of the system than the other, and the system would
be stabilized (relative to structure I) by an amount of resonance
energy less than the interaction energy.   A curve showing the
effect of difference in energy of two resonating structures in in-
hibiting resonance is shown in Figure 4-5.   As structure I becomes more and more stable relative to structure II it makes up a
larger and larger part of the normal state of the system, and
resonance with structure II stabilizes the system by a smaller
and smaller amount.   For this reason we expect the one-electron

bond to be formed only between like atoms or occasionally between unlike atoms which happen to be of such a nature (similarity in electronegativity) as to make structures I and II approximately equal in energy.   The hydrides of boron (Sec. 32) are the only stable neutral molecules to the structure of which the one-electron bond is supposed to make a significant contribution.

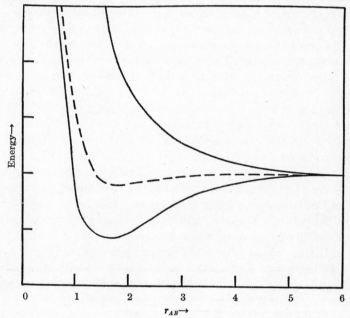

Fig. 5-1.—Curves showing the energy of interaction of two normal hydrogen atoms.

5. THE HYDROGEN MOLECULE AND THE ELECTRON-PAIR BOND

Before 1927 there was no satisfactory theory regarding the nature of the covalent bond.   The chemist had postulated the existence of the valence bond between atoms and had built up a body of empirical information regarding it, but his inquiries into its structure and nature had been futile.   The step taken by Lewis of associating two electrons with a bond can hardly be called the development of a theory, since it left unanswered the fundamental questions as to the nature of the interactions involved and the source of the energy of the bond. Only a decade ago, in 1927, was the development of the theory of the covalent bond initiated by the work of Heitler and London[1] on the hydrogen molecule, described in the following section.

5a. The Heitler-London Treatment of the Hydrogen Molecule.—The hydrogen molecule consists of two nuclei, which may be designated A and B, and two electrons, 1 and 2. As in the treatment of the hydrogen molecule-ion, we calculate the interaction energy for various values of the internuclear distance r_{AB}. When the nuclei are far apart the normal state of the system involves two normal hydrogen atoms. Let us assume that one of the electrons, electron 1, say, is associated with nucleus A, and the other, electron 2, with nucleus B. On calculating the interaction energy as a function of the internuclear distance, it is found that at large distances there is a weak attraction, which soon turns into strong repulsion as r_{AB} is further diminished (dashed curve of Figure 5-1). According to this calculation the two atoms would not combine to form a stable molecule.

Here again, however, we have neglected the resonance phenomenon; for the structure with electron 2 attached to nucleus A and electron 1 to nucleus B is just as stable as the equivalent structure assumed above, and in accordance with quantum-mechanical principles we must consider as a representation of the normal state of the system neither one structure nor the other, but rather a combination to which the two contribute equally; that is, we must make the calculations in such a way as to take into consideration the possibility of the exchange of places of the two electrons.

Structure I: $H_A \cdot^1$ $^2 \cdot H_B$

Structure II: $H_A \cdot^2$ $^1 \cdot H_B$

On doing this there is obtained an interaction-energy curve (the lower full curve in Figure 5-1) which shows a pronounced minimum, corresponding to the formation of a stable molecule. The energy of formation of the molecule from separated atoms as calculated by Heitler, London, and Sugiura is about 67% of the experimental value of 102.6 kcal./mole, and the calculated equi-

[1] W. Heitler and F. London, *Z. f. Phys.* 44, 455 (1927). A mathematical improvement of this work was made by Y. Sugiura, *ibid.* 45, 484 (1927).

librium distance between the nuclei is 0.05 Å larger than the observed value 0.74 A.   A small refinement in the resonance calculation (made by Wang[1]) improves these values somewhat, the calculated bond energy being increased to 80% of its correct value and the equilibrium internuclear distance decreased to 0.75 Å.

Hence we see that a very simple treatment of the system of two hydrogen atoms leads to an explanation of the formation of a stable molecule, *the energy of the electron-pair bond being in the main the resonance energy corresponding to the interchange of the two electrons between the two atomic orbitals.*

5b. The Pairing of Electron Spins.—There is another very important property of the electron-pair bond which is given a theoretical basis by the quantum-mechanical treatment.   In addition to the properties of mass and electric charge, an electron has associated with it certain other properties which are usually described as resulting from the *spin* of the electron.[2]   The electron has a certain intrinsic angular momentum ($\sqrt{3}\, h/4\pi$), which can be oriented by an external magnetic field in either one of two ways, with the field or against the field.   These orientations are usually described as *positive spin* and *negative spin*, respectively, and they are associated with the values $+\frac{1}{2}$ and $-\frac{1}{2}$ for the spin-orientation quantum number m_s.   Accompanying the angular momentum of the electron spin there is also a *magnetic dipole moment*, equal in magnitude to $\sqrt{3}$ Bohr magnetons.   This magnetic moment can contribute to the magnetic susceptibility of substances, making them paramagnetic.

The *Pauli exclusion principle*[3] requires that no more than two electrons occupy a single orbit, and that the two electrons in the same orbit have opposed spins, and thus mutually neutralize their magnetic moments.   The most stable orbit in every atom is the 1s orbit of the K shell.   In the normal hydrogen atom this is occupied by one electron, the spin magnetic moment of which makes monatomic hydrogen gas paramagnetic. In the normal helium atom the 1s orbit is occupied by two electrons, which are required by the exclusion principle to have opposed spins; in con-

---

[1] S. C. Wang, *Phys. Rev.* **31**, 579 (1928).
[2] G. E. Uhlenbeck and S. Goudsmit, *Naturwiss.* **13**, 953 (1925); *Nature* **107**, 264 (1926).
[3] See "Introduction to Quantum Mechanics." Sec. 29.

sequence of this helium is diamagnetic, the spin magnetic moments of the two electrons neutralizing one another.[1]

It is found on analysis[2] that *in order to form a stable bond in the hydrogen molecule the spins of the two electrons must be opposed*, the hydrogen molecule thus being diamagnetic, like the helium atom. Two hydrogen atoms which approach one another can form a stable molecule only if the spins of the two electrons are opposed; in case that they are parallel, the interaction energy for the two atoms will have the form shown by the upper full curve in Figure 5-1, and the two atoms will repel one another.

It is customary to refer to electrons with opposed spins as paired, whether they occupy the same orbit in one atom or are involved in the formation of a bond.

5c. Partial Ionic Character and Deformation.—We have so far considered only structures for the hydrogen molecule in which the two electrons remain near different nuclei. The two ionic structures III and IV

Structure III:　　$H_A:^-$　　　H_B^+

Structure IV:　　H_A^+　　　$:H_B^-$

in which both electrons are attached to the same nucleus must also be considered. These structures involve a positive hydrogen ion H^+ and a negative hydrogen ion $H:^-$ with the helium structure (K shell completed).

One of the most important rules regarding resonance states that *resonance can occur only among structures with the same number of unpaired electrons.* Since the electrons in the negative hydrogen ion, occupying the same orbit, are paired and the electrons involved in a bond formed by structures I and II are paired, this condition is satisfied, and we expect structures III and IV as well as I and II to be of significance for the normal hydrogen molecule.

At large internuclear distances the ionic structures III and IV are not of importance. The energy of the reaction

$$H + H \rightarrow H^+ + H^-$$

---

[1] In some atoms and molecules a contribution to the magnetic moment is made by the orbital motion of the electrons; this effect is, however, of less significance for molecules than for atoms (see Sec. 16).

[2] See "Introduction to Quantum Mechanics," Sec. 43.

is -295.6 kcal./mole, the difference between the electron affinity of hydrogen,

$$H + E^- \rightarrow H^- + 16.4 \text{ kcal./mole,}$$

and the ionization energy of hydrogen,

$$H^+ + E^- \rightarrow H + 312.0 \text{ kcal./mole;}$$

and this makes the structures III and IV so unstable relative to I and II that they make no contribution. As r_{AB} is decreased, however, the Coulomb attraction of H^+ and H^- stabilizes structures III and IV; at the equilibrium distance $r_{AB} = 0.74$ Å each of these two ionic structures makes a contribution of about 2% to the normal state of the molecule. The corresponding extra ionic resonance energy is about 5.5 kcal./mole, or 5% of the total bond energy.[1]

The remaining 15% of the observed bond energy may be attributed to deformation, this term being used to cover all the complicated interactions neglected in the foregoing simple treatments. As the culmination of several attacks on the problem, a thoroughly satisfactory and accurate theoretical treatment of the normal hydrogen molecule was made by James and Coolidge.[2] Their careful and laborious investigation led to a value for the bond energy of the molecule,

$$D_0(H_2) = 102.62 \text{ kcal./mole,}$$

in complete agreement with experiment, with similar agreement for the equilibrium internuclear distance and the vibrational frequency. Theoretical calculations of other properties of the normal hydrogen molecule—the diamagnetic susceptibility, electric polarizability, the anisotropy of the latter quantity, van der Waals forces, etc.—have also been made, with satisfactory results, so that the structure of this simple covalent molecule is now well understood.

As a summary of the results reported above, the bond in the hydrogen molecule would be described as resulting in the main from the resonance of the two electrons between the two nuclei, this phenomenon contributing 80% of the total bond energy.

---

[1] S. Weinbaum, *J. Chem. Phys.* **1**, 593 (1933).
[2] H. M. James and A. S. Coolidge, *J. Chem. Phys.* **1**, 825 (1933).

An additional 5% is contributed by the ionic structures H^-H^+ and H^+H^-, which are of equal importance, and hence lead to no resultant permanent electric moment for the molecule. The remaining 15% of the energy of the bond can be ascribed to complex interactions included under the term deformation.

5d. The Conditions for the Formation of an Electron-pair Bond.—In Section 4c it was pointed out that the resonance which leads to the formation of a stable one-electron bond between two atoms is in general inhibited in case that the two atoms are unlike, and that in consequence such a bond occurs only rarely. We see that for the electron-pair bond no such restriction exists; the two structures I and II (Sec. 5b) which differ only in interchange of the two electrons 1 and 2 by two atoms A and B are equivalent even though the two atoms involved are unlike, and accordingly complete resonance occurs for unlike atoms as well as for like atoms, the resonance energy of the bond being equal to the interaction energy of the two structures. Accordingly there is no special condition as to the nature of the atoms which must be satisfied in order for an electron-pair bond to be formed, and we need not be surprised by the wide-spread occurrence and great importance of this bond.

Resonance with the ionic structures A^+B^- and A^-B^+ also occurs for unlike atoms as well as for like atoms, and is, indeed, of great importance in case that the atoms A and B differ greatly in electronegativity, the contribution of the favored ionic structure then being large. This aspect of the covalent bond is treated in Chapter II.

6. THE FORMAL RULES FOR COVALENT BOND FORMATION

6a. The Structure of Poly-electronic Atoms.—In helium and in all heavier atoms there are two electrons with opposed spin occupying the stable 1s orbit and forming a completed K shell of electrons. The size (linear dimensions) of the K shell varies roughly inversely with the nuclear charge of the atom, being in helium about one-half that of the hydrogen atom, in lithium about one-third, and so on.

The next outer shell is the L *shell*, composed of four orbitals[1]

---

[1] We shall use the word *orbital* in referring to the wave function associated with the orbital motion of an electron.

$2s$, $2p_x$, $2p_y$, and $2p_z$, of which $2s$ is somewhat more stable than the $2p$'s. In the atoms lithium to neon electrons are introduced in these orbitals, two electrons in the same orbital having opposed spins. Neon, with a completed L shell of eight electrons, has the *electronic configuration* $1s^2 2s^2 2p_x{}^2 2p_y{}^2 2p_z{}^2$ or $1s^2 2s^2 2p^6$, the superscript showing the number of electrons occupying the orbitals. In these symbols the numbers 1 and 2 (for K and L shell, respectively) give the values of the *total quantum number n*, and the letters s and p represent the values of the *azimuthal quantum number*[1] l; s, p, d, $f, \cdots$ corresponding to $l = 0$, 1, 2, $3, \cdots$, with a maximum value of $l = n - 1$.

In an atom or monatomic ion the electrons tend first to occupy the more stable orbitals doubly, by pairing; when there are several orbitals of the same energy available, such as $2p_x$, $2p_y$, $2p_z$, they tend not to pair with one another, but instead to occupy different orbitals, keeping their spins parallel. For example, the normal nitrogen atom has the configuration $1s^2 2s^2 2p_x 2p_y 2p_z$, the three $2p$ electrons remaining unpaired. In oxygen the eighth electron must pair with one of these three in order to enter the L shell, leaving only two unpaired electrons; the same process leads to only one in fluorine, and none in neon.

There are n^2 orbitals in the shell with total quantum number n, 1 in the K shell, 4 in L, 9 in M, 16 in N, and so on; the number of electrons occupying a completed shell being thus $2n^2$. The approximate relative energy values for atomic orbitals are indicated in Figure 6-1, the most stable orbitals being lowest (the relative positions vary slowly with atomic number). It is seen that the M shell in light atoms is not completely filled with electrons before the N orbitals begin to be occupied. Instead, after the $3s$ and $3p$ orbitals are occupied by an "octet" of eight electrons, giving the stable argon configuration $1s^2 2s^2 2p^6 3s^2 3p^6$, further electrons enter the $4s$ orbitals (in potassium and calcium), and only later, in the iron-group transition elements, are the five $3d$ orbitals

[1] In the old quantum theory the azimuthal quantum number determined the eccentricity of the elliptical orbit. This interpretation is retained essentially in the quantum mechanics, the s orbital in a given shell being the most eccentric and penetrating most deeply into the core, the p orbitals next, and so on. The greater penetration into the core (the region near the nucleus) leads to greater stability, and thus gives rise to the stability sequence $ns > np > nd$, etc., indicated in Fig. 6-1.

filled by their complement of ten electrons. The palladium and platinum transition elements (ten of each) correspond to filling the five 4d and five 5d orbitals, respectively, and the rare earths (fourteen) to filling the seven 4f orbitals.

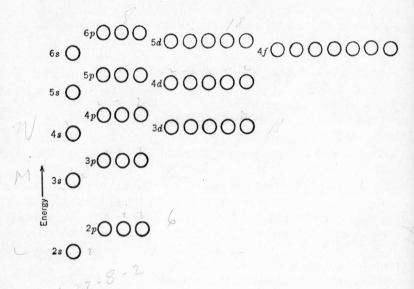

FIG. 6-1.—The approximate stability sequence for atomic orbitals, the lowest circle representing the most stable orbital (1s). Each circle represents one atomic orbital, which can be occupied either by one electron or by two electrons with opposed spins.

The configurations of atoms in their normal states are given in Table 6-1

The outer shell of many stable monatomic ions consists of an octet of eight electrons in s and p orbitals (noble-gas type) or of eighteen electrons in s, p, and d orbitals (eighteen-shell type—Zn^{++}, etc.).

TABLE 6-1.—ELECTRON CONFIGURATIONS OF ATOMS IN THEIR NORMAL STATES

		K	L		M			N				O			P			Q	Term Symbol*
		1s	2s	2p	3s	3p	3d	4s	4p	4d	4f	5s	5p	5d	6s	6p	6d	7s	
H	1	1																	$^2S_{1/2}$
He	2	2																	$^1S_0$
Li	3	2	1																$^2S_{1/2}$
Be	4	2	2																$^1S_0$
B	5	2	2	1															$^2P_{1/2}$
C	6	2	2	2															$^3P_0$
N	7	2	2	3															$^4S_{3/2}$
O	8	2	2	4															$^3P_2$
F	9	2	2	5															$^2P_{3/2}$
Ne	10	2	2	6															$^1S_0$
Na	11	2	2	6	1														$^2S_{1/2}$
Mg	12				2														$^1S_0$
Al	13				2	1													$^2P_{1/2}$
Si	14				2	2													$^3P_0$
P	15		10		2	3													$^4S_{3/2}$
S	16		Neon Core		2	4													$^3P_2$
Cl	17				2	5													$^2P_{3/2}$
Ar	18				2	6													$^1S_0$
K	19	2	2	6	2	6		1											$^2S_{1/2}$
Ca	20							2											$^1S_0$
Sc	21						1	2											$^2D_{3/2}$
Ti	22						2	2											$^3F_2$
V	23						3	2											$^4F_{3/2}$
Cr	24			18			5	1											$^7S_3$
Mn	25		Argon core				5	2											$^6S_{5/2}$
Fe	26						6	2											$^5D_4$
Co	27						7	2											$^4F_{9/2}$
Ni	28						8	2											$^3F_4$
Cu	29	2	2	6	2	6	10	1											$^2S_{1/2}$
Zn	30							2											$^1S_0$
Ga	31							2	1										$^2P_{1/2}$
Ge	32							2	2										$^3P_0$
As	33			28				2	3										$^4S_{3/2}$
Se	34		Copper core					2	4										$^3P_2$
Br	35							2	5										$^2P_{3/2}$
Kr	36							2	6										$^1S_0$

TABLE 6-1.—(continued)

		K	L		M			N				O			P	Q	Term
		1s	2s	2p	3s	3p	3d	4s	4p	4d	4f	5s	5p	5d	p 6d	7s	Symbol*
Rb	37	2	2	6	2	6	10	2	6			1					$^2S_{1/2}$
Sr	38											2					$^1S_0$
Y	39									1		2					$^2D_{3/2}$
Zr	40									2		2					$^3F_2$
Cb	41									4		1					$^6D_{1/2}$
Mo	42					36				5		1					$^7S_3$
Ma	43				Krypton core					6		1					$^6D_{9/2}$
Ru	44									7		1					$^5F_5$
Rh	45									8		1					$^4F_{9/2}$
Pd	46									10							$^1S_0$
Ag	47	2	2	6	2	6	10	2	6	10		1					$^2S_{1/2}$
Cd	48											2					$^1S_0$
In	49											2	1				$^2P_{1/2}$
Sn	50											2	2				$^3P_0$
Sb	51					46						2	3				$^4S_{3/2}$
Te	52				Silver core							2	4				$^3P_2$
I	53											2	5				$^2P_{3/2}$
Xe	54											2	6				$^1S_0$
Cs	55	2	2	6	2	6	10	2	6	10		2	6		1		$^2S_{1/2}$
Ba	56														2		$^1S_0$
La	57					54						2	6	1	2		$^2D_{3/2}$
						Xenon core											
Ce	58	2	2	6	2	6	10	2	6	10	1	2	6	1	2		$^3H_4$
Pr	59										2			1	2		$^4K_{11/2}$
Nd	60										3			1	2		$^5L_6$
Il	61										4			1	2		$^6L_{9/2}$
Sm	62										5			1	2		$^7K_4$
Eu	63										6			1	2		$^8H_{3/2}$
Gd	64										7			1	2		$^9D_2$
Tb	65					46					8	8		1	2		$^8H_{17/2}$
Ds	66				1s to 4d						9	5s, 5p		1	2		$^7K_{10}$
Ho	67										10			1	2		$^6K_{19/2}$
Er	68										11			1	2		$^5L_{10}$
Tm	69										12			1	2		$^4K_{17/2}$
Yb	70										13			1	2		$^3H_6$
Lu	71										14			1	2		$^2D_{3/2}$

TABLE 6-1.—(continued)

	K 1s	L 2s	L 2p	M 3s	M 3p	M 3d	N 4s	N 4p	N 4d	N 4f	O 5s	O 5p	O 5d	P 6s	P 6p	P 6d	Q 7s	Term Symbol*
Hf 72	2	2	6	2	6	10	2	6	10	14	2	6	2	2				$^3F_2$
Ta 73													3	2				$^4F_{3/2}$
W 74													4	2				$^5D_0$
Re 75					68								5	2				$^6S_{5/2}$
Os 76				Hafnium core									6	2				$^5D_4$
Ir 77													9					$^2D_{5/2}$
Pt 78													9	1				$^3D_3$
Au 79	2	2	6	2	6	10	2	6	10	14	2	6	10	1				$^2S_{1/2}$
Hg 80														2				$^1S_0$
Tl 81														2	1			$^2P_{1/2}$
Pb 82														2	2			$^3P_0$
Bi 83					78									2	3			$^4S_{3/2}$
Po 84				Gold core										2	4			$^3P_2$
— 85														2	5			$^2P_{3/2}$
Rn 86														2	6			$^1S_0$
— 87	2	2	6	2	6	10	2	6	10	14	2	6	10	2	6		1	$^2S_{1/2}$
Ra 88																	2	$^1S_0$
Ac 89																1	2	$^2D_{3/2}$
Th 90					86											2	2	$^3F_2$
Pa 91				Radon core												3	2	$^4F_{3/2}$
U 92																4	2	$^5D_0$

* For a discussion of the meaning of term symbols and of line spectra and atomic structure in general see one of the treatises mentioned in the footnote below. The results of spectroscopic investigation of atoms have been collected by R. F. Bacher and S. Goudsmit, "Atomic Energy States," McGraw-Hill Book Co., New York, 1932.

The electron distribution function for a poly-electronic atom or ion shows the presence of electron shells as regions of maximum electron density. In the radial distribution function for the rubidium ion (Fig. 6-2), with configuration $1s^2 2s^2 2p^6 3s^2 3p^6 3d^{10} 4s^2 4p^6$, the K, L, M, and N shells can be distinguished. The dimensions of atoms and ions are discussed in later chapters.[1]

[1] For a detailed treatment of atomic structure see, for example, L. Pauling and S. Goudsmit, "The Structure of Line Spectra," McGraw-Hill Book Co., New York, 1930; H. E. White, "Introduction to Atomic Spectra," McGraw-Hill Book Co., 1934; G. Herzberg, "Atomic Spectra and Atomic Structure," Prentice-Hall, Inc., New York, 1937.

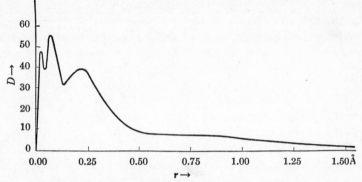

FIG. 6-2.—The radial distribution function D for the rubidium ion (from calculations by Hartree).

The relation between the electron configurations of atoms in their normal states and position in the periodic table of the elements (Fig. 6-3) is seen on comparison of the table with Table 6-1.

The Periodic System of the Elements

0	I	II	III	IV	V	VI	VII
He 2	Li 3	Be 4	B 5	C 6	N 7	O 8	F 9
Ne 10	Na 11	Mg 12	Al 13	Si 14	P 15	S 16	Cl 17

0	Ia	IIa	IIIa	IVa	Va	VIa	VIIa	VIII			Ib	IIb	IIIb	IVb	Vb	VIb	VIIb
Ar 18	K 19	Ca 20	Sc 21	Ti 22	V 23	Cr 24	Mn 25	Fe 26	Co 27	Ni 28	Cu 29	Zn 30	Ga 31	Ge 32	As 33	Se 34	Br 35
Kr 36	Rb 37	Sr 38	Y 39	Zr 40	Cb 41	Mo 42	Ma 43	Ru 44	Rh 45	Pd 46	Ag 47	Cd 48	In 49	Sn 50	Sb 51	Te 52	I 53
Xe 54	Cs 55	Ba 56	La-Lu 57-71	Hf 72	Ta 73	W 74	Re 75	Os 76	Ir 77	Pt 78	Au 79	Hg 80	Tl 81	Pb 82	Bi 83	Po 84	85
Rn 86	87	Ra 88	Ac 89	Th 90	Pa 91	U 92											

FIG. 6-3.—The periodic system of the elements.

6b. Orbitals and Covalent Bonds.—The formal results of the quantum-mechanical treatment of valence (developed by Heitler, London, Born, Weyl, Slater, and other investigators) can be given the following simple statement: *an atom can form an electron-pair* *bond for each stable orbital,* the bond being of the type described for the hydrogen molecule, and owing its stability to the same resonance phenomenon. In other words, there are needed for the formation of an electron-pair bond two electrons with opposed spins and a stable orbital of each of the two bonded atoms.

The hydrogen atom, with only one stable orbital ($1s$), is thus limited to the formation of one covalent bond; the structures originally drawn for the hydrogen bond (Chap. IX), with bi-covalent hydrogen, cannot be accepted.[1]

The carbon atom, nitrogen atom, and other first-row atoms are limited to four covalent bonds, using the four orbitals of the L shell. This restriction forms much of the justification of the importance of the octet postulated twenty years ago.

The quantum-mechanical treatment also leads to the conclusion that in general each additional electron-pair bond formed within a molecule stabilizes the molecule further, so that the most stable electronic structures of a molecule are those in which all of the stable orbitals of each atom are used either in bond formation or for occupancy by an unshared pair of electrons. Stable electronic structures for a molecule containing first-row atoms would accordingly in general involve use of all four orbitals of the L shell; the sharing of electron pairs occurs to as great an extent as is permitted by the number of electrons present.[2] Electronic structures such as $:\!N\!:\!N\!:$, in which each nitrogen atom has only a sextet of electrons in the outer shell, occupying only three L orbitals of each atom, are less stable than structures such as $:N:::N:$, in which use is made of all the L orbitals.[3]

---

[1] L. Pauling, *Proc. Nat. Acad. Sci.* **14**, 359 (1928).

[2] Simple algebraic equations for calculating the number of shared electrons for structures with completed octets and other completed electron shells were given by Langmuir (*J.A.C.S.* **41**, 868 (1919)). These equations usually need not be called upon, since electronic formulas of the sort desired can be written easily with a little practice.

[3] The difference in stability of structures $:\!N\!:\!N\!:$ and $:N:::N:$ is the difference in energy of a single and a triple bond, which is about 146 kcal./mole, in favor of the triple bond (Sec. 18a). The chemical properties of unsaturated substances might suggest the double bond and triple bond to be weaker than the single bond; however, these properties involve comparison of the energy of the double bond with that of *two* single bonds, and similarly of the energy of the triple bond with that of *three* single

For second-row atoms too the octet retains some significance, since the $3s$ and $3p$ orbitals are more stable than the $3d$ orbitals. In a molecule such as phosphine, with the structure

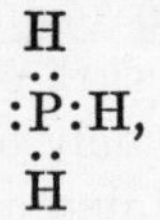

$$\begin{array}{c} \text{H} \\ \text{:}\overset{\displaystyle ..}{\text{P}}\text{:H,} \\ \overset{\displaystyle ..}{\text{H}} \end{array}$$

three of the M orbitals of phosphorus are used for bond formation and one for an unshared pair, and in the phosphonium ion

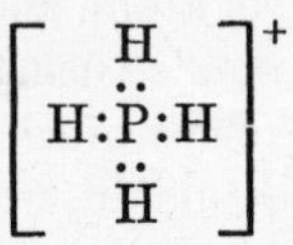

$$\left[\begin{array}{c} \text{H} \\ \text{H:}\overset{\displaystyle ..}{\text{P}}\text{:H} \\ \overset{\displaystyle ..}{\text{H}} \end{array} \right]^{+}$$

four M orbitals are used for bond formation, the five $3d$ orbitals in the M shell not being called on for bond formation. In phosphorus pentachloride, on the other hand, for which the structure

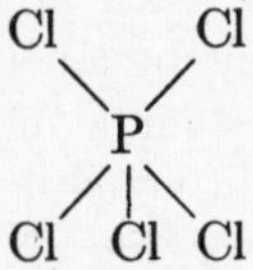

$$\begin{array}{c} \text{Cl} \qquad \text{Cl} \\ \diagdown \quad \diagup \\ \text{P} \\ \diagup \; | \; \diagdown \\ \text{Cl} \quad \text{Cl} \quad \text{Cl} \end{array}$$

can be written, one of the $3d$ orbitals as well as the $3s$ and three $3p$ orbitals must be called on, and in order to form six covalent bonds in the hexafluophosphate ion

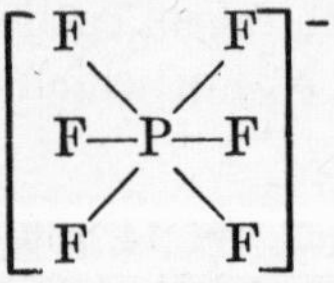

$$\left[\begin{array}{c} \text{F} \qquad \text{F} \\ \diagdown \; \diagup \\ \text{F—P—F} \\ \diagup \; \diagdown \\ \text{F} \qquad \text{F} \end{array} \right]^{-}$$

two $3d$ orbitals are needed.

A maximum of nine covalent bonds can be formed with use of the orbitals of the M shell. This limitation is, however, not of great significance, inasmuch as other factors, discussed later in the book, provide a more serious limitation with respect to the number of atoms which can be bonded to a central atom.[1]

bonds, whereas in the discussion above the comparison is with only one single bond.

[1] A sharp distinction is to be made between the number of atoms bonded to a central atom (the *coordination number* of the central atom) and the

The octet rule similarly retains some significance for third-row atoms and still heavier atoms, aside from those of the transition elements. Thus we can, for example, assign to arsine and stibine structures analogous to those for phosphine, using the four s and p orbitals of the valence shell of the central atom.

For the transition elements use is often made in covalent bond formation of some of the d orbitals of the shell just inside the valence shell, as well as of the s and p orbitals of the valence shell. We write for the hexachloropalladate ion, for example, the structure

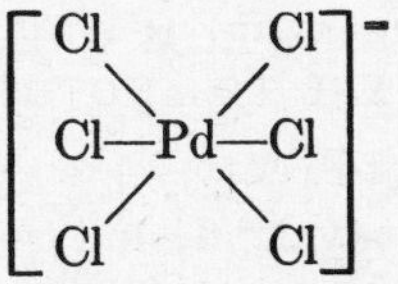

$$
\left[
\begin{array}{ccc}
\text{Cl} & & \text{Cl} \\
 & \diagdown \quad \diagup & \\
\text{Cl} & \!-\!\text{Pd}\!-\! & \text{Cl} \\
 & \diagup \quad \diagdown & \\
\text{Cl} & & \text{Cl}
\end{array}
\right]^{-}
$$

with six covalent bonds from the palladium atom to the six surrounding chlorine atoms. There are in the palladium atom, in addition to the six bonding electron pairs, forty-two electrons. These, in pairs, occupy the $1s$, $2s$, three $2p$, $3s$, three $3p$, five $3d$, $4s$, three $4p$, and three of the $4d$ orbitals. The six bonds are formed by use of the remaining two $4d$ orbitals, the $5s$ orbital, and the three $5p$ orbitals. A detailed discussion of the selection and use of atomic orbitals in bond formation is given in Chapter III and later chapters.

---

number of covalent bonds formed by the central atom (its *covalence*). These numbers may, and often do, differ, as a result of the attachment of some of the surrounding atoms by bonds of type other than single covalent bonds, such as double bonds or electrostatic bonds.

CHAPTER II

THE PARTIAL IONIC CHARACTER OF COVALENT BONDS AND THE RELATIVE ELECTRO-NEGATIVITY OF ATOMS

7. THE TRANSITION FROM ONE EXTREME BOND TYPE TO ANOTHER

After the development twenty years ago of the modern ideas of the ionic bond and the covalent bond the following question was formulated and vigorously discussed: if it were possible to vary continuously one or more of the parameters determining the nature of a molecule or a crystal, such as the effective nuclear charges of the atoms, then would the transition from one extreme bond type to another take place continuously, or would it show discontinuities? With the extension of our understanding of the nature of the chemical bond it has now become possible to answer this question; the pertinent argument is given in the following paragraph, leading to the conclusion that in some cases the transition would take place continuously, whereas in others an effective discontinuity would appear.[1]

7a. Continuous Change in Bond Type.—Let us first consider the case of a molecule involving a single bond between two atoms A and B, which for certain values of the structural parameters for the molecule is a normal covalent bond of the type formed by like atoms and discussed in Sections 5 and 6, and for other

---

[1] Lewis has since 1916 supported the idea that the transition would be continuous, and that the shared electron pair is in general attracted more strongly by one than by the other of two unlike bonded atoms, the bond having a corresponding amount of ionic or "polar" character. Sidgwick ("The Covalent Link in Chemistry," 1933, p. 42 ff.) and London (*Naturwiss.* 17, 525 (1929)) have expressed the opinion that, although the transition between two extreme bond types might occur without discontinuity, there is an essential difference between the two types of bonds and that only rarely will there occur a molecule containing a bond of intermediate type. This latter opinion is contrary to that which we shall form as a result of the discussion given in this chapter.

34

values of the parameters is an ionic bond A^+B^-, the more electronegative of the two atoms holding both of the electrons as an unshared pair occupying one of the orbits of its outer shell. For intermediate values of the structural parameters of the molecule the wave function $a\psi_{A:B} + b\psi_{A^+B^-}$, formed by linear combination of the wave functions corresponding to the normal covalent structure $A:B$ and the ionic structure A^+B^-, with numerical coefficients a and b, can be used to represent the structure of the molecule, the value of the ratio of the coefficients, b/a, being for each set of values of the structural parameters such as to make the bond energy a maximum.[1] As the parameters of the molecule (in particular, the relative electronegativity of A and B) were changed, the ratio b/a would change from zero to infinity, the bond changing in type without discontinuity from the covalent extreme to the ionic extreme by passing through all intermediate stages. In the case under discussion the two extreme structures are of such a nature (each involving only paired electrons and essentially the same configuration of the atomic nuclei) as to permit resonance, and hence the transition from one extreme type of bond to the other would be continuous.

For an intermediate value of the relative electronegativity of A and B, such that the coefficients a and b in the wave function $a\psi_{A:B} + b\psi_{A^+B^-}$ are about equal in magnitude, the bond might be described as *resonating between the covalent extreme and the ionic extreme*, the contributions of the two being given[2] by the values of a^2 and b^2. In case that the extreme covalent structure $A:B$ and the extreme ionic structure A^+B^- correspond separately to the same bond energy value, then the two structures will contribute equally to the actual state of the molecule, and the actual bond energy will be greater than the bond energy for either structure alone by an amount equal to the interaction energy of the two structures; that is, resonance between the two structures will stabilize the molecule. If one of the two extreme structures corresponds to a greater bond energy than the other, the more stable structure will contribute more to the actual state of the molecule than the less stable one, and the actual bond energy

---

[1] That is, to minimize the energy of the system (Sec. 3).

[2] The squares of the coefficients of terms in a composite wave function are interpreted as representing the magnitudes of the contributions of the corresponding structures.

will be increased somewhat by resonance over that for the more stable structure. The relation between the extra resonance energy stabilizing the bond, the interaction energy of the two structures, and the bond energy values of the two structures is the same as that described in an analogous case in Section 4c.

For a molecule such as hydrogen chloride we write the two reasonable electronic structures H:Cl̈: and H⁺ :Cl̈:⁻. (The third structure which suggests itself, H:⁻ Cl̈:⁺, is not given much importance because hydrogen is recognized as less electronegative than chlorine; a discussion of the extent to which such a structure contributes to the normal state of a molecule is given in Section 8.) In accordance with the foregoing argument the actual state of the molecule can be described as corresponding to resonance between these two structures. (The extent to which each structure contributes its character to the actual bond is discussed in detail for hydrogen chloride and other molecules in the following sections of this chapter.) Instead of using this description of the bond as involving resonance between an extreme covalent bond H:Cl̈: and an extreme ionic bond H⁺Cl⁻, we may describe the bond as a *covalent bond with partial ionic character*, and make use of the *valence line*, writing H—Cl (or H—Cl̈:) in place of {H:Cl̈:, H⁺Cl⁻} or some similar complex symbol showing resonance between the two extremes. This alternative description is to be recognized as equivalent to the first; whenever a question arises as to the properties expected for a covalent bond with partial ionic character, it is to be answered by consideration of the corresponding resonating structures.

The amount of ionic character of a bond in a molecule must not be confused with the tendency of the molecule to ionize in a suitable solvent. The ionic character of the bond is determined by the importance of the ionic structure (A⁺B⁻) *when the nuclei are at their equilibrium distance* (1.28 Å for HCl, for example), whereas the tendency to ionize in solution is determined by the relative stability of the actual molecules in the solution and the separated ions in the solution. It is reasonable, however, for the tendency toward ionization in solution to accompany large ionic character of bonds in general, since both result from great difference in electronegativity of the bonded atoms.

Transitions between other extreme types of bonds (covalent to metallic, covalent to ion-dipole, etc.) can also occur without discontinuity, and the bonds of intermediate character can be discussed in terms of resonance between structures of extreme type in the same way as for covalent-ionic bonds.

7b. Discontinuous Change in Bond Type.[1]—In molecules and complex ions of certain types continuous transition from one extreme bond type to another is not possible.   In order for continuous transition to be possible between two extreme bond types, the conditions for resonance between the corresponding structures must be satisfied.   The most important of these conditions is that the two structures must involve the same numbers of unpaired electrons.   *If the two structures under consideration involve different numbers of unpaired electrons, then the transition between the two must be discontinuous, the discontinuity being associated with the pairing or unpairing of electrons.*[2]

The most important molecules and complex ions for which this phenomenon occurs are those containing a transition-group atom. Let us discuss as an example the octahedral complexes FeX_6 of ferric iron.   If the Fe—X bonds are of the extreme ionic or ion-dipole type, the electronic structure about the iron nucleus will be the same as for the Fe^{+++} ion; of the 23 electrons of this ion, 18 occupy the $1s$, $2s$, three $2p$, $3s$, and three $3p$ orbitals in pairs, and the remaining five occupy the five $3d$ orbitals without pairing, as described in Section 6a.   If, however, covalent Fe—X bonds are formed with use of two of the $3d$ orbitals (as well as some of the other orbitals—see Sec. 15a), as in the ferricyanide ion, $[Fe(CN)_6]^{\equiv}$, then the five unshared $3d$ electrons of the iron atom must crowd into the remaining three $3d$ orbitals, with formation of two pairs.   This complex contains only one unpaired electron, whereas the complexes with ionic bonds ($[FeF_6]^{\equiv}$) and ion-dipole bonds ($[Fe(H_2O)_6]^{+++}$) contain five unpaired electrons.   Transition between these structures cannot be continuous.

[1] L. Pauling, *J.A.C.S.* **53**, 1367 (1931); **54**, 988 (1932).
[2] This statement is rigorously true in case that spin-orbit and spin-spin interactions are negligible (as for all light atoms), and is practically true in general.

Resonance is possible, of course, between an ionic FeX_6 structure and a covalent structure in which only the outer orbitals $4s$, $4p$, $4d$, etc. are used in bond formation. This covalent structure with five unpaired electrons would be different in character from that using two $3d$ orbitals, however, and continuous transition to the latter could not occur.

The nature of the discontinuity under discussion is shown in Figure 7-1. Two states of a complex FeX_6 are represented, one

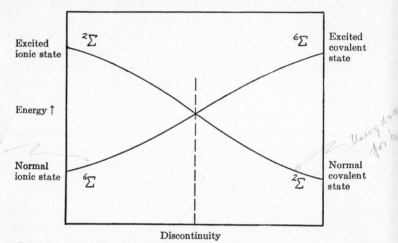

FIG. 7-1.—Energy curves for a ferric complex FeX_6. The curve $^2\Sigma$ represents a stable covalent structure or unstable ionic structure, and the curve $^6\Sigma$ represents an unstable covalent structure or stable ionic structure.

with five unpaired electrons and the other with one. For certain atoms or groups X one of the states is the more stable, and represents the normal complex, and for others the other state is the stable one. At the discontinuity in the nature of the normal state of the complex the energy curves of the two states cross. An actual system would contain complexes in both states, with concentrations determined by the energy difference of the two; an appreciable number of complexes in the less stable state would be present, however, only for the region near the intersection of the two curves.

These complexes and others of similar character are discussed further in Chapter III, in which a magnetic criterion for bond type applicable to complexes of the transition elements is described.

7c. Bond Type and Atomic Arrangement.— The properties of a substance depend in part upon the type of bonds between the atoms of the substance and in part upon the atomic arrangement and the distribution of the bonds. The atomic arrangement is itself determined to a great extent by the nature of the bonds: the directed character of covalent bonds (as in the tetrahedral carbon atom) plays an especially important part in determining the configurations of molecules and crystals; an important part is also played by the interatomic repulsive forces which give "size" to atoms and ions (Chaps. V, X).

During the last twenty-five years there has been collected a great amount of information regarding the atomic arrangement in molecules and crystals. This information can often be interpreted in terms of the nature and distribution of bonds; a detailed discussion of the dependence of interatomic distances and bond angles on bond type will be given in later chapters.

An abrupt change in properties in a series of compounds, such as in the melting points or boiling points of metal halides, has sometimes been considered to indicate an abrupt change in bond type. Thus of the fluorides of the second-row elements,

	NaF	MgF_2	AlF_3	SiF_4	PF_5	SF_6
Melting point	980°	1400°	1040°	−77°	−83°	−55°C.

those of high melting points have been described as salts, and the others as covalent compounds; and the great change in melting point from aluminum fluoride to silicon fluoride has been interpreted as showing that the bonds change sharply from the extreme ionic type to the extreme covalent type.[1] I consider the bonds in aluminum fluoride to be only slightly different in character from those in silicon fluoride, and attribute the abrupt change in properties to a change in the nature of the atomic arrangement.[2] In NaF, MgF_2, and AlF_3 the relative sizes of the metal and non-metal atoms is such as to make the stable co-ordination number of the metal six; each of the metal atoms is surrounded by an octahedron of fluorine atoms, and the stoichiometric relations then require that each fluorine atom be held jointly by six sodium atoms in NaF (which has the sodium

---

[1] N. V. Sidgwick, "The Electronic Theory of Valency," Oxford, 1929, p. 88; "The Covalent Link in Chemistry," Cornell, 1933, p. 52.

[2] L. Pauling, *J.A.C.S.* **54**, 988 (1932).

chloride structure, Fig. 2-1), by three magnesium atoms in
MgF₂ (with the rutile structure, Fig. 7-2), or by two aluminum
atoms in AlF₃.   In each of these crystals the molecules are thus
combined into giant polymers, and the processes of fusion and
vaporization can take place only by breaking the strong chemical
bonds between metal and non-metal atoms; in consequence the
substances have high melting points and boiling points.   The
stable coordination number of silicon relative to fluorine is, on
the other hand, four, so that the SiF₄ molecule has little tendency

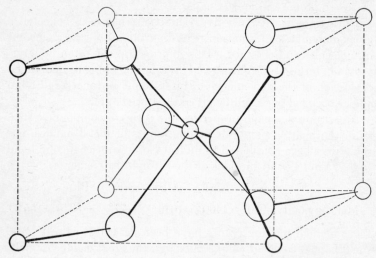

Fig. 7-2.—The atomic arrangement of the tetragonal crystal rutile, TiO₂.
Large circles represent oxygen atoms, small circles titanium atoms.

to form polymers.[1]   The crystal of silicon fluoride consists of
SiF₄ molecules piled together and held together only by weak
van der Waals forces.   Fusion and vaporization of this substance involve no great change in the molecule; the strong Si—F
bonds are not broken, but only the weak intermolecular bonds,
and hence the melting point and boiling point are low.   In
phosphorus pentafluoride and sulfur hexafluoride too there is no
tendency for the coordination numbers of the central atoms to be
increased by polymerization, and the physical properties of these
substances are accordingly similar to those of silicon fluoride.   It
was mentioned eighteen years ago by Kossel that ease of fusion

[1] Silicon also assumes the coordination number six with fluorine in the
fluosilicate ion.

and volatilization would be expected for ionic molecules in which a central cation is surrounded by several anions, and is not good evidence for the presence of covalent bonds.[1] Volatility, as well as many other properties such as hardness, cleavability, etc., depends mainly not so much on bond type as on the atomic arrangement and the distribution of bonds.

There is, to be sure, some correlation between bond type and type of atomic arrangement. Ionic crystals often possess a coordinated structure such that ionic bonds extend throughout the crystal, leading to low volatility. The low volatility of substituted ammonium salts, for example, arises in this way. Another structural feature which leads to high melting points and striking hardness of crystals is the hydrogen bond between molecules (Chap. IX); it is interesting to note that since the hydrogen bond is essentially ionic in nature its effects may be ascribed to its ionic character.

8. THE NATURE OF THE BONDS IN DIATOMIC HALIDE MOLECULES

In the hydrogen molecule a quantum-mechanical treatment has shown that the two ionic structures H^+H^- and H^-H^+ enter into resonance with the extreme covalent structure $H:H$ to only a small extent, each ionic structure contributing only about 2% to the actual normal state of the molecule (Sec. 5c). The reason for this small contribution of the ionic structures is that these structures are unstable relative to the covalent structure, the large amount of energy (295 kcal./mole) required to transfer an electron from one nucleus to the other and form a positive and a negative ion not being completely counterbalanced by the mutual Coulomb energy of the ions. There is not much evidence as to the amount of ionic character of other single bonds between like atoms, as in the chlorine molecule Cl_2. Consideration of energy values makes it probable,[2] however, that in this molecule the

---

[1] W. Kossel, *Z. f. Phys.* 1, 395 (1920).

[2] The ionization energy of chlorine is 299 kcal./mole and its electron affinity 93 kcal./mole, making separated ions Cl^+ and Cl^- unstable relative to atoms by 206 kcal./mole. The Coulomb energy $-e^2/R$ of two ions at the Cl—Cl equilibrium distance $R = 1.988$ Å is -166 kcal./mole, and the extreme covalent bond energy is about 55 kcal./mole. Hence in the equilibrium configuration the ionic structures Cl^+Cl^- and Cl^-Cl^+ are unstable relative to the covalent structure by at least 95 kcal./mole. (The characteristic repulsion of the two ions is neglected.) This energy differ-

ionic structures Cl^+Cl^- and Cl^-Cl^+ make a still smaller contribution to the actual normal state than for the hydrogen molecule.   In general we shall use the symbols Cl—Cl or $:\overset{..}{C}l$—$\overset{..}{C}l:$ to represent a single covalent bond of the sort existent between the two like atoms, including the small equal contributions of the two ionic structures.

Now let us consider the bond between two unlike atoms which however do not differ greatly in electronegativity, such as chlorine and bromine.   The energy required to form the ions Br^+ and Cl^- from the atoms Br and Cl is only 179 kcal./mole, whereas that required to form the ions Br^- and Cl^+ is 212 kcal./mole; accordingly the ionic structure Br^-Cl^+ makes only a very small resonance contribution to the normal state of the BrCl molecule (smaller than that made by the ionic structures in Br_2 and Cl_2), and the ionic structure Br^+Cl^- makes a somewhat larger contribution than that made by the ionic structures in the symmetric molecules.

In hydrogen chloride the energy of formation of the ions H^+ and Cl^- from atoms is 219 kcal./mole, and that of the ions H^- and Cl^+ is 283 kcal./mole.   The ionic structure H^-Cl^+ is accordingly very much less important than the structure H^+Cl^-.   A qualitative estimate of the extent to which the ionic structures H^+X^- and the extreme covalent structures $H:\overset{..}{X}:$ contribute to the normal states of the four hydrogen halides can be made by the consideration of energy curves.   In Figure 8-1 calculated energy curves are shown for the structures H^+X^- and $H:\overset{..}{X}:$ for each of the molecules HF, HCl, HBr, and HI.   It is seen that in the neighborhood of the equilibrium internuclear distances (at the minima of the curves) the covalent curves for HCl, HBr, and HI lie below the ionic curves, the separation increasing from HCl to HI.   This shows that the bonds in these molecules are essentially covalent, with, however, a small amount of H^+X^- ionic character, which is presumably greatest in HCl (of the three) and least in HI.   (The reasonable assumption is here made that the interaction-energy integral of the two structures H^+X^- and HX is about the same in the three molecules, and that the

___

ence is so great as to permit the ionic structures to enter into resonance with the covalent structure to only a small extent.

manifestation of this interaction as resonance energy is
decreased by increase in the
energy difference of the resonating structures, as discussed in Section 4c.) The
effect of resonance on the
energy is shown by the full
lines in the figure, representing actual states (normal and
excited) of the molecules.

In hydrogen fluoride the
situation is different. For
this molecule the ionic curve
falls below the covalent curve
in the neighborhood of the
equilibrium internuclear distance. In consequence of
this *the ionic structure H^+F^-
makes a larger contribution to
the normal state of the molecule than the covalent structure* $H:F:$; the hydrogen-
fluoride bond has a little
more than 50% ionic char-
acter.[1] Because the two energy curves lie close to-
gether, resonance is nearly
complete, and almost the entire interaction energy between the two structures is
effective as resonance energy.

The curves of Figure 8-1 have
been drawn in the following way.
The extreme covalent curves are
Morse curves[2] with equilibrium

[1] This follows from the general
theorem that of two structures
in resonance, the more stable
makes a greater contribution to
the normal state of the system
than the less stable.

[2] See "Introduction to Quantum Mechanics," Sec. 35d.

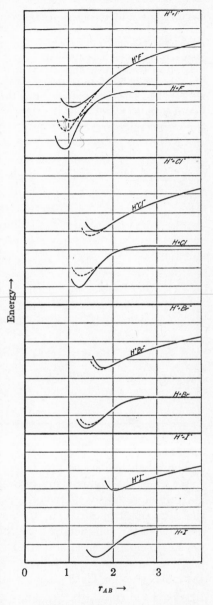

Fig. 8-1.—Calculated energy curves for
the hydrogen halide molecules. The two
dashed curves for each molecule represent
extreme ionic and extreme covalent structures, the two full curves the actual structures resulting from resonance between
these. The dashed curves for HI lie very
close to the full curves.

distances given by the sums of the single-bond covalent radii (Sec. 21), curvatures calculated by Badger's rule (Sec. 21d), and bond energies calculated by the method of the geometric mean (Sec. 9a).   The curves for the ionic structures H^+X^- represent the interaction of a proton with negative ions with electron distribution functions calculated by use of hydrogenlike wave functions with suitable screening constants, polarization being neglected.[1]   The curves representing the normal states are Morse curves drawn with the experimentally determined values of the parameters.

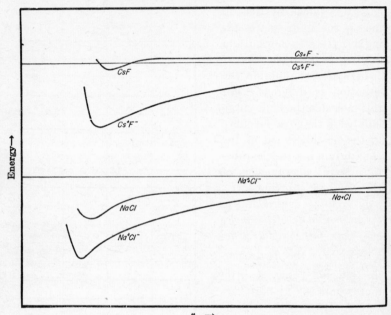

Fig. 8-2.—Energy curves for alkali halide gas molecules.

The alkali halide gas molecules MX present a still more extreme case, the bonds being essentially ionic with only a small amount of covalent character.   For cesium fluoride, involving the most electropositive of the metals and the most electronegative of the non-metals, the electron affinity of the non-metal (98 kcal./mole) is greater than the ionization potential of the metal (89 kcal./mole), so that even at large internuclear distances the ionic structure Cs^+F^- is more stable than the covalent structure $Cs:\overset{..}{\underset{..}{F}}:$.   With decreasing internuclear distance the Coulomb

---

[1] L. Pauling, *J A C.S.* **54**, 988 (1932); *Proc. Roy. Soc.* **A114**, 181 (1927); L. Pauling and J. Sherman, *Z. Krist.* **81**, 1 (1932); see also F. T. Wall, *J.A.C.S.* **61**, 1051 (1939).

energy of the ions causes the ionic structure to be favored further relative to the covalent structure, until at the equilibrium distance the energy difference amounts to over 100 kcal./mole (Fig. 8-2). This molecule contains a bond which is nearly completely ionic in character, the covalent contribution being very small—of the order of magnitude of a few percent.

The other alkali halide molecules are also largely ionic. The energy curves for a representative molecule, sodium chloride, are shown in Figure 8-2. At very large internuclear distances the covalent structure is more stable than the ionic structure; but at about 10 Å the Coulomb attraction causes the curves to cross, and the ionic structure remains the more stable one at smaller internuclear distances. The bonds in all of these molecules are essentially ionic, with only a small amount of covalent character.

The covalent curves of Figure 8-2 have been drawn in the same way as described for the HX curves. The ionic curves represent a Coulomb attractive potential and a repulsive potential b/R^9, in which the constant b is given values which lead (with use of the Madelung constant and corresponding constant in the repulsive potential) to the correct interatomic distances in the corresponding crystals (Chap. X). Polarization is neglected.

An effort has at times been made to determine the type of bond in a molecule by consideration of the nature of the products of dissociation of the molecule. It can be shown, however, that there is no close relation. From the energy curves of Figure 8-2 we see that on separation of the nuclei the normal CsF molecule would dissociate into ions. The NaCl molecule, however, would dissociate into atoms; the energy curve of the normal state, formed by resonance between the ionic and the covalent structures, lies below the lower of the two corresponding curves, following below the ionic curve to the intersection and then switching to the covalent curve. Hence these two alkali halide molecules, both with essentially ionic bonds, would dissociate into different products.[1]

In all of the molecules discussed above the bond is intermediate between the covalent extreme M:Ẍ: and the ionic ex-

[1] The above argument requires that the separation of the nuclei take place sufficiently slowly for the resonance between the structures to occur. The interaction of the structures at 10 Å is small, and there is a chance that rapid separation of the nuclei would lead to dissociation into ions.

treme M^+X^-, varying from an essentially covalent bond with only a small amount of ionic character (hydrogen iodide), through a bond with about equal amounts of covalent and ionic character (hydrogen fluoride), to an essentially ionic bond with only a small amount of covalent character (cesium fluoride).

We may attempt to make a rough quantitative statement regarding the bond type in these molecules with use of dipole-moment data. For the hydrogen halides only very small electric dipole moments would be expected in case that the bonds were purely covalent. For the ionic structure H^+X^-, on the other hand, moments approximating the product of the electronic charge and the internuclear separations would be expected. (Some reduction would result from polarization of the anion by the cation; this we neglect.) In Table 8-1 there are given values of the equilibrium internuclear distances R_0, the electric moments eR_0 calculated for the ionic structure H^+X^-, the observed values of the electric moments μ, and the ratios of these to the values

TABLE 8-1.—ELECTRIC DIPOLE MOMENTS AND IONIC CHARACTER
OF HYDROGEN HALIDE MOLECULES

	R_0	eR_0	μ	μ/eR_0
HCl	1.28 Å	6.07×10^{-18} e.s.u.	1.03×10^{-18} e.s.u.	0.170
HBr	1.43	6.82	0.78	0.114
HI	1.62	7.74	0.38	0.049

of eR_0. These ratios may be interpreted in a simple way as representing the magnitudes of the contributions of the ionic structures to the normal states of the molecules; that is, the amounts of ionic character of the bonds. It is seen that on this basis the bond in hydrogen chloride is 17% ionic, that in hydrogen bromide is 11% ionic, and that in hydrogen iodide is 5% ionic. The dipole moment of hydrogen fluoride is not known; from the calculated energy curves we see, however, that the bond in this molecule must have just over one-half ionic character, and we may make the estimate that it is about 60% ionic. The comparison of the energy curves of the alkali halides with those of the hydrogen halides suggests that in the alkali halides the bonds have 5 to 10% covalent character.

It must be mentioned that the attempt to discuss bond type in this rough quantitative way without giving a complete quantum mechanical treatment of the molecules cannot be rigorously justified. We have adopted the procedure of discussing the structure of molecules and the nature of chemical bonds as completely as possible with use only of the most stable of the atomic orbitals; following this procedure, we are led to base our discussion on the simple structures $M:X$, M^+X^-, and M^-X^+. It is possible,[1] on the other hand, to develop (at least in principle) a complete discussion of the structure of a molecule from either the purely ionic point of view (with extreme polarization or deformation of the ions), or the covalent point of view, provided that all the unstable atomic orbitals are used in the discussion. No treatment of either of these types has been carried out for molecules of any complexity, however, whereas the reasonable procedure which forms the basis of our argument has found extensive application to the problems of structural chemistry.

9. BOND ENERGIES OF HALIDE MOLECULES. THE POSTULATE OF THE ADDITIVITY OF THE ENERGIES OF NORMAL COVALENT BONDS[2]

The wave function representing the single bond in a symmetric molecule A—A can be written in the form

$$a\psi_{A:A} + b\psi_{A^+A^-} + b\psi_{A^-A^+}, \qquad (9\text{-}1)$$

and a similar expression can be written for another molecule B—B. The ratio b/a, determining the contributions of the ionic structures, is small, and probably about the same for all bonds between like atoms.

Now let us consider a molecule A—B, involving a single bond between two unlike atoms. If the atoms were closely similar in character, the bond in this molecule could be represented by a wave function such as 9-1, an average of those for the symmetric molecules A—A and B—B. Let us describe such a bond as a *normal covalent bond*.

If, now, we consider a molecule A—B in which the atoms A and B are dissimilar, one being more electronegative than the other, then we must use a more general wave function,

$$a\psi_{A:B} + c\psi_{A^+B^-} + d\psi_{A^-B^+}, \qquad (9\text{-}2)$$

[1] J. C. Slater, *Phys. Rev.* **41**, 255 (1932).
[2] L. Pauling and D. M. Yost, *Proc. Nat. Acad. Sci.* **18**, 414 (1932); L. Pauling, *J.A.C.S.* **54**, 3570 (1932).

to represent the bond, the best values of c/a and d/a being those which make the bond energy a maximum (minimize the total energy of the molecule).   These values will in general be different from b/a, of 9-1, one being smaller and one greater.   Since they make the bond energy a maximum, we see that *the energy of an actual bond between unlike atoms is greater than (or equal to) the energy of a normal covalent bond between these atoms.*   This additional bond energy is due to the *additional ionic character of the bond;* that is, it is the *additional ionic resonance energy* which the bond has as compared with a bond between like atoms.   In referring to these quantities later we shall omit the word "additional," and say "ionic character of the bond" and "ionic resonance energy."

To test this conclusion, we need values of the energies of normal covalent bonds between unlike atoms.   These values might be calculated by quantum-mechanical methods; it is simpler, however, to make a postulate and test it empirically.   Since a normal covalent bond A—B is similar in character to the bonds A—A and B—B, we expect the value of the bond energy to be intermediate between the values for A—A and B—B.   This result follows from the *postulate of the additivity of normal covalent bonds.*   That is, we assume that the arithmetic mean of the two bond energy values $D(A—A)$ and $D(B—B)$ is the energy of the normal covalent bond between the unlike atoms A and B.

If this postulate were true, actual bond energies $D(A—B)$ between unlike atoms would always be greater than or equal to the arithmetic means of the corresponding symmetrical bond energies; the difference Δ defined as

$$\Delta = D(A—B) - \tfrac{1}{2}\{D(A—A) + D(B—B)\} \qquad (9\text{-}3)$$

would never be negative.   In Table 9-1 there are given values of bond energies and of Δ for the hydrogen halides and halogen halides.[1]

---

[1] In Tables 9-1, 9-2, 9-3, and 9-4 the heat contents at 291°K are used as the basis for the calculation of bond energies, which accordingly include not only the energies of dissociation D_0 of the molecules but also small terms corresponding to the rotational, oscillational, and translational energy of the molecules and a pressure-volume term.   These small terms are not significant for our arguments.   Heat contents rather than energy values are used to give uniformity with Section 10.

TABLE 9-1.—BOND ENERGIES FOR HYDROGEN HALIDE AND
HALOGEN HALIDE MOLECULES

	H—H	F—F	Cl—Cl	Br—Br	I—I
Bond energy	103.4	63.5	57.8	46.1	36.2
					kcal./mole

	H—F	H—Cl	H—Br	H—I
Bond energy	147.5	102.7	87.3	71.4
$\frac{1}{2}\{D(\text{H—H}) + D(\text{X—X})\}$	83.5	80.6	74.8	69.8
Δ	64.0	22.1	12.5	1.6

	Cl—F	Br—Cl	I—Br	I—Cl
Bond energy	86.4	52.7	42.9	51.0
$\frac{1}{2}\{D(\text{X—X}) + D(\text{X'—X'})\}$	60.7	52.0	41.2	47.0
Δ	25.7	0.7	1.7	4.0

It is seen that *for each of the eight molecules Δ is positive.* More-over, the magnitudes of the Δ values, which measure the res-onance energy due to ionic character of the unsymmetrical bonds, are in agreement with our previously formed conceptions as to the nature of the bonds in these molecules. In the series HI, HBr, HCl, HF we have estimated the amounts of ionic character of the bonds to be 5, 11, 17, and 60%, respectively. The corresponding values of Δ, 1.6, 12.5, 22.1, and 64.0 kcal./mole, increase in the same general way, and show the expected large change from HCl to HF. (The only unexpected feature is the very small value of Δ for HI.) The molecule BrCl approaches the normal covalent type still more closely, with Δ equal to only 0.7 kcal./mole. This is the expected result for a bond between two atoms which resemble one another as closely as chlorine and bromine. The values of Δ for IBr and ICl are also small, but that for ClF is even larger than that for HCl, showing that chlorine fluoride is more ionic in character than hydrogen chloride. Chlorine, bromine, and iodine do not differ greatly in electronegativity, chlorine and bromine being more closely similar than bromine and iodine in this way as in other ways. But fluorine is very much more electronegative than the other halogens, and de-serves to be classed by itself as a superhalogen.

It is seen that the quantity Δ is just the heat liberated in the reaction

$$\tfrac{1}{2}\text{A}_2 + \tfrac{1}{2}\text{B}_2 \rightarrow \text{AB}, \qquad (9\text{-}4)$$

the substances all being in the gaseous state; and our requirement that Δ be greater than or equal to zero is equivalent to the requirement that a reaction of this type be not endothermic.

It will be shown in a later section that the postulate of additivity is valid for a very large number of single bonds, and that the values of Δ can be used as the basis for the formulation of an extensive scale of electronegativities of the elements. In a few cases, however, the postulate of additivity is found not to hold. The following section is devoted to the discussion of these.

9a. The Postulate of the Geometric Mean.—The alkali metals form double molecules, M_2, which are present in small concentrations in their vapors. The bonds in these molecules are covalent bonds formed by the valence electrons of the atoms; for example, the $2s$ electron of each lithium atom is used in bond formation in the molecule Li:Li. Because of the large spatial extension of the orbitals and small binding energy of the valence electrons, the bonds in the alkali metal molecules are weak, with bond energies between 27.2 (in Li_2) and 10.4 kcal./mole (in Cs_2). The alkali metals also form hydride molecules, MH. In crystals of the alkali hydrides, which have the sodium chloride arrangement, hydrogen forms the anions, H^-, and the alkalis the cations. We might accordingly expect the bonds in the alkali hydride gas molecules to have some ionic character M^+H^-, leading to ionic resonance energy and positive values of Δ. It is seen from Table 9-2, however, that the values of Δ for LiH, NaH, and KH are negative.

TABLE 9-2.—BOND ENERGY VALUES FOR ALKALI HYDRIDE MOLECULES

	H—H	Li—Li	Na—Na	K—K
Bond energy	103.4	27.2	18.4	12.6 kcal./mole

	Li—H	Na—H	K—H
Bond energy	57.7	52.3	44.5
$\frac{1}{2}\{D(M\!-\!M) + D(H\!-\!H)\}$	65.3	60.9	58.0
Δ	−7.6	−8.6	−13.5

This result shows that the postulate of the additivity of the energies of normal covalent bonds is not valid for these molecules. A quantum-mechanical treatment of one-electron bonds has been carried out[1] which leads to the conclusion that the postulate of additivity should be replaced by a similar postulate involving the geometric mean of the bond energies $D(A\!-\!A)$ and $D(B\!-\!B)$

[1] L. Pauling and J. Sherman, *J.A.C.S.* **59**, 1450 (1937).

(that is, the square root of their product) in place of the algebraic mean. This *postulate of the geometric mean* states that the energy of a normal covalent bond between atoms A and B is equal to $\{D(A—A)D(B—B)\}^{1/2}$, and that in consequence the quantity Δ', defined as

$$\Delta' = D(A—B) - \{D(A—A)D(B—B)\}^{1/2}, \qquad (9\text{-}5)$$

should always be greater than or equal to zero. With the new postulate Δ' replaces Δ as the ionic resonance energy of the unsymmetrical bond.

In case that the bond energies $D(A—A)$ and $D(B—B)$ do not differ greatly in value, there is only a small difference between their geometric and algebraic means (which for 30 and 40, for example, are 34.6 and 35.0, respectively); and for this reason the arguments based on the earlier postulate are in general valid for the new one. For the alkali hydrides, however, the new postulate leads to results much different from those given by the earlier one, since the bond energy of the hydrogen molecule is very much greater than those of the alkali molecules, and the geometric and algebraic means are correspondingly different. The values of Δ' for the molecules LiH, NaH, and KH given in Table 9-3 are seen to be positive, as required by the fundamental resonance theorem in case that the postulate of the geometric mean is valid; and, moreover, they increase slightly from LiH to KH, indicating a small increase in ionic character in this order as expected from the increase in electropositivity of the alkali metals with increasing atomic number.

TABLE 9-3

	Li—H	Na—H	K—H
Bond energy	57.7	52.3	44.5 kcal./mole
$\{D(M—M)D(H—H)\}^{1/2}$	*53.0*	*43.6*	*36.1*
Δ'	4.7	8.7	8.4

The postulate of the geometric mean leads for halide molecules to the Δ' values given in Table 9-4, which is analogous to Table 9-1. On comparison of these tables it is seen that the Δ' and Δ values are not greatly different. The most significant change, from $\Delta = 1.6$ to $\Delta' = 10.2$ kcal./mole for HI, is an improvement; the sequence of values $\Delta' = 10.2, 18.3, 25.4$, and 66.5 kcal./mole for the molecules HI, HBr, HCl, and HF, respectively, can be correlated more satisfactorily with the estimated amounts of ionic character of the bonds (5, 11, 17, and 60%) than could the values of Δ.

It is probable that in general the postulate of the geometric mean leads to somewhat more satisfactory values for the energy of normal covalent bonds between unlike atoms than the postulate of additivity. It is more difficult to apply than the postulate of additivity, however, since values of Δ can be obtained directly from heats of reaction, whereas knowledge of individual bond energies is needed for the calculation of values of Δ'; and we shall find it convenient in the following sections of this chapter to make some use of the postulate of additivity as well as of the postulate of the geometric mean.

TABLE 9-4.—IONIC RESONANCE ENERGY FOR HYDROGEN HALIDE AND HALOGEN HALIDE MOLECULES CALCULATED WITH THE POSTULATE OF THE GEOMETRIC MEAN

	H—F	H—Cl	H—Br	H—I
Bond energy	147.5	102.7	87.3	71.4 kcal./mole
$\{D(\text{H—H})D(\text{X—X})\}^{1/2}$	81.0	77.3	69.0	61.2
Δ'	66.5	25.4	18.3	10.2

	Cl—F	Br—Cl	I—Br	I—Cl
Bond energy	86.4	52.7	42.9	51.0
$\{D(\text{X—X})D(\text{X'—X'})\}^{1/2}$	60.6	51.6	40.9	45.7
Δ'	25.8	1.1	2.0	5.3

10. EMPIRICAL VALUES OF SINGLE BOND ENERGIES

Empirical values of bond energies in diatomic molecules are given directly by the energies of dissociation into atoms, which may be determined by thermochemical or spectroscopic methods. In the case of a polyatomic molecule thermochemical data provide a value for the total heat of dissociation into atoms, that is, for the sum of the bond energies in the molecule, but not for the individual bond energies. Thus from the heat of formation of gaseous water from the elements (57.82 kcal./mole) and the heats of dissociation of hydrogen and oxygen (103.4 and 118.2 kcal./mole, respectively), we find that the heat of the reaction

$$2\text{H} + \text{O} \rightarrow \text{H}_2\text{O}$$

is 220.3 kcal./mole. This is the sum of the amounts of energy required to remove first one hydrogen atom from the water molecule, breaking one O—H bond, and then the second hydrogen atom, breaking the other O—H bond. These two energy quantities are not equal, although they are not much different in value. It is convenient for us to define their (average,) 110.2 kcal./mole, as the energy of the O—H bond in the water molecule. In a similar way values can be obtained for bond energies in polyatomic molecules in which all the bonds are alike. It is to be emphasized that each of these bond energy values represents not the amount of energy required to break one bond in the molecule, but instead the average amount required to break all the bonds.

Values for single bond energies, defined in this way, for many bonds can be found by this process—for the S—S bond from the S_8 molecule (an eight-membered ring containing eight S—S bonds), for the P—P bond from the P_4 molecule (a tetrahedron, with six P—P bonds along the tetrahedron edges), for N—H, P—H, S—H, etc. from NH_3, PH_3, H_2S, etc. These values are given in Table 10-1.

TABLE 10-1.—ENERGY VALUES FOR SINGLE BONDS

Bond	Bond energy (kcal./mole)	Bond	Bond energy	Bond	Bond energy
H—H	103.4	O—H	110.2	Si—I	51.1
C—C	58.6	S—H	87.5	Ge—Cl	104.1
Si—Si	42.5	Se—H	73.0	N—F	68.8
Ge—Ge	42.5	H—F	147.5	N—Cl	38.4
N—N	20.0	H—Cl	102.7	P—Cl	62.8
P—P	18.9	H—Br	87.3	P—Br	49.2
As—As	15.1	H—I	71.4	P—I	35.2
O—O	34.9	C—Si	57.6	As—Cl	60.3
S—S	63.8	C—N	48.6	As—Br	48.0
Se—Se	57.6	C—O	70.0	As—I	33.1
F—F	63.5	C—S	54.5	O—F	58.6
Cl—Cl	57.8	C—F	107.0	O—Cl	49.3
Br—Br	46.1	C—Cl	66.5	S—Cl	66.1
I—I	36.2	C—Br	54.0	S—Br	57.2
C—H	87.3	C—I	45.5	Se—Cl	66.8
Si—H	75.1	Si—O	89.3	Cl—F	86.4
N—H	83.7	Si—S	60.9	Br—Cl	52.7
P—H	63.0	Si—F	143.0	I—Cl	51.0
As—H	47.3	Si—Cl	85.8	I—Br	42.9
		Si—Br	69.3		

There is no allotropic form of oxygen in which the atoms are connected by single O—O bonds. The value of the O—O bond energy given in the table has been obtained from the heat of formation of hydrogen peroxide, with use of the assumption that the H—O bond energy in H_2O_2 is the same as in H_2O. The calculation, typical of those used in evaluating bond energies from thermochemical data, is made in the following way. The heat of formation of H_2O_2 (g) from the elements in the standard state is 33.59 kcal./mole. By adding 103.4 and 118.2 (for H_2 and O_2), we obtain 255.2 kcal./mole as the heat of formation of H_2O_2 (g) from atoms 2H and 2O. Subtraction of 220.3 for two O—H bonds leaves 34.9 kcal./mole as the energy of the O—O bond; this is the value given in the table.

The methods used in obtaining the remaining values in the table are described below.

The thermochemical data used in this work have been taken for the most part from the valuable book by F. R. Bichowsky and F. D. Rossini, "The Thermochemistry of the Chemical Substances" (Reinhold Publishing Corporation, New York, 1936). The bond energy values are so chosen that their sums represent the heat changes $(-\Delta H)$ at 291° accompanying the formation of gaseous molecules from gaseous atoms. There is no significance in the inclusion of the vibrational, rotational, and translational energy of the molecules in the bond energies; it is more convenient to do this than to correct the thermochemical data to 0°K (the information required for this correction being often not available), and there are no appreciable disadvantages involved in this procedure.

The following values were used for the heat contents of the gases of atoms in their normal states (the reference states for the bond energies) relative to the standard states of the elements, to which the heats of formation given by Bichowsky and Rossini refer:

TABLE 10-2.—HEAT OF FORMATION OF ELEMENTS IN STANDARD
STATES FROM MONATOMIC GASES (IN KCAL./MOLE)

H	51.7	Cs	18.8	N	85.1	Se	61.0
Li	39.0	C	124.3	P	31.6	F	31.8
Na	25.9	Si	85.0	As	30.3	Cl	28.9
K	19.8	Ge	85.0	O	59.1	Br	26.9
Rb	18.9	Sn	78.0	S	66.3	I	25.6

The heat of formation of a molecule from atoms is obtained by adding these quantities, summed over all the atoms in the molecule, to the heat of formation from the elements in their standard states.

The energy value given for each of the bonds H—H, F—F, Cl—Cl, Br—Br, I—I, H—F, H—Cl, H—Br, H—I, Cl—F, Br—Cl, I—Cl, and I—Br is the thermochemically or spectroscopically determined value of the heat of dissociation of the corresponding diatomic molecule. The values for the bonds Si—Si and Ge—Ge are one-half the heats of sublimation (per gram-atom) of the crystals of these elements, which have the diamond arrangement, with each atom connected by single bonds to its four nearest neighbors, which surround it tetrahedrally. The values for

P—P and As—As are one-sixth of the heats of formation of the molecules $P_4(g)$ and $As_4(g)$ from separated atoms, and those for S—S and Se—Se are one-eighth of the heats of formation of $S_8(g)$ and $Se_8(g)$ from atoms. The O—O bond energy is obtained from the heat of formation of $H_2O_2(g)$ in the way described above.   That for N—N is obtained in a similar way from the heat of formation of hydrazine ($N_2H_4(g)$) with use of the N—H bond energy in NH_3; this calculation has been made possible by the recent thermochemical studies of hydrazine by Gilbert and his collaborators,[1] who found for the heat of formation of anhydrous hydrazine the value 22.25 kcal./mole, in excellent agreement with the value 22.1 kcal./mole predicted[2] with use of the electronegativity scale.

For the bonds Si—H, N—H, P—H, As—H, O—H, S—H, Se—H. Si—F, Si—Cl, Si—Br, Si—I, Ge—Cl, N—F, N—Cl, As—Cl, As—Br, As—I, O—F, and O—Cl energy values are obtained by dividing the heats of formation of the corresponding gas molecules (SiH_4, etc.) from atoms by the numbers of equivalent bonds. In a few cases estimated values (based on boiling points) of heats of vaporization or sublimation have been used to calculate the heat of formation of a gaseous substance from the value reported for the liquid or solid.

The bond energy values for S—Cl, S—Br, and Se—Cl have been obtained from the heats of formation of S_2Cl_2, S_2Br_2, and Se_2Cl_2, respectively, with use of the S—S and Se—Se values, structures such as Cl—S—S—Cl being assumed for these molecules.

For Si—O and Si—S the heats of formation of crystalline SiO_2 (quartz) and SiS_2 divided by the number of bonds per stoichiometric molecule (four) have been used.   These crystals are giant polymers,[3] each silicon atom being connected by single bonds to four surrounding oxygen or sulfur atoms, each of which is bonded to two silicon atoms.

The energy values for bonds involving carbon have been selected in the following way.   For the C—H bond energy the value given by methane has been used.   (The value 124.3 kcal./mole for the heat of sublimation of diamond to gaseous carbon atoms[4] has been used in place of the earlier value given by Bichowsky and Rossini.)   It is found on calculating the C—C bond energy from the heats of formation of ethane and the higher

[1] V. C. Bushnell, A. M. Hughes, and E. C. Gilbert, *J.A.C.S.* 59, 2142 (1937), A. M. Hughes, R. J. Corruccini, and E. C. Gilbert, *ibid.* 61, 2639 (1939).

[2] L. Pauling, *ibid.* 54, 3570 (1932). The values for the N—N bond energy obtained by N. V. Sidgwick, L. E. Sutton, and W. Thomas, *J. Chem. Soc.* 1933, 406, from the heats of combustion of phenylhydrazine and methylphenylhydrazine, 22.3 and 25.0 kcal./mole, respectively (recalculated on the basis of the new heat of dissociation of nitrogen), are larger than the value 20.0 kcal./mole given by hydrazine itself.

[3] The crystal structure of SiS_2, while not the same as that of any of the crystalline modifications of silica, is somewhat similar: see Figure 48-12; A. Zintl and K. Loosen, *Z. f. phys. Chem.* A174, 301 (1935); W. Büssem, H. Fischer, and E. Gruner, *Naturwiss.* 23, 740 (1935).

[4] This corresponds to the value 124.1 kcal./mole for the heat of sub-

aliphatic hydrocarbons with use of this C—H value and also from diamond itself that not a constant value but somewhat variable results are obtained, covering a range of about 3 kcal./mole.[1] Following an earlier decision,[2] I have chosen to neglect the diamond value, and to choose a value for the C—C bond energy which when combined with the C—H value leads to sums which agree closely with the observed heats of formation of saturated hydrocarbons. The agreement is in general reasonably good (to within 1 or 2 kcal./mole). Because of the fact that the heats of formation of molecules can be represented only approximately by sums of constant bond energies, there is some arbitrariness in the selection of values for inclusion in the table. For the considerations in this chapter and later chapters uncertainties of the order of one or two kcal./mole are of little importance, and we shall not attempt to present a more refined treatment.

The energy value for the C—N bond has been obtained from the aliphatic amines, that for the C—O bond from ethers, and that for the C—S bond from thio-ethers and mercaptans. The values for carbon-halogen bonds have been obtained from the halogen-substituted methanes, and that for C—Si is from crystalline carborundum.

Of the values given in the table, many were originally published several years ago.[3] The values given in the original publication differ from those in the table in part because of change in the value used for the heat of sublimation of carbon and in the state of reference,[4] this change leading to a decrease of 12.8 kcal./mole for each single bond to carbon, and also of a change in the value accepted for the heat of dissociation of nitrogen, leading to a decrease of 6.6 kcal./mole for each bond to nitrogen. These revisions in the states of reference for bond energy values are of no significance in discussions based on energy differences, such as the calculation of extra ionic resonance energy with the postulate of the additivity of energy of normal covalent bonds or the calculation of the energy of resonance of a molecule among several valence-bond structures (Chap. IV), and in general the conclusions drawn with use of the earlier values are still valid.

---

limation of graphite reported by G. Herzberg, *Chem. Rev.* **20**, 145 (1937); see also P. Goldfinger and W. Jeunehomme, *Trans. Faraday Soc.* **32**, 1591 (1936).

[1] This lack of constancy of bond energies in these substances was pointed out by K. Fajans, *Ber.* **53**, 643 (1920); **55**, 2826 (1922); *Z. f. phys. Chem.* **99**, 395 (1921), and has been given a thorough discussion recently by F. D. Rossini, *Bur. Standards J. Res.* **13**, 21 (1934). See also J. B. Conant and G. B. Kistiakowsky, *Chem. Rev.* **20**, 181 (1937).

[2] L. Pauling, *J.A.C.S.* **54**, 3570 (1932).

[3] L. Pauling, *loc. cit.* Somewhat similar values have also been published by Sidgwick, "The Covalent Link in Chemistry," 1933.

[4] An estimated correction was also made in the early work for the difference between the normal ^3P state and the ^5S state of the carbon atom, the latter being used as the reference state. The present values are based on the normal ^3P state.

A fundamental assumption adopted in the formulation and use of the bond energy values of Table 10-1 is that the energy of a molecule to which a single valence-bond structure can be confidently assigned can be approximated closely by the sum of constant terms corresponding to the bonds. This assumption is found to be justified empirically to a considerable extent, the heats of formation calculated by summing the bond energies agreeing with the experimental values to within a few kcal./mole for nearly all molecules. As an example selected at random, the heat of formation of $CH_2FCH_2OH(g)$ from elements in their standard states is 97.0 kcal./mole; this leads to 695.0 kcal./mole on addition of the suitable terms from Table 10-2 for the heat of formation from monatomic gases. The sum of the bond energies for four C—H bonds, one C—F bond, one C—C bond, one C—O bond, and one O—H bond from Table 10-1 is 695.0 kcal./mole, the agreement in this case thus being excellent.

The bond energy values are devised for use only with molecules containing atoms which show their normal covalences (four for carbon, three for nitrogen, etc.). An ammonium salt or a substance such as trimethylamine oxide cannot be treated in this way. The bond energies are also not expected to be valid for a molecule such as phosphorus pentachloride. It is interesting to point out that the heat of the reaction $PCl_3(g) + 2Cl(g) \rightarrow PCl_5(g)$, 78.7 kcal./mole, corresponds to the formation of two new P—Cl bonds of energy 39.4 kcal./mole, which is much less than the normal P—Cl bond energy, 62.8 kcal./mole.

Bond energies can be used in the discussion of the structure of molecules. For example, six years ago it was pointed out that the heat of formation expected for ozone from molecular oxygen would be −75.6 kcal./mole or less (if a correction were made for strain in the three-membered ring), in case that the molecule had

the structure ; the observed value −34.5 kcal./ mole

differs from this by so great an amount as to permit this structure for ozone to be eliminated. A similar discrepancy between the

value −100.8 calculated for the structure and the

observed heat of formation 0.13 kcal./mole of the molecule O_4 eliminates this structure. Evidence is now available from spectroscopic sources also showing that these single-bonded structures are not correct for O_3 and O_4.

The use of bond energies in the discussion of molecules containing multiple bonds and of molecules which can not be represented satisfactorily by one valence-bond structure will be presented in Chapters IV and VI.

11. THE ELECTRONEGATIVITY SCALE OF THE ELEMENTS

11a. The Formulation of the Electronegativity Scale.—In Section 9 it was pointed out that the values of $\Delta(A—B)$, the difference between the energy $D(A—B)$ of the bond between two atoms A and B and the energy expected for a normal covalent bond, assumed to be the arithmetic mean of the bond energies $D(A—A)$ and $D(B—B)$, increase as the two atoms A and B become more and more unlike with respect to the qualitative property which the chemist calls *electronegativity*, the power of an atom in a molecule to attract electrons to itself. Thus Δ increases rapidly in the sequence HI, HBr, HCl, HF, in which the halogen changes from iodine, which is recognized by its general chemical properties to be only a little more electronegative than hydrogen, to fluorine, the most electronegative of all the elements.

The property of the electronegativity of an atom in a molecule is different from the electrode potential of the element, which depends on the difference in free energy of the element in its standard state and in ionic solution, and it is different from the ionization potential of the atom, and from its electron affinity; although it is related to these properties in a general way.

It has been found possible to formulate an electronegativity scale of the elements by the analysis of the Δ values given by the single bond energies. In Table 11-1 there are given values of Δ for the bonds between non-metallic atoms whose energies are given in Table 10-1. These are obtained in the same way as those in Table 9-1. It is seen on inspection that the values of Δ do not satisfy an additivity relation; they cannot be represented as differences of terms characteristic of the two atoms in the bond. However, the square roots of the Δ values do satisfy approximately a relation of this sort. In the table there are given values of $0.208\sqrt{\Delta}$. (These are the square roots of the Δ

values expressed in electron volts; that is, $\sqrt{\Delta/23.06}$. In the original formulation of the electronegativity scale[1] the electron-volt was used as the unit of energy, and it seems desirable to adhere to this, since it leads to a convenient range for the electronegativity scale.) These values for H—Br and Br—Cl, for example, add to 0.92, not far from the H—Cl value 0.98, whereas the sum of Δ(H—Br) and Δ(Br—Cl) is 13.2, which is much smaller than Δ(H—Cl), 22.1. It is, indeed, possible to assign to the elements *electronegativity values* such that their differences are approximately equal to the square roots of the Δ values in electron-volts.

The electronegativity values selected for the elements occurring in Table 11-1 are given in Table 11-2. Their differences are determined by the values of $0.208\sqrt{\Delta}$ in Table 11-1. An additive constant has been so chosen as to give the first-row elements C to F the values 2.5 to 4.0.   *values were used to define x*
put back in to check deviation.

TABLE 11-1.—EXTRA IONIC ENERGY OF BONDS AND ELECTRONEGATIVITY DIFFERENCES OF ATOMS

Bond	Δ	$0.208\sqrt{\Delta}$	$x_A - x_B$	Bond	Δ	$0.208\sqrt{\Delta}$	$x_A - x_B$
C—H	6.3	0.52	0.4	Si—F	90.0	1.97	2.2
Si—H	2.1	.30	.3	Si—Cl	35.6	1.24	1.2
N—H	22.0	.98	.9	Si—Br	25.0	1.04	1.0
P—H	1.8	.28	.0	Si—I	11.7	0.71	0.7
As—H	−12.0	—	.1	Ge—Cl	53.9	1.53	1.2
O—H	41.0	1.33	1.4	N—F	27.0	1.08	1.0
S—H	3.9	0.41	0.4	N—Cl	−0.5	—	0.0
Se—H	−7.5	—	.3	P—Cl	24.4	1.03	.9
H—F	64.0	1.67	1.9	P—Br	16.7	0.85	.7
H—Cl	22.1	0.98	0.9	P—I	7.6	.58	.4
H—Br	12.5	.74	.7	As—Cl	23.8	1.01	1.0
H—I	1.6	.26	.4	As—Br	17.4	0.87	0.8
C—Si	7.0	.55	.7	As—I	7.4	.57	.5
C—N	9.3	.64	.5	O—F	9.4	.64	.5
C—O	23.2	1.00	1.0	O—Cl	2.9	.36	.5
C—S	6.7	0.54	0.5	S—Cl	5.3	.48	.5
C—F	45.9	1.41	1.5	S—Br	2.2	.31	.3
C—Cl	8.3	0.61	0.5	Se—Cl	9.1	.63	.6
C—Br	1.6	.26	.3	Cl—F	25.7	1.05	1.0
C—I	−1.9	—	.0	Br—Cl	0.7	.18	0.2
Si—O	50.6	1.48	1.7	I—Cl	4.0	.42	.5
Si—S	7.7	0.58	0.7	I—Br	1.7	.27	.3

[1] L. Pauling, *J.A.C.S.* **54**, 3570 (1932).

TABLE 11-2.—ELECTRONEGATIVITY VALUES FOR SOME ELEMENTS

H			
2.1			

C	N	O	F
2.5	3.0	3.5	4.0

Si	P	S	Cl
1.8	2.1	2.5	3.0

Ge	As	Se	Br
1.8	2.0	2.4	2.8

			I
			2.5

In constructing Table 11-2 all of the available data have been considered, and the x value (x = electronegativity) which leads to the best general agreement for each atom has been selected. These values are given only to one decimal place on the scale; it is my opinion now that this is the limit of their reliability.

The original table contained the electronegativity values given below immediately after the symbols of the corresponding elements:

H	0.00	2.05	2.1	Br	0.75	2.80	2.8
P	.10	2.15	2.1	Cl	.94	2.99	3.0
I	.40	2.45	2.5	N	.95	3.00	3.0
S	.43	2.48	2.5	O	1.40	3.45	3.5
C	.55	2.60	2.5	F	2.00	4.05	4.0

Following these there are given the values obtained by adding 2.05 to them, representing only a change in origin of the scale, from x_H = 0.00 to x_H = 2.05. It is seen that the new values are within 0.05 of the old except for carbon, which has been decreased from 2.60 to 2.5.

The differences in electronegativity of atoms for the bonds in Table 11-1 are given in the columns headed $x_A - x_B$. If the extra ionic energy $\Delta(A\text{—}B)$ were given accurately by the equation

$$\Delta(A\text{—}B) = 23.06 \ (x_A - x_B)^2, \qquad (11\text{-}1)$$

and the bond energy (in kcal./mole) by the equation

$$D(A\text{—}B) = \tfrac{1}{2}\{D(A\text{—}A) + D(B\text{—}B)\} + 23.06 \ (x_A - x_B)^2, \ (11\text{-}2)$$

the values in the two columns headed $0.208\sqrt{\Delta}$ and $x_A - x_B$ would be equal. It is seen that this is approximately true, the average deviation between the two being 0.09 for forty pairs.[1]

Of the four bonds which give negative values of Δ, two (N—Cl, with $\Delta = -0.5$, and C—I, with $\Delta = -1.9$) are between atoms with the same electronegativity, for which Δ should be zero if the additivity postulate were valid; the small negative values may be due in part to deviation from this postulate and in part to small errors in the bond energies. The large negative value found for As—H($\Delta = -12.0$) can be accounted for as due to the inapplicability of the additivity postulate, the postulate of the geometric mean leading to a calculated positive value for Δ'; for the bond Se—H, however, with $\Delta = -7.5$ and $\Delta' = -4.2$, the thermochemical data are not compatible with our arguments.

The relation of the electronegativity values of Table 11-2 to the periodic system is the expected one. Fluorine and oxygen are by far the most electronegative of the atoms, with fluorine much more electronegative than oxygen. It is interesting that nitrogen and chlorine have the same electronegativity, as have also carbon, sulfur, and iodine. The contours of equal electronegativity cut diagonally across the periodic table, from the upper left to the lower right hand region.

For all of the elements of Table 11-2 except nitrogen and oxygen a thermochemical interpretation of the electronegativity scale more direct than that discussed above can be made. By extending the argument given in Section 9, it is seen that the quantity $\Delta(A-B) = 23.06 \, (x_A - x_B)^2$ is the contribution of the bond A—B to the heat of formation of a gas molecule containing the bond from the elements in the following states (which differ in heat content by only a small amount from the standard states for P, As, S, Se, Br, and I; namely, by the heat of vaporization or sublimation): $H_2(g)$, C(diamond), $F_2(g)$, Si(c), $P_4(g)$, $S_8(g)$, $Cl_2(g)$, Ge(c), $As_4(g)$, $Se_8(g)$, $Br_2(g)$, and $I_2(g)$. These heats of formation should be positive for all compounds of these elements involving only single bonds.

For nitrogen and oxygen the standard states $N_2(g)$ and $O_2(g)$ are far more stable than they would be if the molecules involved single N—N and O—O bonds. From the bond energy values N—N = 20.0 and O—O = 34.9 kcal./mole and the values $2N = N_2 + 170.2$ kcal./mole and $2O = O_2 + 118.2$ kcal./mole

---

[1] Equations 11-1 and 11-2 lead to values of Δ and $D(A-B)$ which are in general somewhat too large in case that $x_A - x_B$ is very large (greater than 1.5), HF for example having $x_F - x_H = 1.9$ and $0.208\sqrt{\Delta} = 1.67$.

we see that this extra stability of the standard state amounts to 110.2 kcal./mole for N_2 and to 48.4 kcal./mole for O_2. The heat of formation of a gas molecule containing single bonds from elements in the states described in the preceding paragraph and from $N_2(g)$ and $O_2(g)$ can accordingly be calculated roughly by the expression

$$Q = 23.06 \sum (x_A - x_B)^2 - 55.1 \, n_N - 24.2 \, n_O, \qquad (11\text{-}3)$$

in which n_N is the number of nitrogen atoms in the molecule and n_O the number of oxygen atoms, and the indicated summation is to be carried over all of the bonds in the molecule.

It is this unusual stability of multiple bonds for first-row atoms, stabilizing the normal states of oxygen and especially of nitrogen, which leads to negative heats of formation. The heat of formation of a molecule containing an atom of nitrogen held by single bonds to other atoms of the same electronegativity should be about -55.1 kcal./mole; the compound would accordingly be very unstable relative to the elements. Nitrogen trichloride is such a compound; in this molecule the bonds are normal covalent bonds, similar to N—N and Cl—Cl single bonds; it is not the weakness of the N—Cl bonds, but rather the extraordinary strength of the triple bond in N_2 which makes nitrogen trichloride unstable. In nitrogen trifluoride the ionic resonance energy of the N—F bonds is great enough to overcome this handicap and give the molecule a positive heat of formation. For F_2O and Cl_2O (with $x_A - x_B = 0.5$) the ionic character is not enough to counteract the term -24.2 kcal./mole for the oxygen atom; these substances have small negative heats of formation.

11b. Heats of Formation of Compounds in their Standard States. The Complete Electronegativity Scale.[1]—The method just described for formulating the electronegativity scale cannot be used for the remaining elements in general because of lack of knowledge of heats of formation of their compounds as gases and of the values of single bond energies for the elements themselves. The following extension of the method can, however, be used.

Except for nitrogen and oxygen, the elements in their standard states probably do not differ very much in energy from states involving single covalent bonds between the atoms, with an additional small stabilization for condensed systems resulting

---

[1] I am indebted to Dr. Fred Stitt for assistance with this section.

from the van der Waals interaction of adjacent non-bonded atoms. Thus the standard states of bromine, iodine, sulfur, diamond, and many other non-metallic elements have just this character. Moreover, the standard states of the metals too are probably not much different from states involving single bonds, since there is a close resemblance in certain properties of the metallic bond and the covalent bond (Chap. XI).

Now let us consider the heat of formation of a substance, liquid or solid in its standard state and containing only single bonds, from elements in their standard states. This heat of formation will be given by Equation 11-3 in case that the van der Waals stabilization and other factors contributing to the heat content have the same value for the reacting elements as for the product. It is not unreasonable that this should be approximately true, since the energy of van der Waals forces is roughly additive in the atoms involved. Moreover, except for first-row atoms, the formation of stable multiple bonds is unusual, and we may assume with reasonable safety that a substance of unknown bond type does not contain multiple bonds of sufficiently greater energy than the corresponding number of single bonds to introduce very great error in the electronegativity calculations.

With the assumption that the heat of formation of a compound in its standard state from elements in their standard states is given by Equation 11-3 a value for the electronegativity of an element can be calculated from the thermochemical data for a compound between the element and an element included in Table 11-1. For B_2O_3 (glass) for example, with $Q = 279.9$ kcal./mole, the extra ionic energy per bond is $(279.9 + 3 \times 24.2)/6 = 58.8$ kcal./mole, which leads to $x_O - x_B = 1.59$ and $x_B = 1.91$. The average value of x_B for B_2O_3, BF_3, BCl_3, and BBr_3 is 1.95, and the value 2.0 can accordingly be assigned to boron. For beryllium and lithium averages of 1.44 and 0.95 respectively are found from the halides, suggesting the values 1.5 and 1.0, which complete the regular sequence with equal differences for the first-row atoms.

In this way Table 11-3 has been constructed.[1] This table is

---

[1] Some verification of the values is provided by the first ionization potentials of the elements. These might be expected to be related to the electronegativities by a constant factor for atoms of the same type of electronic structure, that is, in the same column of the periodic system.

related to the periodic table in a simple way, shown in Figure 11-1. It is seen that in the second row and lower rows the constancy of differences in x values found for the first row elements does not hold. The differences are smaller for the metals than for the non-metals, and the values change less for a given column of the periodic table in the metallic region than in the non-metallic region.[1]

TABLE 11-3.—ELECTRONEGATIVITY VALUES

	x		x		x
H	2.1	Si	1.8	Br	2.8
Li	1.0	P	2.1	Rb	0.8
Be	1.5	S	2.5	Sr	1.0
B	2.0	Cl	3.0	Y	1.3
C	2.5	K	0.8	Zr	1.6
N	3.0	Ca	1.0	Sn	1.7
O	3.5	Sc	1.3	Sb	1.8
F	4.0	Ti	1.6	Te	2.1
Na	0.9	Ge	1.7	I	2.4
Mg	1.2	As	2.0	Cs	0.7
Al	1.5	Se	2.4	Ba	0.9

We have accordingly succeeded in bringing into the field of inorganic thermochemistry, in which on first survey little order can be detected, a certain amount of systematization. It is possible to calculate rough values expected for heats of formation with use of the x values of Table 11-3, which vary in a regular way from atom to atom in the periodic system, the heats of reaction of elements to form compounds being attributed in the main to the extra resonance energy resulting from the partial ionic character of the bonds between unlike atoms, and correspondingly increasing as the atoms become more and more unlike. This order is brought out of apparent lack of order in the thermo-

---

This relation is found to hold to within 0.1 or 0.2 units in x. Values of x calculated for the transition-group elements from ionization potentials (with an average value for the factor) lie between 1.5 and 2.0, as do also the thermochemical values of x for these elements.

[1] The electronegativity values of Table 11-2 could be based on the postulate of the geometric mean rather than the additivity postulate; the postulate of the geometric mean cannot, however, be made the basis of an extended treatment of thermochemical data giving the remaining x values of Table 11-3, because of lack of knowledge of absolute values of some bond energies.

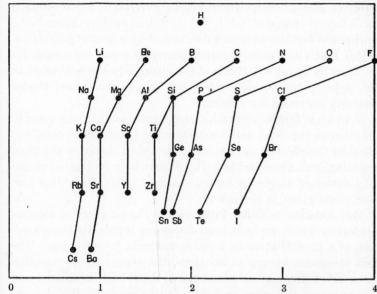

FIG. 11-1.—The electronegativity scale of the elements, showing
relation to the periodic table.

chemical data largely through the corrections for the two elements nitrogen and oxygen, which are alone among the elements in having their standard states much different in stability from single-bonded states.

11c. The Effect of Electric Charge.—The x values of Table 11-3 apply to atoms with formal charge zero. An estimate can be made of the effect of formal charge on the x values in the following way. The increasing electronegativity for a series of atoms such as C, N, O, F can be attributed to increase in the effective nuclear charge acting on the valence electrons. Now the effective nuclear charge is equal to the actual nuclear charge diminished by the screening effects of the electrons. The screening constant of one valence electron for another is about[1] 0.4 (in electron units). Accordingly the increase in effective nuclear charge from N in NR_3 (for which five outer electrons of nitrogen are effective, a shared pair being equivalent to a single unshared electron) to O in OR_2 is 0.6, the increase in actual nuclear charge, $+1$, less the screening constant of an additional electron. The increase in

[1] L. Pauling and J. Sherman, *Z. Krist.* **81**, 1 (1932).

effective nuclear charge from NR_3 to $[NR_4]^+$, in which nitrogen has a formal charge of $+1$, is 0.4, the actual nuclear charge being unchanged but the screening diminished by one electron. Thus we see that a unit positive formal charge increases the x value for an atom by about two-thirds of the distance to the next atom to the right in the periodic table, and a negative formal charge similarly decreases the x value.

If an atom forms bonds which are largely ionic in character in addition to the bond under consideration it may be desirable to consider the effect on the x value of the actual charge on the atom resulting from these bonds. This charge is to be treated in the way described above for formal charge. Examples of this procedure are given in Section 12.

11d. Relation to Other Properties.—The property of electronegativity which we have been discussing represents the attraction of a neutral atom in a stable molecule for electrons. The first ionization energy of an atom, the energy of the reaction $X \rightarrow X^+ + E^-$, may be considered as the average of the electron attraction of the atom and the positive ion; and the electron affinity, the energy of the reaction $X + E^- \rightarrow X^-$, may be thought of similarly as the average of the electron attraction of the atom and the negative ion. It was pointed out by Mulliken[1] that the average of the first ionization energy and the electron affinity of an atom should be a measure of its electronegativity. For multivalent atoms the significance of these energy quantities is complicated by the nature of the states of the atoms and ions,

TABLE 11-4.—COMPARISON OF ELECTRONEGATIVITY WITH AVERAGE OF IONIZATION ENERGY AND ELECTRON AFFINITY

	Ionization energy	Electron affinity	Sum/130	x
F	429.0	98.5	4.06	4.0
Cl	298.9	92.5	3.01	3.0
Br	272.1	87.1	2.76	2.8
I	240.8	79.2	2.46	2.5
H	312.0	16.4	2.52	2.1
Li	123.8	0	0.95	1.0
Na	117.9	0	.91	0.9
K	99.7	0	.77	.8
Rb	95.9	0	.74	.8
Cs	89.4	0	.69	.7

[1] R. S. Mulliken, *J. Chem. Phys.* **2**, 782 (1934); **3**, 573 (1935).

and corrections must be made which need not be discussed here. For univalent atoms (hydrogen, the halogens, the alkali metals) the treatment is straightforward. Values of the energy quantities concerned are given in Table 11-4, it being assumed that the electron affinity of the alkali metals is zero. It is seen that the values of x are closely proportional to those of the sum of the two energy quantities, except for hydrogen, which, with its unique electronic structure, might be expected to misbehave. This comparison and others were used in fixing the origin for the electronegativity scale.

A similar but less satisfactory qualitative correlation is found between the electronegativity values for the elements and other energy quantities, such as the ionization energies and electron affinities independently, and the standard electrode potentials. It was pointed out by Malone[1] that the values of electric dipole moments assigned to single bonds, such that the vector sum of the bond moments for a molecule gives the resultant dipole moment for the molecule, are roughly proportional to differences in electronegativity, the proportionality factor being 1×10^{-18} e.s.u. The relation has, however, only limited validity.

The values given in Table 11-5 for the magnitudes of the electric dipole moment vectors assigned to single covalent bonds[2] have been obtained in the following ways. For bonds between univalent atoms, such as H—Cl, the observed moment of the diatomic molecule is the bond moment. In polyatomic molecules involving equivalent bonds, such as water or phosphorus trichloride, the bond moment can be calculated from the observed moment of the molecule by use of the value of the bond angle found by spectroscopic or electron-diffraction methods, the assumption being made that the interaction of the bond moments produces only a negligible change in the resultant moment of the molecule and that the bond moment vectors are coincident in direction with the internuclear lines. The observed value of the dipole moment of the water molecule, for example, is 1.84×10^{-18} e.s.u., and the H—O—H angle is 105°; from these the value of the H—O bond moment is found to be $1.84/2 \cos 52.5° = 1.51 \times 10^{-18}$ e.s.u.

For the H—C bond moment we accept the value 0.4×10^{-18}, originally

---

[1] J. G. Malone, *J. Chem. Phys.* **1**, 197 (1933); see also C. P. Smyth, *J. Phys. Chem.* **41**, 209 (1937); *J.A.C.S.* **60**, 183 (1938).

[2] These values are those quoted by Smyth, *loc. cit.*, except for changes of ±0.1 in the bonds to carbon, resulting from our choice of 0.4×10^{-18} e.s.u. for the C—H moment, in place of 0.3×10^{-18} used by Smyth. Similar tables have been published by other investigators, including Sidgwick, "The Covalent Link in Chemistry," p. 153.

suggested by Williams[1] and Eucken and Meyer[2] on the basis of arguments which need not be given here. Sutton[3] has suggested 0.2×10^{-18} and Smyth[4] has reported that a theoretical calculation by J. O. Hirschfelder has given the value 0.3×10^{-18}. Our choice of 0.4×10^{-18} is based on the electronegativity difference for carbon and hydrogen.

With this as the starting point values for other bond moments involving carbon can be found in the way illustrated by the following treatment of methyl chloride. The observed moment for this molecule, 1.86×10^{-18} e.s.u., is the resultant of three H—C moments and one C—Cl moment directed toward the corners of a regular tetrahedron. The three H—C moments have as their resultant a moment of 0.4×10^{-18} e.s.u. directed along the C—Cl axis; hence the observed moment is the algebraic sum of the H—C and the C—Cl moments, and the latter accordingly has the value 1.46 (1.5) $\times 10^{-18}$ e.s.u.

In the foregoing discussion and in Table 11-5 the bond symbols A—B are written with the less electronegative element preceding the more electronegative element, so that the electric moment vector has the orientation $+ \longrightarrow -$; it is sometimes convenient to cross the tail of the arrow, $+\!\!\!-\!\!\!\longrightarrow$, to indicate this convention.

It is seen from Table 11-5 that there is a roughly linear relation between the bond-moment values and the corresponding electronegativity differences, as pointed out by Malone. The factor of proportionality is approximately 1.0×10^{-18} e.s.u.

TABLE 11-5.—COMPARISON OF ELECTRONEGATIVITY DIFFERENCES WITH VALUES OF ELECTRIC DIPOLE MOMENTS ASSIGNED TO SINGLE BONDS

	$\mu \times 10^{18}$	$x_2 - x_1$		$\mu \times 10^{18}$	$x_2 - x_1$
As—H	0.10	0.1	Cl—O	0.73	0.5
H—P	.36	.0	I—Br	.4	.3
H—C	(.4)	.4	I—Cl	.8	.5
H—S	.68	.4	P—I	.0	.4
H—I	.38	.4	P—Br	.36	.7
H—Br	.78	.7	P—Cl	.81	.9
H—Cl	1.03	.9	As—I	.78	.5
H—N	1.31	.9	As—Br	1.27	.8
H—O	1.51	1.4	As—Cl	1.64	1.0
C—O	0.8	1.0	As—F	2.03	2.0
C—I	1.2	0.0	Sb—I	0.8	0.7
C—Br	1.4	.3	Sb—Br	1.9	1.0
C—Cl	1.5	.5	Sb—Cl	2.6	1.2
C—F	1.4	1.5			

Great deviations from this simple relation are shown by the

[1] J. W. Williams, *Phys. Z.* **29**, 174, 274, 683 (1928).

[2] A. Eucken and L. Meyer, *ibid.* **30**, 397 (1929).

[3] L. E. Sutton, *Proc. Roy. Soc.* **A133**, 668 (1931).

[4] C. P. Smyth, *loc. cit.*

bonds of chlorine, bromine, and iodine with carbon, arsenic, and antimony. The reasons for this are not known. It is very improbable that the carbon-iodine bond, connecting two atoms with equal electronegativity, has a significant amount of ionic character; and the high electric dipole moment is probably to be attributed to an unsymmetrical distribution of the electrons of the normal covalent bond and the unshared electrons of the iodine atom.

The most obvious correlation of the electronegativity scale with the general chemical properties of the elements bears on their division into metals and non-metals. It is seen that the value $x = 2$ represents approximately the point of separation, the metals being elements with smaller and the non-metals those with larger electronegativity than 2.

12. THE ELECTRONEGATIVITY OF ATOMS AND THE PARTIAL IONIC CHARACTER OF BONDS

It would be convenient in discussing types of bonds to be able to make quantitative statements—to say that certain bonds are essentially covalent, with only five or ten percent of ionic character, others are about equally ionic and covalent, and still others are essentially ionic. The magnitude of the extra ionic resonance energy or of the separation of the bonded atoms on the electronegativity scale provides this information, but only in a qualitative way, in the absence of a calibration of the scale. The problem of making this calibration is a difficult one. At present the best that can be done is to assume that the values 5%, 11%, 17%, and 60% for the ionic character of the bonds in HI, HBr, HCl, and HF, respectively, given in Section 8 are reliable enough to be used as the basis for drawing an empirical curve relating the percent of ionic character for a bond A—B with the electronegativity difference $|x_A - x_B|$. This curve is shown in Figure 12-1. It is not to be considered as accurate; on the other hand, it does give acceptable approximate information about bond type.

The curve of Figure 12-1 has been drawn with use of the equation

$$\text{Amount of ionic character} = 1 - e^{-c(x_A - x_B)^2}, \qquad (12\text{-}1)$$

in which c has the value $\frac{1}{4}$. This curve passes very close to the points for the four hydrogen halides, giving 4%, 11%, 19%, and

60% ionic character for $x_A - x_B = 0.4$, 0.7, 0.9 and 1.9, respectively.

The curve leads to the following amounts of ionic character for various values of $|x_A - x_B|$:

$|x_A - x_B|$	Amount of ionic character	$|x_A - x_B|$	Amount of ionic character
0.2	1%	1.4	39%
.4	4	1.6	47
.6	8	1.8	55
.8	15	2.0	63
1.0	22	2.2	70
1.2	30	2.4	76

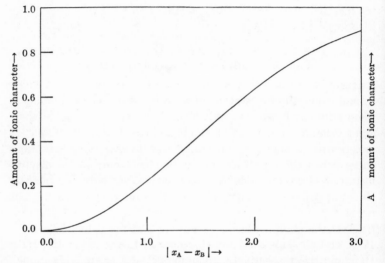

FIG. 12-1.—Curve relating amount of ionic character of a bond A—B to the difference in electronegativity $x_A - x_B$ of the atoms.

According to this curve bonds with $|x_A - x_B| = 1.7$ have 50% ionic character and 50% covalent character. Thus bonds between fluorine and any of the metals or of the elements H, B, P, As, Te with x values near 2 are essentially ionic in character, and bonds between oxygen and any of the metals are 50% or more ionic.

For a molecule like HF containing a single bond we have discussed the bond type in terms of resonance between two structures H^+F^- and $H\!:\!\ddot{F}\!:$. A more complex discussion is needed for molecules containing several bonds. In water, for example, the O—H bond has 39% ionic character, corresponding to $x_O - x_H = 1.4$. The water molecule can accordingly be described as resonating among four electronic structures,

$$\text{H} \qquad \text{H}^+ \qquad \text{H} \qquad \text{H}^+$$
$$:\ddot{\text{O}}:\text{H}, \quad :\ddot{\text{O}}:\bar{\text{H}}, \quad :\ddot{\text{O}}:\ \text{H}^+, \quad :\ddot{\text{O}}:\ \text{H}^+,$$
$$0.37 \qquad 0.24 \qquad 0.24 \qquad 0.15$$

one completely covalent, two with one bond to hydrogen ionic and one covalent, and one with both bonds ionic. If the bonds were independent, the structures would make the contributions indicated to the normal state of the molecule, the completely covalent structure making a contribution of 37%, each of the half-and-half structures contributions of 24%, and the completely ionic structure a contribution of 15%. It is probable, however, that the electrostatic interactions in the completely ionic structure, involving a doubly-charged oxygen ion, cut down its contribution somewhat, and that the contributions of the completely covalent structure and each of the half-and-half structures are increased toward 44% and 28%, respectively.

A similar conception of resonance among many electronic structures is to be formed for other molecules containing more than one bond of intermediate type. Thus for $[NH_4]^+$ it is necessary to consider sixteen structures, one completely covalent structure,

$$\text{H} \qquad\qquad \text{H} \qquad\qquad \text{H}^+$$
$$\text{H}:\overset{+}{\underset{\text{H}}{\ddot{\text{N}}}}:\text{H}, \text{ four such as } \text{H}:\overset{}{\underset{\text{H}}{\ddot{\text{N}}}}:\text{H}^+, \text{six such as } \text{H}:\overset{}{\underset{\text{H}}{\ddot{\text{N}}}}:\text{H}^+, \text{four such as}$$

$$\text{H}^+ \qquad\qquad\qquad\qquad \text{H}^+$$
$$\text{H}:\overset{}{\underset{\text{H}^+}{\ddot{\text{N}}}}:\text{H}^+, \text{ and one completely ionic structure, } \text{H}^+:\overset{}{\underset{\text{H}^+}{\ddot{\text{N}}}}:\text{H}^+. \text{ In}$$

general, in the following discussion, we shall not mention explicitly the resonance of the molecule among these structures; but it is to be borne in mind that the amounts of ionic character of bonds in molecules are to be interpreted in this way. In the following chapters of the book single bonds will as a rule be represented by the symbol A—B; it must be remembered that this symbol represents covalent-ionic resonance, and that the

$$\begin{matrix} & \text{H} \\ & | \\ \text{symbol} \quad \text{H}\text{—}\text{N}^+\text{—}\text{H} \\ & | \\ & \text{H} \end{matrix}$$ for the ammonium ion comprises within itself

all of the sixteen structures shown above, with contributions such as to give each N—H bond a suitable amount of ionic character.

This amount of ionic character can be found in the following way. The x value for N^+ is 3.3, 0.3 greater than that for N (Sec. 11c), giving each of the N—H bonds 30% ionic character. Now the indicated transfer of charge for three bonds (leaving out the bond under consideration) would leave the nitrogen atom nearly neutral, and we accordingly repeat the calculation with the normal value $x = 3.0$ for nitrogen. This leads to 19% ionic character for each bond, representing a positive charge of about one-fifth of a unit on each hydrogen atom. Our conclusion regarding the structure of the ammonium ion $[NH_4]^+$ and the distribution of its charge is accordingly the following: each N—H bond has about 20% ionic character[1] and the unit positive charge of the ion is divided about equally among all five atoms, each having a resultant charge of about $+0.2$.

The treatment given the ammonium ion can be replaced by an alternative one in extreme cases, such as the case of an alkali halide crystal. For a lithium iodide molecule, for example, the electronegativity scale and Figure 12-1 lead to a bond with 43% ionic character. We can be sure that in a lithium iodide crystal, in which a lithium atom is surrounded by six iodine atoms, it will not form more than one covalent bond; that is, we must consider structures

$$\begin{matrix} & \text{I}^- & & \text{I}^- & & :\ddot{\text{I}}: \\ \text{I}^-\,\text{Li}^+\,\text{I}^-, & & \text{I}^-\,\text{Li}\!:\!\ddot{\text{I}}\!:, & & \text{I}^-\,\ddot{\text{Li}}\,\text{I}^-, & \text{etc.} \\ & \text{I}^- & & \text{I}^- & & \text{I}^- \end{matrix}$$

---

[1] The value 20% is quoted in place of 19% because the resultant charge of $+0.2$ for the nitrogen atom (or 0.4 from the three bonds other than the one under consideration) increases the x value for nitrogen by a small amount. These refinements are, however, really beyond the reliability of our treatment.

but we can ignore structures such as I^- $\overset{\cdot\cdot}{\underset{\cdot\cdot}{Li}}\!:\!\overset{\cdot\cdot}{\underset{\cdot\cdot}{I}}\!:$. Hence we may say

that of the six bonds from a lithium atom to its six neighbors one has about 57% covalent character and the others none; this hybrid bond resonates among all six positions, however, so that each of the bonds in the crystal is to be assigned about 10% covalent character.[1] The other alkali halide crystals are still more ionic in character; for crystalline sodium chloride, for example, the bonds have about 5% covalent character.

It is interesting to discuss the silver halides in this way, in view of the extensive argument regarding their nature which has gone on. The x value for silver given by the heats of formation of its halides is 1.8. This leads to 11% ionic character for the AgI molecule, 23% for AgBr, 30% for AgCl, and 70% for AgF. In the crystals of the fluoride, chloride, and bromide, which are reported to have the sodium chloride arrangement, the bonds would have 5%, 12%, and 13% covalent character, respectively, on the assumption that one bond of the gas-molecule type resonates among the six positions; and a similar treatment of the iodide, with the wurtzite structure, would lead to 23% covalent character for each of the four bonds per silver atom. It is probable, however, that these amounts of covalent character of the crystal bonds should be doubled, for the following reason. It is known that silver can form two covalent bonds, as, for example, with carbon in the $[NC{-}Ag{-}CN]^-$ complex ion,[2] each having nearly as much covalent character as for a bond to unicovalent silver (since change in effective nuclear charge does not lead to much change in x values for the transition elements); and resonance of two bonds among the available positions in the silver halide crystals would double the calculated amount of covalent character of the crystal bonds, giving 10% covalent character for AgF, 24% for AgCl, 26% for AgBr, and 46% for AgI.

A detailed discussion of the nature of single bonds in many molecules and crystals will not be given here; instead there fol-

---

[1] In view of the larger value of the interatomic distance in the crystal than in the gas molecule, this estimate of amount of covalent character may be high.

[2] J. L. Hoard, *Z. Krist.* **84**, 231 (1933).

lows a brief survey of the nature of the single bonds formed by the elements.

The Alkali Metals.—Bonds of the alkali metals with all nonmetals are essentially ionic (with more than 50% ionic character—electronegativity difference greater than 1.7) except for the Li—I, Li—C, and Li—S bonds, with 43% ionic character.

The Alkaline-Earth Metals.—Magnesium, calcium, strontium, and barium form essentially ionic bonds with the more nonmetallic elements. Beryllium bonds have the following amounts of ionic character: Be—F, 79%; Be—O, 63%; Be—Cl, 44%; Be—Br, 35%; Be—I, 22%.

The Third-group Elements.—The B—F bond has about 63% ionic character, B—O 44%, B—Cl 22%, etc. Boron forms normal covalent bonds with hydrogen. The aluminum bonds are similar to those of beryllium in ionic character.

The Fourth-group Elements.—The C—F bond, with 44% ionic character, is the most ionic of the bonds of carbon with nonmetallic elements.

The Si—F bond has 70% ionic character, and Si—Cl 30%. The Si—O bond is of especial interest because of its importance in the silicates. It is seen to have 50% ionic character, the value of $x_O - x_{Si}$ being 1.7.

The Remaining Non-metallic Elements.—The bonds formed by fluorine with all of the metals are essentially ionic in character, and those with the intermediate elements (H, B, P, etc.) have a little more than 50% ionic character. The C—F, S—F, and I—F bonds are expected to have 44% ionic character. In CF_4, SF_6, IF_5, and IF_7 the amounts of ionic character of the bonds are probably somewhat less than this value because of the transfer of positive charge to the central atom, which increases its x value and decreases the ionic character of the bonds.

The bonds of oxygen with all metals are essentially ionic.

Since the non-metallic elements in each row of the periodic table are separated by intervals of 0.5, the bonds formed by a non-metallic atom with immediate neighbors in the same row have 6% ionic character and those with its neighbors once removed 22%.

12a. The Partial Ionic Character of Multiple Bonds.—For multiple bonds between atoms of different electronegativity such as the carbon-oxygen double bond in aldehydes and ketones a considerable degree of ionic character is expected, corresponding

to resonance between structures $R_2C::\overset{..}{O}:$ and $R_2C^+:\overset{..}{O}:^-$ (with
a very small contribution from $R_2C^{++}O^-$).   Evidence as to the
amount of the ionic character is provided by the observed electric
dipole moments[1] of about 2.8×10^{-18} e.s.u. (2.70 for acetaldehyde, 2.85 for acetone, 2.77 for methylethylketone, 3.00 for
cyclopentanone, etc.).   For the structure $R_2C::\overset{..}{O}:$ we expect
only a very small dipole moment, and for the structure $R_2C^+:\overset{..}{O}:^-$
a dipole moment of the order of magnitude of 5.95×10^{-18} e.s.u.,
the product of the electronic charge and the carbon-oxygen internuclear distance 1.24 Å.   The observed moment corresponds to
about 47% ionic character for the carbon-oxygen double bond.
The two structures $R_2C::\overset{..}{O}:$ and $R_2C^+:\overset{..}{O}:^-$ thus contribute
almost equally to the normal state of a molecule containing this
bond.[2]

We might have predicted that the bond would have 44% ionic
character, twice that given for the carbon-oxygen single bond by
the electronegativity scale.   The agreement between this value
and the dipole-moment value suggests that in general the amount
of ionic character of a double bond is twice that of the corresponding single bond, or perhaps somewhat larger.   For the
carbon-nitrogen and nitrogen-oxygen double bonds we would
thus expect almost 12% ionic character.   An obvious extension
of this rule leads to about 18% ionic character for the carbon-
nitrogen triple bond.   Actually the observed value of the electric
moment of the alkyl cyanides, 3.5×10^{-18} e.s.u., indicates about
57% ionic character (resonance to $RC^+::\overset{..}{N}:^-$) for this bond, and
thus suggests that the electrons involved in multiple bonds are
more mobile than those involved in single bonds.   The significance of this electronic mobility for the stability of the nitrogen molecule and for the tendency of hydrogen cyanide to
polymerize through formation of hydrogen bonds is discussed
later (Secs. 18a and 39).

[1] Values quoted for electric dipole moments in this book are taken from
the extensive compilation in *Trans. Faraday Soc.* 30 (1934).

[2] The early suggestion by T. M. Lowry (*J. Chem. Soc.* 1923, 822) that
the structure $R_2C^+:\overset{..}{O}:^-$ be used for aldehydes and ketones rather than the
conventional $R_2C::\overset{::}{O}:$ was not uncalled for, since the semi-ionic structure
is actually almost as significant as the purely covalent one.

CHAPTER III

THE DIRECTED COVALENT BOND. BOND
STRENGTHS AND BOND ANGLES. THE
MAGNETIC CRITERION FOR
BOND TYPE.[1]

13. THE NATURE AND BOND-FORMING POWER OF ATOMIC ORBITALS

The energy of a covalent bond is largely the energy of resonance of two electrons between two atoms (Sec. 5). The examination of the form of the resonance integral shows that the resonance energy increases in magnitude with increase in the *overlapping* of the two atomic orbitals involved in the formation of the bond, the word "overlapping" signifying the extent to which the regions in space in which the two orbital wave functions have large values coincide. (Since the square of an orbital wave function is the probability distribution function for the electron, the overlapping is essentially a measure of the amount of interpenetration of the bond-electron distributions of the two atoms.) Consequently it is expected that *of two orbitals in an atom the one which can overlap more with an orbital of another atom will form the stronger bond with that atom, and, moreover, the bond formed by a given orbital will tend to lie in that direction in which the orbital is concentrated.*

The orbitals of an atom differ from one another in their dependence on the distance r of the electron from the nucleus and on the polar angles θ and ϕ, that is, on their angular distribution. The dependence on r has been discussed for the hydrogen atom in Section 4a. It is this dependence which determines in the main the *stability* of the atomic orbital, and the primary significance of the orbital for bond formation can be discussed in terms

---

[1] The argument of this chapter is taken for the most part from my paper "The Nature of the Chemical Bond. Application of Results Obtained from the Quantum Mechanics and from a Theory of Paramagnetic Susceptibility to the Structure of Molecules," *J.A.C.S.* **53**, 1367 (1931).

of stability. Stable bonds are formed only with use of stable atomic orbitals—the $1s$ orbital for hydrogen, the $2s$ and $2p$ orbitals for the first-row atoms, and so on.

The different stable orbitals of an atom which can be used for bond formation do not differ very much from one another in their dependence on r, but they may show a great difference in their angular distribution. This can be seen from Figure 13–1,

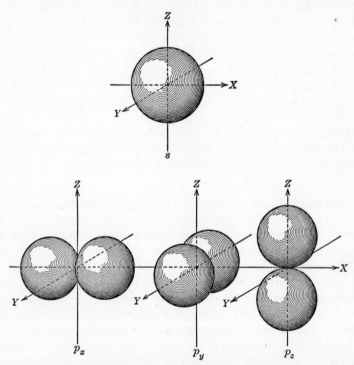

FIG. 13–1.—Representations of the relative magnitudes of s and p orbitals in dependence on angle.

representing the angular distribution of an s orbital and the three p orbitals.[1] The s orbital is spherically symmetrical, and so can form a bond in one direction as well as in any other, whereas the three p orbitals are directed along the three Cartesian axes,

[1] This figure gives a general idea of the distribution of an electron occupying these orbitals so far as orientation is concerned, but it does not show the dependence on r.

and will tend to form bonds in these directions.[1] Moreover, the
p orbitals are concentrated in these directions and have magnitudes $\sqrt{3}$ times as great as that of an s orbital, so far as the angular dependence is concerned. Since the radial part of an s
orbital and that of the p orbitals of the same shell do not differ
much, the p orbitals can overlap the orbital of another atom
more effectively than can the s orbital of the same shell; *p bonds
are stronger than s bonds*. It has been found on quantitative
study of a simple problem of this type[2] that the energy of a bond
is about proportional to the product of the magnitudes of bond
orbitals of the two atoms (in their angular dependence); an s—p
bond would have bond energy about $\sqrt{3}$ times that of an s—s
bond, and a p—p bond would be stronger than an s—s bond by
a factor of about 3. It is convenient to call the magnitude of a
bond orbital in its angular dependence the *strength* of the bond
orbital, with value 1 for an s orbital and 1.732 for a p orbital.

The conclusion that *p bonds tend to be at right angles to one
another*[3] is verified to some extent by experiment. In water,

$$\ddot{\text{H}}$$

with the structure : $\overset{..}{\underset{..}{\text{O}}}$:H, the bond angle[4] is 104°31′. We expect the

bonds to be p bonds rather than s bonds for the following reason.
A $2s$ electron of oxygen is more stable than a $2p$ electron by
about three hundred kcal./mole; and if the s orbital were used
in bond formation (being then occupied effectively by only one
electron) rather than for an unshared pair the molecule would be
made unstable to this extent. The difference of 15° between the
observed value of the bond angle and the expected value of 90° is
probably to be attributed in the main to the partial ionic character
of the O—H bonds, estimated in the preceding chapter to be
39%. This would give a resultant positive charge to the hydrogen atoms, which would repel one another and thus cause an
increase in the bond angle.

[1] The orientation of the axes of reference for the orbitals of an atom is
of course arbitrary; we should say only that the bond directions for the
three p orbitals are at right angles to one another.

[2] L. Pauling and J. Sherman, *J.A.C.S.* 59, 1450 (1937).

[3] This conclusion was first given by J. C. Slater, *Phys. Rev.* 37, 481
(1931).

[4] R. Mecke and W. Baumann, *Physikal. Z.* 33, 833 (1932); B. T. Darling
and D. M. Dennison, *Phys. Rev.* 57, 128 (1940).

In hydrogen sulfide, in which the bonds are nearly normal covalent bonds, the H—S—H angle is observed[1] to have the value 92°20'. Experimental values are not available for H_2Se and H_2Te. The large value reported for ammonia, 108°, may be due in the main to partial ionic character, as for water.

With larger atoms attached to the central atom the bond angles may be increased above the value 90° by steric effects.[2] It is seen that most of the experimental values given in Table 13-1 lie between 90° and 110°.

TABLE 13-1.—OBSERVED VALUES OF BOND ANGLES[3]

Substance	Method[4]	Bond Angle	Experimental Value[5]
$H_2O(g)$	Sp.	H—O—H	105°
$OF_2(g)$	E.D.	F—O—F	100°
$Cl_2O(g)$	E.D.	Cl—O—Cl	115°
$(CH_3)_2O(g)$	E.D.	C—O—C	111°
$H_2S(g)$	Sp.	H—S—H	92°20'
$S_8(c)$	C.S.	S—S—S	106°
$S_8(g)$	E.D.	S—S—S	100°
$BaS_3(c)$	C.S.[6]	S—S—S	103°
$K_2S_3O_6(c)$	C.S.	S—S—S	103°
SCl_2	E.D.	Cl—S—Cl	103°
$Se(c)$	C.S.	Se—Se—Se	105°
$Te(c)$	C.S.	Te—Te—Te	102°

[1] P. C. Cross, *Phys. Rev.* **47**, 7 (1935); B. L. Crawford, Jr., and P. C. Cross, *J. Chem. Phys.* **5**, 371 (1937).

[2] See also Sec. 14a.

[3] Values given in this table are, with a few exceptions, for bond angles which are not determined by the nature of the atomic configuration; for an exceptional example, the value of the phosphorus bond angle in P_4 is determined by the presence of the 3-membered rings and is not characteristic of the atom.

[4] Sp. = spectroscopic, E.D. = electron diffraction, C.S. = crystal structure. For crystal-structure references see the Strukturbericht, for electron-diffraction references the review by L. O. Brockway, *Rev. Modern Phys.* **8**, 231 (1936); see also the references quoted for Table 21-3. The values for PBr_3, PI_3, $AsBr_3$, AsI_3, $SbCl_3$, $SbBr_3$, and SbI_3 are from the electron-diffraction investigations of A. H. Gregg, G. C. Hampson, G. I. Jenkins, P. L. F. Jones, and L. E. Sutton, *Trans. Faraday Soc.* **33**, 852 (1937); and D. P. Stevenson, V. Schomaker, and S. Swingle (unpublished work).

[5] These values have in most cases probable errors of about 3°.

[6] W. S. Miller and A. J. King, *Z. Krist.* **94**, 439 (1936).

TABLE 13-1.—*Continued*

Substance	Method	Bond Angle	Experimental Value
NH₃(g)	Sp.	H—N—H	108°
N(CH₃)₃(g)	E.D.	C—N—C	108°
P(c, black)	C.S.	P—P—P	99°, 103.5°
P₄(g)	E.D.	P—P—P	60°
P(CH₃)₃(g)	E.D.	C—P—C	100°
PF₃(g)	E.D.	F—P—F	104°
PFCl₂(g)	E.D.	Cl—P—Cl	102°
PCl₃(g)	E.D.	Cl—P—Cl	101°
PBr₃(g)	E.D.	Br—P—Br	100°
PI₃(g)	E.D.	I—P—I	98°
As(c)	C.S.	As—As—As	97°
As₄(g)	E.D.	As—As—As	60°
As(CH₃)₃(g)	E.D.	C—As—C	96°
AsCl₃(g)	E.D.	Cl—As—Cl	103°
AsBr₃(g)	E.D.	Br—As—Br	100°
AsI₃(g)	E.D.	I—As—I	100°
Sb(c)	C.S.	Sb—Sb—Sb	96°
SbCl₃	E.D.	Cl—Sb—Cl	104°
SbBr₃	E.D.	Br—Sb—Br	96°, 97°
SbI₃	E.D.	I—Sb—I	98°, 99°
Bi(c)	C.S.	Bi—Bi—Bi	94°

The smallest oxygen bond angle reported, 100°, is for OF_2, in which the bonds have little ionic character and steric forces between the small fluorine atoms should be small. In most molecules the oxygen and nitrogen bond angles are close to 110°.

For heavier atoms of the sixth and seventh columns of the periodic table bond angles of about 100° are usually observed. There seems to be a tendency for the bond angle to decrease with increasing atomic number, as in the sequence P, As, Sb, Bi, with bond angles 105°, 97°, 96°, and 94°, respectively, in the elementary substances.

It is surprising that 60° bond angles are stable for P_4 and As_4, which have the configuration of a regular tetrahedron, the four atoms lying at the tetrahedron corners and the bonds along the tetrahedron edges. The molecules probably involve some strain.

14. HYBRID BOND ORBITALS. THE TETRAHEDRAL CARBON ATOM

From the foregoing discussion it might be inferred that the quadrivalent carbon atom would form three bonds at right angles to one another and a fourth weaker bond (using the s orbital) in some arbitrary direction. This is, of course, not so; and, instead, it is found on quantum-mechanical study of the problem that *the four bonds of carbon are equivalent and are directed towards the corners of a regular tetrahedron*,[1] as had been inferred from the data of organic chemistry.

A rigorous quantum-mechanical treatment of directed valence bonds has not been given, for the reason that the Schrödinger wave equation has not been rigorously solved for any complicated molecule. However, several approximate treatments have been carried out, leading in a reasonable way to results such as those described below. Of these treatments we shall describe only the simplest one, which is, indeed, the most powerful one, in that it leads directly to the largest number of satisfactory results.

The simple theory which we use is based on the postulate given at the beginning of this chapter regarding the dependence of the bond-forming power (the strength) of a bond orbital on its angular distribution, this postulate being a reasonable one. From it, with use of general quantum-mechanical principles, there is derived the whole body of results regarding directed valence, including not only the tetrahedral arrangement of the four single bonds of the carbon atom, but also octahedral and square configurations of bonds (as well as other configurations), together with rules regarding the occurrence of these configurations, the strengths of the bonds, and the relation of configuration to magnetic properties. In this way a single reasonable postulate is made the basis of a large number of the rules of stereochemistry, and is found to lead to several new stereochemical results.

There are four orbitals in the valence shell of the carbon atom. We have described these as the 2s and the three 2p orbitals, with bond strengths 1 and 1.732, respectively. These are, however, not the orbitals used directly in bond formation by the atom.

[1] L. Pauling, *Proc. Nat. Acad. Sci.* 14, 359 (1928), and *loc. cit.*; J. C. Slater, *loc. cit.*; J. H. Van Vleck, *J. Chem. Phys.* 1, 177, 219 (1933); 2, 20 (1934); R. S. Mulliken, *ibid.* 1, 492 (1933), etc.

(They are especially suited to the description of the free carbon atom; if quantum theory had been developed by the chemist rather than the spectroscopist it is probable that the tetrahedral orbitals described below would play the fundamental rôle in the theory, in place of the s and p orbitals.) Now in general a wave function for a system can be constructed by adding together other functions, the wave function for the normal state being the one which minimizes the energy of the system (Sec. 3). The

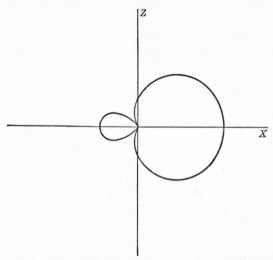

Fıg. 14-1.—The angular dependence of a tetrahedral orbital with bond direction along the x axis.

energy of a system of a carbon atom and four attached atoms is minimized by making the bond energies as large as possible. It is found that a bond orbital formed by linear combination of s and p orbitals, taken with a certain ratio of numerical coefficients, has a bond strength greater than that for an s or p orbital alone, the strength of the best s—p hybrid bond orbital being as great as 2. The angular dependence of this orbital is shown in Figure 14–1; it is seen that the orbital is greatly concentrated in the bond direction (its axis of rotational symmetry), and it can be understood that this orbital would overlap greatly with the orbital of another atom, and would form a very strong bond. We expect this hybridization to take place, in order that the bond energy may be a maximum.

A surprising result of the calculations, of great chemical significance, is the following: when it is sought to make the energy of a second bond as large as possible, by forming another hybrid orbital of maximum bond-forming power, it is found that this second best bond orbital is equivalent to the first, with strength 2, and that *its bond direction makes the tetrahedral angle* 109°28′ *with that of the first.* Moreover, a third and a fourth equivalent orbital can be constructed, the four being directed toward the corners of a regular tetrahedron; but then no more orbitals are left in the valence shell. It is convenient to call these four best *s—p* bond orbitals *tetrahedral orbitals.*[1]

The postulate of the tetrahedral carbon atom in classical stereochemistry requires that the atom have a configuration which is tetrahedral but is not necessarily that of a regular tetrahedron; so long as the four bonds have a general tetrahedral orientation the phenomenon of optical activity is accounted for. There is no need that the R_1—C—R_2 bond angle in $CR_1R_2R_3R_4$ be near 109°28′; it might be 150° or more.[2] The result of the bond orbital treatment described above requires however that the carbon bond angles be close to the tetrahedral angle, since change from this value is associated with loss in bond strength of the carbon orbitals and hence decrease in stability of the system. It is of great interest that in methylene chloride,[3] chloroform, propane, isobutane, and many such molecules the angles between single bonds to the carbon atom are found to have values of about 110° or 112°, very close to the tetrahedral angle 109°28′. Some of these values are given in Table 14–1.

In the molecules POF_3, $POCl_3$, POF_2Cl, and $POFCl_2$ the angles

---

[1] L. Pauling, *Proc. Nat. Acad. Sci.* 14, 359 (1928); *J.A.C.S.* 53, 1367 (1931); J. C. Slater, *Phys. Rev.* 37, 481 (1931).

[2] The non-existence of evidence for the existence of isomers of substances such as methylene chloride requires either that the nature of the distortion from the regular tetrahedral configuration about the central carbon atom be determined uniquely by the attached atoms or groups, or that isomeric molecules differing in the nature of this distortion be readily interconvertible.

[3] A decade ago the value 125° was assigned to the Cl—C—Cl bond angle in methylene chloride by an interpretation of the observed value of the electric dipole moment of the molecule, and the same value was reported from experiments on the diffraction of x-rays by the gas molecules; the correct result was obtained later by electron diffraction study.

TABLE 14-1.—OBSERVED VALUES OF BOND ANGLES FOR
QUADRICOVALENT ATOMS

Substance	Method	Bond Angle	Experimental Value[1]
Propane	E.D.	C—C—C	$111°30' \pm 3°$
Isobutane	E.D.	C—C—C	$111°30' \pm 2°, 113°30' \pm 2°$
$C(CH_3)_3Cl$	E.D.	C—C—C	$111°30' \pm 2°$
$C(CH_3)_3Br$	E.D.	C—C—C	$111°30' \pm 2°$
C_2H_5Cl	E.D.	C—C—Cl	$111°30' \pm 2°$
C_2H_5Br	E.D.	C—C—Br	$109° \pm 2°$
$CH(CH_3)_2Cl$	E.D.	C—C—Cl	$109° \pm 3°$
$CH(CH_3)_2Br$	E.D.	C—C—Br	$109°30' \pm 3°$
CH_3CCl_3	E.D.	C—C—Cl	$109° \pm 2°$
CH_2F_2	E.D.	F—C—F	$110° \pm 1°$
CH_2Cl_2	E.D.	Cl—C—Cl	$112° \pm 2°$
CH_2FCl	E.D.	F—C—Cl	$110° \pm 2°$
$CHCl_3$	E.D.	Cl—C—Cl	$112° \pm 2°$
CH_2Br_2	E.D.	Br—C—Br	$112° \pm 2°$
$CHBr_3$	E.D.	Br—C—Br	$111° \pm 2°$
Hexamethylene tetramine, $C_6H_{12}N_4$	C.S., E.D.	N—C—N[2]	$110° \pm 2°$
Tetramethyl-ethylene	E.D.	C=C—C	$124°20' \pm 1°$
Isobutene	E.D.	C=C—C	$124°20' \pm 1°$
$SiHCl_3$	E.D.	Cl—Si—Cl	$110° \pm 1°$
$SiHBr_3$	E.D.	Br—Si—Br	$110° \pm 2°$

[1] The electron-diffraction results are taken for the most part from the following papers: L. O. Brockway, *J. Phys. Chem.* 41, 747 (1937); L. Pauling and L. O. Brockway, *J.A.C.S.* 59, 1223 (1937); H. E. Lévy and L. O. Brockway, *ibid.* 59, 1662 (1937). The second value for the isobutane angle and the values for the tertiary butyl halides are due to J. Y. Beach and D. P. Stevenson, *ibid.* 60, 475 (1938), and those for the ethyl and isopropyl halides and for methyl chloroform to J. Y. Beach and D. P. Stevenson, *ibid.* 61, 2643 (1939).

[2] The N—C—N and C—N—C bond angles in this molecule are not independent.

halogen-phosphorus-halogen are close to 106° instead of 109°28'.[1] This indicates that the bond from phosphorus to oxygen is not a single covalent bond $\overset{+}{P}:\overset{..}{\underset{..}{O}}:^-$, but presumably has some double-bond character, with use of one of the 3d orbitals of phosphorus.

For quadricovalent silicon, germanium, and tin (and also for other quadricovalent atoms, such as nitrogen in a substituted ammonium ion) the same tetrahedral orientation of bonds is

[1] L. O. Brockway and J. Y. Beach, *J.A.C.S.* 60, 1836 (1938).

expected, since $3s$—$3p$, $4s$—$4p$, and $5s$—$5p$ hybridization is the same as that for the $2s$—$2p$ system. Observed values of bond angles in unsymmetrical compounds of these substances are also included in Table 14–1.

There are many symmetrically substituted compounds (CH_4, $C(CH_3)_4$, CCl_4, $Si(CH_3)_4$, $Ge(CH_3)_4$, $Sn(CH_3)_4$, etc.) in which the bond angles are known to be tetrahedral; these are not included in the table, since they provide no serious test of the theory.

A still more surprising result regarding the significance of the concept of the carbon atom as a regular tetrahedron is provided by the methylethylenes. The picture of the carbon-carbon double bond as involving the sharing of an edge by two regular tetrahedra leads to the tetrahedral value $125°16'$ for the single bond-double bond angle. The experimental value for this angle in both isobutene and tetramethylethylene is $124°20' \pm 1°$.

The results regarding tetrahedral bond orbitals described above are derived in the following way. We assume that the radial parts of the wave functions ψ_s and ψ_{p_x}, ψ_{p_y}, ψ_{p_z} are so closely similar that their differences can be neglected. The angular parts are

$$\left.\begin{aligned}
s &= 1, \\
p_x &= \sqrt{3}\ \sin\vartheta\ \cos\varphi, \\
p_y &= \sqrt{3}\ \sin\vartheta\ \sin\varphi, \\
p_z &= \sqrt{3}\ \cos\vartheta
\end{aligned}\right\} \tag{14-1}$$

ϑ and φ being the angles used in spherical polar coordinates. These functions are *normalized to 4π*, the integral

$$\int_0^{2\pi}\int_0^{\pi} f^2 \sin\vartheta\ d\vartheta\ d\varphi$$

of the square of the function taken over the surface of a sphere having the value 4π. The functions are *mutually orthogonal*, the integral of the product of any two of them (sp_x, say) over the surface of a sphere being zero.

Now we ask whether a new function

$$f = as + bp_x + cp_y + dp_z, \tag{14-2}$$

normalized to 4π (this requiring that $a^2 + b^2 + c^2 + d^2 = 1$), can be formed which has a larger bond strength than 1.732, and if so, what function of this type has the maximum bond strength. The direction of the bond is immaterial; let us choose the z axis. It is easily shown that p_x and p_y do not increase the strength of a bond in this direction, but decrease it, so they are ignored, the function thus assuming the form

$$f_1 = as + \sqrt{1 - a^2}\ p_z, \tag{14-3}$$

in which d is replaced by $\sqrt{1 - a^2}$ for normalization. The value of this in the bond direction $\vartheta = 0$ is, on substituting the expressions for s and p_z,

$$\cdot(\vartheta = 0) = a + \sqrt{3(1 - a^2)}.$$

This is made a maximum by differentiating with respect to a, equating to zero, and solving, the value $a = \frac{1}{2}$ being obtained. Hence the best bond orbital in the z direction is

$$= \frac{1}{2}\, s + \frac{\sqrt{3}}{2}\, p_z = \frac{1}{2} + \frac{3}{2}\, \cos \vartheta. \tag{14-4}$$

This has the form shown in Figure 14-1. Its strength is seen to be 2 by placing $\vartheta = 0$, $\cos \vartheta = 1$.

We now consider the function

$$f_2 = as + bp_x + dp_z$$

which is orthogonal to f_1, satisfying the requirement

$$\int_0^{2\pi} \int_0^{\pi} f_1 f_2 \sin \vartheta \; d\vartheta \; d\varphi = 0$$

and which has the maximum value possible in some direction. (This direction will lie in the xz plane; i.e., $\varphi = 0$, since p_y has been left out.) It is found on solving the problem that the function is

$$f_2 = \frac{1}{2}\, s + \frac{\sqrt{2}}{\sqrt{3}}\, p_x - \frac{1}{2\sqrt{3}}\, p_z; \tag{14-5}$$

this function is seen on examination to be identical with f_1 except that it is rotated through $109°28'$ from f_1. In the same way two more functions can be constructed, each identical with f_1 except for orientation.

An equivalent set of tetrahedral bond orbitals, differing from these only in orientation, is

$$t_{111} = \tfrac{1}{2}(s + p_x + p_y + p_z),$$
$$t_{1\bar{1}\bar{1}} = \tfrac{1}{2}(s + p_x - p_y - p_z),$$
$$t_{\bar{1}1\bar{1}} = \tfrac{1}{2}(s - p_x + p_y - p_z),$$
$$t_{\bar{1}\bar{1}1} = \tfrac{1}{2}(s - p_x - p_y + p_z).$$

The strength of an s—p hybrid orbital increases with increase in the amount of p involved from 1 (pure s) to a maximum value of 2 (tetrahedral orbital) and then decreases to 1.732 (pure p), in the way shown by the dashed curves in Figure 14-2, in which the square of the bond strength (that is, the product of the strengths of equivalent orbitals of two atoms forming a bond) is shown as a function of the nature of the orbitals. That the strength of the orbital is a measure of its bond-forming power is shown by the approximation of these curves to the full curves, which represent the calculated energy of a one-electron bond as a function of the nature of the bond orbitals.[1]

14a. The Effect of an Unshared Pair on Hybridization.—Since tetrahedral orbitals form stronger bonds than other s—p orbitals, it might be thought that hybridization to tetrahedral orbitals would always occur in bond formation. The tendency to use the best bond orbitals is, however, resisted in the case of atoms with

[1] L. Pauling and J. Sherman, *J.A.C.S.* **59**, 1450 (1937).

an unshared pair (or more than one) by the tendency to keep the
unshared pair in the s orbital, which is more stable than the p

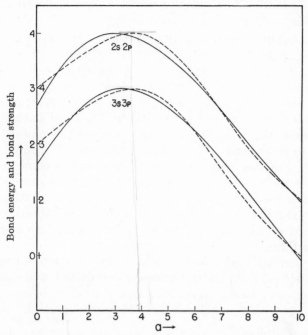

Fig. 14-2.—Square of bond strength (dashed curves) and calculated bond energy
values (full curves) for hybrid s—p orbitals varying from pure p orbitals ($a = 0$,
left) to pure s orbitals ($a = 10$, right).   The upper pair of curves are for L orbitals
($2s$ and $2p$), the lower, with shifted vertical scale, for M orbitals ($3s$ and $3p$).

orbitals.   In OF_2, for example, the use of tetrahedral orbitals in
bond formation would require that half of the s orbital (which is
divided equally among the four tetrahedral orbitals) be used for
shared pairs and only half for unshared pairs. Since a shared
pair counts as only one electron for each atom, this would involve
the loss of one-quarter of the extra stability due to a pair of s
electrons, and the atom will strive to prevent this.   On the other
hand, the bonds will strive to be as strong as possible.   In consequence a compromise will be reached;[1] the bond orbitals will
have a small amount of s character, and be intermediate between
p bonds and tetrahedral bonds, the unshared pair utilizing most
of the s orbital.   The bond strengths of these bonds will be between 1.732 and 2; and the angles between the bond directions

[1] The compromise is, of course, such as to minimize the energy for the
molecule as a whole.

will be increased somewhat from the p-bond value 90° toward the tetrahedral value 109°28′. It is probable that this effect is of some significance in connection with the bond angle values discussed in Section 13.

14b. Orbitals for Incomplete s—p Shells.—In boron trimethyl, $B(CH_3)_3$, only three of the four orbitals of the valence shell are used. If the best bond orbitals were utilized, the C—B—C bond angles would be near 109°28′. However, the molecule obtains added stability by using the s orbital as completely as possible, and this tends to cause the s orbital to be divided among three bond orbitals, which are found by the simple theoretical treatment to be coplanar and to make angles of 120° with one another.[1] Whether this effect would take place completely or whether the bonds would resist this weakening to some extent cannot be predicted; it is found experimentally[2] that the boron trimethyl molecule is coplanar, with 120° angles, indicating that the bond orbitals are those obtained by dividing the s orbital among three.

The formation of a fourth bond by boron would strengthen the bonds (all bond orbitals becoming tetrahedral) and stabilize the molecule; we can thus understand the ability of boron trimethyl to add ammonia to give the compound

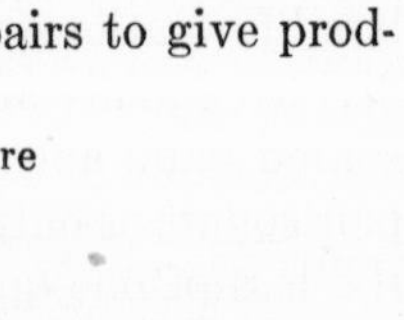

$$H_3C\diagdown \atop H_3C\diagup B—N {\diagup H \atop \diagdown H}.$$

The boron halides, whose structures are discussed in Section 29c, similarly add molecules containing unshared pairs to give prod-

---

[1] The three bond orbitals (taken in the xy plane) are

$$\frac{1}{\sqrt{3}}\, s + \frac{\sqrt{2}}{\sqrt{3}}\, p_x,$$

$$\frac{1}{\sqrt{3}}\, s - \frac{1}{\sqrt{6}}\, p_x + \frac{1}{\sqrt{2}}\, p_y,$$

and

$$\frac{1}{\sqrt{3}}\, s - \frac{1}{\sqrt{6}}\, p_x - \frac{1}{\sqrt{2}}\, p_y.$$

Their bond strength is 1.991, only slightly less than that of tetrahedral orbitals.

[2] H. A. Lévy and L. O. Brockway, *J.A.C.S.* **59**, 2085 (1937).

ucts such as $Cl-B \overset{\displaystyle Cl}{\underset{\displaystyle Cl}{\Big\langle}} N \equiv C-CH_3$, formed from boron trichloride

and methyl cyanide.

In a molecule such as mercury dimethyl the two bond orbitals would be expected to use all of the *s* orbital between them.[1] The simple treatment shows that the two bonds would then be opposed. This is substantiated by the observation of a linear configuration for gas molecules of $HgCl_2$, $HgBr_2$, and HgI_2, and also of a linear configuration for the molecules Hg_2Cl_2, Hg_2Br_2, and Hg_2I_2 (with electronic structures $:\overset{..}{\underset{..}{X}}-Hg-Hg-\overset{..}{\underset{..}{X}}:$) in crystals. A similar configuration is expected for bicovalent complexes of univalent copper, silver, and gold. It has been verified for the $[AuCl_2]^-$ ion[2] and the $[Ag(CN)_2]^-$ ion.[3]

14c. Orbitals for Multiple Bonds.—No general discussion of the orbitals involved in multiple-bond formation analogous to that just described for single bonds has been given. For a double bond two orbitals of each atom are required, which should project in the bond direction in order that the bond be strong. It seems probable[4] that the orbitals involved in double-bond formation by a carbon atom in a molecule such as ethylene are of the following type. The molecule is coplanar, and of the four orbitals s, p_x, p_y, and p_z three lie in the plane of the molecule (taken as the xy plane). From these three, s, p_x, and p_y, there can be constructed by linear combination three strong bond orbitals with their bond directions in the plane, with which single bonds can be formed to the two hydrogen atoms and the other carbon atom.[5] The p_z orbital, with lobes extending above and

---

[1] The two corresponding bond orbitals (with bond directions taken along the x-axis) are $\frac{1}{\sqrt{2}}(s + p_x)$ and $\frac{1}{\sqrt{2}}(s - p_x)$; their bond strength is 1.932.

[2] N. Elliott and L. Pauling, *J.A.C.S.* **60**, 1846 (1938); see Figure 15-4.

[3] J. L. Hoard, *Z. Krist.* **84**, 231 (1932).

[4] W. G. Penney, *Proc. Roy. Soc.* A144, 166 (1934); A146, 223 (1934).

[5] Equations for these orbitals are given in a footnote to the preceding section for the case that the *s* orbital is divided equally among the three bond orbitals. It seems probable that the influence of the double bond

below the plane of the molecule, is then involved in the formation of the second half of the double bond; the simple considerations regarding strengths of bond orbitals used for single bonds are not applicable to it.

14d. Restricted Rotation about Single Bonds.—The single bond orbitals discussed above are cylindrically symmetrical about the bond direction, and hence the energy of a molecule, insofar as it is determined by the bond orbital, should be independent of the orientation of the two parts of a molecule about the axis of a single bond. Other interactions also between the two parts of a molecule such as ethane would be expected not to depend much on this orientation, so that the molecule should show essentially free rotation about the single bond. This is in agreement with chemical experience—no case of isomerism corresponding to restriction of rotation about a pure single bond has been reported.

It has been found recently that the forces restricting rotation about single bonds, while not large enough to permit the isolation of isomers, are large enough to be of significance in structural chemistry, as, for example, in the calculation of entropy values from structural information. It was shown two years ago by Kemp and Pitzer[1] that the value of the entropy of ethane indicates very strongly that as the two methyl groups are rotated about the single carbon-carbon bond relative to one another the potential energy of the molecule changes by about 3000 cal./mole, the potential function having three maxima and three minima in a complete rotation, corresponding to the trigonal symmetry of the methyl groups. Further evidence supporting this restriction of rotation has been reported by Kistiakowsky, Lacher, and Stitt,[2]

---

to carbon causes the corresponding orbital to assume more s character, the two bond orbitals to hydrogen being essentially tetrahedral orbitals. The orbitals are then given by the equations

$$\psi_1 = \frac{1}{2} s + \frac{1}{2} p_x + \frac{1}{\sqrt{2}} p_y$$

$$\psi_2 = \frac{1}{2} s + \frac{1}{2} p_x - \frac{1}{\sqrt{2}} p_y,$$

$$\psi_3 = \frac{1}{\sqrt{2}} s - \frac{1}{\sqrt{2}} p_x,$$

the third corresponding to half of the double bond.

[1] J. D. Kemp and K. S. Pitzer, *J.A.C.S.* 59, 276 (1937).

[2] G. B. Kistiakowsky, J. R. Lacher, and F. Stitt, *J. Chem. Phys.* 7, 289 (1939).

who found from heat-capacity data the value 2750 cal./mole for the height of the potential barrier. A similar barrier of height about 3300 cal./mole has been found by Kemp and Egan[1] for propane, and the values 3800 cal./mole for isobutane and 4200 cal./mole for tetramethylmethane have been reported by Pitzer,[2] all from entropy measurements.

Although the thermodynamic measurements and spectroscopic data[3] for ethane do not permit the decision to be made as to whether the stable configuration of the molecule is that for which there is a plane of symmetry between the methyl groups (point group D_{3h}) or is the staggered configuration (point group D_{3d}), there is strong indirect evidence for the staggered configuration. Thus in many crystals which contain hydrocarbon chains these chains have been found by x-ray examination to have an extended zigzag configuration, corresponding to the staggered configuration for ethane. Dr. V. Schomaker (unpublished work) has also pointed out that the variation of values of heats of hydrogenation of unsaturated cyclic hydrocarbons can be interpreted in a convincing manner if it be assumed that the zigzag configuration is stable. For example, the cyclopentane molecule, which is coplanar, with bond angles 108°, is made less stable than cyclohexane, with the staggered configuration, by an amount of energy equal to the height of the potential barrier per methylene group.

Electron-diffraction studies of 1,2-dichloroethane,[4] 1,2-dibromoethane,[5] 1,2-chlorobromoethane,[5] and racemic and meso 2,3-dibromobutane[6] have been made, and it has been found that for all of these molecules there is restricted rotation about the carbon-carbon single bond, the stable orientation in each molecule being that in which the two halogen atoms are on opposite sides of the carbon-carbon axis. For 1,1,2-trichloroethane[7] the stable orientation is similar, the 2-chlorine atom being nearly opposite one of the 1-chlorine atoms.

The evidence for restricted rotation in ethane and related

[1] J. D. Kemp and J. Egan, *J.A.C.S.* 60, 1521 (1938).

[2] K. S. Pitzer, *J. Chem. Phys.* 5, 473 (1937).

[3] B. L. Crawford, Jr., W. H. Avery, and J. W. Linnett, *ibid* 6, 682 (1938); F. Stitt, *ibid.* 7, 297 (1939).

[4] J. Y. Beach and K. J. Palmer, *ibid.* 6, 639 (1938).

[5] J. Y. Beach and A. Turkevich, *J.A.C.S.* 61, 303 (1939).

[6] D. P. Stevenson and V. Schomaker, *ibid.* 61, 3173 (1939).

[7] A. Turkevich and J. Y. Beach, *ibid.* 61, 3127 (1939).

molecules is accordingly very strong.   The nature of the interaction which is responsible for the phenomenon is, however, still in doubt; none of the various suggestions which have been made[1] seems to be satisfactory.   The fact[2,3] that the methyl groups in dimethylacetylene undergo rotation with very little restriction (the potential barrier being less than 500 cal./mole high) is of some significance with respect to the nature of the phenomenon.

Restriction of rotation about single bonds other than the carbon-carbon bond has been observed.   The height of the potential barrier for rotation about the carbon-nitrogen bond is about 3000 cal./mole in methylamine[4] and 3500 cal./mole (for each methyl group) in dimethylamine.[5]   In methyl alcohol the barrier restricting rotation about the carbon-oxygen bond has a height[6] of about 3000 cal./mole, and somewhat larger values have been reported[7] for other alcohols.

In acetone[7] and propylene,[8] in which the carbon-carbon bond about which rotation of the methyl groups occurs is adjacent to a double bond with another atom, the heights of the potential barriers have been assigned the values 1000 cal./mole and 2100 cal./mole, respectively.

Since the height of the potential barrier in all these molecules is larger than the equipartition energy value RT at room temperature, which is about 600 cal./mole, the restriction is effective in determining the configuration usually assumed by the molecules.

15. BONDS INVOLVING d ORBITALS

The first-row atoms have only four valence orbitals. For the second-row atoms the s and p orbitals are the stable ones, and are usually used in bond formation and for unshared pairs; there also exist, however, five $3d$ orbitals in the M shell, and these, although much less stable than the $3s$ and $3p$ orbitals, might be

---

[1] E. Gorin, J. Walter, and H. Eyring, *J.A.C.S.* **61**, 1876 (1939); J. B. Conn, G. B. Kistiakowsky, and E. A. Smith, *ibid.* **61**, 1868 (1939); A. Eucken and K. Schäfer, *Naturwiss.* **27**, 122 (1939).

[2] B. L. Crawford, Jr., and W. W. Rice, *J. Chem. Phys.* **7**, 437 (1939).

[3] D. W. Osborne, C. S. Garner, and D. M. Yost, *ibid.* **8**, 131 (1940).

[4] J. G. Aston, C. W. Siller, and G. H. Messerly, *J.A.C.S.* **59**, 1743 (1937).

[5] J. G. Aston, M. L. Eidinoff, and W. S. Forster, *ibid.* **61**, 1539 (1939)

[6] L. S. Kassel, *J. Chem. Phys.* **4**, 492 (1936).

[7] S. C. Schumann and J. G. Aston, *J.A.C.S.* **60**, 985 (1938); *J. Chem. Phys.* **6**, 480, 485 (1938).

[8] B. L. Crawford, Jr., *et al.*, *J.A.C.S.* **61**, 2980 (1939).

used when necessary.   The existence of compounds such as PF_5, PF_3Cl_2, PCl_5, $[PF_6]^-$, and SF_6 suggests that one or two $3d$ orbitals are here being used together with the $3s$ and three $3p$ orbitals (all hybridized to bond orbitals) for bond formation.   It seems probable, however, that the completely covalent structures such

as

F   F
 \   /
  F—P   are of little significance, and that the molecules in-
 /   \
F   F

stead resonate mainly among structures such as

:F:⁻   F
        /
F—P⁺
        \
F   F   ,

etc., involving at most four covalent bonds.   (The four covalent bonds resonate among the five positions, making all bonds in the molecule equivalent in bond type.)   This is suggested by the fact that covalences higher than four are shown by second-row atoms only with very electronegative atoms, with which bonds with considerable ionic character would be formed.   On the other hand, the substance PBr_5 exists, and in view of the small difference in electronegativity of phosphorus and bromine it is probable that in this molecule the quinquecovalent structure is of considerable significance.

Heavier atoms such as tin form complexes $[MX_6]^{--}$ with chlorine, bromine and even iodine; it is likely that some use is made of the d orbitals of the valence shell of the central atom in these complexes.

It is, however, the d orbitals of the shell with total quantum number one less than that of the valence shell which are of great significance for bond formation.   In the transition elements the inner d orbitals have about the same energy as the s and p orbitals of the valence shell; and if they are not completely occupied by unshared electron pairs they play a very important part in bond formation.   For the hexamminocobaltic ion (and other cobaltammines) structures such as

$$
\begin{bmatrix}
H_3N & & NH_3 \\
 & \diagdown & \diagup \\
H_3N & -Co- & NH_3 \\
 & \diagup & \diagdown \\
H_3N & & NH_3
\end{bmatrix}^{+++}
$$

are written. It is seen on counting electrons that the cobalt
atom (with atomic number 27) holds 24 unshared electrons in
addition to the six pairs shared with nitrogen. Now the number
of available orbitals is such that six of the stable orbitals (not
including 4d) can be used for bond formation, with enough remaining for the unshared pairs. This is seen from the following
diagram:

1s	2s	2p	3s	3p	3d	4s	4p
..	..	.. .. ..	..	.. .. ..	.. .. ..	— —	— — —

The 24 unshared electrons occupy the orbitals 1s, 2s, three 2p,
3s, three 3p, and three of the 3d orbitals, leaving two 3d orbitals,
the 4s orbital, and the three 4p orbitals available for use as bond
orbitals.

For the atoms of the first transition group (the iron group)
there is little difference in energy of the 3d orbitals and the 4s and
4p orbitals (see Figure 6–1), so that the question as to how these
orbitals can be combined to form good bond orbitals becomes an
interesting one.   Similarly the orbitals 4d, 5s, and 5p have about
the same energy for atoms of the palladium group, and 5d, 6s,
and 6p for atoms of the platinum group. The following discussion of d—s—p hybridization applies to all three transition
groups.

The maximum bond strength of a d orbital is 2.236. That of
the best bond orbital which can be formed by d—s—p hybridization is 3; hence when stable d orbitals are available for use in
bond formation by an atom much stronger covalent bonds can
be formed than with s and p orbitals only, for which the maximum
bond strength is 2.

15a. Octahedral Bond Orbitals.—It is found on analysis of
the mathematical problem that when only two d orbitals are
available for combination with s and p, six equivalent bond
orbitals of strength 2.923 (nearly as great as the maximum 3)
can be formed, and that *these six orbitals have their bond directions
toward the corners of a regular octahedron.* From this theoretical
discussion we accordingly conclude that complexes such as
$[Co(NH_3)_6]^{+++}$, $[PdCl_6]^{--}$, $[PtCl_6]^{--}$, etc., should be octahedral
in configuration. This conclusion is of course identical with
the postulate made by Werner to account for isomerism in com-

plexes with different substituent groups[1], and verified also by the
x-ray examination of $Co(NH_3)_6I_3$, $(NH_4)_2PdCl_6$, $(NH_4)_2PtCl_6$,
and other crystals (see Figure 46–2).

A polar graph of an octahedral bond orbital is shown in Figure
15–1, from which its great concentration in the bond direction,
leading to large overlapping and the formation of a very strong
bond, can be seen.

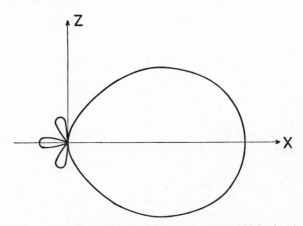

Fig. 15-1.—The angular dependence of an octahedral *dsp* bond
orbital with bond direction along the *x* axis.

It is interesting to note, as was pointed out to me some years
ago by Dr. J. L. Hoard, that these considerations lead to an
explanation of the difference in stability of bivalent and trivalent
cobalt as compared with bivalent and trivalent iron in covalent
octahedral complexes. The formation of covalent complexes
does not change the equilibrium between bivalent and trivalent
iron very much, as is seen from the values of the oxidation-

[1] There is only one form of a monosubstituted octahedral complex
MA_5B. A disubstituted complex MA_4B_2 can exist in two isomeric forms,
cis and trans:

Cis form.   Trans form.

Two forms can be shown by a trisubstituted complex MA_3B_3:

reduction potentials,[1] whereas a great change is produced in the equilibrium between bivalent and trivalent cobalt:

$$Fe^{++} = Fe^{+++} + E^-, \qquad -0.77 \text{ v.}$$
$$[Fe(CN)_6]^{----} = [Fe(CN)_6]^{---} + E^-, \qquad -0.36 \text{ v.}$$

Potential, -0.41 v.

$$Co^{++} = Co^{+++} + E^-, \qquad -1.84 \text{ v.}$$
$$[Co(CN)_6]^{----} = [Co(CN)_6]^{---} + E^-, \qquad +0.83 \text{ v.}$$

-2.67 v.

The effect is so pronounced that covalent compounds of bivalent cobalt can decompose water with liberation of hydrogen, whereas the trivalent cobalt ion decomposes water with liberation of oxygen, being one of the most powerful oxidizing agents known.[2] The explanation is contained in Figure 15-2. In the ions Co^{++}, Co^{+++}, Fe^{++}, and Fe^{+++} there is room for all unshared electrons in the $3d$ orbitals and inner orbitals. When octahedral bonds are formed in the covalent complexes, with use of two of the $3d$ orbitals, only three $3d$ orbitals are left for occupancy by unshared electrons. These are enough for bivalent and trivalent iron and for trivalent cobalt, but they can hold only six of the seven outer unshared electrons of bivalent cobalt. The seventh electron must accordingly occupy an outer unstable orbital, causing the

Optically active stereoisomers can be obtained of a complex like $M(C_2O_4)_3$, containing oxalate groups which occupy two adjacent octahedral corners:

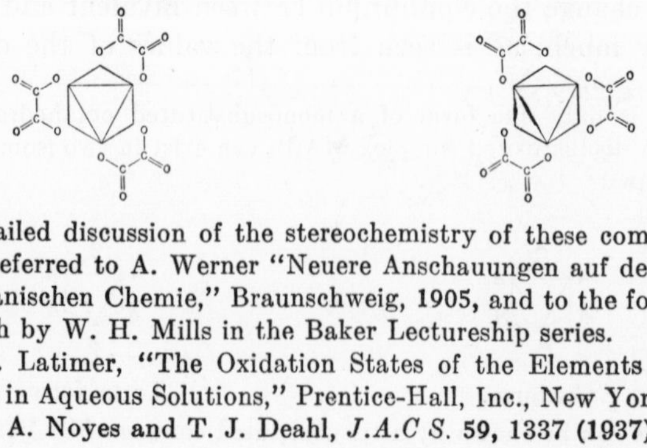

For a detailed discussion of the stereochemistry of these complexes the reader is referred to A. Werner "Neuere Anschauungen auf dem Gebiete der anorganischen Chemie," Braunschweig, 1905, and to the forthcoming monograph by W. H. Mills in the Baker Lectureship series.

[1] W. M. Latimer, "The Oxidation States of the Elements and their Potentials in Aqueous Solutions," Prentice-Hall, Inc., New York, 1938.

[2] See A. A. Noyes and T. J. Deahl, *J.A.C S.* **59**, 1337 (1937).

complex to be unstable.[1] A further discussion of the stability
of covalent complexes of transition elements is given in Section 31.

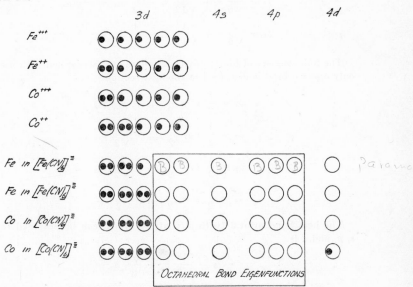

FIG. 15-2.—Occupancy of orbitals by electrons in ionic and covalent
complexes of bivalent and trivalent iron and cobalt.

The five d orbitals, in their angular dependence, are

$$d_s = \sqrt{5/4}\,(3\cos^2\vartheta - 1),$$
$$d_{y+s} = \sqrt{15}\,\sin\vartheta\,\cos\vartheta\,\cos\varphi,$$
$$d_{x+s} = \sqrt{15}\,\sin\vartheta\,\cos\vartheta\,\sin\varphi$$
$$d_{x+y} = \sqrt{15/4}\,\sin^2\vartheta\,\sin 2\varphi,$$
$$d_{xy} = \sqrt{15/4}\,\sin^2\vartheta\,\cos 2\omega.$$

The set of six equivalent octahedral orbitals formed from two d, the s, and
the three p orbitals is

$$\psi_1 = \frac{1}{\sqrt{6}}\,s + \frac{1}{\sqrt{2}}\,p_s + \frac{1}{\sqrt{3}}\,d_z,$$

$$\psi_2 = \frac{1}{\sqrt{6}}\,s - \frac{1}{\sqrt{2}}\,p_s + \frac{1}{\sqrt{3}}\,d_s$$

$$\psi_3 = \frac{1}{\sqrt{6}}\,s + \frac{1}{\sqrt{12}}\,d_s + \frac{1}{2}\,d_{xy} + \frac{1}{\sqrt{2}}\,p_x,$$

[1] An alternative structure, also leading to instability, is that in which
the seventh unshared electron occupies the fourth 3d orbital, and the
covalent bond orbitals make use of the unstable 4d orbital.

$$\psi_4 = \frac{1}{\sqrt{6}} \, s + \frac{1}{\sqrt{12}} \, d_z + \frac{1}{2} \, d_{xy} - \frac{1}{\sqrt{2}} p_x,$$

$$\psi_5 = \frac{1}{\sqrt{6}} \, s + \frac{1}{\sqrt{12}} \, d_z - \frac{1}{2} \, d_{xy} + \frac{1}{\sqrt{2}} \, p_y,$$

$$\psi_6 = \frac{1}{\sqrt{6}} \, s + \frac{1}{\sqrt{12}} \, d_z - \frac{1}{2} \, d_{xy} - \frac{1}{\sqrt{2}} \, p_y.$$

The following set of four equivalent square orbitals formed with use of only one d orbital is discussed in the next section:

$$\psi_1 = \frac{1}{2} \, s + \frac{1}{2} \, d_{xy} + \frac{1}{\sqrt{2}} \, p_x,$$

$$\psi_2 = \frac{1}{2} \, s + \frac{1}{2} \, d_{xy} - \frac{1}{\sqrt{2}} \, p_x,$$

$$\psi_3 = \frac{1}{2} \, s - \frac{1}{2} \, d_{xy} + \frac{1}{\sqrt{2}} \, p_y,$$

$$\psi_4 = \frac{1}{2} \, s - \frac{1}{2} \, d_{xy} - \frac{1}{\sqrt{2}} \, p_y.$$

The best bond orbital (with strength 3) which can be obtained from s, p, and d is

$$\frac{1}{3} \, s - \frac{1}{\sqrt{3}} \, p_z + \frac{\sqrt{5}}{3} \, d_z.$$

Three best bond orbitals of this type can be constructed at mutual angles of 73°9′ and 133°37′, each of the three bond angles having independent choice of these two values.

The two equivalent orbitals

$$\frac{1}{2\sqrt{3}} \, s + \frac{1}{\sqrt{2}} \, p_z + \frac{\sqrt{5}}{2\sqrt{3}} \, d_z,$$

and

$$\frac{1}{2\sqrt{3}} \, s - \frac{1}{\sqrt{2}} \, p_z + \frac{\sqrt{5}}{2\sqrt{3}} \, d_z$$

are oppositely directed and have the bond strength 2.96.

A thorough discussion of equivalent dsp bond orbitals has been published by Hultgren.[1]

15b. Square Bond Orbitals.—In a covalent complex of bivalent nickel such as the nickel cyanide ion $[Ni(CN)_4]^{--}$ the twenty-six inner electrons of the nickel atom can be placed in the $1s$, $2s$, three $2p$, $3s$, three $3p$, and four of the $3d$ orbitals. This leaves available for use in bond formation the fifth $3d$ orbital as well as the $4s$ and three $4p$ orbitals. It is found on hybridizing these orbitals that *four strong bonds directed to the corners of a*

[1] R. Hultgren, *Phys. Rev.* **40**, 891 (1932).

square can be formed, the corresponding orbitals, for which expressions are given at the end of the preceding section, having the bond strength 2.694, much greater than that of *s—p* tetrahedral orbitals (2). These four square orbitals are formed with use of only two of the $4p$ orbitals; a fifth very weak p bond might accordingly also be formed by the nickel atom.

From this argument these nickel complexes are expected to have a square coplanar configuration, rather than the tetrahedral configuration usually assumed for four groups about a central

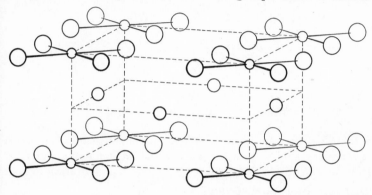

Fig. 15–3.—The structure of the tetragonal crystals K_2PdCl_4 and K_2PtCl_4. The smallest circles represent palladium or platinum atoms, those of intermediate size potassium ions, and the largest chlorine atoms. The four chlorine atoms about each palladium or platinum atom lie at the corners of a square.

atom. In 1931, when the argument was first presented, this configuration had not been recognized for complexes of nickel. The discussion given is also applicable to the coordination complexes of bivalent palladium and platinum, with suitable change in the total quantum numbers of the atomic orbitals. For these complexes the square configuration had been deduced thirty years ago by Werner from the observed existence of isomers and had been verified later by Dickinson[1] by the x-ray investigation of crystals of the chloropalladites and chloroplatinites (Figure 15–3). In the last few years a large amount of evidence in support of this view has been gathered both by chemical investiga-

[1] R. G. Dickinson, *J.A.C.S.* **44**, 2404 (1922). The square configuration has been verified for the tetramminopalladous cation in $[Pd(NH_3)_4]Cl_2 \cdot H_2O$ by B. N. Dickinson, *Z. Krist.* **88**, 281 (1934).

tion and by structural study by x-ray diffraction, the measurement of electric dipole moments, etc.   For example, cis and trans forms of palladium benzylmethylglyoxime have been prepared,[1] with the following configurations:

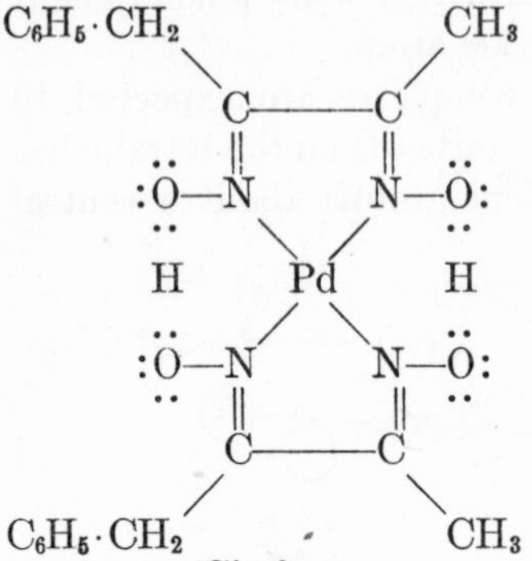

Cis form. 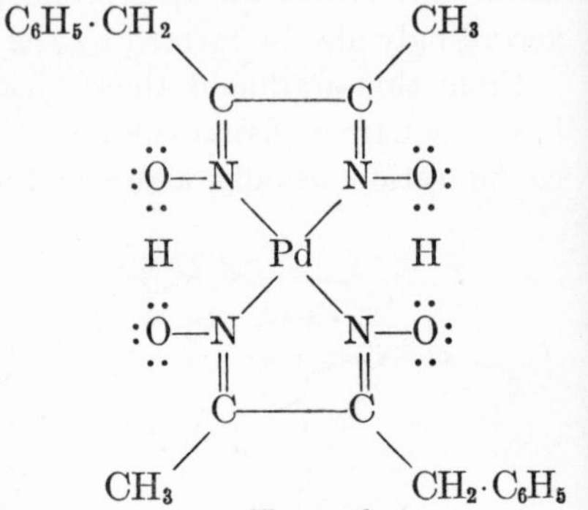   Trans form.

Similar investigations have also been carried out with compounds of trivalent gold.[2]   It has been found that compounds of type R_2AuBr and R_2AuCN complete the square configuration of gold by polymerization to structures such as

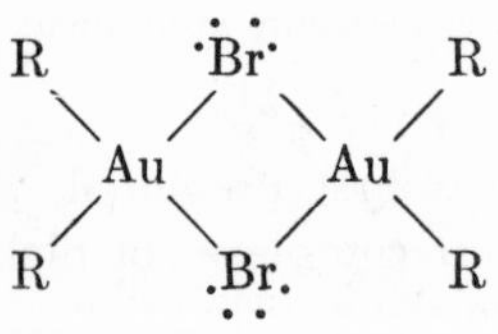

and

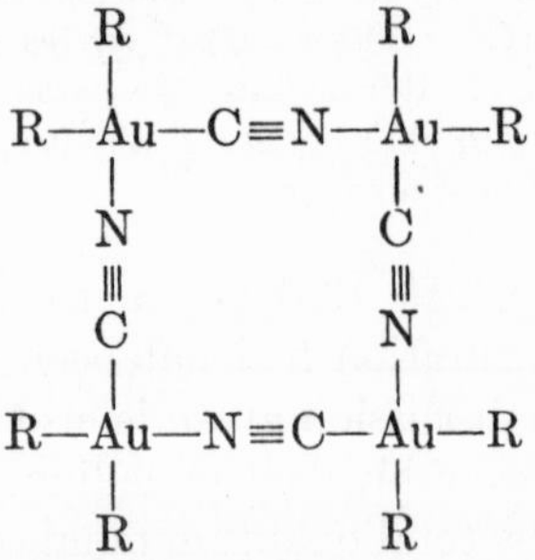

(with R = ethyl, n-propyl, etc.).   The difference in observed degree of polymerization is to be attributed to the difference in bond angles of bromine (normal bond angle about 95°, as for

[1] F. P. Dwyer and D. P. Mellor, *J.A.C.S.* **57**, 605 (1935).

[2] W. J. Pope and C. S. Gibson, *J. Chem. Soc.* **91**, 2061 (1907); C. S. Gibson and J. L. Simonsen, *ibid.* **1930**, 2531; M. S. Kharasch and H. S. Isbell, *J.A.C.S.* **53**, 2701 (1931); A. Burawoy and C. S. Gibson, *J Chem. Soc.* **1934**, 860; **1935**, 219; A. Burawoy, C. S. Gibson, G. C. Hampson, and H. M. Powell, *ibid.* **1937**, 1690.

selenium) and cyanide (linear), the coplanar configurations which are represented being without strain. Compounds with the empirical formula $RAuBr_2$ polymerize to the dimeric form

$$
\begin{array}{ccccc}
:\overset{\cdot\cdot}{\underset{\cdot\cdot}{Br}} & & \overset{\cdot}{\underset{}{Br}}\overset{\cdot}{} & & R \\
& \diagdown & \diagup\diagdown & \diagup & \\
& Au & & Au & \\
& \diagup & \diagdown & \diagup & \diagdown \\
R & & .Br. & & \overset{}{\underset{\cdot\cdot}{Br}}: \\
& & \overset{}{\underset{\cdot\cdot}{}} & &
\end{array}
\quad,
$$

and even auric bromide has a similar dimeric form, as shown by its molecular weight in bromine solution.[1] A similar coplanar structure (with $R = As(CH_3)_3$) has been assigned the molecule $Pd_2Br_4[As(CH_3)_3]_2$, and verified by x-ray examination of crystals of this substance and its chlorine analogue.[2]

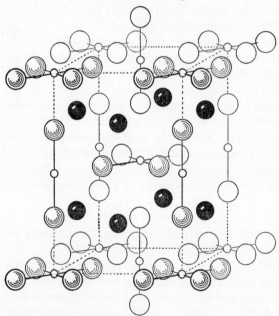

Fig. 15–4.—The atomic arrangement in crystals of $Cs_2AgAuCl_6$ and $Cs_2AuAuCl_6$. Large full circles represent cesium atoms, large open circles chlorine atoms, and small circles gold or silver atoms.

[1] A. Burawoy and C. S. Gibson, *J. Chem. Soc.* 1935, 217.
[2] A. F; Wells, *Proc. Roy. Soc.* A167, 169 (1938).

The tetragonal crystals[1] $Cs_2AgCl_2AuCl_4$ and $Cs_2AuCl_2AuCl_4$, with the structure shown in Figure 15-4, contain square complexes $[AuCl_4]^-$ of trivalent gold, as well as linear complexes $[AgCl_2]^-$ or $[AuCl_2]^-$ of univalent silver or gold.

An interesting case of infinite polymerization is provided by palladous chloride. In crystals of this substance[2] there are coplanar strings of indefinite length with the configuration

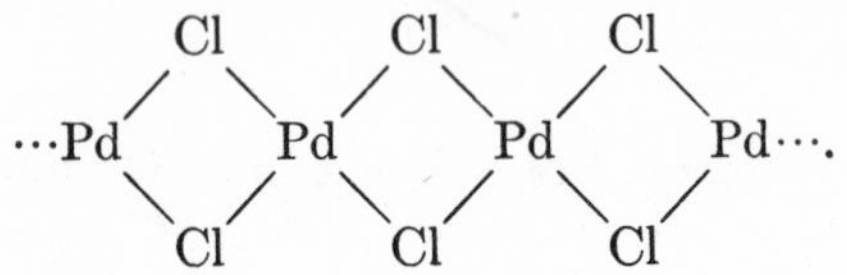

These strings contain rectangular $PdCl_4$ groups which share edges in such a way as to lead to the composition $PdCl_2$. The $PdCl_4$ groups are only slightly distorted from the square configuration, the Cl—Pd—Cl angles being 93° and 87°.

It may be mentioned that quadricovalent complexes of quadrivalent platinum and palladium are expected to have the tetrahedral rather than the square configuration, since two d orbitals are available for bond orbital formation, instead of only one as in the bivalent complexes. Molecules of the recently discovered substances[3] tetramethylplatinum, $Pt(CH_3)_4$, and hexamethyldiplatinum, $Pt_2(CH_3)_6$, might be expected to be similar in structure to neopentane and hexamethylethane, respectively, with a platinum-platinum bond in the second. However, an investigation (as yet incomplete) of the structure of crystalline tetramethylplatinum and trimethylplatinum chloride by J. H. Sturdivant and R. E. Rundle has indicated that tetramers $Pt_4(CH_3)_{16}$ and $Pt_4(CH_3)_{12}Cl_4$ exist in the crystals, with each platinum atom forming six octahedral bonds.

Evidence for the square configuration for $[Ni(CN)_4]^{--}$ was provided in 1931 only by the magnetic properties of salts containing this ion and by the observed isomorphism of $K_2Ni(CN)_4 \cdot H_2O$ and $K_2Pd(CN)_4 \cdot H_2O$. In the last few years many investigations have been carried out which show the presence of this configuration in nickel complexes. The first of these, made by

[1] N. Elliott and L Pauling, *J.A.C.S.* **60**, 1846 (1938).

[2] A. F. Wells, *Z. Krist.* **100**, 189 (1938).

[3] H. Gilman and M. Lichtenwalter, *J.A.C.S.* **60**, 3085 (1938).

Sugden,[1] was the synthesis of cis and trans forms of the nickel compound of benzylmethylglyoxime, with the configurations shown above for the corresponding palladium compound. Similar pairs of isomers of compounds of nickel as well as palladium and platinum with other groups have also been obtained.[2] The x-ray study of crystalline potassium nickel dithio-oxalate[3] has shown it to be isomorphous with the palladium and platinum compounds and has provided a detailed verification of the coplanar structure

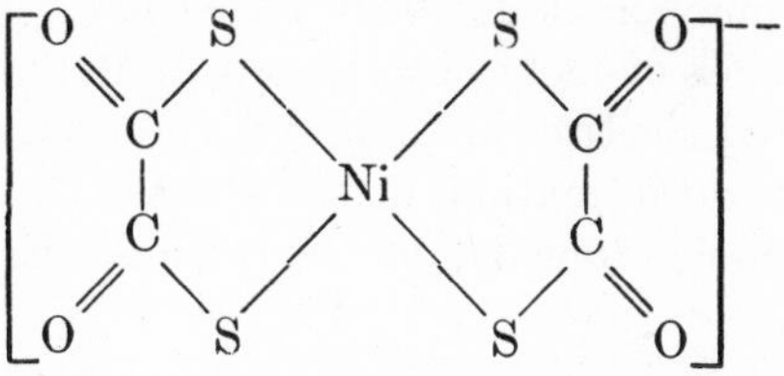

for the complex ion. Isomorphism has been shown for many other sets of substances,[4] such as $BaM(CN)_4 \cdot 4H_2O$, with M = Ni, Pd, and Pt.[5]

[1] S. Sugden, *J. Chem. Soc.* 1932, 246.

[2] K. A. Jensen, *Z. anorg. allg. Chem.* 221, 6 (1934).

[3] E. G. Cox, W. Wardlaw, and K. C. Webster, *J. Chem. Soc.* 1935, 1475; N. Elliott, *Dissertation*, California Institute of Technology, 1938. See also E. G. Cox, F. W. Pinkard, W. Wardlaw, and K. C. Webster, *J. Chem. Soc.* 1935, 459; and E. G. Cox, W. Wardlaw, and K. C. Webster, *ibid.* 1935, 1475, for x-ray work on related crystals.

[4] H. Brasseur, A. de Rassenfosse, and J. Pierard, *Z. Krist.* 88, 210 (1934), and later papers.

[5] In the compounds obtained by replacing the N hydrogen atoms of two substituted pyrromethene molecules

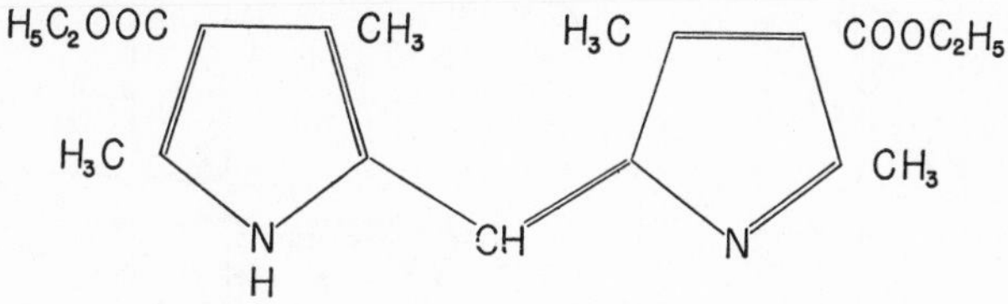

by palladium, nickel, or copper (C. R. Porter, *J. Chem. Soc.* 1938, 368) it is found that the metal atoms form covalent bonds with the four nitrogen atoms. Steric interactions of the α methyl groups prevent the molecule from being completely coplanar, however, so that the four metal-nitrogen bonds must be distorted somewhat from their normal square coplanar configuration.

A survey of the magnetic evidence for the dsp^2 quadricovalent state of nickel is given in Section 16d.

It is seen on analysis of the problem that bivalent copper would be expected to form four covalent bonds of the dsp^2 coplanar type rather than tetrahedral sp^3 covalent bonds. The dsp^2 bonds are much stronger than the sp^3 bonds (strength 2.694 instead of 2). Bivalent copper has, however, one electron more than bivalent nickel, and in the usual assignment of unshared electrons to orbitals this electron would occupy the fifth $3d$ orbital, making it unavailable for bond formation. There is, on the other hand, no loss of energy by the copper atom caused by placing the unshared electron in the third $4p$ orbital and using the $3d$ orbital for bond formation, inasmuch as each of the five orbitals under discussion (one $3d$, one $4s$, three $4p$) is occupied either

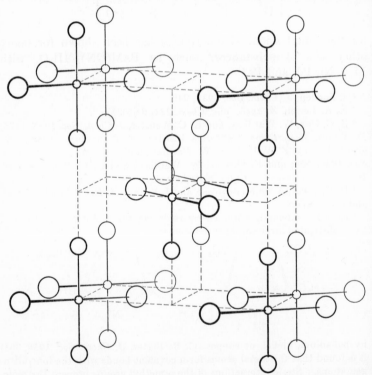

Fig. 15-5.—The atomic arrangement in crystalline cupric chloride dihydrate, $CuCl_2 \cdot 2H_2O$. The circles represent copper atoms, oxygen atoms, and chlorine atoms, in order of increasing size.

by a shared pair or by the single unshared electron on either formulation (single electron in $3d$ with sp^3 bonds or single electron in $4p$ with dsp^2 bonds), and the interaction energy of a shared pair with the copper atom is the same as that of a single unshared electron. The greater strength of dsp^2 bonds than of sp^3 bonds is accordingly the determining factor; a complex of bivalent copper involving four covalent bonds will have the square rather than the tetrahedral configuration.

The planar configuration of quadricovalent cupric copper was discovered by Cox and Webster[1] in the compounds of copper with β-diketones (copper disalicylaldoxime, copper acetylacetonate, copper benzoylacetonate, the copper salt of dipropionylmethane) and by Tunell, Posnjak, and Ksanda[2] in the mineral tenorite, CuO. In crystalline cupric chloride dihydrate (Figure 15–5) there are molecules with the coplanar configuration[3]

$$
\begin{array}{c}
\mathrm{H_2O} \\
| \\
\mathrm{Cl-Cu-Cl,} \\
| \\
\mathrm{H_2O}
\end{array}
$$

and the same group occurs[4] in crystalline $K_2CuCl_4 \cdot 2H_2O$. Some evidence has been reported for the trans coplanar configuration for the stable form of dipyridine cupric chloride,[5]

$$
\begin{array}{ccccc}
\mathrm{CH-CH} & & \mathrm{Cl} & \mathrm{CH-CH} \\
\diagup\diagup & & | & \diagup\diagdown \\
\mathrm{CH} & \mathrm{N-Cu-N} & & \mathrm{CH} \\
\diagdown & \diagup & | & \diagdown \\
\mathrm{CH=CH} & \mathrm{Cl} & \mathrm{CH=CH}
\end{array}
$$

[1] E. G. Cox and K. C. Webster, *J. Chem. Soc.* 1935, 731.

[2] G. Tunell, E. Posnjak, and C. J. Ksanda, *Z. Krist.* 90, 120 (1935).

[3] D. Harker, *Z. Krist.* 93, 136 (1936).

[4] S. B. Hendricks and R. G. Dickinson, *J.A.C.S.* 49, 2149 (1927); L. Chrobak, *Z. Krist.* 88, 35 (1934). In $K_2CuCl_4 \cdot 2H_2O$ each copper atom has as nearest neighbors two chlorine atoms at the distance 2.32 Å and two oxygen atoms (of the water molecules) at 1.97 Å, with the coplanar configuration represented in the text. There are also two neighboring chlorine atoms above and below the plane of this group at the distance 2.95 Å; these are considered not to be covalently bonded to copper, since the distance is much greater than expected for a covalent bond. The crystal $K_2CuCl_4 \cdot 2H_2O$ may be considered as a closely packed aggregate of $CuCl_2 \cdot 2H_2O$ molecules, chloride ions, and potassium ions.

[5] E. G. Cox, E. Sharratt, W. Wardlaw, and K. C. Webster, *J. Chem. Soc.* 1936, 129.

and a coplanar configuration for copper methylethylglyoxime is probable in view of its isomorphism with the corresponding compound of nickel.

Quadricovalent complexes of bivalent silver should have the same coplanar configuration as those of bivalent copper. This has been verified[1] for the argentic salt of picolinic acid, which is isomorphous with the cupric salt and which shows moreover the high birefringence expected for a parallel arrangement of coplanar molecules with the structure

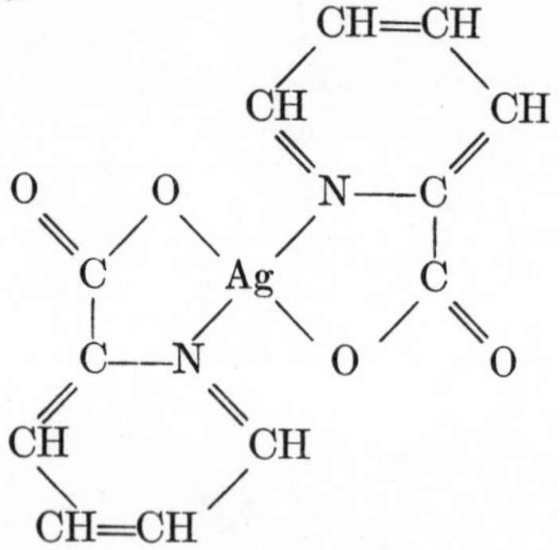

15c. Other Configurations Involving d Orbitals.—In molybdenite, MoS_2, the quadrivalent molybdenum atom, with only one unshared pair of $4d$ electrons, has four $4d$ orbitals available for bond formation. The configuration of the six sulfur atoms about each molybdenum atom in this crystal[2] is not octahedral, but is that of a trigonal prism with unit axial ratio, as shown in Figure 15–6. The S—Mo—S bond angles have values 82° and 136°, which are not far from those for the strongest d—s—p bonds (73°09′ and 133°37′); it is, indeed, found[3] that six equivalent orbitals of strength 2.983 with the trigonal-prismatic orientation of bond directions can be constructed.

This configuration also occurs in tungstenite, WS_2, but it has not been recognized in any other compounds of molybdenum or tungsten.

Both quadrivalent and quinquevalent molybdenum and tungsten form complexes with eight cyanide groups. In these complexes a molybdenum atom has available five $4d$ orbitals, one $5s$

---

[1] E. G. Cox, W. Wardlaw, and K. C. Webster, *J. Chem. Soc.* **1936**, 775.
[2] R. G. Dickinson and L. Pauling, *J.A.C.S.* **45**, 1466 (1923).
[3] R. Hultgren, *loc. cit.*

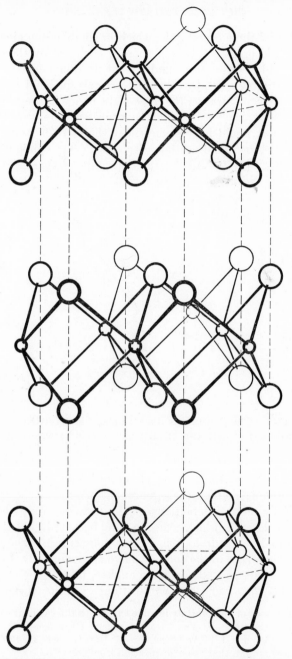

Fig. 15-6.—The structure of the hexagonal crystal molybdenite, MoS₂, showing the arrangement of sulfur atoms (large circles) at the corners of a trigonal prism about each molybdenum atom (small circles).

orbital, and three $5p$ orbitals, which in combination give rise to nine hybrid orbitals. One of these is occupied by the electron pair or odd electron (for quadrivalent or quinquevalent molybdenum, respectively), leaving eight orbitals for bond formation. The stable configuration for these eight bonds has not been predicted theoretically;[1] it might be expected, however, that the bond angles would have values near those, 73°9′ and 133°37′, for the best *spd* bond orbitals (Sec. 13a). The configuration of the complex $[Mo(CN)_8]^{----}$, as determined experimentally by Hoard and Nordsieck in their recent x-ray study[2] of crystalline

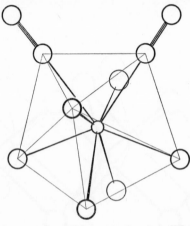

FIG. 15–7.—The structure of the complex ion $[Mo(CN)_8]^{----}$. The nitrogen atoms of only two of the eight cyanide groups are shown.

potassium molybdocyanide dihydrate, $K_4Mo(CN)_8 \cdot 2H_2O$, is shown in Figure 15–7. It is of interest that the coordination polyhedron is neither the square antiprism, which would be favored by steric interactions of the cyanide groups (see Sec. 48a), nor the cube, which comes to mind because it, like the tetrahedron and octahedron, is a regular polyhedron. The twenty-eight bond angles in the complex have approximately the following ideal values: 73°42′ (fourteen angles), 129°50′ (four), 138°55′ (two), 147°23′ (four), and 95°36′ (four). All of these but the

[1] The nature of the orbitals involved in the eight covalent bonds has been discussed by J. H. Van Vleck, *J. Chem. Phys.* **3**, 803 (1935), and W. G. Penney and J. S. Anderson, *Trans. Faraday Soc.* **33**, 1363 (1937), on the assumption that the configuration is cubic.

[2] J. L. Hoard and H. H. Nordsieck, *J.A.C.S.* **61**, 2853 (1939).

last lie close to one of the theoretical angles for best *spd* bonds, the average deviation for the twenty-eight angles being 3°; this may be the reason for the assumption of this configuration by the complex. The angles for the antiprism (sixteen at 74°52′, four at 118°32′, and eight at 141°52′) are also close to the theoretical values (average deviation 5°), whereas those for the cube (twelve at 70°32′, twelve at 109°28′, and four at 180°) show larger deviations from them.

Five covalent bonds can be formed by the phosphorus atom in the molecules PF_5, PF_3Cl_2, and PCl_5 with use of one $3d$ orbital.

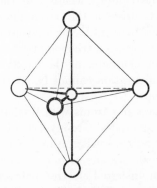

Fig. 15–8.—The structure of the molecule PCl_5, showing the arrangement of the five chlorine atoms at the corners of a trigonal bipyramid about the phosphorus atom.

Allthree of these molecules have been shown by the electron diffraction method[1] to have the configuration of a trigonal bipyramid of halogen atoms with the phosphorus atom at its center (Figure 15–8). In PF_3Cl_2 the two chlorine atoms are at the apices of the two pyramids and the three fluorine atoms at the corners of their common base. The trigonal bipyramidal con-

---

[1] L. O. Brockway and J. Y. Beach, *J.A.C.S.* **60**, 1836 (1938); M. Rouault, *C. r. Acad. Sci.* **207**, 620 (1938); V. Schomaker, unpublished investigation. Brockway and Beach reported the interatomic distances P—F = 1.59 ± 0.03 and P—Cl = 2.05 ± 0.03Å in PF_3Cl_2 and P—F = 1.57 ± 0.02Å in PF_5. The two chlorine atoms at the apices of the pyramids in PCl_5 are 2.11 Å from the phosphorus atom, the other three being at 2.04 Å. It is indicated by Raman spectroscopic data that the phosphorus pentachloride molecule does not retain this configuration in the crystal or in solution in solvents of high dielectric constant.

figuration has been reported also for molybdenum pentachloride,[1] $MoCl_5$, and for the trimethylstibine dihalides,[2] $(CH_3)_3SbX_2$. The theoretical treatment of covalent bonds of this type has not been carried out.

The configuration of the molecule IF_7 has not been determined, and there exists little information about the most stable configurations for seven bonds. In the A-modification of the rare earth sesquioxides[3] and in the ion $[ZrF_7]_=$ each metal atom is surrounded by seven oxygen or fluorine atoms with the configuration of an octahedron distorted by spreading one face and introducing the seventh atom at its center,[4] whereas in the ions $[CbF_7]^-$ and $[TaF_7]^-$ the configuration of the seven fluorine atoms can be described as obtained by introducing a seventh atom at the center of one of the square faces of a trigonal prism.[5] It is possible that the amount of ionic character of the bonds involved here is so great that this configuration cannot be considered as stable for seven covalent bonds.

15d. Configurations for Atoms with Unshared Electron Pairs. —There has been gathered so far only a small amount of information regarding the relative orientations of bonds formed by an atom which also possesses one or more unshared electron pairs.

In a few cases an unshared electron pair seems to have no effect on bond directions. This is observed[6] for Se^{IV} in the octahedral complex ion $[SeBr_6]^-$ and for Sb^{III} in $[SbBr_6]^{---}$.

Usually, however, an unshared pair seems to occupy one of the corners of a coordination polyhedron, and to replace the shared pair of a bond. The molecules NH_3, PCl_3, etc., have pyramidal configurations which might be described as involving bonds directed towards three corners of a tetrahedron with the fourth corner occupied by the unshared pair, and a similar description can be given for H_2O, $(CH_3)_2S$, etc.

The extension of this postulate to atoms with five bonds and one unshared pair suggests that the bonds should be directed toward the five corners of a square pyramid, which with the un-

[1] R. V. G. Ewens and M. W. Lister, *Trans. Faraday Soc.* **34**, 1358 (1938).

[2] A. F. Wells, *Z. Krist.* **99**, 367 (1938).

[3] L. Pauling, *ibid.* **69**, 415 (1929).

[4] G. C. Hampson and L. Pauling, *J.A.C.S.* **60**, 2702 (1938).

[5] J. L. Hoard, *ibid.* **61**, 1252 (1939).

[6] J. L. Hoard and B. N. Dickinson, *Z. Krist.* **84**, 436 (1933); N. Elliott, *J. Chem. Phys.* **2**, 298 (1934); see also Sec. 23b.

shared pair would form an octahedron. The configuration of no molecule or complex of this type (such as IF_5) has so far been determined experimentally. The recent study[1] of the crystal $KICl_4$ has shown, however, that the four chlorine atoms of the $[ICl_4]^-$ complex are located at the corners of a square about the iodine atom; we may consider that the octahedron about iodine is completed by the two unshared electron pairs of the iodine atom, one above and one below the ICl_4 plane.

A similar interpretation can be given the ions $[ClICl]^-$, $[BrIBr]^-$, $[III]^-$, and $[ClIBr]^-$, which are known to be linear in crystals of alkali compounds of these anions.[2] The electronic structure of the ions is $:\ddot{X}:\ddot{\ddot{I}}:\ddot{X}:$; it can be considered that the configuration is the trigonal bipyramid of PF_5, PF_3Cl_2, and PCl_5 with halogen atoms at the two pyramidal apices and the three unshared electron pairs in the equatorial plane.

Dipole-moment determinations for $SeCl_2(C_6H_5)_2$ and $TeCl_4$ in benzene solution have been made,[3] giving the values 3.47 and 2.54×10^{-18} e.s.u., respectively. These non-vanishing values show that the molecules are neither tetrahedral nor square (rejecting the improbable cis square configuration for the selenium compound). Our postulate suggests that the configuration is similar to that of PCl_5 and related molecules; that is, that the four bonds and one unshared pair occupy the five corners of a trigonal bipyramid. The unshared pair would probably occupy one of the equatorial positions rather than one of the apical positions. It has, indeed, been found by Dr. J. D. McCullough[4] that a preliminary x-ray study of crystalline $SeBr_2(C_6H_5)_2$ indicates that the phenyl groups occupy the apical positions and the bromine atoms two of the equatorial positions.

The x-ray investigation[5] of the crystal KIO_2F_2 has shown that the $[IO_2F_2]^-$ ion can be described as having the trigonal bipyramidal configuration, with the two oxygen atoms and the unshared electron pair in the equatorial positions and the two fluorine atoms at the apices.

[1] R. C. L. Mooney, *Z. Krist.* **98**, 377 (1938).

[2] R. W. G. Wyckoff, *J.A.C.S.* **42**, 1100 (1920); R. C. L. Mooney, *Z. Krist.* **90**, 143 (1935); **98**, 324 (1937).

[3] C. P. Smyth, A. J. Grossman, and S. R. Ginsberg, *J.A.C.S.* **62**, 192 (1940).

[4] Personal communication.

[5] L. Helmholz and M. T. Rogers, unpublished work.

16. THE MAGNETIC CRITERION FOR BOND TYPE

16a. Magnetic Susceptibility and Magnetic Moment.—A magnetic polarization resulting from an accelerating influence of the field on the electrons in the substance (the "Larmor precession") is produced in every substance on application of a magnetic field. The direction of the polarization is negative, that is, it gives rise to a field which is opposed to the applied field. A substance polarized in this way is said to be *diamagnetic;* it is repelled by a magnet. The diamagnetic polarization of a substance is practically independent of temperature, and almost independent of structure; it can be calculated with reasonable accuracy as the sum of terms corresponding to the atoms composing the substance, with perhaps some small corrections for the types of bonds involved. Diamagnetic polarization has not been found to be of much value in the investigation of the structure of molecules, and we shall not discuss it further.[1]

Some substances show, in addition to diamagnetic polarization, a polarization of opposite sign (that is, with the field) and often of large magnitude. This *paramagnetic polarization* results from the presence in the substance of atoms, ions, or molecules with permanent magnetic dipole moments, which in general are due in part to the spin magnetic moments of unpaired electrons and in part to the magnetic moments associated with the orbital motions of the electrons. These permanent magnetic dipoles tend to orient themselves with the field; the orienting tendency is opposed by the effect of temperature, the ratio of the number of dipoles in the more stable orientations with the field to the number of those in the less stable orientations against the field decreasing with increasing temperature. The paramagnetic polarization is accordingly dependent on the temperature; for ideal systems (with small interaction between the dipoles) it is inversely proportional to the absolute temperature.

---

[1] Efforts to extend the work of Pascal and to use values of diamagnetic susceptibility in the discussion of the structure of molecules have been made recently by F. W. Gray and J. H. Cruickshank, *Trans. Faraday Soc.* **31**, 1491 (1935); A. Clow, *ibid.* **33**, 381 (1937); A. Clow and J. M. C. Thompson, *ibid.* **33**, 894 (1937).

The diamagnetism of aromatic molecules has been discussed by L. Pauling, *J. Chem. Phys.* **4**, 673 (1936); K. Lonsdale, *Proc. Roy. Soc.* A159, 149 (1937); *J. Chem. Soc.* **1938**, 364; F. London, *Compt. rend.* **205**, 28 (1937); *J. Physique* **8**, 397 (1937).

The molal magnetic susceptibility[1] of an ideal system containing dipoles of only one kind can be represented by the equation

$$\chi_{molal} = N\alpha + \frac{N\mu^2}{3kT}, \tag{16-1}$$

in which N is Avogadro's number, k Boltzmann's constant, T the absolute temperature, α the molecular diamagnetic susceptibility (a negative quantity), and μ the permanent magnetic dipole moment. The paramagnetic term is often written in the form C/T, with $C = N\mu^2/3k$ called the *Curie constant* of the substance. The dipole moment μ is usually measured in Bohr magnetons, with magnitude $eh/4\pi mc$. In this unit μ is easily obtained from C by the equation

$$\mu = \sqrt{3kC/N} = 2.839\sqrt{C}. \tag{16-2}$$

The spin dipole moments of the unpaired electrons in an atom, ion, or molecule usually cooperate in contributing (together with the orbital moment, if there is any) to a resultant magnetic dipole moment for the system. The spin dipole moment of one electron has the magnitude $\sqrt{3} = 1.73$ Bohr magnetons. The resultant of the spin moments of n unpaired electrons has the value

$$\mu = \sqrt{n(n + 2)} \text{ Bohr magnetons.} \tag{16-3}$$

In case that the orbital magnetic moment of the electrons is zero or that a correction for its contribution can be made, the observed value of μ can be substituted in this equation to provide a value for the number of unpaired electrons.

16b. The Magnetic Moments of Ions of the Iron-group Elements.—Most of the compounds of the iron-group elements are paramagnetic. This is to be expected for the monatomic ions, inasmuch as the rules of atomic structure require that the $3d$ electrons remain unpaired until required to pair, which occurs first when they reach six in number, the sixth having to occupy one of the five $3d$ orbitals by pairing with another electron. The calculated value of the spin moment (Equation 16–3) rises to a

[1] For the detailed discussion of magnetic phenomena the reader is referred to E. C. Stoner, "Magnetism and Matter," Methuen, 1934, and J. H. Van Vleck, "The Theory of Electric and Magnetic Susceptibilities," Oxford University Press, 1932.

maximum of 5.92, corresponding to five unpaired electrons, and then decreases, as shown in Table 16–1.

The observed values for the iron-group ions in aqueous solution are seen from the table to agree reasonably well with the theoretical values. The deviations observed can be explained as resulting from contributions of the orbital moments of the electrons.

TABLE 16-1.— MAGNETIC MOMENTS OF IRON-GROUP IONS
IN AQUEOUS SOLUTION

Ion	Number of $3d$ electrons	Number of unpaired electrons	Calculated spin moment*	Observed moment*
K^+, Ca^{++}, Sc^{+++}, Ti^{4+}	0	0	0.00	0.00
V^{4+}	1	1	1.73	1.7
V^{+++}	2	2	2.83	2.4
V^{++}, Cr^{+++}	3	3	3.88	3.8–3.9
Cr^{++}, Mn^{+++}	4	4	4.90	4.8–4.9
Mn^{++}, Fe^{+++}	5	5	5.92	5.9
Fe^{++}	6	4	4.90	5.3
Co^{++}	7	3	3.88	5.0–5.2
Ni^{++}	8	2	2.83	3.2
Cu^{++}	9	1	1.73	1.9–2.0
Cu^+, Zn^{++}	10	0	0.00	0.00

* In Bohr magnetons.

TABLE 16-2.—MAGNETIC MOMENTS OF IRON-GROUP IONS
IN SOLID COMPOUNDS

Substance	Calculated spin moment*	Observed moment*	Substance	Calculated spin moment*	Observed moment*
$CrCl_3$	3.88	3.81	$CoCl_2$	3.88	5.04
$Cr_2O_3 \cdot 7H_2O$		3.85	$CoSO_4 \cdot 7H_2O$		5.06
			$(NH_4)_2Co(SO_4)_2 \cdot 6H_2O$		5.00
$MnCl_2$	5.92	5.75	$Co(N_2H_4)_2SO_4 \cdot H_2O$		4.31
$MnSO_4$		5.87	$Co(N_2H_4)_2(CH_3COO)_2$		4.56
$MnSO_4 \cdot 4H_2O$		5.87	$Co(N_2H_4)_2Cl_2$		4.93
$Fe_2(SO_4)_3$		5.86			
$NH_4Fe(SO_4)_2$		5.86	$NiCl_2$	2.83	3.3
$(NH_4)_3FeF_6$		5.88	$NiSO_4$		3.42
$(NH_4)_3FeF_6 \cdot H_2O$		5.91	$Ni(N_2H_4)_2SO_4$		3.20
$FeCl_3$		5.84	$Ni(N_2H_4)_2(NO_3)_2$		2.80
			$Ni(NH_3)_6SO_4$		2.63
$FeCl_2$	4.90	5.23			
$FeCl_2 \cdot 4H_2O$		5.25	$CuCl_2$	1.73	2.02
$FeSO_4$		5.26	$CuSO_4$		2.01
$FeSO_4 \cdot 7H_2O$		5.25	$Cu(NH_3)_4(NO_3)_2$		1.82
$(NH_4)_2Fe(SO_4)_2 \cdot 6H_2O$		5.25	$Cu(NH_3)_4SO_4 \cdot H_2O$		1.81
$Fe(N_2H_4)_2Cl_2$		4.87			

* In Bohr magnetons.

In many solid salts of these elements values of μ are observed which are close to those for the aqueous ions; some of these are given in Table 16–2. The significance of this will be discussed in the following sections.

16c. The Magnetic Moments of Covalent Octahedral Complexes.—In the ferric ion the five $3d$ electrons occupy the five $3d$ orbitals by remaining unpaired, and these unpaired electrons give rise to a large magnetic moment of 5.92 Bohr magnetons. In an octahedral ferric complex in which the central atom forms six d^2sp^3 bonds with the surrounding groups only three of the $3d$ orbitals are available for occupancy by the five unshared $3d$ electrons, which must accordingly form two pairs. The remaining unpaired electron gives to the complex the small spin magnetic moment 1.73 Bohr magnetons.

It was pointed out in Section 7b that a ferric complex FeX_6, which may have in its normal state a structure of ionic type, with five unpaired electrons, or a structure of the d^2sp^3 covalent type, with one unpaired electron, cannot have an intermediate structure corresponding to resonance between these two, since the conditions for resonance require that the resonating structures have the same number of unpaired electrons. It is accordingly possible by measuring the magnetic moment of an octahedral ferric complex to determine which of these two types it represents.[1]

The observation that a ferric complex contains five unshared electrons does not require that the bonds in the complex be of the extreme ionic type. As many as four rather weak covalent bonds could be formed with use of the $4s$ and $4p$ orbitals without disturbing the $3d$ shell, and a corresponding amount of covalent character of the bonds would not change the magnetic moment of the complex.[2] Similarly the octahedral d^2sp^3 bonds could have some ionic character without relinquishing their hold on the two $3d$ orbitals. At some point in the change in bond type from the ionic extreme to the octahedral covalent extreme

---

[1] Ferric complexes of a possible third type, with three odd electrons occur only very rarely. Ferrihemoglobin hydroxide, with $\mu = 4.47$ Bohr magnetons per heme, has been assigned to this class.

[2] It has also been suggested by M. L. Huggins, *J. Chem. Phys.* 5, 527 (1937), that the $4d$ orbitals might be used in bond formation. These orbitals are very unstable, however, and probably play no significant part in the structure of complexes of the type under discussion.

TABLE 16-3.—OBSERVED MAGNETIC MOMENTS OF OCTAHEDRAL
COMPLEXES OF TRANSITION ELEMENTS[a]

Essentially covalent complexes	μ^* observed	μ^* calculated	Essentially ionic complexes	μ^* observed	μ^* calculated
$K_4[Cr^{II}(CN)_6]$	3.3	2.83			
$K_5[Mn^{III}(CN)_6]$	3.0				
$K_4[Mn^{II}(CN)_6]$	2.0	1.73			
$K_3[Fe^{III}(CN)_6]$	2.33		$(NH_4)_3[Fe^{III}F_6]$	5.9	5.92
$K_4[Fe^{II}(CN)_6]$	0.00	0.00	$(NH_4)_2[Fe^{III}F_5 \cdot H_2O]$	5.9	
$Na_3[Fe^{II}(CN)_5 \cdot NH_3]$	.00		$[Fe^{II}(H_2O)_6](NH_4SO_4)_2$	5.3	4.90
$[Fe^{II}(dipyridyl)_3]SO_4$	.00				
$K_2Ca[Fe^{II}(NO_2)_6]$	1.0^b				
$K_3[Co^{III}(CN)_6]$	0.00				
$[Co^{III}(NH_3)_3F_3]$	$.00^c$		$K_3[Co^{III}F_6]$	5.3^c	4.90
$[Co^{III}(NH_3)_6]Cl_3$	.00				
$[Co^{III}(NH_3)_5Cl]Cl_2$	.00				
$[Co^{III}(NH_3)_4Cl_2]Cl_3$	.00				
$[Co^{III}(NH_3)_4(NO_2)_2]$	.00				
$[Co^{III}(NH_3)_4 \cdot H_2O]_2(C_2O_4)_3$	.00				
$Na_3[Co^{III}(NO_2)_6]$	$.5^b$				
$[Co^{III}(NH_3)_4CO_3]NO_3 \cdot \frac{1}{2}H_2O$	.00				
$K_2Ca[Co^{II}(NO_2)_6]$	1.9	1.73	$[Co^{II}(H_2O)_6](NH_4SO_4)_2$	5.1	3.88
$K_2[Pd^{IV}Cl_6]$	0.00	0.00			
$[Pd^{IV}Cl_4(NH_3)_2]$	.00				
$Na_3[Ir^{III}Cl_3(NO_2)_3]$	.00				
$[Ir^{III}(NH_3)_2NO_2]Cl_2$	.00				
$[Ir^{III}(NH_3)_4(NO_2)_2]Cl$	.00				
$[Ir^{III}(NH_3)_3(NO_2)_3]$	.00				
$K_2[Pt^{IV}Cl_6]$	.00				
$[Pt^{IV}(NH_3)_2]Cl_4$	.00				
$[Pt^{IV}(NH_3)_5Cl]Cl_3$	.00				
$[Pt^{IV}(NH_3)_4Cl_2]Cl_2$	.00				
$[Pt^{IV}(NH_3)_3Cl_3]Cl$	.00				
$[Pt^{IV}(NH_3)_2Cl_4]$	.00				

* In Bohr magnetons.

[a] The values quoted are taken in the main from W. Biltz, *Z. anorg. allg. Chem.* **170**, 161 (1928); D. M. Bose, *Z. Physik* **65**, 677 (1930); and the International Critical Tables.

[b] These values, which should be zero, may be in error. They were reported by L. Cambi, A. Ferrari, and C. Colla, *Gazz. chim. ital* **65**, 1162 (1936).

[c] Private communication from Professor G. H. Cartledge of the University of Buffalo.

the discontinuity in the nature of the normal state will occur, and the argument given above permits us to describe the octahedral complexes with five unpaired electrons as essentially ionic in character and those with only one unpaired electron as essentially covalent.[1]

In Table 16–3 there are given observed values of magnetic moments of some compounds containing octahedral complexes

[1] It has been shown by J. H. Van Vleck, *J. Chem. Phys.* **3**, 807 (1935), that extremely strong ionic forces might lead to pairing of the $3d$ electrons. This phenomenon does not occur, however, in the complex of iron with the most electronegative of all atoms, fluorine, and so it is not to be expected to occur in any complex.

not only of the iron-group elements but also of the palladium-group and platinum-group elements, to which the discussion is also applicable. It is seen that the octahedral complexes of iron with fluorine and with water are essentially electrostatic in character, whereas those with the cyanide, nitrite, and dipyridyl groups are essentially covalent.[1] All of the complexes of trivalent cobalt which have been investigated are essentially covalent, except that with fluorine, $[CoF_6]^{\equiv}$, in which the bonds are essentially ionic. It is interesting that in the sequence $[Co(NH_3)_6]^{+++}$, $[Co(NH_3)_3F_3]$, $[CoF_6]^{\equiv}$ the transition from essentially ionic to essentially covalent bonds occurs between the second and third complex. It will be of interest to locate it still more precisely; this investigation is being carried on by Professor G. H. Cartledge. Bivalent cobalt forms with water essentially ionic bonds and with nitrite groups essentially covalent bonds. The magnetic method cannot be applied to trivalent chromium, the structures of the two extreme types having the same number of unpaired electrons and entering into resonance with each other. The chemical properties of the chromium complexes indicate that chromium, like the other iron-group elements, forms bonds of large covalent character with groups such as cyanide and of small covalent character with water and ammonia.[2] The complexes of the iron-group elements are discussed further in Section 31b.

[1] In some derivatives of ferrohemoglobin and ferrihemoglobin the iron atoms (bivalent or trivalent) are shown to be surrounded octahedrally (probably by four nitrogen atoms of the porphyrin complex, one nitrogen atom of the globin, and the attached group) by the observed values of the magnetic moments, which correspond to d^2sp^3 octahedral bonds (oxyferrohemoglobin, $\mu = 0.0$; carbonmonoxyferrohemoglobin, $\mu = 0.0$; ferrihemoglobin cyanide, $\mu = 2.5$; ferrihemoglobin hydrosulfide, $\mu = 2.3$). In other derivatives the bonds are essentially ionic (ferrohemoglobin, $\mu = 5.4$; ferrihemoglobin, $\mu = 5.8$; ferrihemoglobin fluoride, $\mu = 5.9$). The value $\mu = 4.5$ for ferrihemoglobin hydroxide suggests a structure with three unpaired electrons, not known to be represented among the simpler iron complexes. The derivatives of the prosthetic group of hemoglobin (hemin, ferroheme, hemochromogens) are in part ionic and in part covalent in structure. (L. Pauling and C. D. Coryell, *Proc. Nat. Acad. Sci.* **22**, 159 (1936); **22**, 210 (1936); C. D. Coryell, F. Stitt, and L. Pauling, *J.A.C.S.* **59**, 633 (1937).)

[2] It has been inferred by C. H. Johnson, *Trans. Faraday Soc.* **28**, 845 (1932), that chromium forms d^2sp^3 covalent bonds with oxalate in the ion $[Cr(C_2O_4)_3]^{+++}$ from the following facts: The chromium trioxalate com-

All of the octahedral complexes of the elements of the palladium and platinum groups which have been investigated are diamagnetic, showing the strong tendency of these elements to form covalent bonds.

The magnetic data for prussian blue and similar substances are of unusual interest. X-ray investigations[1] have shown that substances such as $KFeFe(CN)_6 \cdot H_2O$ form cubic crystals in which iron atoms lie at the points of a simple cubic lattice, each being connected with its six neighbors by CN groups extending along the cube edges. The potassium ions and water molecules lie in the cubes outlined in this way. The magnetic data[2] show that half of the iron atoms, presumably those bonded to the carbon atoms of the six adjacent cyanide groups, form essentially covalent bonds, whereas the other iron atoms form ionic bonds.[3]

16d. The Magnetic Moments of Tetrahedral and Square Coordinated Complexes.—The bivalent nickel atom forming four covalent dsp^2 bonds has only four $3d$ orbitals available for the eight unshared $3d$ electrons, which must thus form four pairs, the square complex NiX_4 being diamagnetic. Bivalent nickel in a complex involving only the $4s$ and $4p$ orbitals (electrostatic bonds or weak covalent bonds) distributes the eight $3d$ electrons among the five $3d$ orbitals in such a way as to leave two unpaired, the complex having a magnetic moment of 2.83 Bohr magnetons. From this argument it is seen that the assignment of nickel complexes to the tetrahedral and square coplanar classes can be made by magnetic measurements.

The crystals $K_2Ni(CN)_4$ and $K_2Ni(CN)_4 \cdot H_2O$, shown by isomorphism to contain the coplanar complex $[Ni(CN)_4]^{--}$, are diamagnetic. Many other nickel complexes, some of which have

---

plex and the cobaltic trioxalate complex can be resolved into optical isomers, whereas resolution has not been effected for the trioxalates of trivalent manganese, iron, and aluminum. Observed magnetic moments ($K_3Mn(C_2O_4)_3 \cdot 3H_2O$, $\mu = 4.88$; $K_3Fe(C_2O_4)_3 \cdot 3H_2O$, $\mu = 5.75$; $K_3Co(C_2O_4)_3 \cdot 3\frac{1}{2}H_2O$, $\mu = 0.00$) show the manganese and iron complexes to be essentially ionic and the cobalt complex to be essentially covalent in character.

[1] J. F. Keggin and F. D. Miles, *Nature* **137**, 577 (1936); N. Elliott (unpublished work at the California Institute of Technology) has obtained similar results for $KMFe(CN)_6 \cdot H_2O$, with M=Mn, Co, and Ni.

[2] D. Davidson and L. A. Welo, *J. Phys. Chem.* **32**, 1191 (1928).

[3] The data do not show whether the covalently bonded iron is trivalent or bivalent.

been shown to be coplanar by the methods mentioned in Section 15b, have been found to satisfy the magnetic criterion.   These include the nickel glyoximes,[1,4] potassium nickel dithio-oxalate,[2] nickel diacetyldioxime,[3] nickel ethylxanthogenate[4] [$Ni(C_2H_5O\cdot CS_2)_2$], nickel ethyldithiocarbamate[4] [$Ni(C_2H_5\cdot NH\cdot CS_2)_2$], and many other complexes.

On the other hand, the compounds [$Ni(NH_3)_4$]SO_3, [$Ni(N_2H_4)_2$](NO_2)$_2$, [$Ni(C_2H_4(NH_2)_2)_2$](SCN)$_2\cdot H_2O$, and [$Ni(C_5H_7O_2)_2$] (nickel acetylacetone) are paramagnetic, with values of μ between 2.6 and 3.2.   In these complexes the four atoms attached to nickel are presumably arranged tetrahedrally; this has not yet been shown, however, by x-ray examination or by the synthesis of isomers.

The values found for the molal paramagnetic susceptibility of hydrated nickel cyanides of composition between $Ni(CN)_2\cdot 2H_2O$ and $Ni(CN)_2\cdot 4H_2O$ are about one-half those for ionic nickel compounds, indicating that these substances contain square covalent complexes [$Ni(CN)_4$]$^{--}$ and tetrahedral ionic complexes [$Ni(H_2O)_4$]$^{++}$ or [$Ni(H_2O)_6$]$^{++}$ in equal numbers.[5] Anhydrous nickel cyanide is also paramagnetic, with molal susceptibility about 10% as great as for compounds of ionic nickel, the value found depending somewhat on the method of preparing the sample.   This indicates that about 90% of the nickel atoms form square covalent bonds with carbon or nitrogen atoms of the cyanide groups, and the remaining 10% of the nickel atoms form ionic bonds.

The factors which determine whether the diamagnetic square or the paramagnetic tetrahedral configuration will be assumed by a nickel complex can not be stated precisely.   Groups containing sulfur atoms, which have a strong tendency to form covalent bonds, form square complexes; for nitrogen and oxygen the decision seems to depend on the presence and disposition of double bonds in the group.

[1] S. Sugden, *J. Chem. Soc.* **1932**, 246; H. J. Cavell and S. Sugden, *ibid.* **1935**, 621.

[2] Norman Elliott, unpublished research.

[3] W. Klemm, H. Jacobi, and W. Tilk, *Z. anorg. allgem. Chem.* **201,** 1 (1931).

[4] L. Cambi and L. Szegö, *Ber.* **64,** 2591 (1931).

[5] L. Cambi, A. Cagnasso, and E. Tremolada, *Gazz. Chim. Ital.* **64,** 758 (1934).

The complexes of bivalent palladium and platinum are all diamagnetic. Diamagnetism has been verified[1] for $PdCl_2 \cdot 2H_2O$, $PdCl_2 \cdot 2NH_3$, K_2PdCl_4, $K_2Pd(CN)_4$, K_2PdI_4, $K_2Pd(SCN)_4$, $K_2Pd(NO_2)_4$, palladium dimethylglyoxime, and even for palladous nitrate in solution (probably containing the ion $[Pd(H_2O)_4]^{++}$). The crystalline substances $PdCl_2$, PdI_2, $Pd(CN)_2$, $Pd(SCN)_2$, and $Pd(NO_3)_2$ are also diamagnetic. Their atomic arrangements are unknown, except that of $PdCl_2$, described in Section 15b, but it is probable that they all involve square-coordinated palladium. With the cyanide, for example, this could occur by continued polymerization to give sheets with the structure

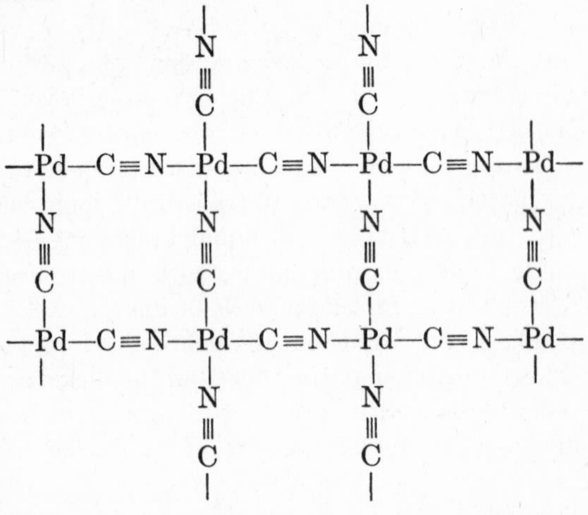

Continued polymerization is observed in crystals[2,3] of PdO and PtS (cooperite), which contain coplanar rectangular PtO_4 or PtS_4 groups, with shared O or S, as shown in Figure 16–1. Braggite, (Pt, Pd, Ni)S, and PdS, however, seem to have a related but more complex structure,[4] involving slight distortions from the cooperite configuration. The values reported for the Pd—S bond distances are 2.26, 2.29, 2.34, and 2.43 Å.

Compounds of bivalent platinum similar to those of palladium listed above and including also $Pt(NH_3)_4SO_4$, $K_2Pt(C_2O_4)_2 \cdot \cdot$

[1] R. B. Janes, *J.A.C.S.* **57**, 471 (1935).

[2] L. Pauling and M. L. Huggins, *Z. Krist.* **87**, 205 (1934).

[3] F. A. Bannister and M. H. Hey, *Mineral. Mag.* **23**, 188 (1932).

[4] T. F. Gaskell, *Z. Krist.* **96**, 203 (1937); F. A. Bannister, *ibid.* **96**, 201 (1937).

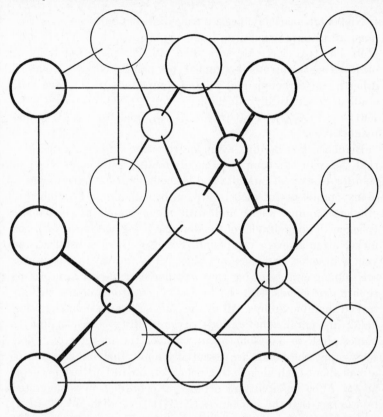

Fig. 16-1.—The atomic arrangement of the tetragonal crystals PdO and PtS. Small circles represent palladium or platinum atoms, large circles oxygen or sulfur atoms.

$2H_2O$, $PtCl_2 \cdot 2CO$, and $PtCl_2 \cdot CO$ are diamagnetic. The latter substance is probably a tetramer.

The magnetic method cannot be used to distinguish easily between the square and the tetrahedral configurations for complexes of bivalent copper or silver, since for each configuration one unpaired electron is expected.[1]

[1] A small difference between the moments for the two configurations might arise in the following way. The moment of cupric ion in solution, 1.95, is larger than the spin moment of one electron, 1.73, by reason of a small contribution of the orbital moment. This contribution should be smaller for square complexes than for tetrahedral complexes because of the greater quenching effect of the more unsymmetrical field of the attached groups. There is some indication that this occurs; for $CuSO_4 \cdot 5H_2O$ and

Nickel tetracarbonyl has a tetrahedral configuration; this does not lead to paramagnetism, however, because the neutral nickel atom has two electrons more than bivalent nickel, and the $3d$ orbitals are completely occupied by pairs. $Ni(CO)_4$, like all other metal carbonyls and related compounds which have been studied magnetically (including $Co(CO)_3NO$, $Fe(CO)_2(NO)_2$, $Fe(CO)_5$, $Fe_2(CO)_9$, $Fe_3(CO)_{12}$, $Cr(CO)_6$, and $Mo(CO)_6$), is diamagnetic.

Evidence has become available recently supporting the idea that the color of a complex is closely related to its bond type and coordination type. Lifschitz and his collaborators[1] have prepared many complexes of nickel with stilbenediamine (1,2-diphenyl-ethylenediamine, stien) and with monophenylethylenediamine (phenen), two molecules of the diamine being combined with one nickel atom in each compound. Some of these substances are yellow in color, and some are blue. All of the yellow substances are diamagnetic, showing that in these each nickel atom forms square dsp^2 bonds with the four nitrogen atoms of the two attached diamine groups. All of the blue substances, on the other hand, are paramagnetic, with susceptibilities corresponding to values close to 3.0 Bohr magnetons for the nickel atom. This shows that the bonds are essentially ionic, the configuration of atoms about each nickel atom being tetrahedral or perhaps octahedral. (The possibility of octahedral coordination is suggested by the fact that the substances $(Ni(NH_3)_6X_2$, with $X = Cl$, Br, I, and NO_3, in which there is octahedral coordination about nickel,[2] are blue in color. In the stien and phenen complexes four octahe-

---

$Cu(NO_3)_2 \cdot 6H_2O$ values of μ of 1.95 to 2.02 are reported, whereas for $CuCl_2 \cdot 2H_2O$, $K_2CuCl_4 \cdot 2H_2O$, $Cu(NH_3)_4(NO_3)_2$, and similar substances the observed values lie between 1.79 and 1.87. A decrease in susceptibility of cupric bromide solutions corresponding to a decrease of 0.11 Bohr magnetons in moment on addition of 12 N. hydrobromic acid was observed by S. S. Shaffer and N. W. Taylor, *J.A.C.S.* **48**, 843 (1926). An interesting anisotropy of the paramagnetic susceptibility of $CuSO_4 \cdot 5H_2O$ has been reported by K. S. Krishnan and A. Mookherji, *Phys. Rev.* **54**, 841 (1938). These investigators found the effective magnetic moment of the $[Cu(H_2O)_4]^{++}$ complex to be 2.12 Bohr magnetons with the magnetic field normal to the plane of the complex and 1.80 with the field in the plane.

[1] I. Lifschitz, J. G. Bos, and K. M. Dijkema, *Z. anorg. allg. Chem.* **242**, 97 (1939).

[2] R. W. G. Wyckoff, *J.A.C.S.* **44**, 1239, 1260 (1922).

dral positions about nickel might be occupied by the nitrogen atoms of the amino groups and two by water molecules or anion atoms.)

The substances studied by Lifschitz and his collaborators include the following:

Yellow diamagnetic substances; square coordination about nickel	Blue paramagnetic substances; tetrahedral or octahedral coordination
Ni stien$_2$SO$_4$·H$_2$O	Ni stien$_2$SO$_4$·2H$_2$O
Ni stien$_2$(Cl$_3$CCOO)$_2$	Ni stien$_2$(Cl$_3$CCOO)$_2$
Ni stien$_2$(HCOO)$_2$·4H$_2$O	Ni stien$_2$(HCOO)$_2$
Ni phenen$_2$(ClO$_4$)$_2$	Ni phenen$_2$(ClO$_4$)$_2$
Ni phenen$_2$(NO$_3$)$_2$	Ni phenen$_2$(NO$_3$)$_2$
Ni stien$_2$Cl$_2$·2H$_2$O	Ni phenen$_2$(NO$_3$)$_2$·2H$_2$O
Ni stien$_2$Cl$_2$	Ni stien$_2$(C$_6$H$_5$COO)$_2$
Ni stien$_2$(NO$_3$)$_2$	Ni stien$_2$(CH$_3$COO)$_2$
Ni stien$_2$(ClO$_4$)$_2$	Ni phenen$_2$Cl$_2$·2H$_2$O

It is seen that in several cases the same substance occurs in both the yellow and the blue form, either with or without change in water content.

The color is determined not only by the coordination but also by the nature of the attached atoms. Thus the diamagnetic compounds Ni(P(C$_2$H$_5$)$_3$)$_2$X$_2$ with X = Cl, Br, and ClO$_4$ are red, whereas the paramagnetic nitrate is green;[1] and the diamagnetic nickelous disalicylaldimine is orange, the paramagnetic disalicylaldehyde green.[2]

[1] K. A. Jensen, *Z. anorg. allg. Chem.* **229,** 265 (1936); Lifschitz *et al., loc. cit.*

[2] G. N. Tyson, Jr., and S. C. Adams, unpublished investigation.

CHAPTER IV

THE RESONANCE OF MOLECULES AMONG SEVERAL VALENCE-BOND STRUCTURES

17. RESONANCE IN NITROUS OXIDE AND BENZENE

For many molecules it is possible to formulate valence-bond structures which are so reasonable and which account so satisfactorily for the properties of the substances that they are accepted by everyone without hesitation. The following structures may be shown for illustration:

Oxygen fluoride,

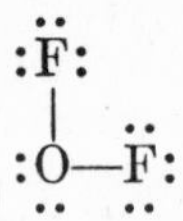

$$
\begin{array}{c}
: \ddot{F} : \\
| \\
: \ddot{O} - \ddot{F} :
\end{array}
$$

Trimethylamine,

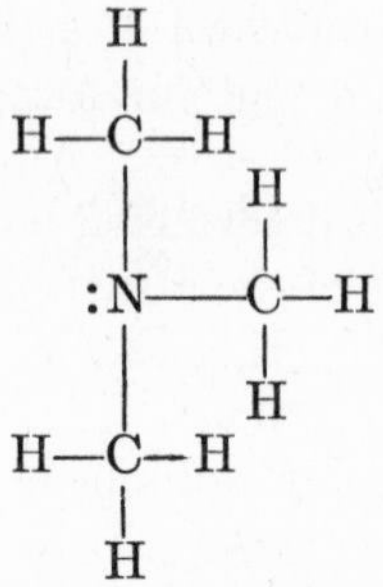

$$
\begin{array}{c}
H \\
| \\
H - C - H \quad\quad H \\
\quad\quad\quad\quad\quad | \\
: N \underline{\quad\quad} C - H \\
| \quad\quad\quad\quad | \\
H - C - H \quad\quad H \\
| \\
H
\end{array}
$$

Ethane,

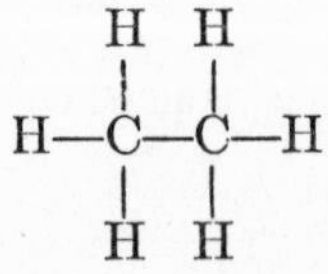

$$
\begin{array}{c}
H \quad H \\
| \quad | \\
H - C - C - H \\
| \quad | \\
H \quad H
\end{array}
$$

Ethylene,

$$
\begin{array}{c}
H \quad\quad\quad\quad H \\
\diagdown \quad\quad\quad\diagup \\
C = C \\
\diagup \quad\quad\quad\diagdown \\
H \quad\quad\quad\quad H
\end{array}
$$

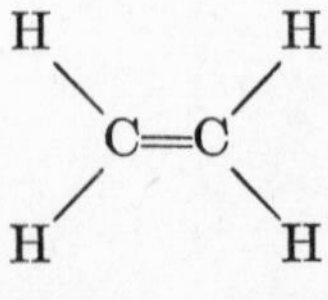

The physical and chemical properties of substances and the configurations of molecules associated with structures of this type are well understood, and this understanding forms the basis for a large part of chemical reasoning.

It is sometimes found, however, that an unambiguous assignment of a single valence-bond structure to a molecule cannot be made—two or more structures which are about equally stable may suggest themselves, no one of which accounts in a completely satisfactory way for the properties of the substance. Under these circumstances some new structural concepts and symbols might be introduced; we might, for example, use the

symbol ⬡ for benzene, without attempting to interpret this

in terms of single and double bonds. With the development of the idea of quantum-mechanical resonance a more illuminating and useful solution to this difficulty has been found: *the actual normal state of the molecule is not represented by any one of the alternative reasonable structures, but can be represented by a combination of them*, their individual contributions being determined by their nature and stability. The molecule is then described as *resonating among the several valence-bond structures.*[1]

The resonance of molecules among various electronic structures has been discussed in detail in Chapter II for the case that the resonating structures differ in regard to bond type (ionic and covalent). The resonance under discussion in this

[1] The idea of the quantum-mechanical resonance of molecules among several valence-bond structures was developed about seven years ago: see J. C. Slater, *Phys. Rev.* 37, 489 (1931); E. Hückel, *Z. Physik* 70, 204 (1931); 72, 310 (1931); 76, 628 (1932); 83, 632 (1933); L. Pauling, *J.A.C.S.* 53, 1367, 3225 (1931); 54, 988, 3570 (1932); *Proc. Nat. Acad. Sci.* 18, 293 (1932); L. Pauling and G. W. Wheland, *J. Chem. Phys.* 1, 322 (1933); etc. During the twentieth century rapid progress had been made in the development of chemical theories which bear some relationship to the theory of resonance. A small resemblance to it is shown by Thiele's theory of partial valence (J. Thiele, *Ann.* 306, 87 (1899)), and it is much more closely approximated by Arndt's theory of intermediate stages (F. Arndt, E. Scholz, and F. Nachtwey, *Ber.* 57, 1903 (1924); F. Arndt, *ibid.* 63, 2963 (1930)) and the theory of the mesomeric state developed by the English and American organic chemists (T. M. Lowry, *J. Chem. Soc.* 1923, 822, 1866; H. J. Lucas and A. Y. Jameson, *J.A.C.S.* 46, 2475 (1924); R. Robinson et. al. *J. Chem. Soc.* 1926, 401; C. K. Ingold and E. H. Ingold, *ibid.* 1926, 1310; etc.).

chapter is not greatly different; it involves structures which differ in the distribution of bonds rather than in their type.

The nitrous oxide molecule may be used as an example. This molecule is linear, with the oxygen atom at one end. It contains sixteen valence electrons; and it is seen that these can be assigned to the stable L orbitals of the atoms in either one of the two following reasonable ways:

A: $:\overset{-}{\overset{..}{N}}=\overset{+}{N}=\overset{..}{O}:,$

B: $:N\equiv\overset{+}{N}-\overset{..}{\underset{..}{O}}:.$

Each of these involves four covalent bonds (counting a double bond as two and a triple bond as three), and a separation of charge to adjacent atoms. Other structures which might be written are recognized at once as being much less stable than these, such as

C: $\cdot\overset{-}{\overset{..}{\underset{..}{N}}}-\overset{+}{N}\equiv\overset{+}{O}:,$

on which instability is conferred by the arrangement of electric charges, and

D: $:\overset{-}{\overset{..}{N}}=\overset{..}{N}-\overset{..}{O}:^{+},$

E: $:\overset{..}{N}-\overset{..}{N}=\overset{..}{O}:,$ etc.,

with instability arising from the smaller number of covalent bonds.

A decision cannot be made between structures A and B, which are, indeed, so closely similar in nature that there can be no appreciable energy difference between them. Moreover, they satisfy the other conditions for resonance: they involve the same number of unpaired electrons (zero), and they correspond to about the same equilibrium configuration of the nuclei (linear, for a central tetrahedral atom forming either two double bonds or a single bond and a triple bond). We accordingly expect the normal state of the molecule to correspond to *resonance between structures A and B*, with perhaps also very small contributions by the other less stable structures, which can be neglected in our discussion. The molecule is more stable than it would be if either A or B alone represented its normal state by an amount of energy equal to the resonance energy between the two structures. Its interatomic distances and force constants are not those corresponding to either A or B alone, but to resonance between them (Chap. V). Its electric dipole moment is not large, but is very close to zero, the opposed moments of the two structures cancelling each other.

The value of the electric dipole moment provides an illustration of the significance of resonance as compared with tautomerism. If nitrous oxide gas were a tautomeric mixture of molecules of types A and B its dielectric constant would be very large, since the molecules of each type would have large dipole moments and would make a large contribution to the dielectric constant of the gas. The frequency of resonance between structures A and B is, however, very large, of the order of magnitude of electronic frequencies in general, and the nuclei do not have time to orient themselves in an applied electric field in order to contribute to the dielectric constant of the medium before the electrons of the molecule have run through their phases, which results in a very small average electric moment.

The discussion of Section 3 regarding the element of arbitrariness in the concept of resonance may be recalled at this point with reference to the nitrous oxide molecule and the other molecules which are described in this chapter as resonating among several valence-bond structures. It is not necessary that the structures A and B be used as the basis of discussion of the nitrous oxide molecule. We might say instead that the molecule cannot be satisfactorily represented by any single valence-bond structure, and abandon the effort to correlate its structure and properties with those of other molecules. By using valence-bond structures as the basis for discussion, however, with the aid of the concept of resonance, we are able to account for the properties of the molecule in terms of those of other molecules in a straightforward and simple way. It is for this practical reason that we find it convenient to speak of the resonance of molecules among several electronic structures.

It is to be emphasized again that in writing two valence-bond structures for the nitrous oxide molecule and saying that it resonates between them we are making an effort to extend the valence-bond picture to molecules to which it is not strictly applicable, and that we are not required to do this but choose to do it in the hope of obtaining a satisfactory description of these unusual molecules, permitting us to correlate and "understand" the results of experiments on their chemical and physical properties and to make predictions in the same way as for molecules to which a single valence-bond structure can be assigned. Nitrous oxide does not consist of a mixture of tautomeric molecules, some with one and some with the other of the two structures written above; instead, all of the molecules have the same electronic structure, this being of such a nature that it cannot be satisfactorily represented by any one valence-bond diagram but can be reasonably well represented by two. The properties of the molecule are essentially those expected for an average of the two valence-bond structures, except for the stabilizing effect of the resonance energy.

To represent the molecule we may use the symbol $\{$:N̄=N⁺=Ö:, :N⁺≡N—Ö:⁻ $\}$, the resonating structures being enclosed in brackets. I do not believe that it is wise to attempt to simplify the symbol further—to write, for example, N≡N=O, even though, as we shall see later, the N—N bond and the N—O bond have properties approaching those of a triple bond and a double bond, respectively (Sec. 22). If the formula N≡N=O were to be used it would be confused with formulas for non-resonating molecules. This formula suggests that the nitrogen atom can form five covalent bonds, which is not true. Moreover, the formula carries with it no stereochemical implications—we do not know the relative orientation to expect for a double bond and a triple bond—whereas the resonating formula shows at once that the molecule is linear.[1]

Benzene provides an interesting and important illustration of a resonating molecule. The two Kekulé structures for benzene, A and B, are the most stable valence-bond structures which can

---

[1] The English structural chemists make use of formulas such as :N≡N—Ö:; the arrows indicate changes in positions of electron pairs, corresponding to resonance with the structure :N̈=N=Ö:. F. Arndt and B. Eistert, *Ber.* **71**, 237 (1938), have suggested the use of the double arrow ⟷ to indicate resonance, writing :N̈=N=Ö: ⟷ :N≡N—Ö: for normal nitrous oxide.

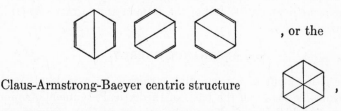

A:

B:

be written for the known hexagonal coplanar configuration. Other
structures, such as the Dewar structures

, or the

Claus-Armstrong-Baeyer centric structure   ,

correspond to diminished stability because of their weak bonds
between distant atoms, and they need not be considered in a
simple discussion.   (A more detailed study of the benzene problem is described in Section 19.)   The Kekulé structures individually do not provide a satisfactory representation of the benzene
molecule; the high degree of unsaturation which by comparison
with hexene or cyclohexene would be expected for a molecule
containing three double bonds is not shown by benzene, which
instead is surprisingly stable and unreactive.   It is resonance
which gives to benzene its aromatic properties.   The two Kekulé
structures are equivalent, and have the same energy; they accordingly enter into complete resonance.   The molecule is stabilized in this way by the resonance energy of about 39 kcal./mole
(Sec. 18).   The unsaturation of a compound containing a double
bond is due, from the thermodynamic point of view, to the instability of a double bond relative to two single bonds, amounting to about 17 kcal./mole per double bond,[1] or 51 kcal./mole
for three double bonds.   The resonance energy removes the
greater part of this instability, and gives to the molecule a degree
of saturation approaching that of the paraffins.

[1] The values 100.1 and 58.6 kcal./mole for the energy of the C=C and
C—C bonds, respectively, are given in Sections 18 and 10.

The stereochemical properties of the benzene molecule can be predicted from the concept of resonance between the two Kekulé structures.   This resonance gives to each of the carbon-carbon bonds a large amount of double-bond character, with its stereochemical implications.   The bonds adjacent to a double bond are coplanar; accordingly the entire benzene molecule must be coplanar.   The six carbon-carbon bonds are equivalent; hence the carbon hexagon must be regular; and the carbon-hydrogen bonds must be directed radially.   All of these statements have been verified experimentally in recent years, by the study of electric dipole moments of benzene derivatives, of electron-diffraction photographs of benzene vapor, of x-ray data for crystalline benzene derivatives, and of the Raman and infrared spectra of benzene.

18. RESONANCE ENERGY

The assignment of a resonating structure to a molecule can sometimes be made on the basis of theoretical arguments, as in the two cases discussed above.   In general such an assignment should be supported by experimental evidence, such as that provided by chemical properties, resonance energies, interatomic distances, force constants of bonds, bond angles, electric dipole moments, etc.   If the reasonable valence-bond structures are not equivalent, knowledge of the magnitudes of the contributions of different structures to the normal state of a molecule can be obtained from such data.

Of these methods of studying resonance in molecules the most fruitful at present are the determination and interpretation of values of interatomic distances, discussed in the following chapter, and the calculation of values of resonance energies from thermochemical data.   It is to the latter that we now turn our attention.

18a. Values of Bond Energies for Multiple Bonds.—In Section 10 there is given a table of values of bond energies for single bonds.   In the construction of this table care was taken to make use of data for only those molecules to each of which an unambiguous assignment of a valence-bond formula could be made. This consideration of bond energies is extended in Table 18-1, which contains values for some multiple bonds, obtained by methods similar to those described in Section 10.

TABLE 18-1.—VALUES OF BOND ENERGIES FOR MULTIPLE BONDS

Bond	Bond energy	Compounds
C=C	100 kcal./mole	
C≡C	123	
C=O	142	Formaldehyde
C=O	149	Other aldehydes
C=O	152	Ketones
C=N	94	
C≡N	144	Hydrogen cyanide
C≡N	150	Other cyanides
C=S	103	
O=O	96	$^1\Delta$ state of O_2
N≡N	170	Normal N_2

By the addition of the suitable quantities from Tables 10-1 and 18-1 an approximate value can be predicted for the heat of formation of a gas molecule from the elements in the state of monatomic gases, provided that the molecule in its normal state is well represented by a single electronic structure of the valence-bond type. For example, the heat of formation of acetylene from the elements in their standard states is -53.9 kcal./mole, and that from atoms is 298.1 kcal./mole. The sum of bond energies 2 C—H + C≡C is 297 kcal./mole. The error of 1 kcal./mole is indicative of the degree of reliability of the bond energy values, which are averages of those found by consideration of the thermochemical data for many substances.

The energy values given are not those for extreme covalent bonds, but for actual bonds with partial ionic character. In Section 12a it was pointed out that the observed value of the electric dipole moment of acetone provides evidence that the carbon-oxygen double bond has nearly 50% ionic character, so that the molecule should be represented by the resonating structure $\{(H_3C)_2C::\overset{..}{O}:, \quad (H_3C)_2\overset{+}{C}:\overset{..}{\underset{..}{O}}:^-\}$. The carbon-oxygen bond energy corresponding to either the bond $C::\overset{..}{O}:$ or that $^+C:\overset{..}{\underset{..}{O}}:^-$ must be less than that for the C=O bond in acetone, because the resonance energy for these two structures stabilizes the molecule.[1] In view of the large amount of ionic resonance for multiple

---

[1] The amount of ionic resonance energy in this bond is very large—about 54 kcal./mole, as given by the following calculation. Using for the oxygen-oxygen double-bond energy the value 96 kcal./mole, corresponding to the excited $^1\Delta$ state of the oxygen molecule (which is 22.4 kcal./mole

bonds between atoms differing in electronegativity, it is to be expected that these bonds will be affected more strongly (as to amount of ionic character) by neighboring bonds than are single bonds of small ionic character; and it is observed that the values calculated for the energies of multiple bonds vary for different compounds.   This has been taken into consideration to some extent by the tabulation of more than one value for some bonds; it may lead, however, to a greater error in energy calculations for molecules containing multiple bonds than for those containing only single bonds.

18b. Empirical Values of Resonance Energies.—The table of bond energies permits the calculation of values of the heats of formation of molecules to which a single valence-bond structure can be assigned which agree with the experimental values to within a few kcal./mole.   On carrying out a similar calculation for a resonating molecule on the basis of any single valence-bond structure which can be formulated, it is found that *in every case the actual energy of formation of the molecule is greater than the calculated value*; that is, the molecule is actually more stable than it would be if it had the valence-bond structure assumed for it in making the bond-energy calculation.   This result is required by the fundamental quantum-mechanical principle on which the concept of resonance is based (Sec. 3); it provides, however, a pleasing confirmation of the arguments used in the construction of the table of bond energies.

The difference between the observed heat of formation and that calculated for a single valence-bond structure for a molecule with use of the table of bond energies is an empirical value of the

---

less stable than the normal state, the structure of which is discussed in Sec. 35), the postulate of the arithmetic mean, with $C=C = 100$ kcal./mole, leads to 98 kcal./mole for the energy of the normal covalent bond $C::\overset{..}{O}:$. This is 54 kcal./mole less than the $C=O$ bond-energy value given in the table for ketones.

It is interesting to note that the $C\equiv N$ bond shows no ionic resonance energy, its tabulated values (144, 150 kcal./mole) lying close to the mean (146) of the bond energies for $C\equiv C$ and $N\equiv N$.   Indeed, the large value for the energy of the $N\equiv N$ bond is surprising.   A possible explanation is that for this triple bond, and perhaps for triple bonds in general, there is a large amount of resonance between the normal covalent structure $:N:::N:$ and the equivalent ionic structures of type $:N^{+}::\overset{..-}{N}:$.

resonance energy of the molecule, relative to the assumed valence-bond structure.

It is desirable that the structure used as the basis for the resonance energy calculation be the most stable (or one of the most stable) of those among which resonance occurs.   It is not always convenient for this choice to be made, for the following reason. The tabulated bond energies are designed for use only between atoms with zero formal charge; no simple method of calculating the heats of formation of molecules containing charged atoms has been devised, because of the difficulties introduced by the Coulomb energy terms for the separated charges.   For this reason there is no empirical value available for the resonance energy of the nitrous oxide molecule; both of the stable structures $:\overset{-..}{N}=\overset{+}{N}=\overset{..}{O}:$ and $:N\equiv\overset{+}{N}-\underset{..}{\overset{..}{O}}:$ involve atoms with formal charges.   Moreover, it is possible that the structure $:\underset{..}{\overset{-}{C}}\equiv\overset{+}{O}:$ for carbon monoxide is more stable than the structure $:C=\overset{..}{O}:$; the formal charges for the first structure, however, prevent its use as the basis for the resonance energy calculation.

It must be remembered that one of the conditions for resonance of molecules among several electronic structures is that the configuration of the molecule (the arrangement of the nuclei) remain constant during the electronic resonance; it is the composite electronic structure which provides a single potential function determining the equilibrium configuration and modes of oscillation for the molecule.   It is not possible for an amide to

resonate between the structures $R-C\diagdown\overset{\overset{..}{O}:}{}\diagdown NH_2$ and $R-C\diagdown\overset{\overset{..}{O}H}{}\diagdown NH$; it

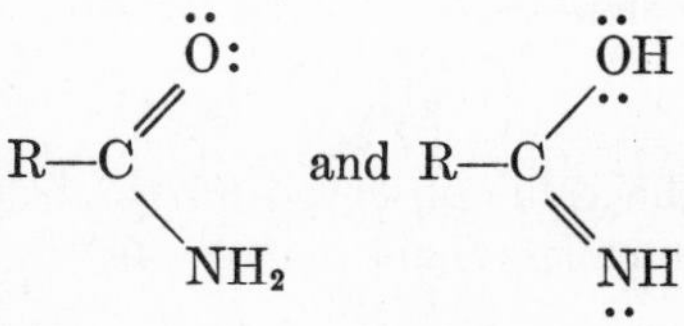

is resonance between the structures

$$R-C\Big\langle{\overset{\overset{..}{O}:}{\underset{\underset{..}{NH_2}}{}}}\qquad\text{and}\qquad R-C\Big\langle{\overset{\overset{..}{\overset{-}{O}}:}{\underset{\overset{+}{NH_2}}{}}}$$

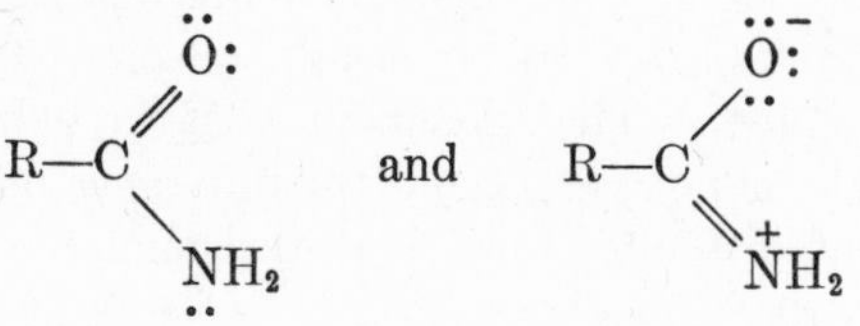

which occurs.

The heat of formation of the benzene gas molecule from separated atoms is found from the heat of combustion (789.2 kcal./mole) and the heats of formation of the products of combustion, water and carbon dioxide, to have the value 1039 kcal./mole. The sum of the bond energies 6C—H + 3C—C + 3C=C gives the value 1000 kcal./mole for the heat of formation of a hypothetical molecule with the Kekulé structure [Kekulé hexagon] or [Kekulé hexagon], involving non-interacting double bonds. The difference between these, 39 kcal./mole, is the resonance energy of the molecule.

In calculating resonance energies it is for simplicity and convenience only that the thermochemical data are converted into energies of formation of molecules from separated atoms and compared with sums of bond energies; the same results can be obtained by dealing directly with heats of formation from elementary substances in their standard states or with heats of combustion or of hydrogenation reactions or other reactions, the resonating substance being compared with suitable non-resonating substances. This may be illustrated by the calculation of the resonance energy of benzene from data obtained in the very important series of direct measurements of heats of hydrogenation being carried on by Kistiakowsky and his collaborators.[1] The value expected for the heat of hydrogenation of a hypothetical molecule with a Kekulé structure involving non-interacting double bonds is 85.77 kcal./mole, three times the heat of hydrogenation of cyclohexene:

$$C_6H_{10} + H_2 \rightarrow C_6H_{12} + 28.59 \text{ kcal./mole.}$$

The value observed for the heat of hydrogenation of benzene is much less than this:

$$C_6H_6 + 3H_2 \rightarrow C_6H_{12} + 49.80 \text{ kcal./mole.}$$

The difference, 35.97 kcal./mole, is the resonance energy for benzene, which stabilizes the molecule relative to the individual Kekulé structures. The agreement with the value found above, 39 kcal./mole, is not very good (the difference of 3 kcal./mole is to be attributed to uncertainties in the bond-energy values); but

---

[1] G. B. Kistiakowsky, J. R. Ruhoff, H. A. Smith, and W. E. Vaughan, *J.A.C.S.* **57**, 876 (1935); **58**, 137 (1936); **58**, 146 (1936); etc.

it provides sound substantiation of the order of magnitude of the benzene resonance energy.[1]

As a second illustration let us consider the carbon monoxide molecule. For years there has been discussion as to which of the structures :C̈=Ö: and :C≡O:⁻⁺ is the better one. We would consider it probable that resonance occurs between them; or, splitting :C̈=Ö: into its constituents, among the three structures (a) ⁺:C̈:Ö:⁻ , (b) :C::Ö:, and (c) ⁻:C:::O:⁺. From the discussion of the carbon-oxygen double bond in ketones the conclusion can be drawn that the structures a and b make about equal contributions, a being nearly as stable as b despite its smaller number of covalent bonds because the great electronegativity of oxygen stabilizes a structure containing negative oxygen. The third structure c would also be expected to be significant because of its stabilization through the formation of a triple covalent bond, which counteracts the instability resulting from the unfavorable distribution of charge. The observed very small or zero value of the electric dipole moment provides evidence that the contribution made by structure c is about the same as that made by structure a. The structure b would have no large dipole moment, whereas those of a and c are very large, about equal in magnitude, and opposed in direction; and only if a and c contribute about equally would the moment of the molecule be small.

We may well inquire as to how it is possible for three structures as different in character as a, b, and c to contribute about equally to the normal state of the molecule. The answer, indicated above, is this: the three structures have about the same energy, as the result of two opposing effects, those of the number of covalent bonds and of the separation of charge. In the sequence a, b, c the number of covalent bonds changes from one to three; this would tend to make a the least stable and c the most stable. However, the charge distribution for a, with the more electro-

---

[1] A surprisingly large variability in bond-energy values is shown to exist by the range of values (26.6 to 30.1 kcal./mole) found for the heats of hydrogenation of different olefins. The double-bond energy value given in Table 18-1 corresponds to an average olefin, with heat of hydrogenation 29.8 kcal./mole (calculated with use of the C—C, C—H, and H—H bond-energy values). The comparison of benzene with cyclohexene is obviously reasonable.

negative atom negative, is the favorable one, and this stabilizes the structure, making it nearly equal in energy to b; whereas the charge distribution for c is unfavorable, the more electronegative atom having a positive charge, which counteracts the extra stability of the triple covalent bond and brings structure c also into approximate energy equality with b.

The resonance energy of carbon monoxide relative to the structure $:C{=}\ddot{O}:$ (which itself corresponds to resonance between $^{+}:C:\ddot{O}:^{-}$ and $:C::\ddot{O}:$, as in the ketones) can be found by comparing its heat of formation from atoms, 210 kcal./mole, with the ketone value of the double-bond energy, 152 kcal./mole.[1] The very large difference, 58 kcal./mole, represents the energy of resonance with the third structure $^{-}:C:::O:^{+}$. It is interesting that this resonance energy with structure c is about the same as that between a and b, 54 kcal./mole, as evaluated in a footnote to Section 18a. The total resonance energy relative to structure b, the normal covalent double-bonded structure, is over one hundred kcal./mole. It is the very large resonance energy in carbon monoxide which stabilizes the substance despite its lack of saturation of the carbon valences.

The empirical resonance-energy values[2] given in Table 18-2 are discussed in the following sections of this chapter and in Chapter V.

TABLE 18-2.—EMPIRICAL RESONANCE-ENERGY VALUES

Substance	Resonance energy (in kcal./mole)	Reference structure
Benzene, C_6H_6	39	
Naphthalene, $C_{10}H_8$	75	
Anthracene, $C_{14}H_{10}$	105	

[1] The bond energy values are not designed for use with a molecule as unconventional as carbon monoxide, containing bivalent carbon. It seems probable, however, that the error involved in this application is not great.

[2] L. Pauling and J. Sherman, *J. Chem. Phys.* **1**, 606 (1933).

TABLE 18-2.—(continued)

Substance	Resonance energy (in kcal./mole)	Reference structure
Phenanthrene, $C_{14}H_{10}$	110	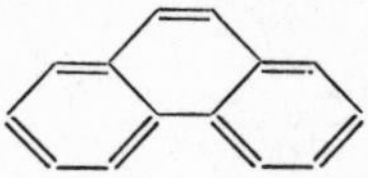
Biphenyl, $C_{12}H_{10}$	8*	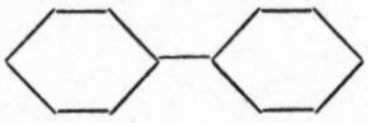
1,3,5-Triphenylbenzene, $C_{24}H_{18}$	25*	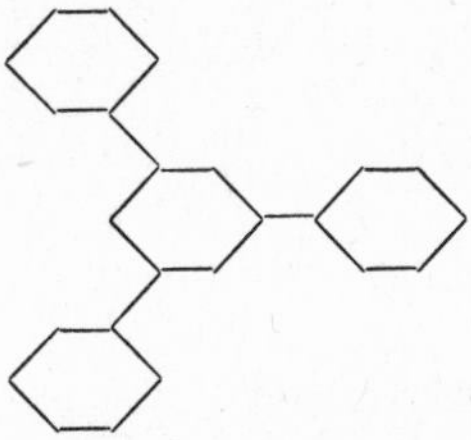
Phenylethylene, C_8H_8	7*	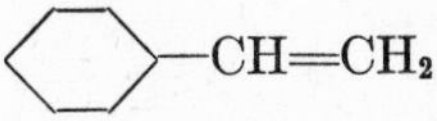 $-CH=CH_2$
Stilbene, $C_{14}H_{12}$	15*	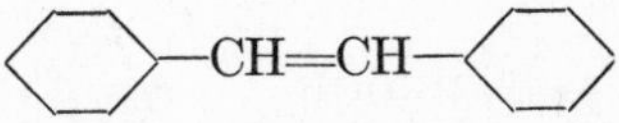 $-CH=CH-$
Phenylacetylene, C_6H_5CCH	10*	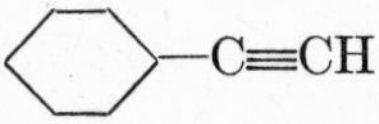 $-C\equiv CH$
Pyridine, C_5H_5N	43	 N
Quinoline, C_9H_7N	69	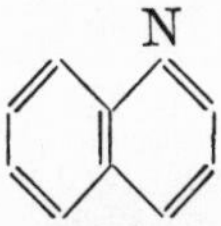 N
Pyrrole, C_4H_5N	31	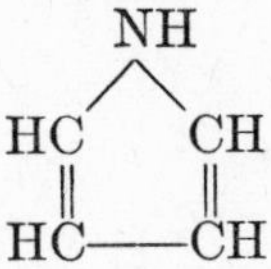 NH HC CH HC——CH
Indole, C_8H_7N	54	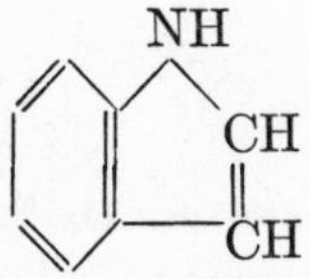 NH CH CH

* Extra resonance energy, not including that within the benzene ring.

Table 18-2.—(continued)

Substance	Resonance energy (in kcal./mole)	Reference structure
Carbazole, $C_{12}H_9N$	91	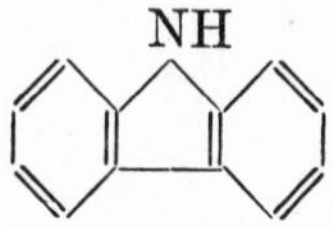 (structure) NH
Furan, C_4H_4O	23	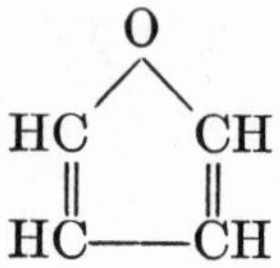 $\begin{array}{c} O \\ HC \quad CH \\ \| \quad \| \\ HC{-}{-}CH \end{array}$
Thiophene, C_4H_4S	31	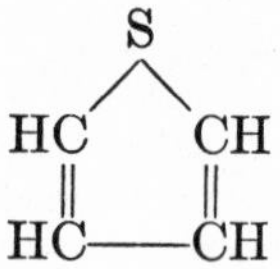 $\begin{array}{c} S \\ HC \quad CH \\ \| \quad \| \\ HC{-}{-}CH \end{array}$
Acids, RCOOH	28	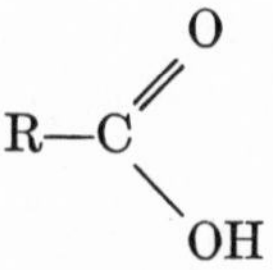 $R-C\begin{array}{c} O \\ \\ OH \end{array}$
Esters, RCOOR′	24	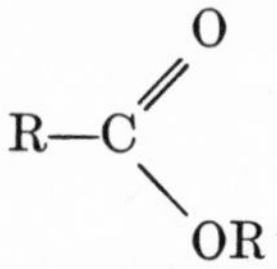 $R-C\begin{array}{c} O \\ \\ OR \end{array}$
Amides, $RCONH_2$	21	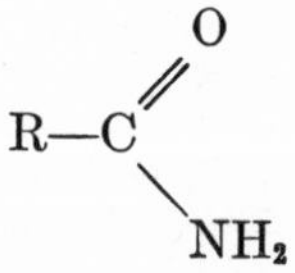 $R-C\begin{array}{c} O \\ \\ NH_2 \end{array}$
Urea, $CO(NH_2)_2$	37	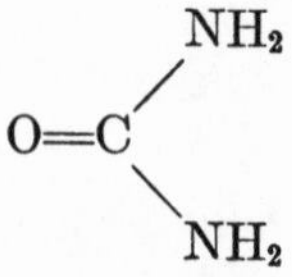 $O=C\begin{array}{c} NH_2 \\ \\ NH_2 \end{array}$
Dialkylcarbonates, R_2CO_3	42	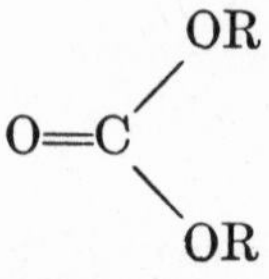 $O=C\begin{array}{c} OR \\ \\ OR \end{array}$

TABLE 18-2.—(continued)

Substance	Resonance energy (in kcal./mole)	Reference structure
Phenol, C_6H_5OH	7*	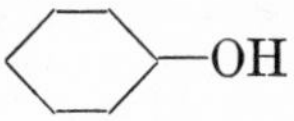 ⬡—OH
Aniline, $C_6H_5NH_2$	6*	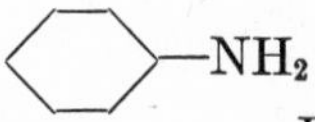 ⬡—NH_2
Benzaldehyde, C_6H_5CHO	4*	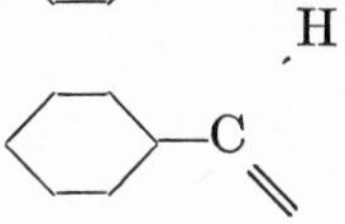 ⬡—C (with H and double bond)
Phenyl cyanide, C_6H_5CN	5*	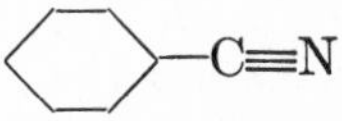 ⬡—C≡N
Benzoic acid, C_6H_5COOH	4**	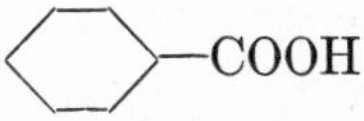 ⬡—COOH
Acetophenone, $C_6H_5COCH_3$	7*	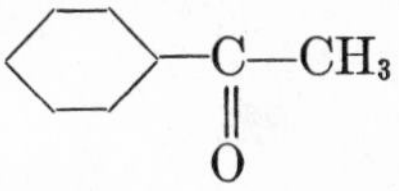 ⬡—C—CH_3 (‖O)
Benzophenone, $C_6H_5COC_6H_5$	10*	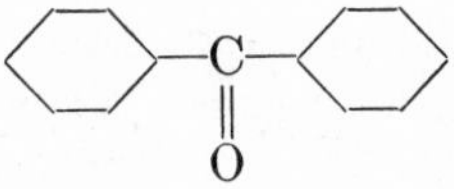 ⬡—C—⬡ (‖O)
Carbon monoxide, CO	58	C≡O
Carbon dioxide, CO_2	33	O=C=O
Carbon oxysulfide, SCO	20	S=C=O
Carbon disulfide, CS_2	11	S=C=S
Alkyl cyanates, RNCO	7	R—N=C=O

** Extra resonance energy, not including that within the benzene ring or the carboxyl group.

19. THE STRUCTURE OF AROMATIC MOLECULES

In the foregoing discussion of the structure of benzene the stability and characteristic aromatic properties of the substance have been attributed to resonance of the molecule between the two Kekulé structures. A similar treatment, which provides a similar explanation of their outstanding properties, can be given the condensed polynuclear aromatic hydrocarbons.

For naphthalene the conventional valence-bond structure is the Erlenmeyer structure:

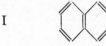

There are two other structures which differ from this only in a redistribution of the bonds:

These three structures, the most stable valence-bond structures which can be formulated for naphthalene, are seen to have about the same energy, and to correspond to about the same molecular configuration. It is to be expected then that they will be combined to represent the normal state of the naphthalene molecule, to which they should contribute about equally. Resonance among these three stable structures should stabilize the molecule to a greater extent than the Kekulé resonance in benzene, involving two equivalent structures; it is seen from Table 18-2 that the resonance energy of naphthalene, 75 kcal./mole, is indeed much greater than that of benzene.

For anthracene four stable valence-bond structures can be formulated,

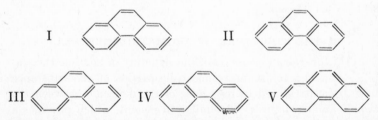

and for phenanthrene five,

The observed values of the resonance energy are 105 kcal./mole for anthracene and 110 kcal./mole for phenanthrene. These are reasonable in comparison with those of benzene and naphthalene and also with each other, the angular ring system having a larger number of stable resonating structures and a larger resonance energy than the linear ring system.

The higher condensed ring systems can be similarly represented as resonating among many valence-bond structures.   The resonance energy increases in rough proportion to the number of hexagonal rings in the system.   In addition it is somewhat greater for the branched and angular ring systems than for the corresponding linear ones, the former resonating among more stable valence-bond structures than the latter (as in the case of phenanthrene and anthracene).

The configurations of the molecules are those expected for the resonating structures.   Through resonance each bond acquires some double-bond character, which causes the adjacent bonds to strive to be coplanar.   The molecules are thus brought into completely coplanar configurations, with 120° bond angles. This has been verified for naphthalene and anthracene by the careful x-ray studies of Robertson,[1] and is shown also by x-ray work on other members of the series.[2]

The general chemical properties of the substances are also accounted for.   The stabilization of the molecules by resonance gives them aromatic character in the same way as for benzene.

A simple consideration of the resonating structures leads to an explanation for observed differences in behavior of different carbon-carbon bonds in these molecules.   In benzene we may say that each bond has $\frac{1}{2}$ double-bond character, since it occurs as a single bond in one Kekulé structure and as a double bond in the other.   This does not mean that the bond behaves half the time as a double bond, but rather that it is a bond of a new type, very much different from a double bond, and with properties intermediate between those of a double bond and a single bond.   (The properties are not the average of those for the two bond types; consideration must also be given the stabilizing effect of the resonance energy.)

---

[1] J. M. Robertson, *Proc. Roy. Soc.* A140, 79 (1933); A142, 674 (1933).
[2] For cyclobutadiene and cyclo-octatetraene coplanar configurations would be stabilized by the effect of resonance.   The bond angles in these coplanar molecules, 90° and 135°, are, however, so far from the normal values as to introduce considerable strain, which would make the molecules less stable than expected and remove part of their aromatic character.

In naphthalene, anthracene, and phenanthrene the amounts
of double bond character, found by averaging the stable resonating structures, are the following:

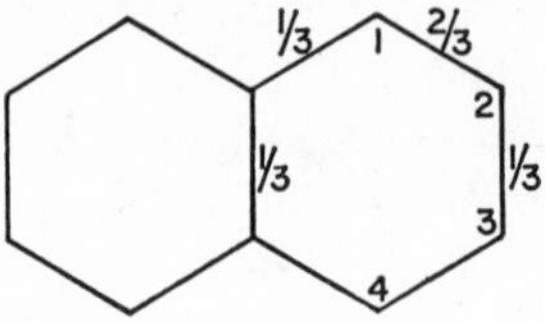

NAPHTHALENE

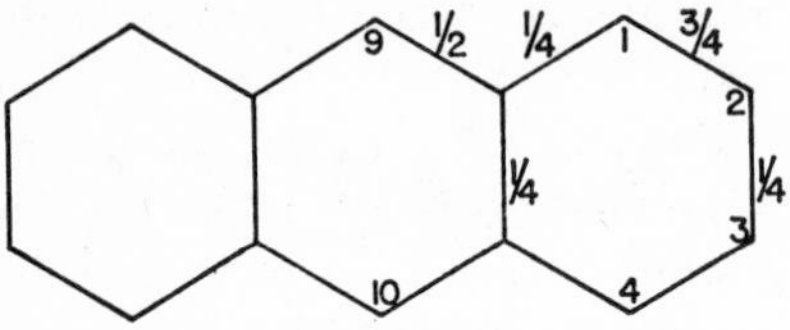

ANTHRACENE

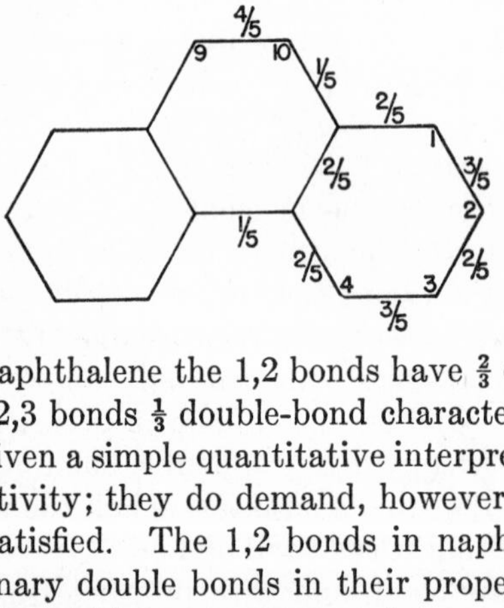

PHENANTHRENE

In naphthalene the 1,2 bonds have $\frac{2}{3}$ double bond character and
the 2,3 bonds $\frac{1}{3}$ double-bond character. These numbers cannot
be given a simple quantitative interpretation in terms of chemical
reactivity; they do demand, however, that qualitative relations
be satisfied. The 1,2 bonds in naphthalene must be closer to
ordinary double bonds in their properties than are the benzene
bonds, which in turn are much more like double bonds than are
the 2,3 bonds in naphthalene, the last, indeed, having practically
no double-bond properties. These statements are in agreement
with general chemical experience. A hydroxyl group on carbon
atom 2 of the system shown

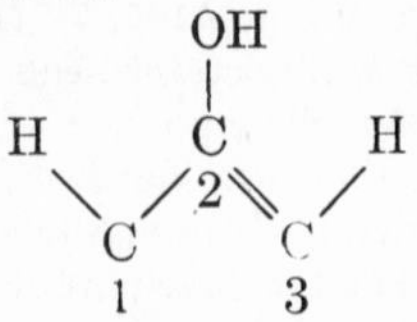

will induce substitution on carbon atom 3 on attack by certain reagents (bromine, diazomethane) rather than carbon atom 1, the double bond serving as the path for the directing influence (Sec. 19b). This phenomenon can be used to test the extent to which different carbon-carbon bonds have the properties of a double bond. It is found[1] that with hydroxyl in position 2 of naphthalene reaction occurs readily in position 1, whereas even when position 1 is blocked with methyl reaction does not occur at position 3. This shows strong double-bond properties for the 1,2 bond and very weak ones for the 2,3 bond, as expected. Moreover, it is also found[2] that the 1,2 bonds in anthracene have stronger double-bond properties than those of the same bond in naphthalene, and that the double-bond properties of the 9,10 bond in phenanthrene are stronger still, as indicated by the amounts of double-bond character. It is for this reason that phenanthrene, despite its greater thermodynamic stability, consequent to its greater resonance energy, is more reactive than anthracene.

An interesting related phenomenon involving the benzene ring, discovered by Mills and Nixon,[3] can be discussed in a similar way.[4] By attaching saturated hydrocarbon rings of different sizes to two *ortho* positions of the benzene molecule it is possible to make the ring react as though the double bonds were fixed in the positions corresponding to one or the other of the Kekulé structures. Mills and Nixon found 5-hydroxyhydrindene (I)

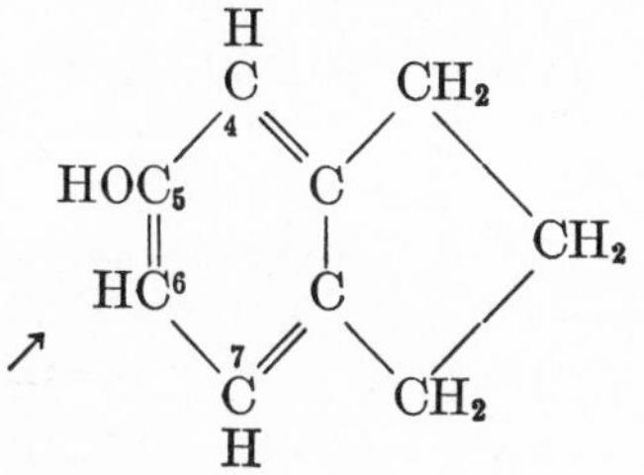

on reaction with the phenyldiazonium ion to undergo substitution in the 6 position, and *ar*-tetrahydro-β-naphthol (II)

[1] L. F. Fieser and W. G. Lothrop, *J.A.C.S.* **57**, 1459 (1935) and earlier references quoted by them.
[2] L. F. Fieser and W. G. Lothrop, *ibid.* **58**, 749 (1936).
[3] W. H. Mills and I. G. Nixon, *J. Chem. Soc.* **1930**, 2510.
[4] L. E. Sutton and L. Pauling, *Trans. Faraday Soc.* **31**, 939 (1935).

$$
\begin{array}{c}
\text{H} \qquad \text{H}_2 \\
\text{C} \qquad \text{C} \\
\end{array}
$$

$$
\text{HOC}_2 \qquad \text{C} \qquad \text{CH}_2 \qquad \text{II}
$$

$$
\text{HC}^3 \qquad \text{C} \qquad \text{CH}_2
$$

$$
\begin{array}{c}
\text{C} \qquad \text{C} \\
\text{H} \qquad \text{H}_2
\end{array}
$$

to undergo substitution in the 1 position.   These results were originally interpreted as showing complete fixation of one or the other of the Kekulé structures, resulting from the influence of the five-membered side ring (with 108° angles) in bringing a single bond into position, with its normal tetrahedral angle of 109°28′, and thus minimizing the strain energy, and from the opposite influence of the six-membered ring, which favors large angles. We see, however, that the stabilization of one Kekulé structure over the other need not be complete in order that one of the bonds adjacent to the hydroxyl-substituted carbon atom assume enough additional double-bond character to dominate the reaction.   The effect of the side rings in stabilizing one Kekulé structure relative to the other probably causes it to contribute a few percent more than the other to the normal state of the molecule, and this slight superiority gives one bond much stronger double-bond properties than the other for the orientation of substituents.[1]

19a. The Quantitative Treatment of Resonance in Aromatic Molecules.—It has been found possible to carry out the quantitative discussion of resonance in aromatic molecules by simplifying the problem in the following way.   Of the four valence orbitals of the carbon atom, shown in Figure 13-1 before hybridization, three lie in the plane of the ring (s, p_x, and p_y, the plane of the ring being taken as the xy plane).   These can be combined to give three bond orbitals which are coplanar and make 120° angles with one another,[2] and are thus adapted to the formation by the

---

[1] Sutton and Pauling, *loc. cit.*   For further discussion see N. V. Sidgwick and H. D. Springall, *Chem. and Ind.* **55**, 476 (1936); *J. Chem. Soc.* **1936**, 1532; L. F. Fieser and W. C. Lothrop, *J.A.C.S.* **58**, 2050 (1936); W. Baker, *Ann. Rep. Chem. Soc.* **33**, 281 (1936); *J. Chem. Soc.* **1937**, 477.

[2] These orbitals are given in a footnote of Section 14b for the case that the s orbital is divided equally among the three bonds.   In benzene it is probable that the strong C—C bonds, with interatomic distances smaller than the single-bond value, use more of the s orbital than does the H—C bond.

carbon atom of single covalent bonds to the two adjacent carbon atoms in the ring and to the attached hydrogen atom.   It is assumed that this single-bond framework of the molecule,

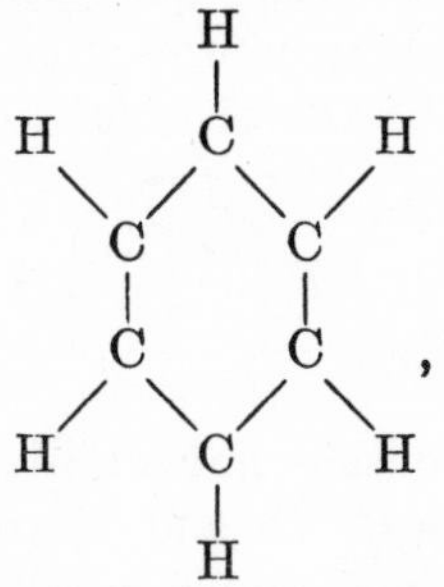

remains unchanged; for each atom the fourth orbital and its electron then remain to be considered.

The fourth orbital is the p_z orbital shown in Figure 13-1.   It possesses lobes above and below the plane of the ring.   Let us assume that each of the six p_z orbitals is occupied by one electron (this involving neglect of ionic structures).   The problem is to calculate the interaction energy of the six electrons in the six orbitals.

If there were only two orbitals and two electrons, as in the hydrogen molecule, the interaction energy would be just the resonance energy associated with the interchange of the two electrons between the two orbitals (Sec. 5).   This is the situation in ethylene; the two p_z electrons here convert the single bond into a double bond.   Let us designate this p_z resonance energy by the symbol α.   It is approximately equal to the difference in energy of the carbon-carbon double bond and the carbon-carbon single bond; that is, to about 41 kcal./mole.[1]

Now, the resonance energy for the two Kekulé structures in benzene can be calculated in terms of α by neglecting all interactions except those between adjacent atoms in the ring.[2]   It is found to have the value 0.9α, this being the extra stability of the ring relative to one of the Kekulé structures.   With $\alpha = 41$

[1] In this discussion, contrary to the usual custom, α has been used to represent the magnitude of the resonance energy of two p_z electrons, taken with positive sign.

[2] E. Hückel, *Z. f. Phys.* **70**, 204 (1931); **72**, 310 (1931); **76**, 628 (1932); L. Pauling and G. W. Wheland, *J. Chem. Phys.* **1**, 362 (1933).

kcal./mole this resonance energy is 37 kcal./mole, which is equal to the value found empirically.

This agreement is, however, fortuitous in part.   It is found on examination of the problem that consideration must also be given, in addition to the Kekulé structures A and B, to the three structures C, D, and E of the Dewar type.

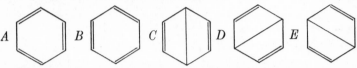

It is not necessary to consider any additional structures.[1]

The three structures C, D, and E are less stable than the Kekulé structures and make much smaller contributions to the normal state of the benzene molecule.   They increase the resonance energy from 0.9α to 1.11α.   By equating this to the empirical resonance energy of benzene α is found to have the value 35 kcal./mole, somewhat smaller than given by the bond-energy difference.   This is not surprising in view of the approximations involved.[2]

A similar treatment of naphthalene[3] leads to the value 2.04α, which on equation to the empirical resonance energy 75 kcal./mole fixes α at 37 kcal./mole, in approximate agreement with the result for benzene.   Approximate calculations for anthracene and phenanthrene[4] lead to 3.09α and 3.15α, respectively, for the resonance energy, giving $\alpha = 34$ and 35 kcal./mole on comparison with the empirical values.

A second method of treatment, called the *molecular-orbital* treatment to differentiate it from the valence-bond treatment described above, has also been applied to the problem.[5]   With

[1] The rule regarding independent structures is the following: with the atoms arranged in a ring, only those valence-bond structures for which the bonds do not cross need be considered; all others can be represented as resonance combinations of these.

[2] It was assumed in evaluating α as 41 kcal./mole that the entire energy of the bonds is interchange energy of the two electrons.   This is not true; the interchange energy is usually estimated to comprise 80 to 90% of the bond energy.

[3] L. Pauling and G. W. Wheland, *loc. cit.*; J. Sherman, *J. Chem. Phys.* **2**, 488 (1934).

[4] G. W. Wheland, *J. Chem. Phys.* **3**, 356 (1935)

[5] E. Hückel, *loc. cit.*

it the six electrons are not combined in pairs to form bonds, but move independently from atom to atom. The calculated resonance energies are expressed in terms of an energy quantity β, their values being 2.00β for benzene and 3.68β for naphthalene. These lead to $\beta = 20$ kcal./mole for both substances on comparison with the empirical values, the ratio for the two being accordingly given satisfactorily by this treatment as well as by the valence-bond treatment. For anthracene and phenanthrene the theory gives as values of the resonance energy 5.32β and 5.45β, corresponding again to $\beta = 20$ kcal./mole (within 0.5 kcal./mole) in each case.

There is, moreover, a reasonable relation between α and β. The first is the energy of interchange of two p_z electrons, analogous to that of the hydrogen molecule, and the second is the energy of resonance of one electron between two p_z orbitals, analogous to that of the hydrogen molecule-ion. The ratio of bond energies in H_2^+ and H_2 is 0.59, and that of β and α is 0.57; the agreement of these two ratios is excellent.

The valence-bond treatment described above involves neglect of the partial ionic character of the bonds in the benzene molecule, and the molecular-orbital treatment overemphasizes it.[1]

The agreement of the two treatments with each other and with the empirical resonance energy values makes it probable that the point of view presented above regarding the structure of aromatic molecules will not need extensive revision in the future, although it may be subjected to further refinement.

19b. The Orientation of Substituents in Aromatic Molecules.— When a substituent is introduced into an aromatic molecule it may enter into certain of the available positions more readily than into others. This phenomenon has been extensively studied, and empirical rules have been formulated which describe the experimental results fairly satisfactorily.

In a monosubstituted benzene C_6H_5R the groups $R = CH_3$, F, Cl, Br, I, OH, NH_2 are ortho-para directing and the groups $R = COOH$, CHO, NO_2, SO_3H, $[N(CH_3)_3]^+$ are meta directing for the cationoid reagents causing substitution.[2] Most ortho-

---

[1] A comparison of the two methods of quantitative discussion of aromatic molecules has been published by G. W. Wheland, *J. Chem. Phys.* **2,** 474 (1934).

[2] R. Robinson ("Outline of an Electrochemical (Electronic) Theory of the Course of Organic Reactions," Institute of Chemistry of Great Britain

para directing groups activate the molecule so that substitution takes place more readily than in benzene itself, and most meta directing groups have a deactivating effect.   In naphthalene substitution occurs at the α position, in furan, thiophene, and pyrrole at the α position, and in pyridine at the β position, all of these molecules except pyridine being more active than benzene.

During the last fifteen years a qualitative theory has been developed[1] which accounts satisfactorily for the phenomenon in its major features, and recently a quantitative treatment based on the quantum mechanics has been carried out,[2] with a degree of success which provides strong support for the theory.

The theory is based on the consideration of the distribution of electric charge in the molecule in which substitution is taking place.   In a benzene molecule the six carbon atoms are equivalent, and the charge distribution is accordingly such as not to make one carbon atom different from another.   In the molecule C_6H_5R, with R attached to carbon atom 1, the electron distribution will in general be affected by the group R in such a way as to change the charges on the ortho (2 and 6), meta (3 and 5), and para carbon atoms.   Moreover, the electron distribution may also be changed somewhat on the approach of the substituting group R' to one of the carbon atoms ("polarization" of the molecule by the group R'); in benzene the polarization of one carbon atom by the group would be the same as for another, but in a substituted benzene the polarization would in general vary from atom to atom, and so might cause a difference in behavior of different positions.   The fundamental postulate of the theory of orientation of substituents is the following: *In an aromatic molecule undergoing substitution by a cationoid group R' the rate of sub-*

---

and Ireland, London, 1932), following Lapworth's suggestion, has classified reagents causing substitution as cationoid or anionoid, the former resembling reactive cations and the latter reactive anions in their behavior. Cationoid reagents include acids, reactive cations such as diazonium cations, alkyl halides, quaternary ammonium compounds, etc.   Anionoid reagents include reactive anions ($[NH_2]^-$, $[OH]^-$, $[CN]^-$, $[OR]^-$, etc.), molecules containing unshared electron pairs (nitrogen atom of ammonia and amines), etc.

[1] Many workers, including Fry, Stieglitz, Lapworth, Lewis, Lucas, Lowry, Robinson, and Ingold, have contributed to the theory.   For a review see C. K. Ingold, *Chem. Rev.* 15, 225 (1934).

[2] G. W. Wheland and L. Pauling, *J.A.C.S.* 57, 2086 (1935).

stitution of R' for hydrogen on the nth carbon atom increases with increase in the negative charge on the nth carbon atom when the group R' approaches it.

Substitution by a cationoid reagent is thus assumed to take place preferentially at that carbon atom on which the negative charge is the largest.   This assumption is a reasonable one, in view of the electron-seeking character of cationoid reagents.

There are two principal ways in which the charge distribution can be affected by the group R, for each of which it has been assumed, and has been verified by quantum-mechanical calculations,[1] that the ortho and para carbon atoms are about equally affected, the meta carbon atoms being affected to a much smaller extent.

The first effect of the group R, called the *inductive effect*, results whenever the electron affinity of the group is larger than or smaller than that of hydrogen.   In the former case electrons are attracted to the group and to the attached carbon atom 1; it can be seen from the following argument that they are removed to a larger extent from the ortho and para carbon atoms than from the meta carbon atoms.   The electronegative group attracts electrons from carbon atom 1, and this in turn attracts electrons from the other atoms of the ring.   This effect is then continued around the ring, carried in part by the single bonds in the plane of the ring, and in part by the six aromatic (p_z) electrons.   The contribution of the latter is of such a nature as to affect the ortho and para carbon atoms preferentially.   The transfer of negative charge from the other atoms of the ring to carbon atom 1 by action of the six aromatic electrons can be described as resulting from resonance with ionic structures. There are only three stable ionic structures of this type,

and they lead to the removal of electrons equally from the two ortho atoms and the para atom.   Consequently the rate of substitution at the ortho and para positions will be greatly decreased

<hr />

[1] Wheland and Pauling, *loc. cit.*   This was first shown, for the inductive effect alone, by E. Hückel, *Z. Physik* **72**, 310 (1931).

and that at the meta positions somewhat decreased; the group R will be meta directing, with deactivation. An example of such a group is $[N(CH_3)_3]^+$, in trimethylphenylammonium ion; the nitrogen atom is more electronegative than hydrogen, and its electronegativity is further intensified in this case by its positive charge. The same effect is seen in pyridine; the nitrogen atom attracts electrons mainly from the α and γ carbon atoms, and consequently pyridine substitutes in the β positions, and is less active than benzene. Toluene shows the opposite effect. Electric moment measurements show that the methyl group loses electrons to the ring;[1] these go mainly to the ortho and para carbon atoms, which are thus activated; in consequence toluene substitutes in these positions, and the substitution occurs with greater ease than in benzene.

We might expect that F, Cl, Br, I, OH, and NH_2 would be meta directing, inasmuch as these groups all are more strongly electronegative than hydrogen. Actually they are all ortho-para directing. The inductive effect is in these cases overcome by another effect, called the *resonance effect* (or sometimes the *tautomeric* or *electromeric effect*).

Let us consider a molecule C_6H_5X in which the group X possesses an unshared pair of electrons on the atom adjacent to the benzene ring. The stable structures among which resonance analogous to that in benzene occurs are the Kekulé structures, *A* and *B* (smaller contributions are also made by other structures Sec. 19a), which will be ignored here for the sake of simplicity).

In addition to these, however, there are three structures *F*, *G*, and *H* which can be written for these benzene derivatives but not for benzene itself. These structures

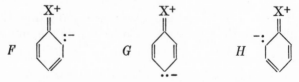

---

[1] This result is surprising, since in the electronegativity scale carbon is more electronegative than hydrogen; this is probably a resonance effect.

are not so stable as *A* and *B*, because, although they contain the same number of double bonds, they involve an unstable separation of charge.   They make a significant, although small, contribution to the normal state of the molecule.   The extra resonance energy resulting from their contribution is about 6 kcal./mole (Table 18-2, phenol and aniline).   As a result of this conjugation of the unshared pair of the group X with the benzene ring there is accordingly built up a negative charge on each of the ortho carbon atoms and the para carbon atom, this effect being superimposed on the inductive effect of the group.   For the groups listed above the resonance effect is stronger than the inductive effect, making the groups ortho-para directing.[1]

In benzaldehyde and many other similar molecules, on the other hand, the resonance effect directs toward the meta positions, this resulting whenever the substituted group R contains an electronegative atom and a double or triple bond conjugated with the benzene ring, (R = $COOH$, CHO, NO_2, $COCH_3$, SO_3H, CN, etc.).   The structures leading to this effect, F′, G′, and H′ are of the types

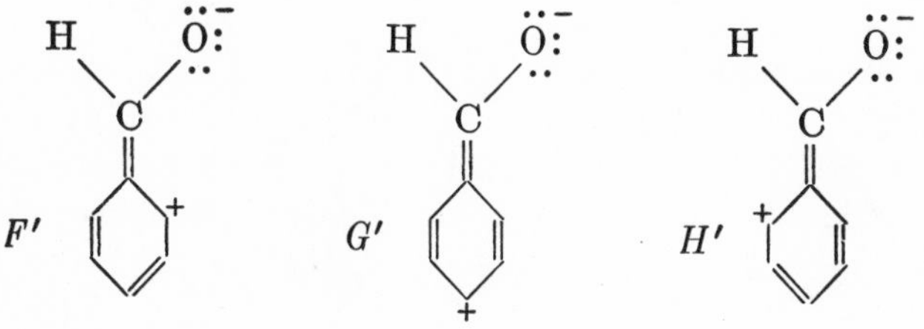

which decrease the electron density on the aromatic nucleus, especially at the ortho and para positions, and thus lead to reaction at the meta positions, but at a slower rate than for benzene itself. The extra resonance energy due to these structures is about 5 kcal./mole.

[1] Resonance of this type is often indicated by use of arrows; the method is obvious from the examples

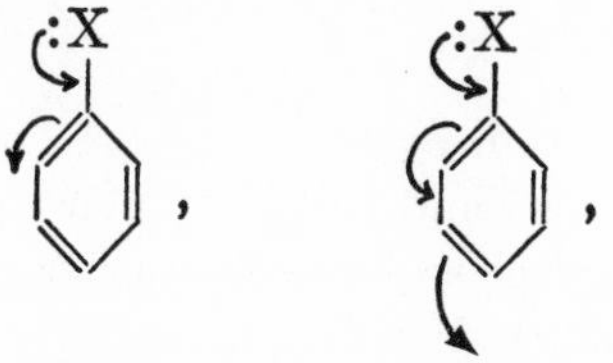

The above discussion for monosubstituted benzene can be summarized as follows. When resonance does not occur, substitution is usually determined by the inductive effect, an electron-attracting group being meta directing and an electron-repelling group ortho-para directing. The resonance effect, which when present is usually more powerful than the inductive effect, is meta directing when the group contains an electronegative atom and a double bond conjugated with the benzene ring, and ortho-para directing when the group contains an unshared electron pair on the atom adjacent to the benzene ring.

In a few cases (naphthalene, for example) it is necessary to consider also the polarization of the molecule by the attacking group; as yet no general qualitative rules have been formulated regarding this effect, although some quantitative calculations have been carried out. The effect can be treated qualitatively by the consideration of the number of stable ionic structures placing an unshared pair on the carbon atom being attacked. For the α position of naphthalene there are seven:

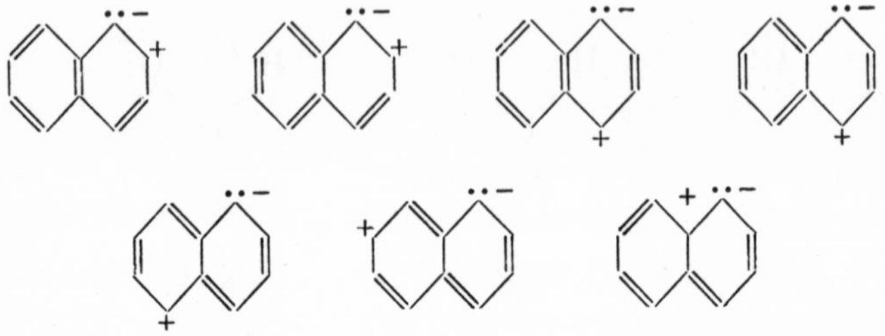

and for the β position only six:

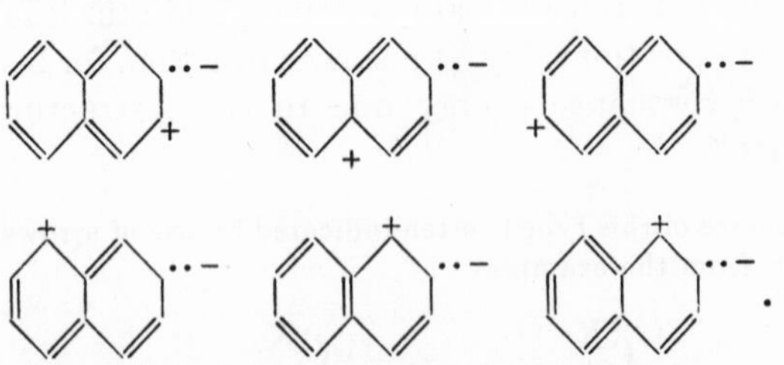

Accordingly the polarization by the attacking group will be the greater for the α position, and substitution will tend to occur there. The orienting effect is, however, rather weak.

19c. The Effect of Resonance on the Electric Dipole Moments of Molecules.—It was pointed out by Sutton[1] in 1931 that resonance of the types discussed in the preceding section for molecules such as chlorobenzene and nitrobenzene would cause the electric dipole moments of these molecules to have values differing from those of the corresponding alkyl derivatives, and that a test of the resonance theory of orientation of substituents could be carried out by the analysis of dipole-moment data.

The dipole-moment vectors $(+ \rightarrow -)$ in both R—Cl and R—NO$_2$ (with R an alkyl group—preferably sec-propyl or tert-butyl for comparison with phenyl compounds) are directed along the R—Cl or R—N axes.   In chlorobenzene resonance to structures such as $:\!\!\overset{-}{\diagdown\!\!\diagup}\!\!=\!\!\overset{..\,+}{\underset{..}{\text{Cl}}}:$ is seen to lead to a decrease in moment,

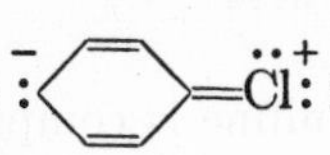

the dipole vector for these less important structures being opposed in direction to that of the primary structure; this is verified by experiment, the change in moment from the alkyl chlorides to phenyl chloride being -0.58×10^{-18} e.s.u.   Similar changes are shown by the bromides and iodides (Table 19-1).

For the meta-directing nitro group an increase in moment is expected, due to the contribution of structures such as

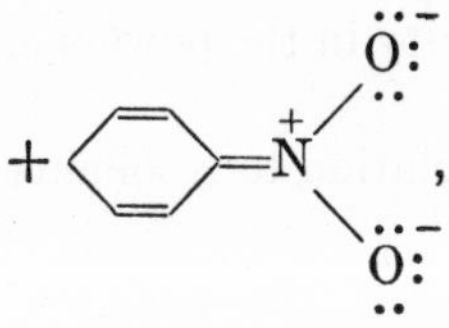

$$+\diagdown\!\!\diagup=\overset{+}{N}\Big\langle\,\overset{\overset{..\,-}{O}:}{\underset{\underset{..}{O}:}{}}$$, in which the nitro group accepts a pair of

electrons from the ring.   This too is verified by experiment, the observed increase in moment being 0.64×10^{-18} e.s.u.

In these molecules the electric dipole vector is well defined in direction, coinciding with the C—Cl or C—N bond.   In an amine, on the other hand, the moment of the molecule is the resultant of several bond moments, and in general it does not coincide with the R—N bond in direction.   It was found by Sutton on analysis of the data that the observed increase in re-

[1] L. E. Sutton, *Proc. Roy. Soc.* A133, 668 (1931); *Trans. Faraday Soc.* 30, 789 (1934).

TABLE 19-1 —ELECTRIC DIPOLE MOMENTS OF ALKYL
AND ARYL DERIVATIVES

Group	—CH(CH$_3$)$_2$ or —C(CH$_3$)$_3$ $\mu \times 10^{18}$	—C$_6$H$_5$ $\mu \times 10^{18}$	Difference
—Cl	2.14	1.56	−0.58
—Br	2.15	1.54	−0.61
—I	2.13	1.38	−0.75
—NH$_2$	1.23	1.55	+0.32
—OCH$_3$	1.29	1.23	−0.06
—OH	1.66	1.73	+0.07
—NO$_2$	3.29	3.93	+0.64
—CHO	2.46	2.75	+0.29
—NO	2.51	3.14	+0.63

sultant moment from alkylamine to aniline is compatible with a decrease in moment of the R—N part of the molecule, and that the dipole moment values for other groups (−OCH$_3$, −OH, etc.) can be correlated satisfactorily with their orienting powers for substitution reactions and with their resonating structures by consideration of the angles between the bond vectors.   We shall not discuss these rather complicated calculations further.

As would be expected, vinyl and naphthyl derivatives are observed to have nearly the same dipole moments as the phenyl derivatives (1.66 × 10^{-18} for vinyl chloride, 1.59 × 10^{-18} for naphthyl chloride), verifying the close similarity in the powers of conjugation of these three groups.

The discussion of dipole moment data in relation to resonance is continued in Section 27.

20. THE STRUCTURE AND STABILITY OF THE HYDROCARBON FREE RADICALS

Ever since the discovery by Gomberg in 1900 of the dissociation of hexaphenylethane into triphenylmethyl radicals the search for a theoretical explanation of the phenomenon has been carried on.   The modern theory of the stability of the aromatic free radicals attributes it in the main to the resonance of the free valence among many atoms.[1]

[1] L. Pauling and G. W. Wheland, *J. Chem. Phys.* **1**, 362 (1933), **2**, 482 (1934); E. Hückel, *Z. f. Phys.* **83**, 632 (1933).   The quantitative theory was foreshadowed by a somewhat similar qualitative discussion by

The hexaalkylethanes, which do not dissociate appreciably, have the valence-bond structure

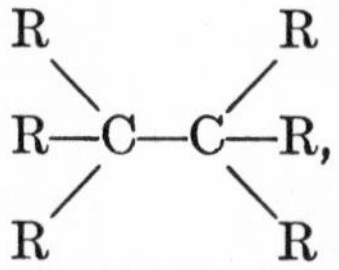

$$\begin{array}{ccc} R & & R \\ \diagdown & & \diagup \\ R\!-\!\!C\!-\!\!C\!-\!R, \\ \diagup & & \diagdown \\ R & & R \end{array}$$

and the corresponding free radicals the structure

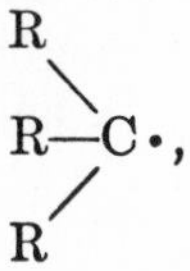

$$\begin{array}{c} R \\ \diagdown \\ R\!-\!\!C\!\cdot, \\ \diagup \\ R \end{array}$$

the odd electron (free valence) being located on the methyl carbon atom. The introduction of an aryl group, however, provides additional structures for the radical; it is principally the energy of resonance among these which stabilizes the free radical and increases the degree of dissociation of the substituted ethane.

For simplicity, let us consider the molecule $C_6H_5CH_2\!-\!CH_2C_6H_5$, 1,2-diphenylethane, and let us restrict the discussion of resonance to the structures with the greatest stability (those with the maximum number of double bonds). For the undissociated molecule there is resonance among the four Kekulé structures

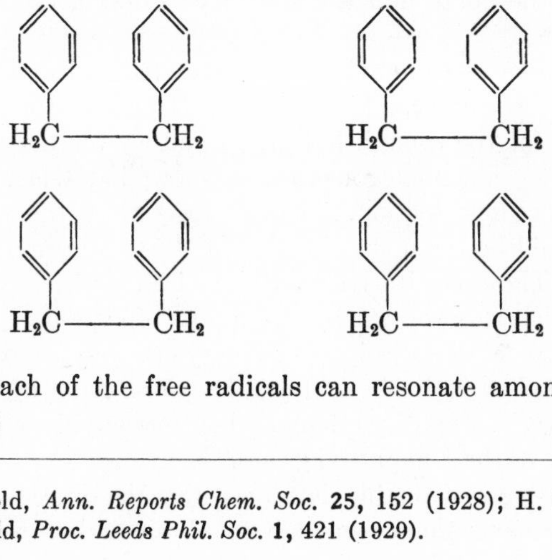

whereas each of the free radicals can resonate among the five structures

C. K. Ingold, *Ann. Reports Chem. Soc.* **25**, 152 (1928); H. Burton and C. K. Ingold, *Proc. Leeds Phil. Soc.* **1**, 421 (1929).

$$A \quad B \quad C\cdot \quad D \quad E$$

$$\cdot CH_2 \qquad \cdot CH_2 \qquad CH_2 \qquad CH_2 \qquad CH_2$$

If the radical were restricted to resonance between the Kekulé structures A and B, with the free valence on the methyl carbon, resonance would stabilize the radicals to just the same extent as the undissociated molecules, which would then have only the same tendency to dissociate as a hexaalkylethane. But actually the five structures A, B, C, D, and E (each with three double bonds) contribute about equally to the structure of the radical, which thus resonates among five structures instead of two, and is correspondingly stabilized by the additional resonance energy.

The extra resonance energy of the phenylmethyl radical is not large enough to lead to appreciable dissociation of 1,2-diphenylethane. In the triphenylmethyl radical, however, the odd electron can resonate among nine positions (the ortho and para positions of the three phenyl groups) in addition to that on the methyl carbon atom. It is found on evaluating the extra resonance energy for this radical by the two methods described in Section 19a that it is of the order of magnitude of one-half the carbon-carbon single-bond energy; the enhanced stability of two radicals is accordingly great enough to overcome in large part the energy of the bond, and the substance shows a large degree of dissociation.

Whereas for the phenyl group three structures with the free valence in the group can be written (C, D, and E), there are seven structures for the α-naphthyl group and six for the β-naphthyl group, these being analogous to those shown in the last paragraph of the preceding section. This suggests that the α-naphthyl group should be the more effective of the two in promoting dissociation. The quantitative treatment leads to the same expectation, which is borne out by the results of experimental studies of the degree of dissociation of hexaarylethanes, the order found being hexaphenylethane < tetraphenyldi-β-naphthylethane < tetraphenyldi-α-naphthylethane. The biphenyl group is about as effective as the β-naphthyl group.

In recent years valuable data regarding the degree of dissociation of hexaarylethanes have been obtained by the magnetic method; the concentration of the triarylmethyl radicals is determined by measuring the magnetic susceptibility of the solution, to which the unpaired spin of the odd electron in the radical makes a paramagnetic contribution. This method, first used by Taylor,[1] at the suggestion of G. N. Lewis, has been extensively applied by Müller[2] and Marvel[3] and their collaborators.

It has been found that hexa-*p*-alkylphenylethanes in solution dissociate to a somewhat greater extent than hexaphenylethane itself, the magnitude of the enhancement of the degree of dissociation by the *p*-alkyl groups being uncertain because of instability of the radicals.[3d,3e]   A possible explanation for this effect, involving resonance of the radical to structures such as

$$
\begin{array}{ccc}
\text{Ar} & & \text{R} \\
| & & | \\
\text{C} = & & = \text{C} \quad \cdot \text{R}, \\
| & & | \\
\text{Ar} & & \text{R}
\end{array}
$$

in which a single bond within the alkyl group is broken, has been suggested by Wheland.[4]   This explanation applies also to the effect of the *t*-butyl group in increasing the degree of dissociation when it is present as a direct substituent in the ethane.

Whereas structures such as

$$
\begin{array}{c}
\text{Ar} \\
| \\
\text{C} = \cdot , \\
| \\
\text{Ar}
\end{array}
$$

which place the odd electron in the outer phenyl group, can be written for a radical containing the *p*-biphenylmethyl group,

[1] N. W. Taylor, *J.A.C.S.* **48**, 854 (1926).

[2] E. Müller, I. Müller-Rodloff, and W. Bunge, *Ann.* **520**, 235 (1935); E. Müller and I. Müller-Rodloff, *ibid.* **521**, 89 (1935).

[3] (a) M. F. Roy and C. S. Marvel, *J.A.C.S.* **59**, 2622 (1937); (b) C. S. Marvel, E. Ginsberg, and M. B. Mueller, *ibid.* **61**, 77 (1939); (c) C. S. Marvel, M. B. Mueller, and E. Ginsberg, *ibid.* **61**, 2008 (1939); (d) C. S. Marvel, W. H. Rieger, and M. B. Mueller, *ibid.* **61**, 2769 (1939); (e) C. S. Marvel, M. B. Mueller, C. M. Himel, and J. F. Kaplan, *ibid.* **61**, 2771 (1939).

[4] G. W. Wheland, *J. Chem. Phys.* **2**, 474 (1934).

there are no corresponding stable structures for the m-biphenyl group; hence the effect of the m-biphenyl group in stabilizing the free radical should be much less than that of the p-biphenyl group, and only a little greater than that of the phenyl group itself.[1] The experimental evidence on this point is not completely consistent. The dissociation constant of hexaphenylethane in benzene solution, which is about 5.7×10^{-4} at 25°C., is increased by a factor of about 60 by substitution of two p-biphenyl groups for phenyl groups, and again by about 60 by a second similar substitution. The observation[2] that hexa-m-biphenylethane in 2.5% benzene solution at 25°C. is 60% dissociated, which corresponds to the value 0.24 for the dissociation constant, shows that the factor for substitution of two phenyl groups by two m-biphenyl groups is only about 7.5, which is much smaller than that for two p-biphenyl groups. The ratio 7.5 to 60 is reasonable in view of the theoretical considerations given above. However, Marvel, Mueller, and Ginsberg have also reported the degrees of dissociation of di-m-biphenyltetraphenylethane and di-p-biphenyltetraphenylethane in 3.6% benzene solution at 25°C. to be 11 or 12% and 13 or 14%, respectively. The difference in these values is surprisingly small. It seems probable that the value for di-m-biphenyltetraphenylethane is incorrect: the application of the theoretically sound principle that each pair of substituted groups should cause about the same change in the free energy of dissociation permits the prediction to be made that the dissociation constant for this substance is 4.3×10^{-3} and its degree of dissociation under the conditions of the experiment only about 2.8%.

Resonance of this type gives to all of the bonds in the triarylmethyl radicals partial double-bond character, and the radicals would strive to assume a completely coplanar configuration. It is found on consideration of the dimensions of the groups, however, that steric effects prevent this; the phenyl groups in triphenylmethyl must be rotated somewhat out of the median plane. Moreover, the steric interactions of large substituent groups in the substituted ethanes probably weaken the carbon-carbon bond somewhat, and are responsible in part for the un-

[1] It has been found by Dr. A. J. Stosick (unpublished work) by quantum-mechanical calculations that the stabilizing effect of the m-biphenyl group is predicted to differ only slightly from that of the phenyl group.

[2] Marvel, Ginsberg, and Mueller, *loc. cit.*

usual properties of these substances.[1] It is likely that the very large degree of dissociation reported for hexa-*o*-methylphenyle-thane[2] (as compared with hexa-*p*-methylphenylethane) is a steric effect.

[1] H. E. Bent and E. S. Ebers, *J.A.C.S.* **57,** 1242 (1935); G. W. Wheland, *J. Chem. Phys.* **2,** 474 (1934).

[2] Marvel, Mueller, Himel, and Kaplan, *loc. cit.*

CHAPTER V

INTERATOMIC DISTANCES AND THEIR RELATION TO THE STRUCTURE OF MOLECULES AND CRYSTALS

21. INTERATOMIC DISTANCES IN NORMAL COVALENT MOLECULES. COVALENT RADII

As a result of the development of the x-ray method of studying the structure of crystals and the band-spectroscopic method and especially the electron-diffraction method of studying gas molecules, a large amount of information regarding interatomic distances in molecules and crystals has been collected. It has been found that the values of interatomic distances corresponding to covalent bonds can be correlated in a simple way in terms of a set of values of *covalent bond radii* of atoms, as described below.[1]

The values found for the equilibrium distance between two atoms A and B connected by a covalent bond of fixed type (single, double, etc.) in different molecules and crystals are in most cases very nearly the same, so that it becomes possible to assign a constant value to the A—B bond distance for use in any molecule involving this bond. For example, the carbon-carbon distance in diamond (representing a single covalent bond) is 1.542 Å, and

---

[1] Interatomic-distance values obtained in various ways are reliable to an extent determined by the nature of the method. Spectroscopic values for diatomic molecules are usually accurate to within 0.01 Å or even 0.001 Å, and those for polyatomic molecules are somewhat less reliable. Electron-diffraction values for gas molecules may be assigned probable errors of from 0.01 to 0.05 Å or more, depending on the care with which the investigation has been carried out and the complexity of the molecule. X-ray values for crystals may be reliable to 0.001 Å, in case that the interatomic distance is determined directly by the size of the unit cell (as in diamond). In general, however, they depend also on some additional parameters evaluated with use of intensity data; they are then reliable to 0.01 Å only in exceptional cases. The probable errors for x-ray crystal structure values involving several parameters are around 0.01 to 0.05 Å for investigations carried out carefully in recent years, and 0.10 Å or more for others. X-ray diffraction values for gas molecules are reliable only to 0.1 or 0.2 Å.

the values found in the seventeen molecules given in Table 21-1 lie between 1.52 and 1.55 Å, all being equal to the diamond value to within their probable errors.   This constancy is of interest in view of the varied nature of the molecules.   Thus there is no significant difference between the values for the paraffins and those for the cyclic aliphatic compounds; even for the three-membered ring in cyclopropane, in which an increase in bond distance might be expected as a result of the strain resulting from the 60° bond angles (the heat of formation being 23 kcal./mole less than that calculated from the bond energies), the normal value is found.   Moreover, the results found for isobutene, tetra-methylethylene, the two 2-butenes, mesitylene (1,3,5-trimethyl-benzene), and hexamethylbenzene show that the single-bond distance from a methyl carbon to a carbon atom in an ethylenic or aromatic group has approximately the normal value.[1]

TABLE 21-1.—EXPERIMENTAL VALUES OF CARBON-CARBON
SINGLE BOND DISTANCES[2]

Substance	C—C distance
Diamond	1.542 Å
Ethane	1.55 ± 0.03 Å
Propane	1.54 ± 0.02
Isobutane	1.54 ± 0.02
Neopentane	1.54 ± 0.02
Cyclopropane	1.53 ± 0.03
Cyclopentane	1.52 ± 0.03
Cyclohexane	1.53 ± 0.03
Isobutene	1.54 ± 0.02
Tetramethylethylene	1.54 ± 0.02
Mesitylene	1.54 ± 0.01
Hexamethylbenzene	1.54 ± 0.01
Trans-2-butene[2]	1.53 ± 0.02
Cis-2-butene[2]	1.54 ± 0.02
Trans-2,3-epoxybutane[2]	1.53 ± 0.02
Cis-2,3-epoxybutane[2]	1.54 ± 0.02
Paraldehyde, $(CH_3CO)_3$	1.54 ± 0.02
Metaldehyde, $(CH_3CO)_4$	1.54 ± 0.03

[1] A change in distance is expected for a single bond between double bonds or aromatic nuclei, which then forms part of a conjugated system (Sec. 27).

[2] The first eleven hydrocarbon values are from the electron-diffraction study by L. Pauling and L. O. Brockway, *J.A.C.S.* 59, 1223 (1937).   The values reported earlier for some of these molecules by R. Wierl (*Ann. d. Phys.* 8, 521 (1931); 13, 453 (1932)) agree with these to within their some-what larger probable errors.   For mesitylene and hexamethylbenzene, as

It has been reported[1] that the spectroscopic study of methyl-acetylene leads to the value 1.462 ± 0.005 Å for the carbon-carbon single-bond distance in this substance, and this value has been verified recently by the electron diffraction method not only for methylacetylene but also for dimethylacetylene and dimethyldi-acetylene.[2]   This is 0.08 Å less than the value 1.54 Å expected in case that constancy of the single-bond distance were main-tained in the presence of an adjacent triple bond, as it seems to be, to within about 0.02 or 0.03 Å, for a single bond with adjacent double bond or aromatic nucleus.   The significance of this short-ening is not clear at the present time.

The shortening may be due in part to the use of a carbon bond orbital differing from a tetrahedral orbital in involving a larger amount of the $2s$ orbital (Secs. 14c, 21c).   The fact that the C—H distance in acetylene (1.06 Å) is 0.03 Å less than that in methane (1.09 Å) suggests, however, that this orbital effect is responsible for only about one-third of the shortening of the carbon-carbon single bond distance.   The remainder may be the result of partial double-bond character arising from resonance

$$\text{with structures such as } \overset{+}{\text{H}} \quad \overset{\displaystyle \text{H}}{\underset{\displaystyle \text{H}}{\vert \atop \vert}} \text{C}{=}\text{C}{=}\overset{..}{\text{C}}{-}\text{H} \quad \text{(Sec. 22).}$$

For a more detailed discussion see the paper by Pauling, Springall, and Palmer.[2]

Similar constancy is shown by other covalent bond distances (with certain exceptions which will be discussed later).   For the carbon-oxygen single bond, for example, the following values have been reported: 1.42 ± 0.03 Å in dimethyl ether;[3] 1.46 ± 0.04 Å in 1,4-dioxane,[3] 1.44 ± 0.02 Å in α-methylhydroxylamine,[4] and

---

well as p-xylene, P. L. F. Jones (*Trans. Faraday Soc.* **31**, 1036 (1935)) reported the value 1.50 Å. A careful x-ray study of crystals of hexa-methylbenzene has been carried out recently by L. O. Brockway and J. M. Robertson, *J. Chem. Soc.* **1939**, 1324, leading to 1.53 ± 0.02 Å for the single-bond distance.

[1] G. Herzberg, F. Patat, and H. Verleger, *J. Phys. Chem.* **41**, 123 (1937); R. M. Badger and S. H. Bauer, *J. Chem. Phys.* **5**, 599 (1937).

[2] L. Pauling, H. D. Springall, and K. J. Palmer, *J.A.C.S.* **61**, 927, April issue (1939).

[3] L. E. Sutton and L. O. Brockway, *J.A.C.S.* **57**, 473 (1935).

[4] L. O. Brockway, J. Y. Beach, and L. Pauling, *J.A.C.S.* **57**, 2693 (1935).

1.43 ± 0.02 Å in paraldehyde,[1] metaldehyde,[2] and the cis and trans-2,3-epoxybutanes;[3] all of these lie close to the value 1.43 Å accepted as standard

It is found, moreover that covalent bond distances are in general related to one another in an additive manner; the bond distance A—B is equal to the arithmetic mean of the distances A—A and B—B. For example, the C—C distance in diamond is 1.54 Å and the Si—Si distance in the element (with the diamond arrangement) is 2.34 Å. The arithmetic mean of these, 1.94 Å, is identical with the Si—C distance 1.93 ± 0.03 Å found in tetramethylsilane to within the probable error of the experimental value. In consequence it becomes possible to assign to the elements *covalent radii* such that the sum of two radii is equal to the equilibrium internuclear distance for the two corresponding atoms connected by a single covalent bond.

These covalent radii are for use in molecules in which the atoms form covalent bonds to a number determined by their positions in the periodic table—carbon four, nitrogen three, and so on. (The effect of change in covalence from the normal valence is discussed in Section 21b.) It is found empirically that the radii are applicable to covalent bonds with considerable ionic character; even in hydrogen fluoride, with the bond more ionic than covalent in type, the observed interatomic distance, 0.92 Å, is close to the sum of the radii, 0.94 Å. For extreme ionic bonds, however, ionic radii are to be used (Chap. X), and in some molecules, discussed in the following chapter, the partial ionic character plays an important part in determining the interatomic distances.

The radii are so chosen that their sums represent average internuclear distances for bonded atoms in molecules and crystals at room temperature. The atoms carry out thermal oscillations, which cause the internuclear distances to vary about their average values. These are at room temperature only slightly different from the values corresponding to the minima in the potential energy functions.

Values of the single-bond covalent radii of the non-metallic elements are given in Table 21-2. These values, which were origi-

[1] D. C. Carpenter and L. O. Brockway, *ibid.* **58,** 1270 (1936).

[2] L. Pauling and D. C. Carpenter, *ibid.* **58,** 1274 (1936).

[3] L. O. Brockway and P. C. Cross, *J.A.C.S.* **58,** 2407 (1936); **59,** 1147 (1937).

TABLE 21-2.—COVALENT RADII FOR ATOMS

H
0.30 Å

	B	C	N	O	F
Single-bond radius	0.88	0.771	0.70	0.66	0.64 Å
Double-bond radius	.76	.665	.60	.55	.54
Triple-bond radius	.68	.602	.547	.50	

	Si	P	S	Cl
Single-bond radius	1.17	1.10	1.04	0.99
Double-bond radius	1.07	1.00	0.94	.89
Triple-bond radius	1.00	0.93	.87	

	Ge	As	Se	Br
Single-bond radius	1.22	1.21	1.17	1.14
Double-bond radius	1.12	1.11	1.07	1.04

	Sn	Sb	Te	I
Single-bond radius	1.40	1.41	1.37	1.33
Double-bond radius	1.30	1.31	1.27	1.23

nally obtained largely from crystal data,[1] may be tested by comparison with the results of the many recent investigations of gas molecules as well as of crystals.[2]

[1] See the references of Table 21-1.

[2] Shortly after the formulation of a rough set of atomic radii for use in crystals of all types (W. L. Bragg, *Phil. Mag.* 40, 169 (1920)) it was recognized that the effective radius of an atom depends on its structure and environment, and especially on the nature of the bonds which it forms with adjacent atoms. Between 1920 and 1927 a complete set of values of ionic radii, for use in ionic molecules and crystals, was developed by Landé, Wasastjerna, Goldschmidt, and Pauling; this work is discussed in Chapter X. In 1926 M. L. Huggins (*Phys. Rev.* 28, 1086 (1926)) published a set of atomic radii for use in crystals containing covalent bonds. V. M. Goldschmidt in the same year published values of atomic radii obtained from metals as well as from covalent non-metallic crystals ("Geochemische Verteilungsgesetze der Elemente," *Skrifter det Norske Videnskaps-Akad. Oslo. I. Matem.-Naturvid. Klasse,* 1926); more recently he has collected these and additional values into a table of radii for use in metals and intermetallic compounds (*Trans. Faraday Soc.* 25, 253 (1929); see Chapter XII). A survey of the interatomic-distance values for covalent crystals was then made by L. Pauling and M. L. Huggins (*Z. Krist.* 87, 205 (1934)), leading to the formulation of the tables of tetrahedral radii, octahedral radii, and square radii given and described in Section 23, and by making small changes in the values of some of the tetrahedral radii, in the way indicated by the data available at that time for a few normal-valence molecules, values of single-bond normal covalent

TABLE 21-3.—BOND DISTANCES AND RADII FOR ELEMENTS

Bond	Substance	Method[1]	One-half of observed distance	Assigned radius
C—C	Diamond	X-ray	0.771 Å	0.77 Å
F—F	F_2(g)	E.D.[2]	.73	.64
Si—Si	Si(c)	X-ray	1.17	1.17
P—P	P_4(g)	E.D.[3]	1.10	1.10
P—P	P(c, black)	X-ray[4]	1.09, 1.10	1.10
S—S	S_8(c)	X-ray[5]	1.05	1.04
S—S	S_8(g)	E.D.[6]	1.05	1.04
Cl—Cl	Cl_2(g)	Sp.	0.992	0.99
Ge—Ge	Ge(c)	X-ray	1.22	1.22
As—As	As_4(g)	E.D.[3]	1.22	1.21
As—As	As(c)	X-ray	1.25	1.21
Se—Se	Se(c)	X-ray	1.16	1.17
Br—Br	Br_2(g)	Sp.	1.140	1.14
Sn—Sn	Sn(c)(grey)	X-ray	1.40	1.40
Sb—Sb	Sb(c)	X-ray	1.43	1.41
Te—Te	Te(c)	X-ray	1.38	1.37
I—I	I_2(g)	Sp.	1.33	1.33

[1] X-ray signifies the x-ray study of crystals, E.D. the electron-diffraction study of gas molecules, and Sp. the spectroscopic study of gas molecules.

[2] L. O. Brockway, *J.A.C.S.* 60, 1348 (1938).

[3] L. R. Maxwell, V. M. Mosley, and S. B. Hendricks, *J. Chem. Phys.* 3, 698 (1935).

[4] R. Hultgren and B. E. Warren, *Phys. Rev.* 47, 808 (1935); approximately the same value is found also in amorphous red phosphorus, amorphous black phosphorus, and liquid phosphorus: C. D. Thomas and N. S. Gingrich, *J. Chem. Phys.* 6, 659 (1938).

[5] B. E. Warren and J. T. Burwell, *J. Chem. Phys.* 3, 6 (1935).

[6] L. R. Maxwell, S. B. Hendricks, and V. M. Mosley, *Phys. Rev.* 49, 199 (1936).

References are not given for the older x-ray and spectroscopic values; they may be obtained from the standard compilations.

Comparison of the radii with half the interatomic distances in elementary molecules or crystals involving single bonds may be made as a first check on the radii (Table 21-3). For the fourth-

radii differing only slightly from those given in Table 21-2 were obtained (see also L. Pauling, *Proc. Nat. Acad. Sci.* 18, 293 (1932)). Since then the electron-diffraction study of gas molecules and further x-ray work on molecular crystals have provided many interatomic-distance values for testing and refining the table of radii. Values of some covalent radii were suggested also by N. V. Sidgwick and E. J. Bowen, *Ann. Reports Chem. Soc.* 28, 384 (1931); see Sidgwick, "The Covalent Link in Chemistry," Cornell, 1933, p. 82.

row elements, crystallizing with the diamond structure, and the halogens (other than fluorine) the agreement is perfect, since these were the sources of the values in the table. The crystals As, Sb, Se, and Te also show agreement to within the rather large probable errors of the experimental values. The electron-diffraction results for P_4, As_4, and S_8, obtained since the table was formulated, provide a good check of the corresponding radii.[1]

An extensive test of the single-bond covalent radii has been made recently by the electron-diffraction study of the methyl derivatives of the elements, with formulas $M(CH_3)_n$. The results of this study of thirteen substances[2] are shown in Table 21-4. It is seen that the agreement is excellent. By subtraction of the carbon radius, these M—C values could be used as the basis for formulating the table of single-bond radii.

The radius of the hydrogen atom is more variable than that of other atoms, as can be seen from the experimental values for M—H distances in compounds of hydrogen collected in Table 21-5. (The spectroscopic values are reliable to about 0.01 Å or less and the electron-diffraction values to 0.03 Å.) An average value 0.30 Å has been given in the table of radii.

The dependence of the covalent radii of the elements on atomic number is shown in Figure 21-1. It is seen that the relation is a simple one; for the first and second rows of the periodic table smooth curves can be drawn through the points, whereas for the other rows there is only a slight discontinuity between the quadrivalent atoms and their neighbors, which may perhaps be at-

[1] One important assumption made in the original formulation of the table of covalent radii was that the S—S single-bond distance is 2.08 Å, as in the crystals pyrite, FeS_2, and hauerite, MnS_2. This has been verified subsequently by measurements not only on $S_8(c)$ and $S_8(g)$ Table 21-3) but also on $S_8(l)$ and S_n (plastic) (S—S = 2.07 Å, 2.08 Å, N. S. Gingrich, *Phys. Rev.* **55**, 236 (1939); *J. Chem. Phys.* **8**, 29 (1940)) and on H_2S_2 (S—S = 2.05 ± 0.02 Å) and $(CH_3)_2S_2$ (S—S = 2.04 ± 0.03 Å. D. P. Stevenson and J. Y. Beach, *J.A.C.S.* **60**, 2872 (1938)).

[2] Similar agreement is also found for a great many other substances, such as hexamethylene tetramine (C—N = 1.47 Å), methylene chloride, chloroform, and carbon tetrachloride (C—Cl = 1.76 Å), etc.; the very extensive table which might be reproduced to show this agreement will be omitted. Lack of agreement is observed for bonds between very electronegative elements: the F—F bond in F_2 (observed, 1.46 ± 0.05 Å; sum of radii, 1.28 Å) and the O—F bond in OF_2 (observed, 1.41 ± 0.05 Å) and $FONO_2$ (observed, 1.42 ± 0.05 Å; sum of radii, 1.30 Å); the reason for this is unknown.

tributed to the change in the nature of the bond orbitals. This regularity in behavior of the covalent radii is to be contrasted with the irregularities shown by the bond-energy values.

TABLE 21-4.—BOND DISTANCES AND RADIUS SUMS FOR
METHYL COMPOUNDS[1]

C—C	N—C	O—C	F—C
1.54 ± 0.02	1.47 ± 0.02	1.42 ± 0.03	1.42 ± 0.02 Å
1.54	1.47	1.43	1.41
Si—C	P—C	S—C	Cl—C
1.93 ± 0.03	1.87 ± 0.02	1.82 ± 0.03	1.77 ± 0.02
1.94	1.87	1.81	1.76
Ge—C	As—C		Br—C
1.98 ± 0.03	1.98 ± 0.02		1.91 ± 0.02
1.99	1.98		1.91
Sn—C			I—C
2.18 ± 0.03			2.10 ± 0.03
2.17			2.10

[1] The upper value for each bond is that found experimentally for the methyl derivative of the indicated atom (C(CH₃)₄, N(CH₃)₃, etc.), and the lower value is the sum of the single-bond radii of Table 21-2. The experimental value for C—C is from L. Pauling and L. O. Brockway, *J.A.C.S.* **59**, 1223 (1937), that for Br—C is from H. A. Lévy and L. O. Brockway, *ibid.* **59**, 1662 (1937), those for P—C and As—C are from H. D. Springall and L. O. Brockway, *ibid.* **60**, 996 (1938), and the others are from the extensive investigation of methyl compounds carried on by L. O. Brockway and H. O. Jenkins, *J.A.C.S.* **58**, 2036 (1936).

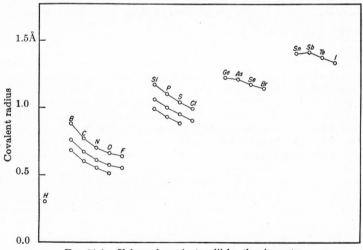

FIG. 21-1.—Values of covalent radii for the elements.

TABLE 21-5.—THE COVALENT RADIUS OF HYDROGEN

Compound	Method	Distance M—H	Radius of hydrogen
H_2	Sp.	0.74 Å	0.37 Å
NH_3	Sp.	1.01	.31
H_2O	Sp.	0.97	.31
HF	Sp.	.92	.28
HCl	Sp.	1.28	.29
HBr	Sp.	1.42	.28
HI	Sp.	1.62	.29
CH_4	Sp.	1.093	.32
C_2H_6	E.D.	1.09	.32
C_2H_4	Sp.[1]	1.087	.32
CH_2CCH_2	Sp.[1]	1.087	.32
C_6H_6	E.D.	1.08	.31
C_2H_2	Sp.	1.06	.29
HCN	Sp.	1.06	.29
H_2S	Sp.	1.35	.31

21a. Double-bond and Triple-bond Radii.—For the carbon-carbon triple bond in acetylene and the nitrogen-nitrogen triple bond in the nitrogen molecule the accurate spectroscopic values 1.204 Å and 1.094Å, respectively, have been reported.[2] These lead to the values 0.602 Å for the triple-bond radius of carbon and 0.547 Å for nitrogen; the sum of these, 1.149 Å, is close to the C≡N distance in hydrogen cyanide,[2] 1.154 Å. The spectroscopic values[3] 1.86 Å for the P≡P bond in P_2 and 1.49 Å for the P≡N bond in PN correspond to 0.93 Å for the triple-bond radius of phosphorus.

For the carbon-carbon double-bond distance the spectroscopic

---

[1] Values calculated from the vibrational frequencies of ethylene and allene (Sec. 21d) by E. H. Eyster, *J. Chem. Phys.* **6**, 580 (1938).

[2] G. Herzberg, F. Patat, and J. W. T. Spinks, *Z. f. Phys.* **91**, 386 (1934); F. Rasetti, *Phys. Rev.* **34**, 367 (1929). The electron-diffraction study of the nitrogen molecule has led to the value 1.095 ± 0.005 Å for the nitrogen-nitrogen triple-bond distance (V. Schomaker and D. P. Stevenson, unpublished investigation). The agreement with the spectroscopic value, with similar agreement found for other molecules (oxygen, chlorine, bromine, iodine, carbon dioxide) provides evidence that electron-diffraction values of interatomic distances are reliable to 0.005 Å in favorable cases, for which a single parameter determines the structure of the molecule.

[3] G. Herzberg, *Ann. d. Phys.* **15**, 677 (1932); J. Curry, L. Herzberg and G. Herzberg, *J. Chem. Phys.* **1**, 749 (1933); *Z. f. Phys.* **36**, 348 (1933).

values 1.325 ± 0.005 Å[1] and 1.331 ± 0.005 Å[2] for ethylene and 1.330 ± 0.005 A[1] for allene are available; the less accurate electron-diffraction values are 1.34 ± 0.02 Å for the two substances.[3] The carbon-oxygen double-bond distance has been assigned the values 1.21 ± 0.01 Å in formaldehyde,[4] 1.22 ± 0.01 Å in acetaldehyde,[5] and 1.20 ± 0.02 Å in glyoxal.[6] On the basis of these values the double-bond radii 0.665 Å for carbon and 0.55 Å for oxygen have been adopted. The other double-bond and triple-bond radii in Table 21-2 have been assigned reasonable values, in most cases less than the single-bond values by the amounts 0.10 and 0.17 Å, respectively. These radii are of use in the discussion of resonance in the following chapters.

21b. The Effect of Electric Charge on Covalent Radii.—The decrease in covalent radius in a sequence of atoms such as C, N, O, F in which the bonds are formed by use of orbitals of the same shell is to be attributed to an increase in the effective nuclear charge accompanying increase in atomic number. It is accordingly to be expected that anything which changes the effective nuclear charge acting on the valence electrons of an atom would also change the covalent radius of the atom. By the argument given in Section 11c it is found that unit positive charge on an atom with atomic number Z should lead to change in covalent radius of that atom toward that of the atom with atomic number $Z + 1$, this change being equal in magnitude to about one-half of the difference of the radii of the two atoms. Negative charge should have the opposite effect. For nitrogen with unit positive charge, for example, as in the tetramethylammonium ion, a decrease of about 0.02 Å in single-bond radius, from 0.70 Å to 0.68 Å, is predicted in this way. The C—N distance in the tetramethylammonium salts has not yet been determined with suffi-

[1] E. H. Eyster, *loc. cit.*

[2] H. W. Thompson, *Trans. Faraday Soc.* 35, 697 (1939).

[3] L. Pauling and L. O. Brockway, *J.A.C.S.* 59, 1223 (1937). A recent electron-diffraction study by V. Schomaker, as yet unpublished, has led to the value 1.330 ± 0.005 Å for the carbon-carbon double-bond distance in ethylene.

[4] D. P. Stevenson, J. E. LuValle, and V. Schomaker, *J.A.C.S.* **61**, 2508 (1939).

[5] D. P. Stevenson, H. D. Burnham, and V. Schomaker, *ibid.* **61**, 2922 (1939).

[6] J. E. LuValle and V. Schomaker, *ibid.* **61**, 3520 (1940).

cient accuracy to provide a test for this; it has been found,[1] however, that the carefully-determined value of the N—O distance in the nitrate ion is 0.03 Å less than expected for the type of single-bond—double-bond resonance involved (Sec. 25e), and this decrease is attributed to the positive formal charge of the nitrogen atom.

It is to be emphasized that the interatomic distance between two atoms of opposite electric charge is not appreciably affected by the charges, since the radius of one atom is increased and that of the other decreased by the charge effect. Thus in trimethyl-amine oxide, $(H_3C)_3N^+—\overset{\cdot\,\cdot}{\underset{\cdot\cdot}{O}}{\,\vphantom{O}}^-$, the normal value 1.36 Å would be expected for the N—O distance, whereas the C—N distance should be decreased from the normal single-bond value 1.47 Å by about 0.03 Å.

21c. The Effect of Incompleteness of the Valence Shell.—In boron trimethyl, with the electronic structure

$$\underset{\underset{\displaystyle CH_3}{|}}{\underset{\displaystyle B}{\overset{\displaystyle H_3C \qquad CH_3}{\diagdown\!\diagup}}} \quad,$$

the boron atom is surrounded by only six *L* electrons (three shared pairs), instead of a completed octet. It might well be anticipated that the single-bond radius of boron for use with these "sextet" bonds (Sec. 14b) would be different from the normal radius. The experimental value for the B—C distance in boron trimethyl is[2] 1.56 Å, corresponding to a boron sextet radius of 0.79 Å. This value is 0.09 Å less than the value given in Table 21-2 for the single-bond radius of boron, obtained by extrapolation from those for the other first-row atoms and applicable to a hypothetical boron atom with a completed octet but with zero electric charge. It seems probable that this difference is due to the presence of the sextet of electrons about the boron atom.

There are no other straightforward ways of determining this sextet correction at present, and its value, given by only one substance, must be considered to be somewhat uncertain. We shall, however, use the boron trimethyl value −0.09 Å to correct for

[1] Norman Elliott, *J.A.C.S.* **59**, 1380 (1937).
[2] H. A. Lévy and L. O. Brockway, *J.A.C.S.* **59**, 2085 (1937).

incompleteness of valence shells of first-row atoms in later sections.

21d. Interatomic Distances and Force Constants of Bonds.—It is seen on examining the available spectroscopic data for simple molecules that the force constants of bonds, which determine the frequencies of vibration of the nuclei in the molecules, are not independent of the corresponding interatomic distances, but are closely related to them.   Various equations expressing this relationship have been advanced.[1]   We select for discussion that of Badger,[2] which has the form

$$k_0 = 1.86 \times 10^5/(R - d_{ij})^3, \qquad (21\text{-}1)$$

in which k_0 is the force constant in dynes per cm., R the interatomic distance in Ångströms, and d_{ij} a constant dependent on the rows of the periodic table containing the two atoms, with values 0.34 for H—1 (that is, hydrogen with a first-row atom), 0.59 for H—2, 0.65 for H—3, 0.68 for 1—1, 0.90 for 1—2, and 1.18 for 2—2.

By virtue of the existence of this relationship experimental data regarding force constants of bonds can be used as a source of information about bond type and molecular structure in the same way as those regarding interatomic distances.   The structural interpretation of vibrational frequencies of polyatomic molecules can be made in general only if the information about the nature of the normal modes of vibration is sufficient to permit the calculation of bond force constants.

22. INTERATOMIC DISTANCES AND RESONANCE[3]

The resonance of the benzene molecule between the two Kekulé

[1] C. H. Douglas-Clark, *Phil. Mag.* **18**, 459 (1934); *Trans. Faraday Soc.* **31**, 1017 (1935); C. H. Douglas-Clark and J. L. Stoves, *Phil. Mag.* **22**, 1137 (1936); H. S. Allen and A. K. Longair, *Nature* **135**, 764 (1935); H. W. Thompson and J. W. Linnett, *J. Chem. Soc.* **1937**, 1396, 1399; G. B. B. M. Sutherland, *J. Chem. Phys.* **8**, 161 (1940).

[2] R. M. Badger, *J. Chem. Phys.* **2**, 128 (1934); a more refined expression has also been suggested by Badger, *ibid.* **3**, 710 (1935).

[3] L. Pauling, *Proc. Nat. Acad. Sci.* **18**, 293 (1932); L. Pauling, L. O. Brockway, and J. Y. Beach, *J.A.C.S.* **57**, 2705 (1935); L. Pauling and L. O. Brockway, *ibid.* **59**, 1223 (1937).   A somewhat different discussion of the effect of resonance on interatomic distances, based on the quantum-mechanical treatments of resonating molecules mentioned in Section 19a, has been published by W. G. Penney, *Proc. Roy. Soc.* **A158**, 306 (1937).

structures (the small contributions of other structures being neglected) can be considered to give each of the six carbon-carbon
bonds fifty percent single-bond character and fifty percent
double-bond character. We would expect that the carbon-
carbon interatomic distance would lie between the single-bond
value 1.54 Å and the double-bond value 1.33 Å: not midway between, but closer to the lower value, both because of the extra
stabilization due to the resonance energy (a strong bond having
smaller interatomic distance than a weak bond) and because of
greater effectiveness of the double-bond potential function (with
its greater curvature in the neighborhood of its minimum, corresponding to its larger force constant) in determining the position
of the minimum of the potential function for the resonating molecule. The observed value for benzene,[1] 1.39 ± 0.01 Å, is only
0.06 Å greater than the double-bond distance.

An empirical curve relating carbon-carbon interatomic distances with the amounts of single-bond and double-bond character for molecules resonating between structures some of which
represent the bond as a single bond and some as a double bond
could be used in interpreting observed values of the interatomic
distances to obtain information as to the type of the bonds.
The pure single-bond and double-bond distances provide the end
points of the curve, and a third point, at fifty percent double-
bond character, is provided by the value 1.39 Å for benzene. A
fourth point on the curve is given by the value 1.42 Å for graphite.
The structure of the graphite crystal is shown in Figure 22-1. It
consists of hexagonal layers of molecules which are separated by
a distance so large (3.40 Å) that there can be no covalent bonds
between them; each of the layers is a giant molecule, and the
superimposed layer molecules are held together only by weak van
der Waals forces. The four valences of each carbon atom are
used to form bonds with its three neighbors; the layer molecule
resonates among many valence-bond structures such as

<hr>

[1] R. Wierl, *Ann. d. Phys.* **8**, 521 (1931); L. Pauling and L. O. Brockway,
J. Chem. Phys. **2**, 867 (1934); the same value is reported for the benzene
nuclei in stilbene by J. M. Robertson, *Proc. Roy. Soc.* **A162**, 568 (1937),
and values within 0.02 Å have been obtained in the x-ray study of several
benzene derivatives. L. O. Brockway and J. M. Robertson, *J. Chem. Soc.*
1939, 1324, have recently found the value 1.39 ± 0.02 Å by x-ray investigation of hexamethylbenzene.

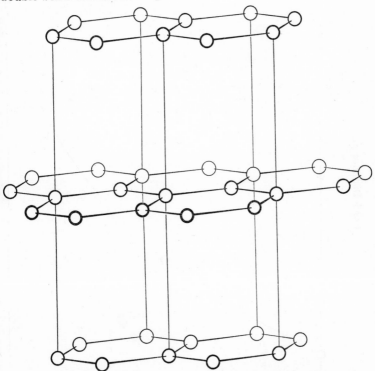

and in this way each carbon-carbon bond achieves one-third double-bond character.

Fig. 22-1.—The arrangement of carbon atoms in the graphite crystal.

Through these four points we draw a smooth curve, as shown in Figure 22-2, which we accept as representing the dependence of carbon-carbon interatomic distance on the amount of double-bond character for single-bond—double-bond resonance. The use of the curve in the discussion of the nature of the carbon-

174 *INTERATOMIC DISTANCES* [V-22]

carbon bonds in resonating molecules is illustrated in the following chapter.

In view of the reasonable behavior of interatomic-distance values in general, it seems probable that by a suitable translation and change of vertical scale (to give the correct end points) the same function can be used for bonds between other atoms, and also for resonance involving triple bonds.   These further uses of the curve are also illustrated in the following chapter.

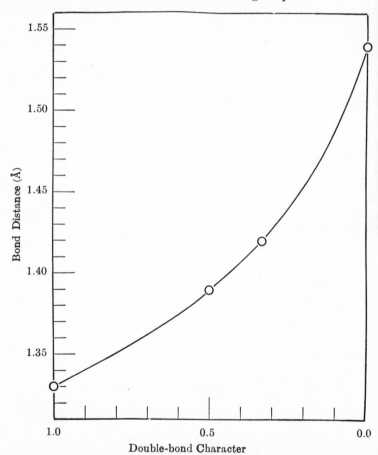

Fig. 22-2.—The relation between interatomic distance and amount of double-bond character for single-bond—double-bond resonance of carbon-carbon bonds.

It is interesting that the curve can be represented with only small deviations from the experimental points by the equation

$$R = R_1 - (R_1 - R_2)\frac{3x}{(2x + 1)}, \qquad (22\text{-}2)$$

in which R is the value of the interatomic distance for a bond of intermediate type, R_1 that for a single bond, R_2 that for a double bond, and x the amount of double-bond character. This equation can be derived in the following simple way. Let the potential function for a resonating bond be given as the sum of two parabolic functions, representing single-bond and double-bond potential functions, with coefficients $1-x$ and x respectively:

$$V(R) = \tfrac{1}{2}(1-x)k_1(R-R_1)^2 + \tfrac{1}{2}xk_2(R-R_2)^2. \qquad (22\text{-}3)$$

By equating to zero the derivative of this with respect to R, its equilibrium value (corresponding to the minimum of the potential function) can be found as a function of x and the ratio of the force constants k_2/k_1. The function becomes identical with that of Equation 22-2 when k_2/k_1 is given the value 3. This value for the ratio of the force constants is approximately that given by Badger's rule, about 2.3 to 2.8; it is possible that some increase is needed to compensate for the neglect of resonance energy in the assumed potential function.[1]

22a. The Conditions for Equivalence or Non-equivalence of Bonds.—It often happens that the most reasonable valence-bond structure which can be written for a molecule or crystal is one which makes bonds between like pairs of atoms non-equivalent. In this circumstance there is another structure equivalent to the first, and differing from it in the distribution of the non-equivalent

[1] The following table is given for convenience in using the resonance-interatomic distance curve; it corresponds to 0.20 Å difference in single-bond and double-bond distance:

x	$\dfrac{0.20\cdot 3x}{2x+1}$	$0.20 - \dfrac{0.20\cdot 3x}{2x+1}$	x	$\dfrac{0.20\cdot 3x}{2x+1}$	$0.20 - \dfrac{0.20\cdot 3x}{2x+1}$
0.00	0.000	0.200	0.40	0.133	0.067
.05	.027	.173	.45	.142	.058
.10	.050	.150	.50	.150	.050
.15	.069	.131	.60	.164	.036
.20	.086	.114	.70	.175	.025
.25	.100	.100	.80	.185	.015
.30	.113	.087	.90	.193	.007
.35	.124	.078	1.00	.200	.000

bonds (or there may be several other equivalent structures). An example is provided by benzene, the two Kekulé structures being the most stable valence-bond structures for this molecule, and another example is sulfur dioxide, for which the reasonable structures

$$\overset{\cdot\cdot}{S^+} \quad \text{and} \quad \overset{\cdot\cdot}{S^+} \quad \text{may be written;}$$

$$-{:}\overset{\cdot\cdot}{O}{:} \quad \overset{\cdot\cdot}{O}{:} \qquad {:}\overset{\cdot\cdot}{O} \quad {:}\overset{\cdot\cdot}{O}{:}-$$

many other molecules of this type are discussed in the following chapters.

Let us consider a molecule A_2B, for which the two equivalent structures A—B—A (I) and A—B—A (II) may be written, each involving two bonds of which one is stronger than the other. We now ask whether the two A atoms in the molecule are to be considered as equivalent or not; that is, whether the two bonds from the atom B to the two atoms A are equivalent or not.

This question, to be intelligible, needs to be discussed in detail. The principles of quantum mechanics require that the normal state of the isolated molecule have a resonance structure to which the equivalent structures I and II contribute equally. The interpretation of this resonance depends on the magnitude of the resonance energy. If the resonance energy is very large, the molecule resonates between the alternative structures with such a high frequency that no experiment can be devised to detect the individual structures I and II. (The frequency of resonance is the resonance energy divided by Planck's constant h.) The two bonds A—B are then made completely equivalent by resonance. This is the situation in benzene and sulfur dioxide.

If, on the other hand, the resonance integral is very small, the resonance between structures I and II occurs so rarely that it is convenient to refer to the substance as containing tautomeric or isomeric molecules, with structures which are represented essentially by I or II alone. The relation of resonance to tautomerism and the distinction between tautomerism and isomerism are discussed in Section 57.

It is convenient for us to draw a (rather broad) line between resonance (in the sense of resonance of a molecule among alternative valence-bond structures) and tautomerism with use of the ratio of the resonance frequency to the frequency of nuclear motion. If the resonance frequency is much greater than the frequency of oscillation of the nuclei, the molecule will be represented by the resonating structure {A—B—A, A—B—A} and the two bonds in the molecule will be equivalent, whereas if it is much less the two atoms A will oscillate for some time about equilibrium positions relative to B which are not equivalent, and will then interchange their rôles.

The discussion can be made more definite by considering the forces between B and the two attached atoms. Structure I alone corresponds to a potential function which brings the equilibrium position of one atom (A' for the molecule A—B—A') closer to B than that for A, whereas structure II places A closer than A' to B. If the resonance energy is small, the molecule will oscillate for a while in a way corresponding to a small distance B—A' and a larger distance A—B, and then oscillate about new equilibrium positions, with A—B smaller than B—A'. This corresponds to tautomerism. If the resonance energy is sufficiently large, however, the potential function for nuclear oscillation will be changed, and the two atoms A and A' will oscillate in equivalent fashion about equilibrium positions equidistant from B. The two bonds in the molecule are then equivalent. The magnitude of resonance integral required to achieve this depends on (among other factors) the difference in the equilibrium configurations of the alternative structures. Thus the configurations of the carbon nuclei corresponding to the two Kekulé structures separately (with C—C = 1.54 Å and C=C = 1.33 Å) would place the carbon atoms only about 0.1 Å from their actual positions (with C—C = 1.39 Å). This distance (0.1 Å) is less than the usual amplitude of nuclear oscillation (about 0.2 Å), so that with each libration of the nuclei the molecule would pass through the configuration appropriate to each of the Kekulé structures. On the other hand, tautomerism may be expected when the stable configurations differ largely from one another.

It has been reported by Braune and Pinnow[1] that the molecules UF_6, WF_6, and probably MoF_6 have octahedral structures which are not regular, but have holohedral orthorhombic symmetry,

[1] H. Braune and P. Pinnow, *Z. phys. Ch.* B **35**, 239 (1937).

the three pairs of M—F distances having the ratios 1:1.12:1.22. It can not be decided from simple *a priori* considerations that this structure is incorrect; it is possible that the central atom would tend to form three kinds of bonds in pairs, and that the resonance energy among the three corresponding structures would be so small that the potential function would not be changed from that for one of the individual structures. This seems improbable, however, and I think that further experimental work is needed before the reported structure is accepted.

The inequality of the apical and equatorial P-Cl distances in phosphorus pentachloride is not cast in doubt by the same argument, since these directions are not geometrically equivalent even for equality of the distances.

23. TETRAHEDRAL AND OCTAHEDRAL COVALENT RADII

23a. Tetrahedral Radii.—In crystals with the diamond, sphalerite, or wurtzite (Fig. 23-1) arrangement each atom is surrounded tetrahedrally by four other atoms. If the atoms are those of fourth-column elements or of two elements symmetrically arranged relative to the fourth column, the number of valence electrons is right to permit the formation of a tetrahedral covalent bond between each atom and its four neighbors. The diamond arrangement is shown by C, Si, Ge, and Sn, and the sphalerite or the wurtzite arrangement (or both) by the compounds SiC, AlN, AlP, AlAs, AlSb, GaP, GaAs, GaSb, InSb, ZnO, ZnS, ZnSe, ZnTe, CdS, CdSe, CdTe, HgS, HgSe, HgTe, CuCl, CuBr, CuI, AgI, MgTe, BeO, BeS, BeSe, and BeTe. In all of these except BeO it is probable that the bonds are essentially covalent in structure.

In ZnS, for example, the extreme covalent structure

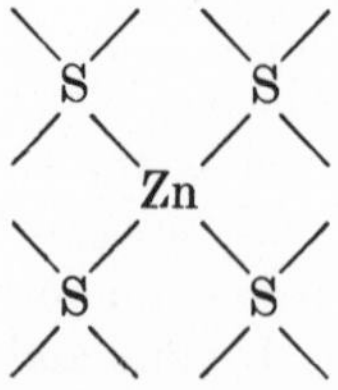

$$\begin{array}{ccc} \diagdown\diagup & \diagdown\diagup \\ S & S \\ \diagup\diagdown & \diagup\diagdown \\ & Zn & \\ \diagdown\diagup & \diagdown\diagup \\ S & S \\ \diagup\diagdown & \diagup\diagdown \end{array}$$

places formal charges 2− on zinc and 2+ on sulfur. It is probable that the bonds have enough ionic character in this crystal and the others of similar structure to make the actual charges of the atoms much smaller.

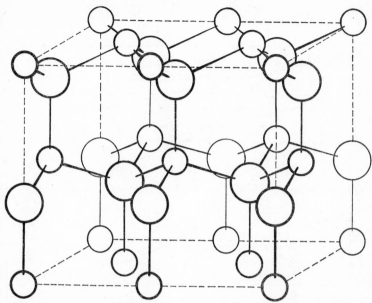

Fig. 23-1.—The arrangement of zinc atoms (small circles) and sulfur atoms (large circles) in the hexagonal crystal wurtzite. Sphalerite, the cubic modification of zinc sulfide, has a closely related structure.

A set of values of tetrahedral covalent radii[1] for use in crystals of these types is given in Table 23-1 and represented graphically in Figure 23-2. These values were obtained from the observed

TABLE 23-1.—TETRAHEDRAL COVALENT RADII

	Be	B	C	N	O	F
	1.06	0.88	0.77	0.70	0.66	0.64
	Mg	Al	Si	P	S	Cl
	1.40	1.26	1.17	1.10	.04	0.99
Cu	Zn	Ga	Ge	As	Se	Br
1.35	1.31	1.26	1.22	1.18	1.14	1.11
Ag	Cd	In	Sn	Sb	Te	I
1.53	1.48	1.44	1.40	1.36	1.32	1.28
Au	Hg	Tl	Pb	Bi		
1.50	1.48	1.47	1.46	1.46		

[1] M. L. Huggins, *Phys. Rev.* **28**, 1086 (1926); L. Pauling and M. L. Huggins, *Z. Krist.* **87**, 205 (1934).

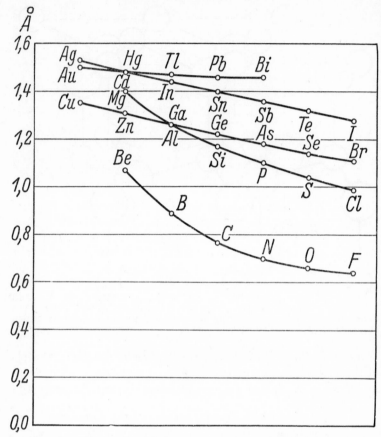

Fig. 23-2.—Values of tetrahedral covalent radii for sequences of atoms.

interatomic distances in crystals of these tetrahedral types and of other types in which the atom of interest forms four covalent bonds with neighboring atoms which surround it tetrahedrally. For example, in pyrite, FeS_2, each sulfur atom is surrounded tetrahedrally by three iron atoms and one sulfur atom, with all of which it forms essentially covalent bonds; the substance is a derivative of hydrogen disulfide, H_2S_2. That the Fe—S bonds are essentially covalent is shown by the magnetic criterion; the substance is only slightly paramagnetic, which corresponds to the formation of octahedral $3d^2 4s 4p^3$ bonds by the ferrous iron ($\mu = 0$) rather than to ionic bonds ($\mu = 4.90$). The sulfur-sulfur distance in this crystal is 2.09 Å or 2.10 Å, which agrees well with the value from the table, 2.08 Å.

It is found that for the substances listed above (omitting BeO) and many others the tetrahedral radius sums agree closely with the experimentally determined values of the interatomic distances (which were, of course, used in their derivation), the average deviation being about 0.02 Å.

The tetrahedral radii for first and second row elements are identical with the normal single-bond covalent radii given in Table 21-2. For the heavier atoms there are small differences, amounting to 0.03 Å for bromine and 0.05 Å for iodine. It is possible that these differences are due to the difference in the nature of the bond orbitals in tetrahedral and normal covalent compounds.

23b. Octahedral Radii.—In pyrite each iron atom is surrounded by six sulfur atoms, which are at the corners of a nearly regular octahedron, corresponding to the formation by iron of $3d^2 4s 4p^3$ bonds. The iron-sulfur distance is 2.27 Å, from which, by subtraction of the tetrahedral radius of sulfur, 1.04 Å, the value 1.23 Å for the $d^2 sp^3$ octahedral covalent radius of bivalent iron is obtained.

From similar data for other crystals with the pyrite structure or a closely related structure (of the marcasite or arsenopyrite types), given in Table 23-3,[1] values can be obtained for the octahedral radii of other transition-group elements. The elements

---

[1] In some cases the M—X distance given in Table 23-3 has been directly determined by x-ray methods; in others, where the parameter has not been accurately evaluated, it has been calculated from the lattice constant by use of a value for the S—S (Se—Se, etc.) distance given by the table of tetrahedral radii.

A recent careful investigation of marcasite (M. J. Buerger, *Z. Krist.* **97**, 504 (1937); *Am. Mineral.* **16**, 361 (1931)) has led to the values 2.25 and 2.23 Å for the Fe—S bond distances, in approximate agreement with that in pyrite, 2.27 Å, and the value 2.21 Å for the S—S distance. This is 0.13 Å larger than twice the sulfur covalent radius whereas the pyrite value, 2.10 Å, has the expected magnitude; the significance of this reported deviation is uncertain.

Buerger (loc. cit.) has tabulated the following values for marcasite-type crystals of quadrivalent iron, taken from the investigations of G. Hägg, *Nova Acta Reg. Soc. Sci. Upsaliensis* **7**, 78 (1929) and M. J. Buerger, *Z. Krist.* **82**, 165 (1932):

	FeP_2	$FeAs_2$	$FeSb_2$
Fe—X	2.24, 2.29	2.33, 2.37	2.57, 2 62 Å
X—X	2.17	2.47	2.78

The values of the X—X distances reported for these crystals too are somewhat larger than expected from the table of radii, except for FeP_2.

Fe^{II} and Co^{III} in the indicated valence states are iso-electronic; it is interesting that there is very little difference in their radii, the decrease in radius with unit increase in atomic number being only 0.01 Å. The same very small decrease is shown in the two sequences Ru^{II}, Rh^{III}, Pd^{IV} and Os^{II}, Ir^{III}, Pt^{IV}, which, moreover, have identical values of the radii.[1]

TABLE 23-2.—OCTAHEDRAL COVALENT RADII

Fe^{II}	1.23 Å	Ru^{II}	1.33 Å	Os^{II}	1.33 Å
Co^{III}	1.22	Rh^{III}	1.32	Ir^{III}	1.32
Ni^{IV}	1.21	Pd^{IV}	1.31	Pt^{IV}	1.31
Co^{II}	1.32			Au^{IV}	1.40
Ni^{III}	1.30				
Ni^{II}	1.39				
Fe^{IV}	1.20				

For all of these atoms the number of electrons is such that all of the stable orbitals are occupied by unshared pairs or are used in bond formation. In CoS$_2$, CoSe$_2$, NiAsS, and AuSb$_2$ the atoms Co^{II}, Ni^{III}, and Au^{IV} contain one more electron than can be fitted into the three $3d$ orbitals ($5d$ for Au) that are left after the d^2sp^3 orbitals are usurped by the bonds. It is not known whether this extra electron is pushed into an outer orbital ($4d$) or whether a compromise is reached, the bonds relinquishing some $3d$ orbital to the electron. The effect of the extra electron is to produce an increase of 0.09 or 0.10 Å in the octahedral covalent radius for each of these atoms. The two extra electrons in Ni^{II} produce a total increase of twice as much, 0.18 Å.

A deficiency of electrons, on the other hand, has, as might be expected, little effect on the radius. The value found for Fe^{IV} is about 1.20 Å, only slightly less than that for Fe^{II}. The values[2] 2.36 Å and 2.51 Å for the Os—Cl distance in K$_2$OsCl$_6$ and the Os—Br distance in K$_2$OsBr$_6$, respectively, lead to the same value, 1.37 Å, for the octahedral radius of quadrivalent osmium; whereas the value 2.28 Å for the Os—Cl distance[3] in K$_2$OsO$_2$Cl$_4$ gives 1.29 Å for the octahedral radius of sexavalent osmium. These lie within 0.04 Å of the radius of bivalent osmium.

[1] The value for Ni^{IV} in the table is extrapolated and those of Rh^{III} and Ir^{IV} are interpolated.

[2] J. D. McCullough, *Z. Krist.* 94, 143 (1936).

[3] J. L. Hoard and J. D. Grenko, *Z. Krist.* 87, 100 (1934).

TABLE 23-3.—INTERATOMIC DISTANCES IN PYRITE-TYPE CRYSTALS

Substance	Distance M—X	Radius of M	Substance	Distance M—X	Radius of M
FeS$_2$	2.27	1.23	PtP$_2$	2.38	1.28
			PtAs$_2$	2.49	1.31
CoAsS	2.40	1.24	PtSb$_2$	2.67	1.31
	2.26	1.24			
			CoS$_2$	2.37	1.33
RuS$_2$	2.35	1.31	CoSe$_2$	2.45	1.31
RuSe$_2$	2.48	1.34			
RuTe$_2$	2.64	1.32	NiAsS	2.48	1.30
				2.34	1.30
PdAs$_2$	2.49	1.31			
PdSb$_2$	2.67	1.31	NiS$_2$	2.42	1.38
			NiSe$_2$	2.53	1.39
OsS$_2$	2.37	1.33			
OsSe$_2$	2.48	1.34	AuSb$_2$	2.76	1.40
OsTe$_2$	2.65	1.33			
			FeP$_2$	2.27	1.17
			FeAs$_2$	2.36	1.18
			FeSb$_2$	2.60	1.24

The octahedral radii of the table are applicable to complex ions such as $[PtCl_6]^{--}$. The radius sum Pt^{IV}—Cl is 2.30 Å, and the several reported experimental values for salts of chloroplatinic acid range from 2.26 Å to 2.35 Å. The radii can also be applied to the sulfides, selenides, and tellurides of quadrivalent palladium and platinum (PdS_2, etc.), which crystallize with the cadmium iodide structure, consisting of layers of MX_6 octahedra so packed together that each X is common to three octahedral complexes. The average deviation between radius sums and reported distances for these substances is about 0.02 Å.

For ferrous iodide, on the other hand, the observed interatomic distance, 2.88 Å, is much greater than the radius sum 2.56 Å. This shows that the bonds in the octahedral complexes (the crystals have the cadmium iodide structure) are not d^2sp^3 covalent bonds; and the observed paramagnetism of the substance ($\mu = 5.4$) supports the conclusion that the bonds are essentially ionic. The essentially ionic character of the bonds in all the halides of manganese, iron, cobalt, and nickel is similarly indicated by the magnetic data and the interatomic distances.

From the observed values of interatomic distances in complex ions such as $[SnCl_6]^{--}$, $[PbBr_6]^{--}$, and $[SeBr_6]^{--}$ and from crystals such as TiS_2 with the cadmium iodide structure the octahedral

radii given in Table 23–4 have been obtained.[1]   These correspond
not to d^2sp^3 bonds, involving d orbitals of the shell within the
valence shell, but to sp^3d^2 orbitals, use being made of the unstable d orbitals of the valence shell itself.

TABLE 23-4.—ADDITIONAL OCTAHEDRAL RADII

Ti^{IV}	1.36 Å	Sn^{IV}	1.45 Å	Se^{IV}	1.40 Å
Zr^{IV}	1.48	Pb^{IV}	1.50	Te^{IV}	1.52

For Sn^{IV} and Pb^{IV} these radii are greater than the corresponding tetrahedral sp^3 radii by the factor 1.03.

There is a pair of unshared electrons in Se^{IV} (in the ion
$[SeBr_6]^{--}$) occupying the $4s$ orbital, which is hence not available
for use in forming $4s4p^34d^2$ bonds.   It has been suggested to me
by Dr. J. Y. Beach that the role of the s orbital in bond formation
is here being played by the $5s$ orbital, the bonds being $4p^34d^25s$
bonds; the large value of the radius (23 percent greater than the
tetrahedral radius of selenium) is to be expected from this point
of view.   A similar effect is shown by Te^{IV}.

In a molecule such as $As(CH_3)_3$ the unshared pair of electrons
in the valence shell occupies the $4s$ orbital and in this way plays
an important part in determining the configuration of the molecule; the As—C bonds are p bonds (with perhaps a small amount
of s character), and make angles of 100° with one another,
whereas in $B(CH_3)_3$, with the $2s$ orbital not occupied by an
unshared pair, the sp^2 bonds are coplanar.   An s unshared pair
in a molecule of this sort is not an "inert pair"[2] so far as stereochemistry is concerned.   On the other hand, the $4s$ pair of sele-

---

[1] The following values of R—Cl distances in cubic crystals M_2RCl_6 have
been reported by G. Engel, *Z. Krist.* **90**, 341 (1935):

	M=K	NH$_4$	Rb	Cs	Tl
R=Ti			2.33	2.35 Å	
Se		2.38	2.39	2.41	
Zr			2.44	2.45	
Sn	2.45	2.41	2.42	2.43	2.39
Te		2.54	2.51	2.51	2.48
Pt	2.33	2.36	2.32	2.34	2.29
Pb		2.48	2.50	2.50	

These are in general agreement with the values of earlier investigators,
such as R. G. Dickinson, *J.A.C.S.* **44**, 276 (1922), who found Sn—Cl
= 2.44 and 2.46 Å for K_2SnCl_6 and $(NH_4)_2SnCl_6$, respectively.

[2] N. V. Sidgwick, "Ann. Reports Chem. Soc." **30**, 120 (1933).

ium in the $[SeBr_6]^{--}$ ion is really an inert pair, since the $5s$ orbital replaces the $4s$ orbital for purposes of bond-formation and the configuration (but not the size) of the complex is the same as it would be if the inert pair were not present. A striking case of this behavior is presented by the compounds $(NH_4)_2SbBr_6$ and Rb_2SbBr_6. The observed diamagnetism of the substances[1] shows that $[SbBr_6]^{--}$ ions, which would contain one unpaired electron, are not present; moreover, the structure of the crystals is found on x-ray examination to be similar to that of potassium chloroplatinate. The substances accordingly contain the two octahedral complex ions $[SbBr_6]^-$ and $[SbBr_6]^{---}$, the former with $5s5p^35d^2$ bonds and the latter with an inert $5s$ pair of electrons and $5p^35d^26s$ bonds.

It is probable that the $[Bi(SCN)_6]^{---}$ ion is octahedral, showing a truly inert pair. The configurations of $SeCl_4$, $[AsCl_4]^-$, and similar molecules and complexes have not been determined; it will be interesting to see whether or not the outer unshared pair is stereochemically inert.

23c. Other Covalent Radii.—Bivalent nickel, palladium, and platinum and trivalent gold form four coplanar dsp^2 bonds, directed to the corners of a square, with attached atoms. It is found on examining the observed values of interatomic distances that *square dsp^2 radii of atoms have the same values as the corresponding octahedral d^2sp^3 radii*, as given in Table 23–2. This is shown by the following comparisons:

Substance	Observed distance	Radius sum
PdO[2]	2.00 Å	1.98 Å
PdS[3]	2.26, 2.29, 2.34, 2.43	2.36
PdCl$_2$[4]	2.31	2.31
K$_2$PdCl$_4$	2.29	2.31
(NH$_4$)$_2$PdCl$_4$	2.35	2.31
PtS	2.32	2.36
K$_2$PtCl$_4$	2.32	2.31

No reliable data are available for bivalent nickel, but it is probable that the equality holds for it also.

[1] N. Elliott, *J. Chem. Phys.* **2**, 298 (1934).
[2] L. Pauling and M. L. Huggins, *loc. cit.*
[3] T. F. Gaskell, *Z. Krist.* **96**, 203 (1937); F. A. Bannister, *ibid.* **96**, 201 (1937).
[4] A. F. Wells, *ibid.* **100**, 189 (1938).

In molybdenite and tungstenite the metal atom is surrounded by six sulfur atoms at the corners of a right trigonal prism with axial ratio unity (Fig. 15–6).[1] From the observed interatomic distances the trigonal-prism radius values 1.37 Å for Mo^{IV} and 1.44 Å for W^{IV} are obtained.

The average Mo—C bond distance in $K_4Mo(CN)_8 \cdot 2H_2O$ is 2.15 A,[2] which corresponds to the value 1.38 Å for the octacovalent radius of Mo^{IV}. The close approximation of this value to the trigonal-prism radius indicates that the bond orbitals are nearly the same for the two types of coordination.

In Cu_2O and Ag_2O crystals each oxygen atom is surrounded tetrahedrally by four metal atoms, each of which is midway between two oxygen atoms, with which it probably forms two covalent bonds of the sp type.[3] The interatomic distances in these crystals lead to the radius values 1.18 and 1.39 Å for Cu^I and Ag^I, which are 0.17 and 0.14 Å less than the tetrahedral radii. The magnitude of this decrease is reasonable in comparison with that found for the change from sp^3 to sp^2 bonds for boron, -0.09 Å (Sec. 21c.).

23d. The Anomalous Manganese Radius.—At the time of the formulation of the tables of covalent radii it was pointed out[4] that the manganese-sulfur distance in hauerite, MnS_2, with the pyrite structure, is surprisingly large. Its magnitude has since been verified[5] and an x-ray study leading to similarly large interatomic distances has been made of manganese diselenide and manganese ditelluride,[6] which also have the pyrite structure. The values found, 2.59 Å for Mn—S, 2.70 Å for Mn—Se, and 2.90 Å for Mn—Te, correspond to 1.55, 1.56, and 1.58 A for the octahedral radius of bivalent manganese; whereas by extrapolation of the values in Table 23–2 there is obtained 1.24 Å for the d^2sp^3 radius of univalent manganese, which should not be different from that of bivalent manganese by more than 0.01 or 0.02 Å

The solution to this difficulty is found by application of the magnetic criterion for bond type. It was shown by Elliott that

[1] R. G. Dickinson and L. Pauling, *J.A.C.S.* **45**, 1466 (1923).

[2] J. L. Hoard and H. H. Nordsieck, *J.A.C.S.* **61**, 2853 (1939).

[3] The two bond orbitals $\frac{1}{2}(s + p_z)$ and $\frac{1}{2}(s - p_z)$ make complete use of the s orbital. They have opposed bond directions and strength 1.95.

[4] L. Pauling and M. L. Huggins, *loc. cit.*

[5] F. Offner, *Z. Krist.* **89**, 182 (1934).

[6] N. Elliott, *J.A.C.S.* **59**, 1958 (1937).

the available magnetic data for hauerite, interpreted by the Weiss-Curie equation, lead to the value 6.1 Bohr magnetons for the magnetic moment of manganese. This is far from the predicted value for d^2sp^3 bonds, 1.73, but close to that for ionic bonds, 5.92, and it shows that the electronic structure of this crystal, and presumably also of the diselenide and the ditelluride, is entirely different from that of pyrite.[1]

The sulfur-sulfur, selenium-selenium, and tellurium-tellurium distances observed in the manganese compounds provide further evidence for this structural interpretation. They correspond to radii which agree more satisfactorily with the normal-valence radii than with the tetrahedral radii of the non-metallic atoms, indicating that the atoms are not forming tetrahedral covalent bonds:

	Distance $\dfrac{X-X}{2}$	Tetrahedral radius	Normal covalent radius
Sulfur	1.04 Å	1.04 Å	1.04 Å
Selenium	1.19	1.14	1.17
Tellurium	1.37	1.32	1.37

24. VAN DER WAALS AND NON-BONDED RADII OF ATOMS

In a molecule of chlorine, with the electronic structure :Cl̈:Cl̈:, the covalent radius of chlorine may be described as representing roughly the distance from the chlorine nucleus to the pair of electrons which is shared with the other chlorine atom. In a crystal of the substance the molecules are attracted together by their van der Waals interactions, and assume equilibrium positions at which the attractive forces[2] are balanced by the characteristic repulsive forces between atoms, resulting from interpenetration of their electron shells. Let us call one-half of the equilibrium internuclear distance between two chlorine atoms in such van der Waals contact, corresponding to the relative positions

---

[1] The bonds from manganese to the surrounding atoms need not be of the extreme ionic type; resonance with covalent bonds of the $4s4p^34d^2$ type, which have the same magnetic properties, could occur.

[2] These are mainly the London dispersion forces, the nature of which we shall not discuss. See F. London, *Z. f. Phys.* **63**, 245 (1930); Pauling and Wilson, "Introduction to Quantum Mechanics," Sec. 47.

$$:\overset{\cdot\cdot}{\underset{\cdot\cdot}{Cl}}:\overset{\cdot\cdot}{\underset{\cdot\cdot}{Cl}}: \qquad :\overset{\cdot\cdot}{\underset{\cdot\cdot}{Cl}}:\overset{\cdot\cdot}{\underset{\cdot\cdot}{Cl}}:$$

for two molecules, the *van der Waals radius* of chlorine.

It is expected that the van der Waals radius be larger than the covalent radius, since it involves the interposition of two electron pairs between the atoms rather than one.   Moreover, the van der Waals radius of chlorine should be about equal to its ionic radius, inasmuch as the bonded atom presents the same face to the outside world in directions away from its bond as the ion, $:\overset{\cdot\cdot}{\underset{\cdot\cdot}{Cl}}:^-$, does in all directions.

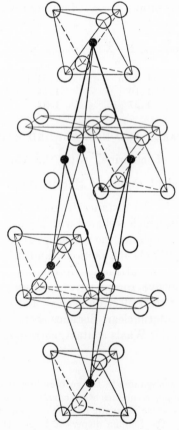

Fig. 24-1.—The atomic arrangement in the cadmium chloride crystal. Small circles represent cadmium atoms, large circles chlorine atoms.

The ionic radius of chlorine has the value 1 81 Å (Chap.). The value of the effective van der Waals radius of chlorine in the crystalline element, the structure of which has not been accurately determined, is not known. The following distances between chlorine atoms of different molecules have been observed in the molecular crystal 1, 2, 3, 4, 5, 6-hexachlorocyclohexane:[1] 3.60, 3.77, 3.82 Å; these are close to twice the ionic radius, 3.62 Å. Similar agreement is shown by inorganic covalent crystals. Cadmium chloride, for example, consists of layers of $CdCl_6$ octahedra condensed together by sharing each chlorine atom among three (Fig. 24-1). These layers are superimposed, with only the weak van der Waals forces holding them together. (The crystals show pronounced basal cleavage, resulting from this layer structure.) The distance between chlorine atoms of different layers is 3.76 Å, which is only slightly larger than the ionic value 3.62 Å.

Other non-metallic elements also are found to have van der Waals radii approximately equal to their ionic radii. For sulfur, for example, in the layer crystal molybdenite, the van der Waals radius effective between layers is 1.75 Å, which is slightly less than the ionic radius 1.85 Å; this decrease may be due to the fact that the sulfur atom, forming three covalent bonds, has only one unshared pair left to take care of its van der Waals contacts.

TABLE 24-1.—VAN DER WAALS RADII OF ATOMS

		H	1.2 Å		
N	1.5 Å	O	1.40 Å	F	1.35 Å
P	1.9	S	1.85	Cl	1.80
As	2.0	Se	2.00	Br	1.95
Sb	2.2	Te	2.20	I	2.15

Radius of methyl group, CH_3, 2.0 Å.
Half-thickness of aromatic molecule, 1.85 Å.

The value of the effective van der Waals radius of an atom in a crystal depends on the strength of the attractive forces holding the molecules together, and also on the orientation of the contact relative to the covalent bond or bonds formed by the atom (as discussed below); it is accordingly much more variable than the corresponding covalent radius. In Table 24-1 there are given the ionic radii of non-metallic elements for use as van der Waals

[1] R. G. Dickinson and C. Bilicke, *J.A.C.S.* 50, 764 (1928).

radii.   They have been rounded off to the nearest 0.05 Å, and
are to be considered as reliable only to 0.05 or 0.10 Å.[1] For the
elements of the nitrogen group values about 0.2 Å less than the
ionic radii are included, as indicated by the few available experimental data.

The methyl group as a whole can be assigned the radius 2.0 Å.
In metaldehyde,[2] for example, each methyl group is surrounded
by eight methyl groups of other molecules, two at 3.90 Å, four
at 4.03 Å, and two at 4.11 A, and in hexamethylbenzene[3] the
methyl-methyl distances between molecules lie between 4.0 and
4.1 Å.   The methylene group, CH_2, may be assigned the same
van der Waals radius as the methyl group, 2.0 Å.   This value is
substantiated by the following distances representing intermolecular contacts: CH_2—CH_2 = 3.96, CH_2—O = 3.32, 3.33, CH_2—N
= 3.55, 3.69 A in diketopiperazine,[4] and CH_2—CH_2 = 4.05,
CH_2—O = 3.38, 3.52 Å in glycine.[5]

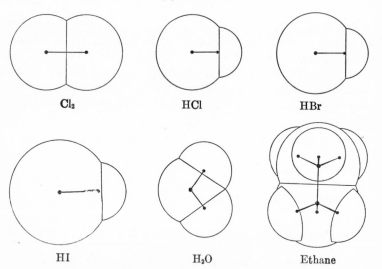

Cl₂   HCl   HBr

HI   H₂O   Ethane

Fɪɢ. 24-2.—Drawings of representative molecules, with atoms shown as spheres
with radii equal to their van der Waals radii.

[1] Interatomic distances between atoms in different molecules have been
discussed briefly by several authors, including S. B. Hendricks, *Chem. Rev.*
7, 431 (1930); M. L. Huggins, *ibid.* **10**, 427 (1932); and N. V. Sidgwick,
Ann. Rep. Chem. Soc. **29**, 64 (1933).

[2] L. Pauling and D. C. Carpenter, *J.A.C.S.* **58**, 1274 (1936).

[3] K. Lonsdale, *Proc. Roy. Soc.* **A123**, 494 (1929).

[4] R. B. Corey, *J.A.C.S.* **60**, 1598 (1938).

[5] G. Albrecht and R. B. Corey, *ibid.* **61**, 1087 (1939).

It has been emphasized by Mack[1] that the dimensions of the methyl group and of other hydrocarbon groups can be accounted for by assigning to the hydrogen atom a van der Waals radius of about 1.29 Å. The effective radius in metaldehyde, diketopiperazine, and glycine varies between 1.06 and 1.34 Å. In Table 24-1 an average value 1.2 Å is given.

Drawings showing the effect of van der Waals radii in determining the shapes of molecules are shown in Figures 24-2, 24-3, 24-4, and 24-5.

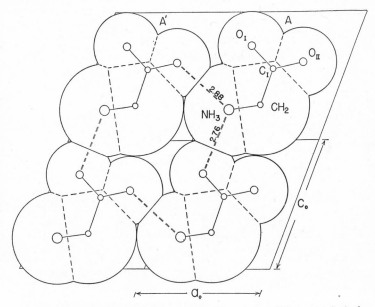

Fig. 24-3.—The arrangement of molecules in a layer of the crystal glycine. It is seen that the packing of the molecules is determined by the van der Waals radii of the groups, except for the N—H · · · O contacts, which are shortened through the formation of hydrogen bonds (Chap. IX).

The distances between saturated hydrocarbon molecules in crystals can be calculated by use of these radii, with consideration also of the possibility of molecular or group rotation. Another factor must be introduced for aromatic molecules.[2] The p_z orbitals in these molecules project above and below the plane of the ring, in such a way as to give to the ring an effective thickness of about 3.7 Å, as observed in naphthalene, anthracene, durene,

[1] E. Mack, Jr., *J.A.C.S.* 54, 2141 (1932).
[2] E. Mack, Jr., *loc. cit.*; *J. Phys. Chem.* 41, 221 (1937).

hexamethylbenzene, and other aromatic hydrocarbons. The value for graphite, 3.4 Å, is somewhat smaller.

It is interesting to note that the van der Waals radii given in Table 24-1 are 0.75 to 0.83 Å greater than the corresponding single-bond covalent radii; to within their limit of reliability

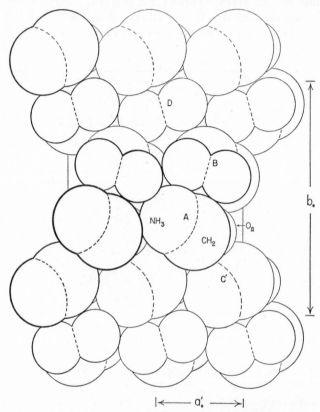

Fig. 24-4.—Another packing drawing of the glycine crystal (Albrecht and Corey).

they could be taken as equal to the covalent radius plus 0.80 Å.

The effective radius of an atom in a direction which makes only a small angle with the direction of a covalent bond formed by the atom is smaller than the van der Waals radius in directions away from the bond. This might well be expected from the fact that the electron pair which would give the chloride ion, $:\overset{..}{\underset{..}{Cl}}:^-$, for example, its size in the direction toward the left is pulled in to form the bond in methyl chloride, $H_3C:\overset{\cdot\cdot}{\underset{\cdot\cdot}{Cl}}:$. In consequence of this atoms which are bonded to the same atom can approach one another much more closely than the sum of the van der Waals radii. In carbon tetrachloride the chlorine atoms are only 2.87 Å apart, and yet the properties of the substance indicate that there

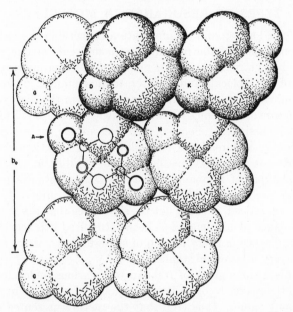

FIG. 24-5.—A packing drawing of the diketopiperazine crystal (Corey).

is no great strain resulting from the repulsion that should result from the van der Waals diameter 3.6 Å. Even in methylene chloride and chloroform, where the strain might be relieved by increasing the bond angle, the chlorine-chlorine distance is only 2.92 A. We conclude that the non-bonded radius of an atom in directions close to the bond direction (within 35°) is about 0.5 A less than the van der Waals radius; a unicovalent atom can be considered as a sphere which is whittled down on the side of the bond.

CHAPTER VI

TYPES OF RESONANCE IN MOLECULES

With the background of information concerning the nature of the phenomenon of the resonance of a molecule among several valence-bond structures and its relation to such properties as the energy of the molecule and its interatomic distances given in the preceding chapters, we are now ready to begin the discussion of the structure of molecules to which a single valence-bond formula can not be assigned. Some of these resonating molecules have been mentioned already as examples; in the selection of others for treatment the effort has been made to illustrate all of the principal types of resonance and to present substantiating evidence in each case. The discussion is not intended to be exhaustive; indeed, it could not be, since once that the nature of the resonance phenomenon has been recognized it is seen that it is of significance in every branch of structural chemistry and for nearly every class of substances.

The discussions given of resonance in various molecules may seem to the reader to be so far from quantitative in nature as to be without value. It is true that the picture presented of the structure of a resonating molecule is in general rather indefinite; but in the half-dozen years that have gone by since the quantum-mechanical resonance phenomenon was first applied to problems of molecular structure encouraging progress has been made in the formulation of a semi-quantitative system, with the aid of both experimental and theoretical methods, and we can hope for similar progress in the future.

25. THE STRUCTURE OF SIMPLE RESONATING MOLECULES

25a. Carbon Monoxide, Carbon Dioxide, and Carbon Suboxide.—It was stated in Chapter IV that carbon monoxide resonates about equally among the three structures $:C^+:\overset{..}{O}:^-$, $:C::\overset{..}{O}:$, and $:C^-:::O:^+$, the resonance energy and electric dipole moment providing evidence. The observed value[1] of the interatomic distance, 1.13 Å, is compatible with the resonating structure but does not give much information about it.[2] The three structures correspond to the values 1.25, 1.13, and 1.10 Å (with corrections of -0.18 and -0.09 Å for the first two for effect of incompleteness of the carbon valence shell); and resonance among these might well give the observed value.

The discussion of interatomic distances corresponding to resonance among several valence-bond structures can be carried out in the following way, representing a simple extension of the quantitative treatment of the single bond-double bond resonance curve in Section 22.

Let the potential function be

$$V(R) = \tfrac{1}{2}x_1 k_1 (R - R_1)^2 + \tfrac{1}{2}x_2 k_2 (R - R_2)^2 + \tfrac{1}{2}x_3 k_3 (R - R_3)^2, \quad (25\text{-}1)$$

in which x_1, x_2, x_3 represent the extents to which the three structures contribute to the state of the molecule (with $x_1 + x_2 + x_3 = 1$), the k's are their force constants, and the R's their interatomic distances. For single, double, and triple bonds the k's may be taken[3] in the ratio $1:3:6$. The equilibrium value of R is found by equating the derivative $\dfrac{dV}{dR}$ to zero and solving for R, which leads to the result

$$R = \frac{x_1 k_1 R_1 + x_2 k_2 R_2 + x_3 k_3 R_3}{x_1 k_1 + x_2 k_2 + x_3 k_3}. \quad (25\text{-}2)$$

that is, R is the weighted averages of the R_i's, with the $x_i k_i$'s as the weights.

The application of this formula to carbon monoxide gives $R = 1.12$ Å, in good agreement with the observed value.

It is not surprising that so unconventional a molecule as carbon monoxide should have a resonating structure of this type I think that the recognition of the fact that the carbon dioxide molecule, for which the valence-bond formula $O=C=O$ has been written ever since the development of valence theory, is not well represented by this structure alone but that other valence-bond structures also make important contributions must come as a surprise to everyone. The carbon-oxygen distance in

[1] L. Gerö, G. Herzberg, and R. Schmid, *Phys. Rev.* **52**, 467 (1937).

[2] In an early discussion of this molecule, before the discovery of the incomplete-shell effect, the interatomic distance was used as an argument for resonance (L. Pauling, *Proc. Nat. Acad. Sci.* **18**, 293 (1932)).

[3] The ratios of force constants observed for single, double, and triple bonds are about $1:2.5:5$. The values used, $1:3:6$, represent an increase (perhaps due to the stabilizing effect of resonance energy), as indicated by the empirical single bond-double bond curve.

this molecule is known[1] to be close to 1.15Å. If the structure O=C=O alone represented the molecule the distance should be 1.22 Å, the sum of the double-bond radii, as in the ketones. We see, however, that other structures should contribute. In the aldehydes and ketones there is resonance between the structures $R_2C::\overset{..}{O}:$ and $R_2C^+:\overset{..}{O}:^-$, with the second almost as important as the first. The corresponding structure for carbon dioxide, $:\overset{..}{O}::C^+:\overset{..}{O}:^-$, is, however, exceeded in stability by another, $:O^+:::C:\overset{..}{O}:^-$, which involves one more covalent bond. There will accordingly occur resonance among five structures:

$$:\overset{..}{\underset{..}{O}}::C::\overset{..}{\underset{..}{O}}:$$

$$:\overset{..}{\underset{..}{O}}::\overset{+}{C}:\overset{..}{\underset{..}{O}}:^-$$

$$^-:\overset{..}{\underset{..}{O}}:\overset{+}{C}::\overset{..}{\underset{..}{O}}:$$

$$:\overset{..}{O}:::C:\overset{..}{\underset{..}{O}}:^-$$

$$^-:\overset{..}{\underset{..}{O}}:C:::\overset{..}{O}:^+$$

The first three of these may be combined into one valence-bond structure, O=C=O. The extent of resonance between the three O=C=O, $^+$O≡C—O$^-$, and $^-$O—C≡O$^+$ is not accurately known. The second and third must be important, in order to bring the interatomic distance down to its observed value, and they are probably about equally important with the conventional structure O=C=O; application of Equation 25-2 (with corrections of 0.03 Å for the formal charges, as in Section 21b) gives the value 1.15 Å for the distance, agreeing with the observed value.

The following detailed calculation of the expected interatomic distance in carbon dioxide is given to illustrate the use of Equation 25-2 in the discussion of resonance among three structures.

[1] W. V. Houston and C. M. Lewis, *Phys. Rev.* **38**, 1827 (1931).

The structures under discussion are

$$A \qquad :\ddot{O}\!=\!C\!=\!\ddot{O}:$$

$$B \qquad :\overset{+}{\ddot{O}}\!\equiv\!C\!-\!\overset{-}{\ddot{O}}:$$

$$C \qquad \overset{-}{:}\!\ddot{O}\!-\!C\!\equiv\!\overset{+}{O}:$$

with B and C contributing equally. Let us assume that A also contributes to the same extent, so that x_1, x_2, and x_3 have the same value $\frac{1}{3}$ in Equation 25-2.

$$R = \frac{x_1 k_1 R_1 + x_2 k_2 R_2 + x_3 k_3 R_3}{x_1 k_1 + x_2 k_2 + x_3 k_3}.$$

The sums of the covalent radii are C–O $= 1.43$, C=O $= 1.22$, and C≡O $= 1.10$ Å, which give $R_1 = 1.46$, $R_2 = 1.22$, and $R_3 = 1.07$ Å when the formal-charge correction is made. With k_1, k_2, and k_3 in the ratios $1:3:6$, the equation for R becomes

$$R = \frac{\frac{1}{3} \times 1.46 + 1 \times 1.22 + 2 \times 1.07}{\frac{1}{3} + 1 + 2}.$$

It is convenient to remove the smallest of the R's from the fraction, giving

$$R = 1.07 + \frac{\times 0.39 + 1 \times 0.15}{\frac{1}{3} + 1 + 2},$$

which leads on evaluation to $R = 1.15$ Å.

The observed resonance energy in the carbon dioxide molecule, relative to the ketonic type of double bond, is 33 kcal./mole.

Resonance of the same type would be expected in carbon oxysulfide and carbon disulfide. The observed interatomic distances,[1] C—O $= 1.16 \pm 0.02$ Å and C—S $= 1.56 \pm 0.03$ Å in SCO and C—S $= 1.54 \pm 0.03$ Å in CS_2, agree well with the values C—O $= 1.15$ Å and C—S $= 1.53$ Å calculated for equal resonance among the three structures O=C=S, $^+$O≡C—S$^-$, $^-$O—C≡S$^+$ and S=C=S, $^+$S≡C—S$^-$, $^-$S—C≡S$^+$. The uncertainty of 0.03 Å in the C—S distance would allow some deviation from equality in the contributions of the three structures, however, and general chemical experience suggests that the structures with a carbon-sulfur triple bond are less important than the others. The resonance energy for carbon oxysulfide is 20 and for carbon disulfide 11 kcal./mole (Table 18-2); these

---

[1] P. C. Cross and L. O. Brockway, *J. Chem. Phys.* **3**, 821 (1935).

low values support the thesis that the structures containing the
C≡S bond are less important than those containing the C≡O
bond.

The carbon suboxide molecule is linear, as expected for the
double-bonded structure A:

$$A \quad :\overset{..}{O}=C=C=C=\overset{..}{O}:.$$

The observed distances,[1] C—C = 1.29 ± 0.02 and C—O = 1.20
± 0.02 Å, do not correspond to this structure, which requires
C=C = 1.33 and C=O = 1.22 Å, but to resonance between it
and structures B and C,

$$B \quad :\overset{+}{O}\equiv C-C\equiv C-\overset{..}{\underset{..}{O}}:^{-}$$

$$C \quad :\overset{-}{\underset{..}{O}}-C\equiv C-C\equiv\overset{+}{O}:,$$

and perhaps others of intermediate type also. The distances indicate that each of the structures B and C makes a contribution
of about 20 percent, with A contributing about 60 percent. This
conclusion is substantiated also by the frequencies of oscillation
of the molecule.[2]

We attribute to the pentacarbon dioxide molecule C_5O_2, which
has not yet been investigated by the electron diffraction method,
a similar linear structure, with somewhat less double-bond character than for C_3O_2, because of the greater separation of charge
involved.[3] It has been pointed out to me by Dr. V. Schomaker
that resonance with structures analogous to B and C can occur
for molecules C_nO_2 for which n is odd but not for those with even
n, and that this explains the observed existence of CO_2, C_3O_2, and
C_5O_2 and apparent non-existence of C_2O_2, C_4O_2, etc.

25b. The Cyanides and Isocyanides.—For an alkyl cyanide
the structure R—C≡N, representing resonance between
R—C:::N: and R—C$^+$::$\overset{..}{N}$:$^-$, may be accepted. The large

[1] L. O. Brockway and L. Pauling, *Proc. Nat. Acad. Sci.* **19**, 860 (1933);
H. Boersch, *Sitz. ber. Akad. Wiss. Wien* **144**, 1 (1935).

[2] H. W. Thompson and J. W. Linnett, *J. Chem. Soc.* **1937**, 1376.

[3] For the preparation and properties of this substance see A. Klemenc
and G. Wagner, *Ber.* **70B**, 1880 (1937). Some doubt as to the existence of
pentacarbon dioxide has been expressed by O. Diels, *Ber.* **71**, 1197 (1938).

dipole moment (over 3×10^{-18} e.s.u.) shows that the triple bond has a large amount of ionic character, the two structures apparently being of about equal importance. The observed C—N distance[1] in methyl cyanide, 1.16 ± 0.02 Å, is compatible with this interpretation, but indicates a smaller contribution of the structure R—C$^+$::N̈:$^-$.

The interesting question as to the relative importance of the two structures R—N̈::C: and R—N$^+$:::C:$^-$ for the alkyl isocyanides is not answered by consideration of the observed value[2] 1.17 ± 0.02 Å for the N—C distance in methyl isocyanide, since the predicted distances for the two structures are nearly the same, 1.19 and 1.15 Å, respectively. The atoms C—N—C are observed to have a linear configuration, which is the stable one for the second structure and not for the first.

25c. Nitrous Oxide and the Azides. The Adjacent Charge Rule.—In Section 17 nitrous oxide was considered to resonate between two structures A and B, which are so similar in nature as to contribute about equally to the normal state of the molecule. There is, however, a third structure, C,

$$A \quad :\overset{-\,..}{N}::\overset{+}{N}::\overset{..}{O}:$$

$$B \quad :N:::\overset{+}{N}:\overset{..\,-}{\underset{..}{O}}:$$

$$C \quad :\overset{-\,..}{\underset{..}{N}}:\overset{+}{N}:::\overset{+}{O}:$$

which must be discussed. It is analogous to the third structure of importance for carbon dioxide, which has the same number of electrons as nitrous oxide, and might be of importance for the latter molecule also. It is found on calculating the interatomic distances by the use of Equation 25–2 that resonance among the three structures A, B, C, contributing equally, leads to the values N—N = 1.15 Å and N—O = 1.07 Å. The sum of these, 2.22 Å, is much smaller than the value 2.31 Å given by the spectroscopic value 65.94×10^{-40} g. cm.^{2} for the moment of

---

[1] L. O. Brockway, *J.A.C.S.* **58**, 2516 (1936); L. Pauling, H. D. Springall, and K. J. Palmer, *ibid.* **61**, 927 (1939).

[2] L. O. Brockway, *loc. cit.*

inertia.[1]   On the other hand, equal resonance between A and B leads to N—N = 1.12 A and N—O = 1.19 A, the sum of which is just equal to the spectroscopic value.

We can attribute the lack of importance of structure C to the instability resulting from the charge distribution, which gives adjacent atoms electric charges of the same sign.   This *adjacent charge rule* has been further substantiated by observations on covalent azides and on fluorine nitrate.[2]   In the ionic crystals NaN_3 and KN_3 the azide ion is linear and symmetrical, each of the end atoms being 1.15 ± 0.02 Å from the central one.[3]   Resonance among the three structures A, B, and C,

$$A \quad \bar{:}\overset{..}{N}\!\!=\!\!\overset{+}{N}\!\!=\!\!\overset{..}{N}\bar{:}$$

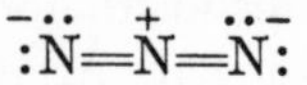

$$B \quad \bar{:}\overset{..}{N}\!\!-\!\!\overset{+}{N}\!\!\equiv\!\!N:$$

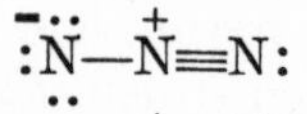

$$C \quad :N\!\!\equiv\!\!\overset{+}{N}\!\!-\!\!\overset{..}{N}\bar{:}$$

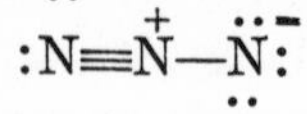

contributing equally, leads to 1.15 Å, in agreement with the observed value, whereas structure A alone would require the unsatisfactory value 1.22 Å.   The covalent molecule methyl azide, on the other hand, has the configuration[2]

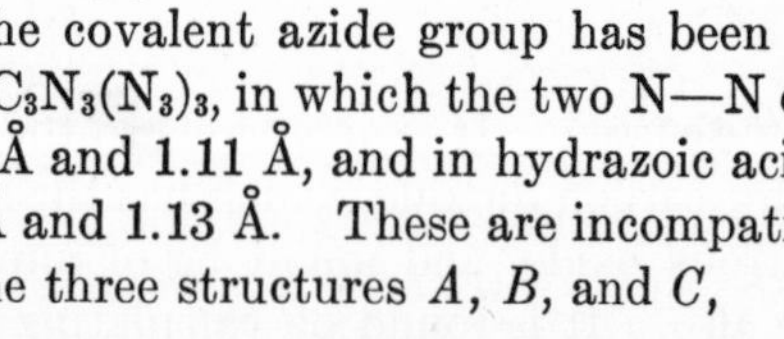

the distances having probable errors of 0.02 Å.   A similar configuration for the covalent azide group has been found in cyanuric triazide,[4] $C_3N_3(N_3)_3$, in which the two N—N distances have the values 1.26 Å and 1.11 Å, and in hydrazoic acid,[5] HN_3, with distances 1.24 Å and 1.13 Å.   These are incompatible with resonance among the three structures A, B, and C,

[1] E. K. Plyler and E. F. Barker, *Phys. Rev.* **38**, 1827 (1931).   The distances N—N and N—O in this molecule have not been separately determined.

[2] L. Pauling and L. O. Brockway, *J.A.C.S.* **59**, 13 (1937).

[3] S. B. Hendricks and L. Pauling, *J.A.C.S.* **47**, 2904 (1925); L. K. Frevel, *ibid.* **58**, 779 (1936).   The value N—N = 1.165 ± 0.02 Å is observed in ammonium azide (L. K. Frevel, *Z. Krist.* **94**, 197 (1936)).

[4] E. W. Hughes, *J. Chem. Phys.* **3**, 1 (1935); I. E. Knaggs, *Proc. Roy. Soc.* A150, 576 (1935).

[5] E. H. Eyster, *J. Chem. Phys.* **8**, 135 (1940).

$$A \quad R—\overset{..}{N}=\overset{+}{N}=\overset{..}{N}\overset{-}{:}$$

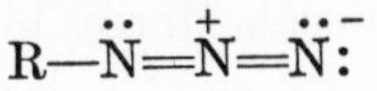

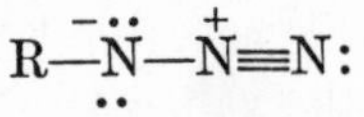

$$B \quad R—\overset{-\,..}{N}—\overset{+}{N}\equiv N:$$

$$C \quad R—\overset{+}{N}\equiv\overset{+}{N}—\overset{..\,-}{N}\overset{}{:}$$

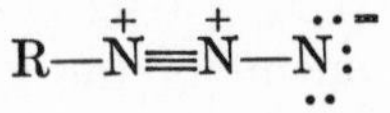

but agree well with equal resonance between A and B, the calculated values being 1.24 Å and 1.12 Å. The significance of the adjacent charge rule is seen clearly from the fact that the elimination of structure C for the covalent azide and not for the azide ion is the result of the positive formal charge given to the nitrogen atom by the formation of a covalent bond.

Another application of the rule, to the fluorine nitrate molecule, will be discussed in a following section, with mention also of the stability of covalent and ionic azides and nitrates.

25d. The Nitro, Carboxyl, and Amide Groups. Acid and Basic Strengths.—Resonance between the two equivalent struc-

tures R—N (with O: and O:) and R—N , with perhaps a small contri-

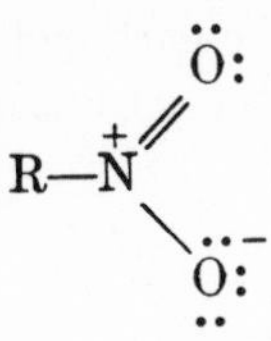

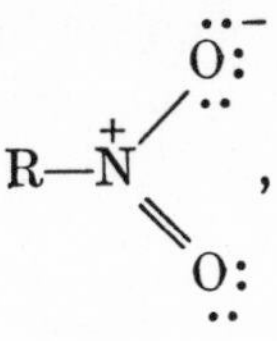

bution by R—N , is expected for the nitro group. This

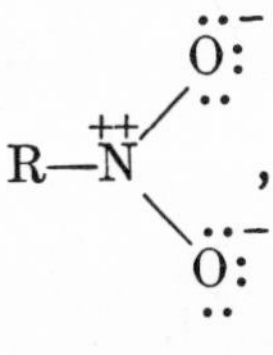

would lead to the tetrahedral value 125°16′ for the O—N=O bond angle and to the predicted value 1.19 Å for the N—O distance, the three atoms of the group and the atom of R attached to nitrogen being coplanar, with the two oxygen atoms symmetrically related to the R—N axis. (The unsymmetrical configuration reported for the group in para-dinitrobenzene,[1] with N—O distances 1.10 and 1.25 Å, can hardly be correct, since the

[1] R. W. James, G. King, and H. Horrocks, *Proc. Roy. Soc.* A153, 225 (1935).

relatively weak intermolecular forces in the crystal could not inhibit the resonance of the double bond.) This configuration has been verified by the electron-diffraction study of nitromethane,[1] which led to the values O—N—O angle $= 127° \pm 3°$ and N—O distance $= 1.21 \pm 0.02$ Å. Moreover, the calculated electric dipole moment for the group, 2.70×10^{-18} e.s.u.

$$\left(\text{corresponding to the average charge distribution} \quad \underset{1.21\,\text{Å}}{\overset{O^{-1/2e}}{\underset{O^{-1/2e}}{\overset{+e}{N}}}}\ \Big\rangle\ 127° \right),$$

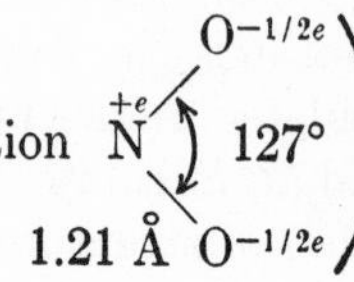

agrees satisfactorily with the observed large value of about 3×10^{-18} e.s.u. for aliphatic nitro compounds. For the nitro group, as for the azide group, there is available no value for resonance energy because of the failure of the system of bond energies to include within its scope structures involving formal charges.

Whereas in the nitro group the two resonating structures are equivalent, they are made non-equivalent in the carboxyl group and its esters, becoming equivalent again in the corresponding ions.

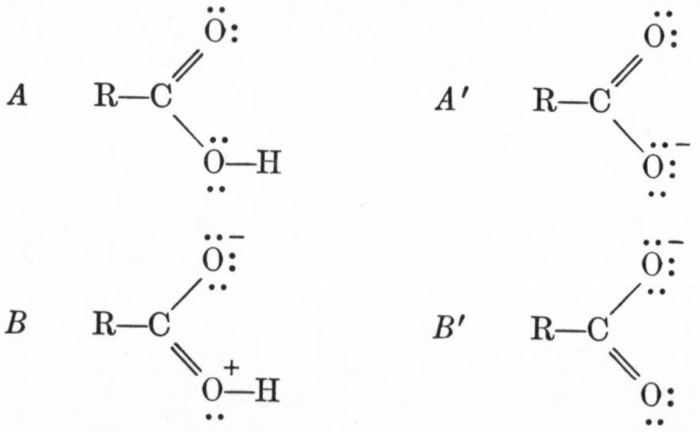

The lack of equivalence of structures *A* and *B* does not inhibit their resonance very thoroughly, however, since the corresponding resonance energy is still large, having the value 28 kcal./mole for acids and 24 kcal./mole for esters.

[1] L. O. Brockway, J. Y. Beach, and L. Pauling, *J.A.C.S.* **57**, 2693 (1935). This configuration is found in tetranitromethane also: A. J. Stosick, *ibid.* **61**, 1127 (1939).

The predicted configuration for the carboxyl group is that with the angle O—C—O equal to 125°28′ and the C—O distance 1.27 Å. The available accurately determined experimental values agree well with these: angle O—C—O = 125° ± 5° and distance C—O = 1.29 ± 0.02 Å in the dimer of formic acid;[1] angle O—C—O = 124° ± 4° and C—O = 1.27 ± 0.01 Å in sodium formate;[2] angle O—C—O = 122° ± 3° and C—O = 1.26 ± 0.02 Å in glycine,[3] NH_2CH_2COOH; angle O—C—O = 124° and C—O = 1.24–1.30 Å in oxalic acid dihydrate;[4] with similar values reported in other investigations.

The concept of resonance provides an obvious explanation of some of the characteristic properties of the carboxyl group, the most striking of which is its acid strength. If the electronic

structure of a carboxylic acid were $R-C\overset{\displaystyle O}{\underset{\displaystyle OH}{\big\Vert}}$, its acid strength

would differ only by a rather small amount from that of an alcohol. The double-bonded oxygen atom would attract electrons from the carbon atom, which in turn would exert the same influence on the hydroxyl oxygen, leaving it with a resultant positive charge. This would repel the proton, and an increase in the acid constant would be produced in this way, through operation of the *inductive effect*. Resonance with structure *B* provides a much more effective way of placing a positive charge on the hydroxyl oxygen, however, and the high acid strength of the carboxyl group can be attributed in the main to this effect.

An alternative point of view regarding the acid strength of the carboxyl group is the following. There is a certain decrease in free energy accompanying the ionization of the hydroxyl group in a non-resonating molecule, corresponding to the value of the acid constant K_A. The free energy decrease for ionization of the carboxyl group is larger than this because of the gain in resonance energy of the group during the change from the unsym-

[1] L. Pauling and L. O. Brockway, *Proc. Nat. Acad. Sci.* **20**, 336 (1934).

[2] W. H. Zachariasen, *Phys. Rev.* **53**, 917 (1938).

[3] G. Albrecht and R. B. Corey, *J.A.C.S.* **61**, 1087 (1939).

[4] J. M. Robertson, *J. Chem. Soc.* **1936**, 1817; W. H. Zachariasen Z. *Krist.* **89**, 442 (1934).

metrical configuration, in which resonance is partially inhibited, to the symmetrical configuration of the ion, with complete resonance. The effect of this on the acid constant is given by the equation

$$\text{Change in resonance energy} = RT \ln \frac{K_{A'}}{K_A}, \text{ in which } K_{A'} \text{ is}$$

the acid constant of the resonating group.[1] If the resonance energy of the carboxyl ion were 36 kcal./mole, that for the acid being 28 kcal./mole, the acid constant would be raised to the observed value 1.8×10^{-5} (for acetic acid and the following members of the series) from the value 2×10^{-11}. The difference between this and the value for the hydroxyl group in alcohols and water, about 10^{-16}, could be attributed to the inductive effect. It is unfortunate that an experimental value for the resonance energy of the carboxyl ion is not available.

Further increase of the acid constant by substitution of electronegative atoms such as chlorine in the hydrocarbon chain (from $K_A = 1.86 \times 10^{-5}$ for acetic acid to 1.5×10^{-3} for chloroacetic acid, 5×10^{-2} for dichloroacetic acid, and 2×10^{-1} for trichloroacetic acid, for example) is attributed to the inductive effect, the effect of the electronegative atom being transmitted through the chain to the oxygen atom,[2] and to electrostatic interactions.

The acid constant of phenol, 1.7×10^{-10}, is much larger than that of the aliphatic alcohols. This we attribute to resonance with the structures F, G, and H,

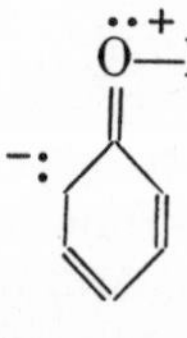

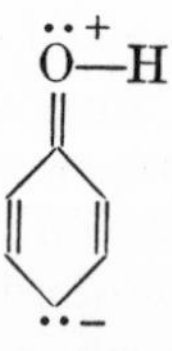

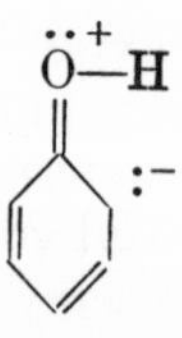

which give the oxygen atom a positive formal charge. The inductive effect of the ring is negligible; accordingly the increase in acid constant by a factor of about 10^6 from aliphatic to aromatic alcohols indicates that the resonance energy of the phenolate ion among the structures I to V

[1] It is easily seen that the entropy effect of resonance is negligible here.
[2] See, for example, G. Schwarzenbach and H. Egli, *Helv. Chim. Acta* **17**, 1183 (1934).

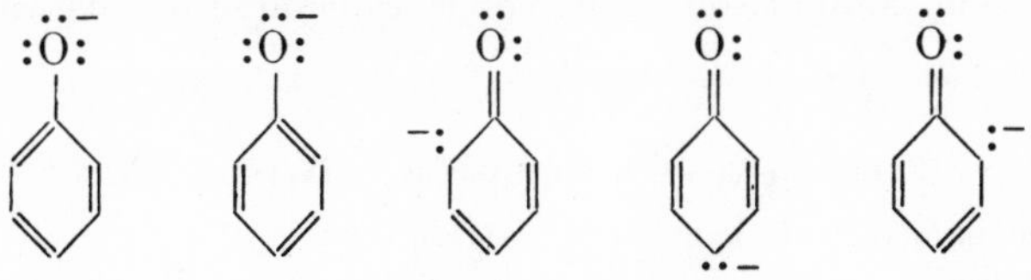

I   II   III   IV   V

is about 8 kcal./mole greater than that for phenol. This is to be expected, since these five structures are closely similar in nature, differing only in the position of the negative charge, whereas for the unionized molecule the structures *F*, *G*, and *H*, with separated charges, are much less stable than the conventional structures, and contribute only a small amount (7 kcal./mole—Table 18-2) to the resonance energy.

A nitro group substituted in phenol should increase the acid constant by virtue of the inductive effect of the electronegative group (with N^+ attached to the ring); moreover, in the ortho and para positions there would occur an additional resonance effect, due to the contribution of structures such as the following:

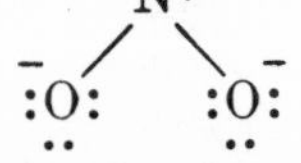

Unionized molecule 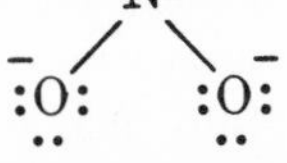   Ion

These place a positive charge on the oxygen atom of the unionized molecule, and so cause it to repel the proton. On analysis of the experimental values for K_A at 25°C it is found that the inductive effect of a nitro group increases K_A by a factor of about 32, and the resonance effect in the ortho and para positions gives another factor of about the same value. The acid constant of a nitrophenol can be found approximately by multiplying that for phenol, itself, 1.7×10^{-10}, by the factor 32 for every meta nitro group and 1000 for every ortho or para nitro group in the molecule.   The comparison of the values calculated in this way with those found by experiment is shown in Table 25-1.

TABLE 25-1.—ACID STRENGTHS OF NITROPHENOLS

Number of nitro groups		Calculated K_A	Observed K_A*	Compound
Meta	Ortho-para			
0	0	(1.7×10^{-10})	1.7×10^{-10}	Phenol
1		5.4×10^{-9}	10×10^{-9}	m-Nitrophenol
2		1.7×10^{-7}	2.1×10^{-7}	3,5-Dinitrophen
	1	1.7×10^{-7}	$\begin{cases} 0.75 \times 10^{-7} \\ 0.96 \times 10^{-7} \end{cases}$	o-Nitrophenol / p-Nitrophenol
1	1	5.4×10^{-6}	$\begin{cases} 12 \times 10^{-6} \\ 7 \times 10^{-6} \\ 3.7 \times 10^{-6} \end{cases}$	2,3-Dinitrophenol / 2,5-Dinitrophenol / 3,4-Dinitrophenol
	2	1.7×10^{-4}	$\begin{cases} 1 \times 10^{-4} \\ 2 \times 10^{-4} \end{cases}$	2,4-Dinitrophenol / 2,6-Dinitrophenol
	3	1.7×10^{-1}	1.6×10^{-1}	2,4,6-Trinitrophenol

* All data are for 25°C.

The extra factor 32 for resonance in the ortho and para positions corresponds to an extra resonance energy of 1.7 kcal./mole ($= RT \ln 32$) for the ion relative to the unionized molecule. This is not unreasonable; there is only one structure of this type involved for each ortho or para nitro group, and the unfavorable distribution of charge makes it of little significance for the unionized molecule.

A straightforward treatment of the basic strength of aniline can be given.   A saturated aliphatic amine such as methylamine has a basic constant K_B, corresponding to the reaction

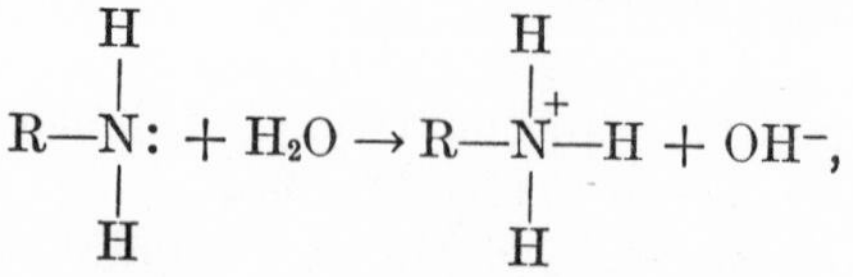

$$\text{R—N:} + H_2O \rightarrow \text{R—N}^+\text{—H} + OH^-,$$

of about 5×10^{-4}.   In these substances an unshared electron pair is available on the nitrogen atom for forming the bond with the proton.   In aniline, on the other hand, this pair of electrons is involved in resonance; and whereas the aniline molecule resonates among the three structures F, G, and H, as well as the normal structures 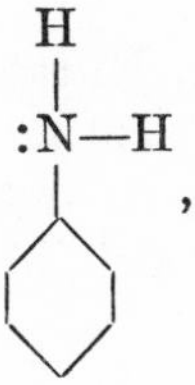 , the phenylammonium

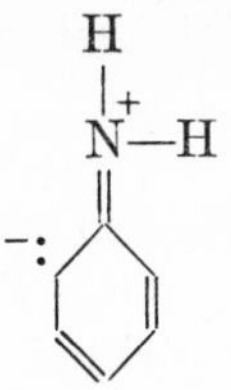

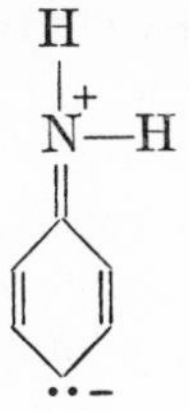

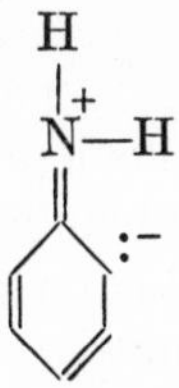

ion is restricted to the normal structures 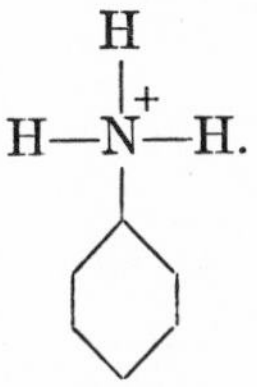 . The ion is

thus made unstable relative to the unionized molecule (using the aliphatic compounds for comparison) by a free energy equal to the resonance energy due to the three structures F, G, and H, and its basic dissociation constant is reduced very greatly, to the value $K_B = 3.5 \times 10^{-10}$.

Since this change by the factor $1/1.4 \times 10^6$ is due entirely to the complete inhibition of the F, G, H resonance by addition of the proton, the quantity $RT \ln 1.4 \times 10^6 = 8.4$ kcal./mole represents the F, G, H resonance energy in aniline. This value is probably more accurate than that given by thermochemical data, 6 kcal./mole (Table 18-2), and the agreement between the two is satisfactory.

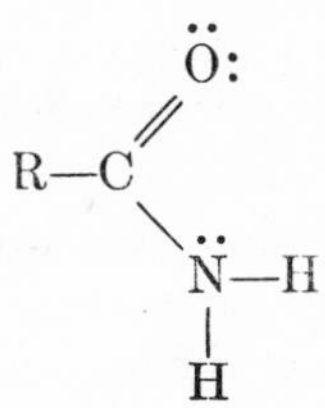

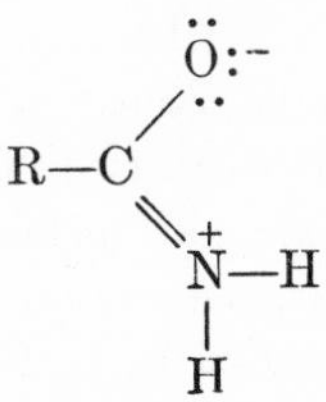

The resonance energy between the structures A and B for the amides, such as acetamide, CH_3CONH_2, is about 21 kcal./mole (Table 18-2). This resonance would be completely inhibited by addition of a proton to the nitrogen atom. The corresponding calculated value for the basic constant, 1×10^{-20}, is so small as to be without significance, except to show, that the amides do not form salts with acids by adding proton to the amino group.

There exist no data regarding the configuration and dimensions of the amide group.

25e. The Carbonate, Nitrate, and Borate Ions and Related Molecules.—Carbonic acid and its derivatives resonate among the three structures A, B, and C, the resonance being complete for the ion and somewhat inhibited in the acid

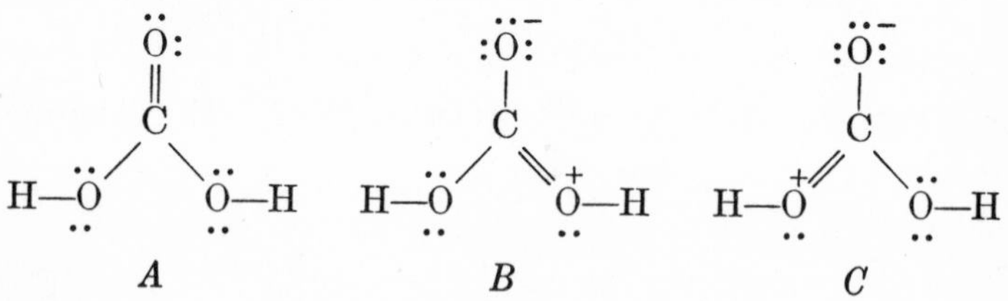

and its esters. (Specific mention need not be made of the structure

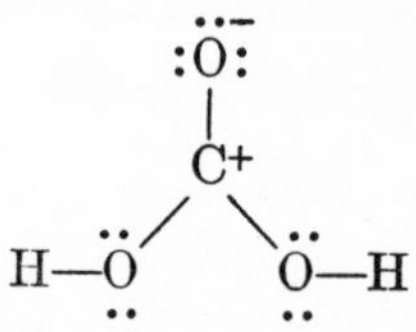

The contribution of structures of this type, which give partial ionic character to bonds, is to be assumed in all cases.)

The value 42 kcal./mole for the resonance energy is given by the thermochemical data for the dialkyl carbonates. This value for resonance of the double bond among three positions is not unreasonable when compared with the corresponding value of 24 kcal./mole for esters of the fatty acids, in which the bond resonates between two positions.

The resonating structure requires that the carbonate ion be coplanar, with bond angles 120°, and the three C—O distances equal to 1.31 Å. This configuration of the ion was found in the original x-ray study of calcite,[1] and has been verified since by examination of other carbonate crystals. The value calculated for the C—O distance is in satisfactory agreement with that found in a thorough recent reinvestigation[2] of calcite, 1.31 ± 0.01 Å.

For the nitrate ion, with the same type of structure as the carbonate ion, a similar configuration is expected and observed:

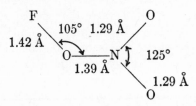

It is interesting to note that the positive formal charge for the nitrogen atom does not influence the single-bond distances, but decreases the double-bond distance by 0.03 Å (Sec. 21b), since the double-bonded oxygen atom is neutral rather than negative. The calculated N—O distance, 1.22 Å, is slightly larger than the observed value,[3] 1.21 ± 0.01 Å.

The electron-diffraction investigation[4] of the explosive gas fluorine nitrate, discovered by Cady,[5] has led to the assignment to it of the following configuration:

The values of the interatomic distances are less reliable than

[1] W. L. Bragg, *Proc. Roy. Soc.* **A89**, 468 (1914).

[2] N. Elliott, *J.A.C.S.* **59**, 1380 (1937).

[3] N. Elliott, *loc. cit.* It was the discrepancy between Elliott's result and that expected without consideration of the formal charge effect which led to the formulation of this correction. The data for the nitrate ion suggest that the correction should be −0.04 Å.

[4] L. Pauling and L. O. Brockway, *J.A.C.S.* **59**, 13 (1937).

[5] G. H. Cady, *ibid.* **56**, 2635 (1934). Cady prepared the substance by passing fluorine through concentrated nitric acid. Its preparation from fluorine and crystalline potassium nitrate has been reported by D. M. Yost and A. Beerbower, *ibid.* **57**, 781 (1935).

usual (to only about 0.05 Å); they indicate, however, that the bond from nitrogen to the oxygen atom with fluorine attached has very little double-bond character. This is to be expected from the adjacent charge rule, which excludes the structure

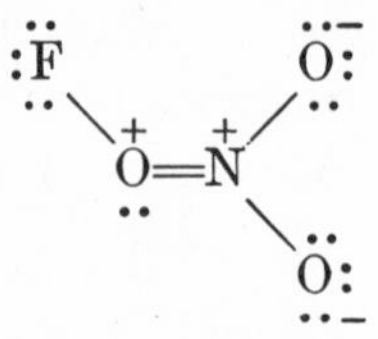

The adjacent charge rule similarly requires that for other covalent nitrates also, such as methyl nitrate, the resonance of the double bond be restricted to two of the three oxygen atoms.   This has as yet not been verified.

It is interesting to note that the adjacent charge rule provides an explanation of the large differences in stability shown by covalent and ionic azides and nitrates.   Covalent azides and nitrates are restricted by the rule to resonance between two important structures, whereas the ions resonate among three structures.   The resonance energy for two structures is of the order of magnitude of 25 kcal./mole (carboxyl group, etc.) and that for three structures is about 45 kcal./mole;[1] hence ionic azides and nitrates are more stable than the covalent substances by about 20 kcal./mole.   We accordingly understand why the alkali and alkaline-earth azides can be exploded only at high temperatures whereas the heavy metal azides, chlorazide, cyanuric triazide, hydrazoic acid, and other covalent azides are extremely explosive.   The ionic nitrates also are relatively stable, and the covalent nitrates (fluorine nitrate, methyl nitrate, nitroglycerine, etc.) are exploded easily.

This destabilizing effect of the adjacent charge rule shown in covalent azides and nitrates does not occur in the analogous compounds containing carbon as the central atom, since the quadricovalent carbon atom is neutral.

The borate group in crystalline boric acid is observed[2] to have a coplanar triangular configuration with the B—O distance

[1] A very simple quantum-mechanical treatment leads to the ratio 1:2 for these.

[2] W. H. Zachariasen, *Z. Krist.* **88,** 150 (1934).

1.35 Å. Similar triangular BO_3 groups occur[1] in hambergite, Be_2BO_3OH, with $B—O = 1.35$ Å. In calcium metaborate,[2] CaB_2O_4, there are infinite chains of BO_3 groups joined by sharing oxygen atoms, and in potassium metaborate,[3] $K_3B_3O_6$, these groups are similarly joined into trimeric ions (Fig. 25-1); in the

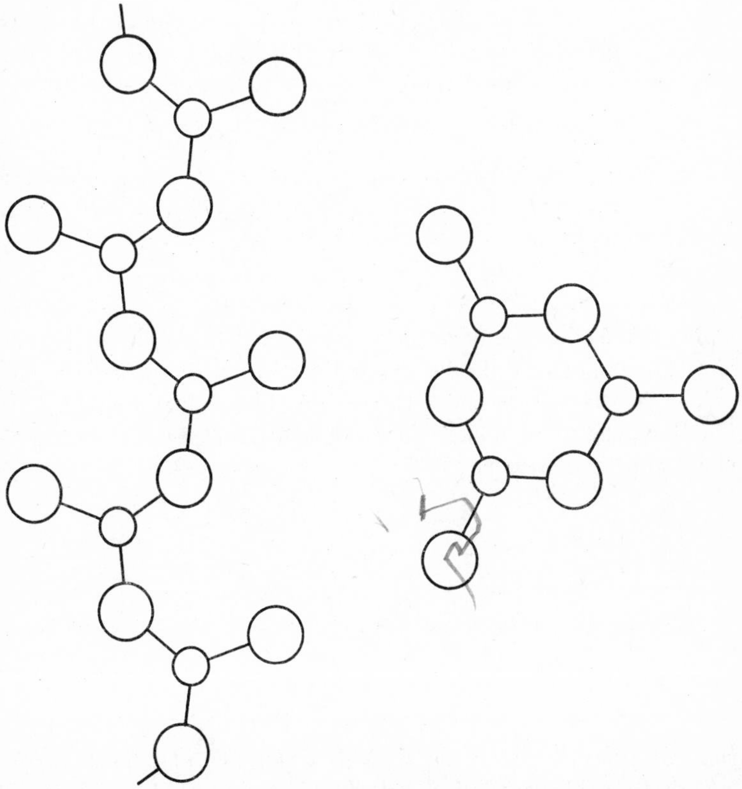

Fig. 25-1.—A portion of the infinite metaborate chain $(BO_2)_\infty$ in CaB_2O_4 (left), and the metaborate ring $[B_3O_6]^{---}$ in $K_3B_3O_6$. Small circles represent boron atoms, large circles oxygen atoms.

former compound the value 1.36 Å is given for the B—O distance, and in the latter the two values 1.33 Å (to the outer oxygen atoms) and 1.38 Å (to the shared oxygen atoms).

[1] W. H. Zachariasen, *ibid.* **76**, 289 (1931).
[2] W. H. Zachariasen, *Proc. Nat. Acad. Sci.* **17**, 617 (1931); W. H. Zachariasen and G. E. Ziegler, *Z. Krist.* **83**, 354 (1932).
[3] W. H. Zachariasen, *J. Chem. Phys.* **5**, 919 (1937).

The sum of the double-bond radii for boron and oxygen is 1.31 Å, and that of the single-bond radii 1.54 Å. Carbonate-like resonance between these leads to B—O = 1.37 Å, which is larger than the reported value; moreover, consideration should be given the negative formal charge of boron, which would increase the discrepancy. It seems probable that in the borate ion a new phenomenon is taking place; that the ionic character of the B—O bonds (the two atoms differ in electronegativity by 1.5 units) gives to the boron atom a positive charge, as in the structure

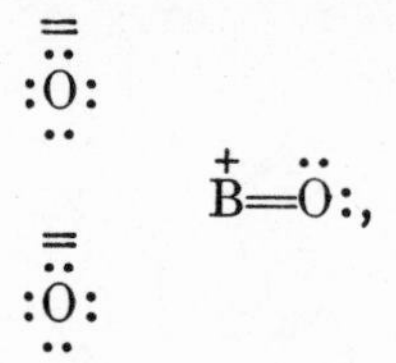

$$\ddot{\underset{\cdot\cdot}{O}}\\ \overset{+}{B}=\ddot{O}:,\\ \ddot{\underset{\cdot\cdot}{O}}$$

which then effects a decrease in the covalent radius of boron. This phenomenon will be discussed further in Chapter VII.

The two B—O distances 1.33 Å and 1.38 Å in the $(B_3O_6)^{---}$ ion show the greater importance of the structure involving uncharged oxygen atoms,

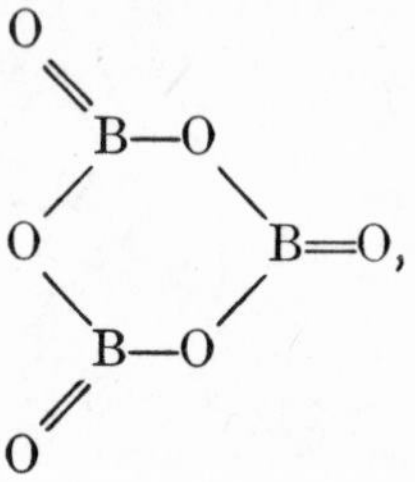

$$\begin{array}{c}
O\\
\diagdown\\
B-O\\
\diagup\qquad\diagdown\\
O\qquad\qquad B=O,\\
\diagdown\qquad\diagup\\
B-O\\
\diagup\\
O
\end{array}$$

than of the other structures. The difference of 0.05 Å corresponds to a difference of about 20% in amount of double-bond character.

Resonance of the carbonate type occurs in urea, $CO(NH_2)_2$, and guanidine, $CNH(NH_2)_2$. For urea the thermochemical value of the resonance energy is 37 kcal./mole, and for guanidine 47 kcal./mole, the latter being calculated with use of the estimated value 24 kcal./mole for the heat of sublimation.

The observed values of interatomic distances for urea are[1] C—O = 1.25 Å and C—N = 1.37 Å. The second of these dis-

[1] R. W. G. Wyckoff and R. B. Corey, *Z. Krist.* **89**, 462 (1934).

tances is sensitive to the amount of double-bond character, as it comes on a steep portion of the resonance curve; the experimental value indicates 20% double-bond character for the C—N bonds, leaving 60% for the C—O bond. The calculated values of the distances are then C—N = 1.37 Å, C—O = 1.26 Å.

Reliable interatomic-distance data are not available for guanidine or the guanidinium ion.

The basic strengths of guanidine and its derivatives present an interesting problem. Guanidine itself is a very strong base, approaching the alkalies in strength. This fact can be accounted for by arguments closely related to those used for the carboxylic acids in the preceding section. The guanidinium ion resonates among the three structures

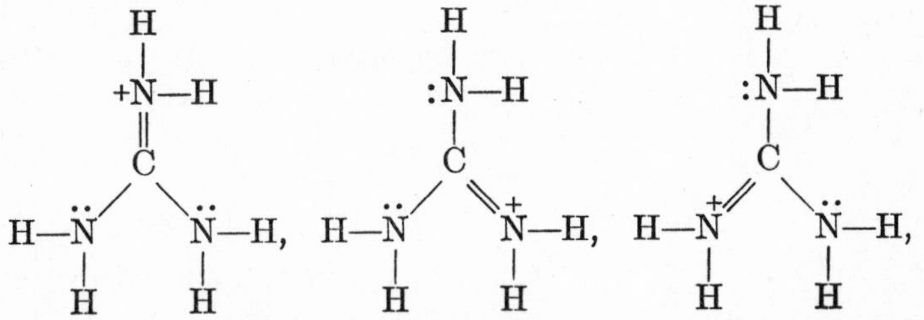

which are all equivalent, whereas guanidine itself resonates among the three structures

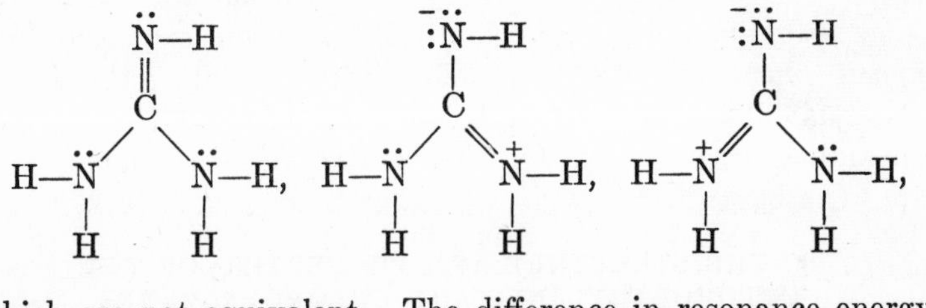

which are not equivalent. The difference in resonance energy can be estimated to be of the magnitude of 6 to 8 kcal./mole, which would increase the basic strength very greatly.

The monoalkylguanidines and NN-dialkylguanidines should be somewhat weaker bases than guanidine itself, for the following reason. The replacement of one or two hydrogens of an —NH_2 group by alkyl radicals tends to prevent the double bond from swinging to this group, because carbon is more electronegative than hydrogen and hence tends to cause the adjacent nitrogen

atom not to assume a positive charge.   In consequence resonance
of the double bond is to some extent restricted to the two other
nitrogen atoms.   This causes a decrease in the basic strength
toward that characteristic of an imidine, the decrease being about

$$
\text{twice as great for } \mathrm{HNC} \begin{cases} \nearrow \mathrm{NH_2} \\ \searrow \mathrm{NR_2} \end{cases} \text{ as for } \mathrm{HNC} \begin{cases} \nearrow \mathrm{NH_2} \\ \searrow \mathrm{NHR} \end{cases}. \text{ A very much}
$$

larger effect is expected for the NN′-dialkylguanidines.   The
alkyl groups on two of the nitrogen atoms would tend to force
the double bond to the third nitrogen atom, the structure

$$
\begin{array}{c}
\mathrm{H} \qquad \mathrm{H} \\
| \qquad\quad | \\
\mathrm{R-N} \qquad \mathrm{N-R} \\
\searrow \quad \swarrow \\
\mathrm{C} \\
\parallel \\
\mathrm{N-H} \\
\cdot\cdot
\end{array}
$$
being more important than the other two.

This nitrogen atom would hence have little tendency to add a
proton, and the substance would be a weak base.   On the other
hand, the NN′N″-trialkylguanidines should be about as strong
bases as guanidine itself, inasmuch as the conditions for resonance in this molecule and its symmetrical ion are exactly the
same as for guanidine and its ion.   These various conclusions are
in agreement with the available data;[1] guanidine, the monoalkylguanidines, NN-dimethylguanidine, and NN′N″-trimethyl-
guanidines are strong bases, whereas the NN′-dialkylguanidines
are weak bases.

26. THE STRUCTURE AND PROPERTIES OF THE CHLOROETHYLENES AND CHLOROBENZENES

The chemical properties of the chlorobenzenes and chloroethylenes differ strikingly from those of saturated aliphatic
chlorine compounds and of aromatic compounds with chlorine
substituted in a side chain.   For example, methyl chloride and
benzyl chloride are hydrolyzed by boiling with alkali, giving the
corresponding alcohols, whereas chlorobenzene is not affected by
this treatment.   In general there is a pronounced diminution in

[1] T. L. Davis and R. C. Elderfield, *J.A.C.S.* **54**, 1499 (1932).

reactivity of a chlorine atom adjacent to an aromatic nucleus or double bond.

The obvious explanation of this involves resonance of the following type, which gives to the C—Cl bond some double-bond character:

$$\left\{ \overset{\cdot\cdot}{\underset{\cdot\cdot}{Cl}}: \quad H_2C=C\diagdown{}_H \quad , \quad \overset{\cdot\cdot}{\underset{\cdot\cdot}{Cl}}:^+ \quad \overset{-}{H_2}C—C\diagup{}_H \right\},$$

$$\left\{ \langle\!\!\!\!\bigcirc\!\!\!\!\rangle—\overset{\cdot\cdot}{\underset{\cdot\cdot}{Cl}}:, \quad \langle\!\!\!\!\bigcirc\!\!\!\!\rangle^{-}=\overset{\cdot\cdot}{Cl}:^+, \quad etc. \right\}.$$

In order to study this phenomenon, which may be described as involving the conjugation of an unshared pair of electrons on the chlorine atom with the double bond or aromatic nucleus, and to determine the amount of double-bond character in carbon-chlorine bonds of this type, values of the carbon-chlorine distance in chloroethylenes[1] and chlorobenzenes[2] have been determined by the electron diffraction method.

The results of the investigations are given in Table 26-1. Whereas in carbon tetrachloride, methyl chloride, and similar molecules the carbon-chlorine distance is 1.76 Å, in these substances the values found are from 0.03 to 0.09 Å less than this

TABLE 26-1.—INTERATOMIC DISTANCES IN CHLOROETHYLENES
AND CHLOROBENZENES

Molecule	C—Cl distance*	Molecule	C—Cl distance*
CH_2CHCl	1.69 Å	C_6H_5Cl	1.69 Å
CH_2CCl_2	1.69	$p\text{-}C_6H_4Cl_2$	1.69
cis-CHClCHCl	1.67	$m\text{-}C_6H_4Cl_2$	1.69
trans-CHClCHCl	1.69	$o\text{-}C_6H_4Cl_2$	1.71
$CHClCCl_2$	1.71	$1,3,5\text{-}C_6H_3Cl_3$	1.69
C_2Cl_4	1.73	$1,2,4,5\text{-}C_6H_2Cl_4$	1.72
		C_6Cl_6	1.70

* These values are reliable to about ±0.02 Å.

and, moreover, there is found for the chloroethylenes a reasonable correlation between the amount of shortening and the number of

[1] L. O. Brockway, J. Y. Beach, and L. Pauling, *J.A.C.S.* 57, 2693 (1935).
[2] L. O. Brockway and K. J. Palmer, *ibid.* 59, 2181 (1937).

chlorine atoms conjugated with the double bond.   The shortening is about 0.08 Å for substituted ethylenes containing one or two chlorine atoms, which corresponds, when interpreted by the method of Section 22, to about 18% double-bond character. The shortening observed for trichloroethylene, 0.05 Å, corresponds to about 10% double-bond character, and that for tetrachloroethylene, 0.03 Å, to about 5% double-bond character.   It seems probable that there is competition between the chlorine atoms in these compounds for the double bond, leading to a decrease in double-bond character as compared with vinyl chloride.   Corresponding to the decrease in double-bond character there is observed for trichloroethylene and tetrachloroethylene somewhat greater reactivity than for vinyl chloride and the dichloroethylenes.

The shortening observed for all of the chlorobenzenes studied is about 0.06 or 0.07 Å, corresponding to about 15% double-bond character.   (The variations from the values 1.69 or 1.70 Å reported in the table have little significance, although there is indication of a small increase in distance with increase in the number of chlorine atoms in the molecule.)   From these results it can be concluded that the benzene ring has about the same power of conjugation with a chlorine atom as has a double bond, and moreover that its capacity for conjugation is somewhat greater, in that little saturation is indicated for hexachlorobenzene, in contrast to tetrachloroethylene.

Decreases in interatomic distances in the bromine and iodine derivatives of ethylene and benzene have also been reported,[1] with magnitudes about the same as for the chlorine derivatives.   In dibromacetylene and diiodacetylene, in which the halogens are conjugated with a triple bond, there are decreases of about 0.10 Å, corresponding to 30% double-bond character;[2] this supports the expectation that the power of conjugation of a triple bond is greater than that of a double bond.

[1] H. de Laszlo, *Proc. Roy. Soc.* **A146,** 690 (1934); J. A. C. Hugill, I. E. Coop, and L. E. Sutton, *Trans. Faraday Soc.* **34,** 1518 (1938).

[2] H. de Laszlo, *Nature* **135,** 474 (1935); L. O. Brockway and H. Lévy, unpublished investigation.   L. O. Brockway and I. E. Coop, *Trans. Faraday Soc.* **34,** 1429 (1938), have recently reported C—Cl = 1.68 ± 0.04 Å in ClCCH and C—Br = 1.80 ± 0.03 Å in BrCCH, and J. Y. Beach and A. Turkevich, *J.A.C.S.* **61,** 299 (1939), have found values 0.01 Å less than these for ClCN and BrCN, respectively.

A theoretical study of the phenomenon described above has been made by Sherman and Ketelaar.[1]

27. RESONANCE IN CONJUGATED SYSTEMS

For a molecule such as butadiene-1, 3, $CH_2=CH-CH=CH_2$, it is customary to write one valence-bond formula involving alternating single and double bonds and to take cognizance of the difference in properties from a molecule containing isolated double bonds by saying that here the double bonds are conjugated.   From the new point of view the phenomenon of conjugation is attributed to resonance between the ordinary structure and certain structures involving one less double bond—

$$\overset{|}{C}H_2-CH=CH-\overset{|}{C}H_2$$ for butadiene, and to a smaller extent $C^+H_2{}^-CH=CH-CH_2{}^-$, etc.[2]   These structures are less stable than the ordinary structure, and contribute only a small amount to the normal state of the molecule, giving the 2,3 bond a small amount of double-bond character.

The quantum-mechanical treatment of this problem[3] indicates that the single bonds in a conjugated system have about 20% double-bond character, and that the extra resonance energy resulting from the conjugation of two double bonds is about 5 to 8 kcal./mole.   The calculations also show that a double bond and a benzene nucleus are approximately equivalent in conjugating power.

The thermochemical data for biphenyl, 1,3,5-triphenylbenzene, phenylethylene, and stilbene (Table 18-2) correspond to a value of about 7 kcal./mole for the conjugation energy of a double bond and a benzene ring or of two benzene rings.   Somewhat lower values, between 2 and 6 kcal./mole, are given for the conjugation energy in dienes by data on heats of hydrogenation.[4]

[1] J. Sherman and J. A. A. Ketelaar, *Physica* 6, 572 (1939).   For further theoretical work on this problem see also J. E. Lennard-Jones, *Proc. Roy. Soc.* A158, 280 (1937); W. G. Penney, *ibid.* A158, 306 (1937); C. A. Coulson, *ibid.* A169, 413 (1939); *J. Chem. Phys.* 7, 1069 (1939); J. E. Lennard-Jones and C. A. Coulson, *Trans. Faraday Soc.* 35, 811 (1939).

[2] It is to be noted that such structures can not be written for molecules with isolated double bonds.

[3] L. Pauling and J. Sherman, *J. Chem. Phys.* 1, 679 (1933).

[4] G. B. Kistiakowsky, J. R. Ruhoff, H. A. Smith, and W. E. Vaughan *J.A.C.S.* 58, 146 (1936).

These values are rendered uncertain by the surprisingly large variation found for the heats of hydrogenation of isolated double bonds in different hydrocarbons.

In butadiene-1,3 and cyclopentadiene the value found[1] for the carbon-carbon distance for the bond between the conjugated double bonds is 1.46 Å. This, interpreted by use of the curve of Section 22, corresponds to 18% double-bond character. The same amount of double-bond character is also indicated by the following x-ray values for the bond between two benzene rings or a benzene ring and a double bond: stilbene (C_6H_5—CH=CH—C_6H_5), 1.44 Å; biphenyl, 1.48 Å; p-diphenylbenzene, 1.46 Å.

This amount of double-bond character should give to the bond in some part the properties of a double bond; in particular the conjugated systems should tend to remain coplanar. Chemical evidence for cis and trans isomers of the type

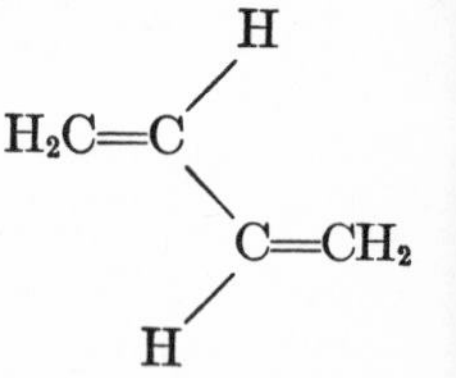

$$H_2C=C \begin{matrix} H \\ \diagup \\ \diagdown \\ C=CH_2 \\ \diagup \\ H \end{matrix}$$

and

$$\begin{matrix} H_2C & CH_2 \\ \diagdown\diagdown & \diagup\diagup \\ C—C \\ \diagup & \diagdown \\ H & H \end{matrix}$$

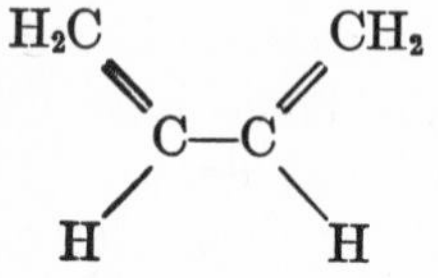

has not been forthcoming; presumably the restriction of rotation about the central bond is not great enough to prevent easy interconversion of these molecular species. It is great enough, however, to cause the conjugated molecules to retain in general the coplanar equilibrium configuration in crystals. Thus the stilbene molecule is coplanar,[2] whereas the closely similar unconjugated molecule dibenzyl is not coplanar;[3] and coplanarity has been observed also for trans-azobenzene,[4] oxalic acid and oxalate ion, and other conjugated molecules. Because the amount of double-bond character of the conjugated "single" bond is small, however, the forces which strive toward

[1] V. Schomaker and L. Pauling, *J.A.C.S.* **61**, 1769 (1939).

[2] J. M. Robertson, *Proc. Roy. Soc.* **A150**, 348 (1935).

[3] J. M. Robertson and I. Woodward, *ibid.* **A162**, 568 (1937).

[4] J. J. de Lange, J. M. Robertson, and I. Woodward, *ibid.* **A171**, 398 (1939).

coplanarity are not very strong, and may be rather easily overcome by steric effects.   This is illustrated by Figure 27-1, showing a molecule of cis-azobenzene drawn to scale, with use of 1.0 Å
as the van der Waals radius of hydrogen.   It is seen that contact
of the ortho hydrogen atoms of the two rings prevents the molecule from assuming the coplanar configuration, and it has in fact
been found by x-ray examination[1] that each of the phenyl groups
is rotated through about 50° out of the coplanar orientation.   A
non-coplanar configuration has been reported for o-diphenylbenzene also.[2]

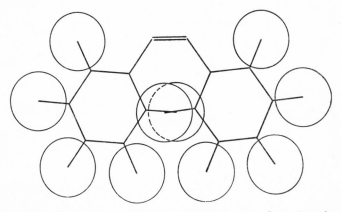

FIG. 27-1.—The coplanar configuration of cis-azobenzene, drawn to scale with
use of 1.0 Å for the van der Waals radius for hydrogen.   It is seen that steric interactions of hydrogen atoms prevent the assumption of this configuration.

A similar scale drawing of 1,3,5-triphenylbenzene, Figure 27-2,
shows that there is some steric repulsion between hydrogen atoms
in this molecule (drawn with non-bonded radius 1.0 Å); the same
amount is expected for biphenyl (Figure 27-3).   It can not be
predicted that this repulsion would be strong enough to overcome
the tendency toward coplanarity resulting from conjugation, and
the available empirical information is conflicting: triphenylben-
zene is reported from x-ray study to be non-coplanar,[3] whereas
older studies of biphenyl[4] and p-diphenylbenzene[5] have led to
coplanar structures.

[1] J. M. Robertson, *J. Chem. Soc.* **1939**, 232.

[2] C. J. B. Clews and K. Lonsdale, *Proc. Roy. Soc.* **A161**, 493 (1937)

[3] K. Lonsdale, *Z. Krist.* **97**, 91 (1937).

[4] J. Dhar, *Indian J. Phys.* **7**, 43 (1932).

[5] L. W. Pickett. *Proc. Roy. Soc.* **A142**, 333 (1933).

The effect of steric hindrance in giving rise to optical activity of o—o′ substituted biphenyls is well known; for a discussion of

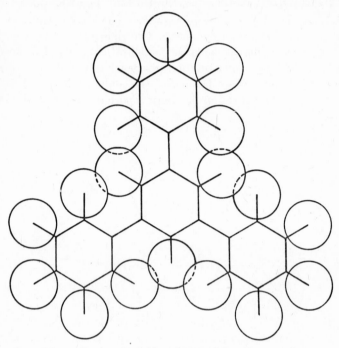

Fig. 27-2.—The coplanar configuration of 1,3,5-triphenylbenzene, drawn to scale with use of 1.0 Å for the van der Waals radius of hydrogen.

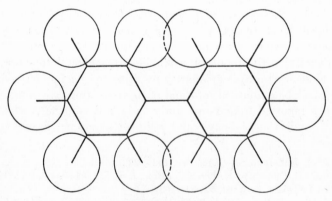

Fig. 27-3.—The coplanar configuration of biphenyl, drawn to scale with use of 1.0 Å for the van der Waals radius of hydrogen.

this phenomenon the reader is referred to treatises on organic chemistry.[1]

An interesting method of determining the amount of conjugation energy of two benzene rings and a nitrogen-nitrogen double bond has been developed recently, subsequent to the discovery[2] that the cis isomer of azobenzene is formed from the ordinary (trans) isomer in solution through the action of light. As mentioned above, steric interaction of the two rings in the cis compound is so great that a coplanar configuration can not be achieved, the benzene rings being rotated 50° out of the coplanar configuration. Since coplanarity is an essential attribute of double-bond character, we may assume that the amount of conjugation energy in cis-azobenzene and related molecules is small (it is probably not greater than 2 or 3 kcal./mole), and accept the difference in energy of the cis and trans isomers as the conjugation energy for the trans configuration. This has been determined by Hartley[3] by the measurement of heats of fusion of the two crystalline substances to the (trans) liquid as 12 kcal./mole and by Corruccini and Gilbert[4] by the measurement of their heats of combustion as 10 kcal./mole.

A very interesting investigation of the effect of the nuclear configuration of a molecule, as influenced by the steric interactions of atoms and groups, on the amount of resonance has been carried out by Birtles and Hampson[5] by the measurement of the electric dipole moments of the substituted durenes.

It was pointed out in Sections 19b and 19c that a nitro group or amino group substituted in benzene interacts with the benzene ring in such a way as to give the molecules values of the electric dipole moments which differ from those for the corresponding alkyl derivatives.[6] For nitrobenzene the moment, 3.95×10^{-18} e.s.u., is increased by 0.64×10^{-18} e.s.u. above the value for alkyl

---

[1] See, for example, H. Gilman, "Organic Chemistry," John Wiley and Sons, New York, 1938, p. 263.

[2] G. S. Hartley, *Nature* 140, 281 (1937).

[3] G. S. Hartley, *J. Chem. Soc.* 1938, 633.

[4] R. J. Corruccini and E. C. Gilbert, *J.A.C.S.* 61, 2925 (1939).

[5] R. H. Birtles and G. C. Hampson, *J.C.S.* 1937, 10; see also C. E. Ingham and G. C. Hampson, *ibid.* 1939, 981.

[6] See also W. D. Kumler and C. W. Porter, *J.A.C.S.* 56, 2549 (1934); C. K. Ingold, *Chem. Rev.* 15, 225 (1934); L. G. Groves and S. Sugden, *J.C.S.* 1937, 1992; C. P. Smyth, *J. Phys. Chem.* 41, 209 (1937).

nitro derivatives because of resonance with structures such as

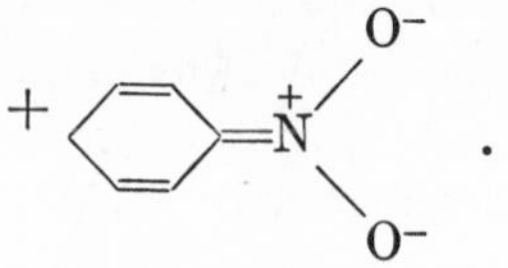

In aniline there occurs similar resonance with structures such as

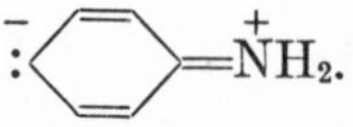

With an electron-donating group and an electron-receiving group para to one another in the same molecule additional resonance occurs with structures such as

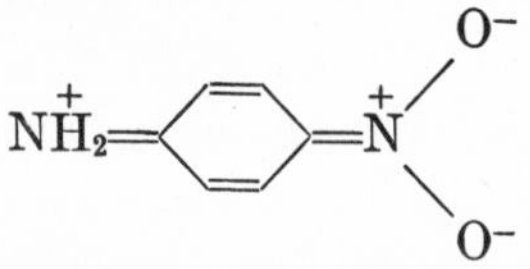

for p-nitrodimethylaniline, for example, this effect causes the dipole moment, 6.87×10^{-18} e.s.u., to be much greater than the sum of the values 3.95 and 1.58×10^{-18} e.s.u. for nitrobenzene and dimethylaniline, respectively.

Now in order that resonance of these types may occur, giving partial double-bond character to the bonds connecting the benzene ring and the attached groups, the molecule must approximate the coplanar configuration appropriate to this double-bond character. This is possible in nitrobenzene itself; but in nitro-

durene, , steric interaction between the oxygen

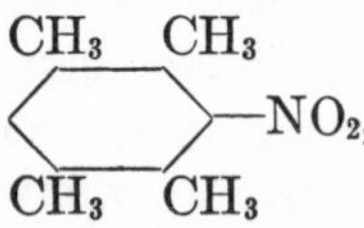

atoms of the nitro group and the ortho methyl groups prevents the assumption of the coplanar configuration, the nitro group being rotated somewhat about the N—C bond. Accordingly the resonance with the ring should be less complete than for nitrobenzene. This prediction is verified by the observed moments: nitrobenzene, 3.93; nitrodurene, 3.39; alkyl nitro compounds, 3.29×10^{-18} e.s.u. It is seen that the moment in nitrodurene is reduced nearly to the alkyl value. A similar result is obtained with nitroaminodurene, with moment 4.98×10^{-18} e.s.u., 1.12 smaller than that, 6.10×10^{-18} e.s.u., for p-nitroaniline. In

this case there is inhibition also of the resonance involving interaction between the nitro and amino groups.

Steric effects of this sort should be small for the amino group,
because of its small size, and non-existent for bromine and other
cylindrically symmetrical groups.   It is found that corresponding
durene and benzene derivatives involving these groups differ
only slightly in moment, the small differences being attributed to
induction in the methyl groups; values found are the following:
aminodurene, 1.39, aniline, 1.53; bromodurene, 1.55, bromo-
benzene, 1.52.

Steric interactions are often of significance in the orientation of
substituents in aromatic molecules.   In the discussion of the
Mills-Nixon effect in Section 19 it was mentioned that *ar*-tetra-
hydro-β-naphthol undergoes substitution in the 1 position on
reaction with the phenyldiazonium ion, this effect being explained
as the result of a somewhat greater contribution by one Kekulé
structure than by the other to the normal state of the molecule.
Bromination also takes place, like diazotization, in the 1 position,
but sulfonation and nitration are anomalous, leading to 3 derivatives.   This we attribute to the effect of steric repulsion of the
sulfonic acid group or nitro group in the 1 position by the adjacent methylene group, leading to an increase in the heat of activation for 1 substitution great enough to overcome the rather small
advantage over 3 substitution resulting from the Mills-Nixon effect.

Other examples showing the importance of steric hindrance of
resonance in anomalous cases of orientation in aromatic substitu-
tions have been pointed out.[1]

The value of the central bond distance in cyanogen[2] and diacetylene[2] is 1.36 Å.   This corresponds to about 45% double-
bond character, showing the large conjugating power of the triple
bond.   (A correction of 0.04 Å is made here for the effect of the
triple bonds on the normal single-bond radii of the carbon atoms.)
The value 1.40 Å has been reported[3] for the bond between benzene
rings and acetylenic carbon atoms in tolane, C_6H_5—C≡C—C_6H_5.
The conjugation energy of the phenyl group and the triple bond
in phenylacetylene is about 10 kcal./mole.

The well-known chemical properties of conjugated systems, in-

[1] G. Baddeley, *Nature* 144, 444 (1939); W. G. Brown, A. H. Widiger,
and N. J. Letang, *J.A.C.S.* 61, 2597 (1940).
   [2] L. O. Brockway, *Proc. Nat. Acad. Sci.* 19, 868 (1933); L. Pauling,
H. D. Springall, and K. J. Palmer, *J.A.C.S.* 61, 927, (1939).
   [3] J. M. Robertson and I. Woodward, *Proc. Roy. Soc.* A164, 436 (1938).

cluding especially their power of transmitting the effects of groups, can be accounted for in a qualitative way by the resonance concept. For example, an electron-donating group such

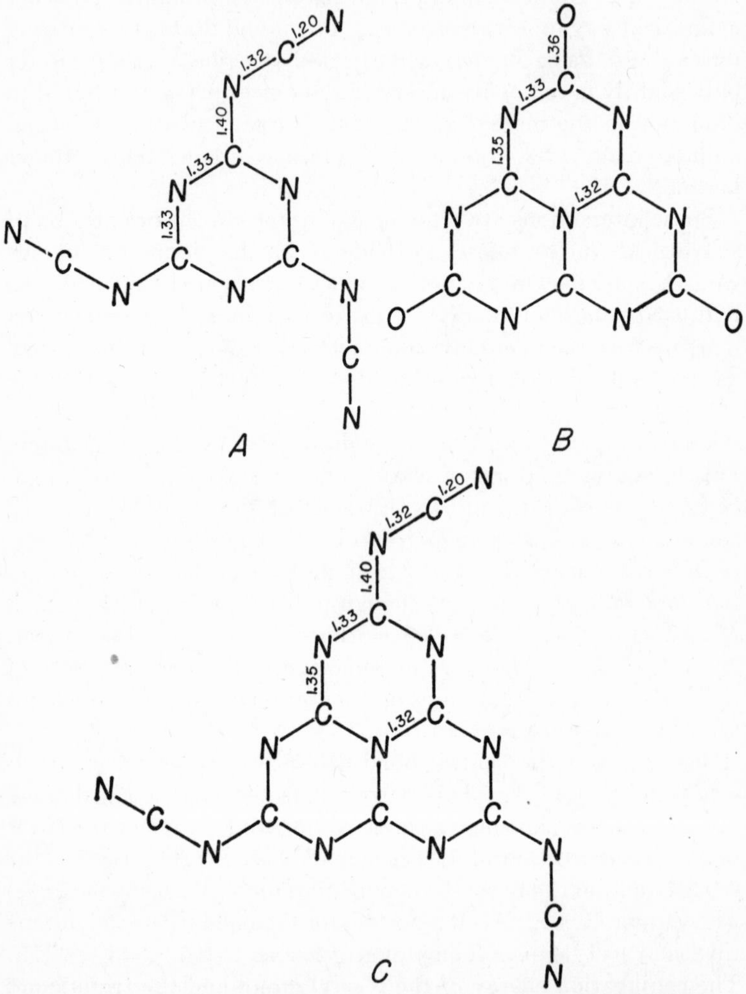

Fig. 28-1.—The structures of (A) the cyanuric tricyanamide ion, [C₆H₃]⁻⁻⁻, (b) the cyamelurate ion, [C₆N₇O₃]⁻⁻⁻ and (c) the cyameluric tricyanamide (hydromelonate) ion, [C₉N₁₃]⁻⁻⁻. Predicted values of interatomic distances are shown. The molecules are coplanar, with all bond angles (except in the linear cyanamide groups) close to 120°.

as $(CH_3)_2N-$ in a molecule $(CH_3)_2\overset{..}{N}CH=CH-CH=R$ can transmit its electrons to the group R by resonance with the structure $(CH_3)_2N^+$=CH—CH=CH—$\overset{..}{R}{}^-$. Phenomena of this type have been discussed especially by Robinson.[1]

28. RESONANCE IN HETEROCYCLIC MOLECULES

For pyridine, pyrazine, and related six-membered heterocyclic molecules Kekulé resonance occurs as in benzene, causing the molecules to be coplanar and stabilizing them by about 40 kcal./ mole. The interatomic distances observed in these molecules,[2] C—C = 1.40 Å and C—N = 1.36 Å, are compatible with this structure. The resonance energy found for quinoline, 69 kcal./ mole, is about the same as that of naphthalene.

In cyanuric triazide,[3] $C_3N_3(N_3)_3$, and the cyanuric tricyanamide ion,[4] $[C_3N_3(NCN)_3]^{---}$, the cyanuric ring has the configuration and dimensions expected for Kekulé resonance. An interesting type of resonance[5] is shown by the cyameluric nucleus, C_6N_7, in the cyamelurate ion, $[C_6N_7O_3]^{---}$, and the hydromelonate ion, $[C_6N_7(NCN)_3]^{---}$ (Fig. 28-1). The electronic structure of this nucleus corresponds to resonance not only between the two **valence-bond structures I and II**

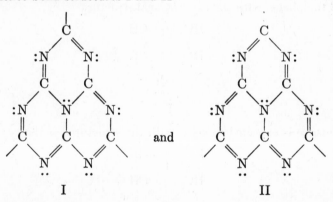

I   II

---

[1] R. Robinson, *loc. cit.*; *Society of Dyers and Colourists, Jubilee Journal,* 1934, 65.

[2] The values given for interatomic distances in pyridine, pyrazine, furan, pyrrole, and thiophene are from an investigation by V. Schomaker and L. Pauling, *J.A.C.S.* **61**, 1769 (1939).

[3] E. W. Hughes, *J. Chem. Phys.* **3**, 1, 650 (1935); I. E. Knaggs, *Proc. Roy. Soc.* A150, 576 (1935); *J. Chem. Phys.* **3**, 241 (1935).

[4] J. L. Hoard, *J.A.C.S.* **60**, 1194 (1938).

[5] L. Pauling and J. H. Sturdivant. *Proc. Nat. Acad. Sci.* **23**, 615 (1937). Chemical evidence regarding the structure of the cyameluric nucleus has been presented by C. E. Redemann and H. J. Lucas, *J.A.C.S.* **61**, 3420 (1939).

(corresponding to the Kekulé structures of benzene), but also among the eighteen structures of the types III to XX,

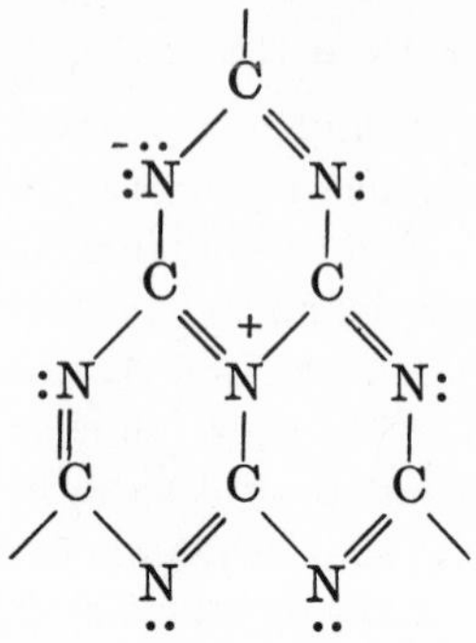

III to XX

each of which, with six double bonds but with separated electric charges, makes a somewhat smaller contribution than structure I or II (probably about one-half or two-thirds as large).

For the five-membered heterocyclic molecules furan, pyrrole, and thiophene, with the conventional structure

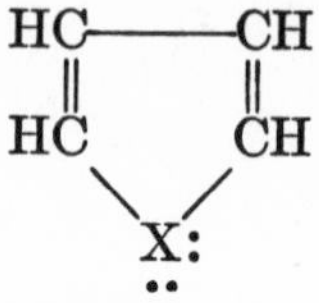

I

resonance is expected to occur with the structures of the types

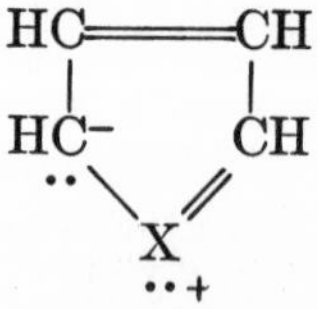

II, III

and

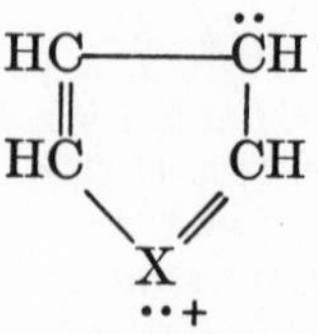

IV, V

The thermochemical data for these substances give the values 23, 31, and 31 kcal./mole, respectively, for the energy of this resonance. It is interesting that the extent of the resonance, as indicated by the magnitude of the resonance energy, increases with decrease in electronegativity of X; the very electronegative oxygen atom has smaller tendency to assume the positive charge accompanying structures II to V than has the less electronegative nitrogen or sulfur atom. This conclusion is further substantiated by the observed interatomic distances, C—O = 1.41 A, C—N = 1.42 Å, and C—S = 1.74 Å in furan, pyrrole, and thiophene, respectively; these correspond (with consideration of the electric charge effect) to about 8% total contribution of structures II to V for furan, 24% for pyrrole, and 28% for thiophene. (The furan value is smaller than expected.)

Similar resonance is shown by indole,

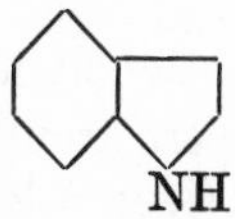

(resonance energy 54 kcal./mole), carbazole,

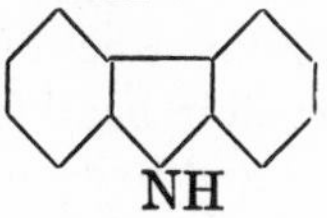

(resonance energy 91 kcal./mole), and related molecules

CHAPTER VII

THE STRUCTURE OF MOLECULES AND COMPLEX IONS INVOLVING BONDS WITH PARTIAL DOUBLE-BOND CHARACTER

From the discussion in the preceding chapters several conclusions have been drawn which are of significance with regard to the structure of molecules and complex ions involving bonds between atoms of the heavier elements—those beyond the first row of the periodic system—and atoms and groups such as the halogens, oxygen, the hydroxyl and amino groups, the carbonyl, cyanide, and nitro groups, etc. It has been seen that the heavier atoms are not rigorously restricted by the octet rule, but can and often do make use of the d orbitals of the valence shell or the next inner shell in bond formation; that electron "donors" such as the halogen and oxygen atoms and the hydroxyl and amino groups held by a single covalent bond are able under certain circumstances to swing another pair of electrons into position for bond formation, converting the bond into a double bond; and that electron "acceptors" such as the cyanide and nitro groups held by a single bond are similarly able to make space (that is, provide an orbital) for a pair of electrons disgorged by the rest of the molecule, the bond being converted into a double bond in this way. By application of these ideas, and by recourse to experimental information to settle doubtful points, a detailed description of the structure of molecules and complex ions of the heavier elements can be formulated, as presented in the following sections.

29. COMPOUNDS OF THE ELEMENTS WITH THE HALOGENS

29a. The Structure of Silicon Tetrachloride and Related Molecules.[1]—It has been customary in the past to assign to silicon tetrachloride (which we select for illustration) the simple valence-bond structure A,

[1] L. O. Brockway and F. T. Wall, *J.A.C.S.* **56**, 2373 (1934).

$$A \quad \ddot{:}\overset{\displaystyle ..}{\underset{\displaystyle ..}{\text{Cl}}}\ddot{:}\overset{\displaystyle ..}{\underset{\displaystyle ..}{\text{Si}}}\ddot{:}\overset{\displaystyle ..}{\underset{\displaystyle ..}{\text{Cl}}}\ddot{:}$$

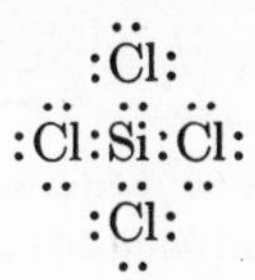

analogous to that of carbon tetrachloride or of silicon tetra-methyl, in which the central atom is surrounded by four shared pairs which make use of its sp^3 bond orbitals. The observation that the configuration of the molecule is that of a regular tetra-hedron is compatible with this picture; but the observed value of the silicon-chlorine distance is not, this value, 2.00 ± 0.02 Å (Table 29-1), being 0.16 Å less than the sum of the single-bond covalent radii of silicon and chlorine.

TABLE 29-1.—INTERATOMIC DISTANCES IN CHLORIDE
MOLECULES MCl_n.[1]

(The upper number of those in each group is the observed value of the M—Cl distance, that below it the sum of the single-bond covalent radii, with their difference on the third line. The fourth number is the sum of the double-bond radii, given for those elements for which it is known.)

Si—Cl	P—Cl	S—Cl	Cl—Cl
2.00 ± 0.02	2.00 ± 0.02	2.00 ± 0.02	1.983 ± 0.005 Å
2.16 1.96	*2.09 1.89*	*2.03 1.83*	(*1.98*)
−0.16	−0.09	−0.03	(0.00)

Ge—Cl	As—Cl
2.08 ± 0.03	2.16 ± 0.03
2.21	*2.20*
−0.13	−0.04

Sn—Cl	Sb—Cl	Te—Cl	I—Cl
2.30 ± 0.03	2.37 ± 0.02	2.36 ± 0.03	2.315 ± 0.005
2.39	*2.40*	*2.36*	*2.32*
−0.09	−0.03	0.00	0.00

[1] The observed values quoted in this table and the following one are due in the main to L. O. Brockway and F. T. Wall, *J.A.C.S.* **56**, 2373 (1934); see also R. Wierl, *Ann. d. Phys.* **8**, 521 (1931); **13**, 453 (1932); L. O. Brock-way, *J.A.C.S.* **57**, 958 (1935); W. Grether, *Ann. d. Phys.* **26**, 1 (1936); D. P. Stevenson and J. Y. Beach, *J.A.C.S.* **60**, 2872 (1938).

The suggestion that this discrepancy shows that the values of the radii are in error can be rejected, inasmuch as these values, obtained from the elements themselves, are verified by the data for their methyl derivatives. The suggestion that it is due directly to the partial ionic character of the bonds can also be discredited: the Si—Cl bond (electronegativity difference, 1.2) is less ionic than the C—F bond (electronegativity difference, 1.5), and the latter bond in methyl fluoride exhibits an interatomic distance equal to its radius sum.

The interpretation which is given to this decrease in interatomic distance below the value expected for a single covalent bond is that it represents the effect of partial double-bond character resulting from the use of a second orbital of the chlorine atom, together with its pair of electrons, in bond formation, the phenomenon being closely similar in nature to that described in Section 26 in connection with the chloroethylenes and chlorobenzenes.

The magnitude of the shortening is very large; it corresponds to about fifty percent double-bond character for each of the silicon-chlorine bonds. This would result from resonance of the molecule among the six structures of the type C

$$
C \qquad
\begin{array}{c}
:\overset{\cdot\cdot}{\text{Cl}}: \\
\overset{+\,\cdot\cdot}{:}\text{Cl}::\overset{\cdot\cdot}{\text{Si}}::\overset{\cdot\cdot}{\text{Cl}}\overset{--\cdot\cdot}{:}{}^{+} \\
:\overset{\cdot\cdot}{\text{Cl}}: \\
\cdot\cdot
\end{array}
$$

(the six differing in the distribution of the two double bonds among the four chlorine atoms). Resonance is of course then to be expected also with the four structures of type B, four of type D, one of type A, and one of type E.

$$
\begin{array}{ccc}
:\overset{\cdot\cdot}{\text{Cl}}: & \overset{\cdot\cdot+}{\text{Cl}}: & \overset{\cdot\cdot+}{\text{Cl}}: \\
:\overset{\cdot\cdot}{\text{Cl}}:\overset{\cdot\cdot-}{\text{Si}}::\overset{\cdot\cdot}{\text{Cl}}{}^{+} & :\overset{\cdot\cdot+}{\text{Cl}}::\overset{\cdot\cdot}{\text{Si}}:----\overset{\cdot\cdot}{:}{}^{+}\text{Cl}: & :\overset{\cdot\cdot+}{\text{Cl}}::\overset{\cdot\cdot}{\text{Si}}:----\overset{\cdot\cdot}{:}{}^{+}\text{Cl}: \\
:\overset{\cdot\cdot}{\text{Cl}}: & :\overset{\cdot\cdot}{\text{Cl}}: & \overset{\cdot\cdot+}{\text{Cl}}: \\
B & D & E
\end{array}
$$

These structures altogether give to the silicon atom a resultant negative charge, and to the chlorine atoms positive charges, whereas charges of opposite sign are indicated by the electronegativity scale. The reversal of charge is accomplished by resonance with the numerous structures of types A', A'', B', etc., shown below:

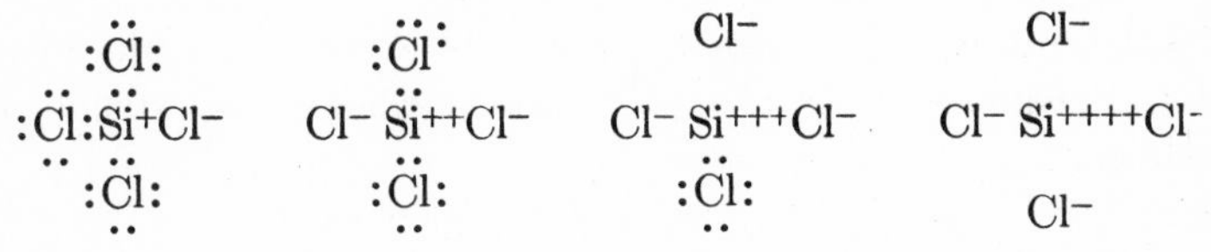

$$
\begin{array}{cccc}
:\overset{\cdot\cdot}{\underset{\cdot\cdot}{Cl}}: & :\overset{\cdot\cdot}{\underset{\cdot\cdot}{Cl}}{\cdot} & Cl^- & Cl^- \\
:\overset{\cdot\cdot}{\underset{\cdot\cdot}{Cl}}:Si^+Cl^- & Cl^-\ Si^{++}Cl^- & Cl^-\ Si^{+++}Cl^- & Cl^-\ Si^{++++}Cl^- \\
:\overset{\cdot\cdot}{\underset{\cdot\cdot}{Cl}}: & :\overset{\cdot\cdot}{\underset{\cdot\cdot}{Cl}}: & :\overset{\cdot\cdot}{\underset{\cdot\cdot}{Cl}}: & Cl^- \\
A' & A'' & A''' & A''''
\end{array}
$$

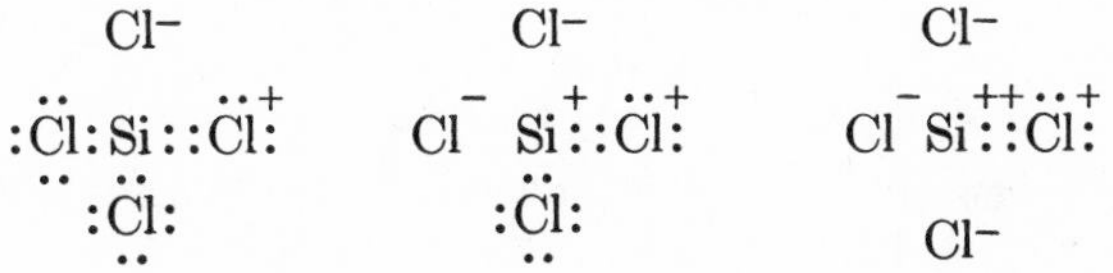

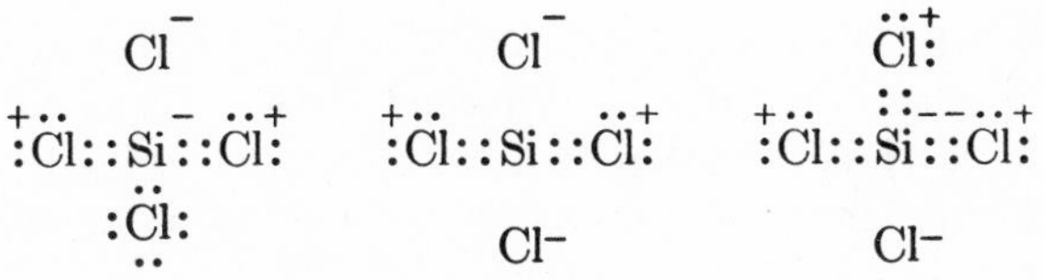

$$
\begin{array}{ccc}
Cl^- & Cl^- & Cl^- \\
:\overset{\cdot\cdot}{Cl}:Si::\overset{\cdot\cdot}{\underset{\cdot\cdot}{Cl}}:^+ & Cl^-\ Si^+::\overset{\cdot\cdot}{\underset{\cdot\cdot}{Cl}}:^+ & Cl^-\ Si^{++}::\overset{\cdot\cdot}{Cl}:^+ \\
:\overset{\cdot\cdot}{\underset{\cdot\cdot}{Cl}}: & :\overset{\cdot\cdot}{\underset{\cdot\cdot}{Cl}}: & Cl^- \\
B' & B'' & B'''
\end{array}
$$

$$
\begin{array}{ccc}
Cl^- & Cl^- & \overset{\cdot\cdot}{Cl}:^+ \\
^+:\overset{\cdot\cdot}{Cl}::Si^-::\overset{\cdot\cdot}{Cl}:^+ & ^+:\overset{\cdot\cdot}{Cl}::Si::\overset{\cdot\cdot}{Cl}:^+ & ^+:\overset{\cdot\cdot}{Cl}::\overset{:}{\underset{--}{Si}}::\overset{\cdot\cdot}{Cl}:^+ \\
:\overset{\cdot\cdot}{\underset{\cdot\cdot}{Cl}}: & Cl^- & Cl^- \\
C' & C'' & D'
\end{array}
$$

Here the symbol Cl^- is used for chlorine with four unshared pairs of valence electrons.

The extent to which these various structures contribute is uncertain. It is seen that whereas structures A, A', A'', A''', A'''', B', B'', B''', and C'' involve four or fewer bonds, which can be formed by use of the $3s3p^3$ orbitals of the silicon atom, the remaining structures require that one or more of the relatively unstable $3d$ orbitals also be drafted into service. It is probable for this reason that the structures of the first class make larger contributions than those of the second class, the silicon atom acquiring in this way a small resultant positive charge and the chlorine atoms corresponding negative charges.

A bond in silicon tetrachloride can be described as resonating among the ionic structure, $Si^+\ Cl^-$, the single normal covalent structure, $Si:\overset{..}{Cl}:$, and the double covalent structure, $Si^-::\overset{..}{Cl}:^+$, with the first somewhat more important that the third.   Or, if we represent by the valence dashes covalent bonds with partial ionic character, as is customary, the bond can be said to resonate between the two bond types Si—Cl and Si=Cl, with the molecule as a whole resonating among various valence-bond structures such as the following:

$$
\begin{array}{ccccc}
\mathrm{Cl} & \mathrm{Cl} & \mathrm{Cl} & \mathrm{Cl} & \mathrm{Cl}\\
| & | & \| & \| & \|\\
\mathrm{Cl{-}Si{-}Cl} & \mathrm{Cl{-}Si{=}Cl} & \mathrm{Cl{-}Si{=}Cl} & \mathrm{Cl{=}Si{=}Cl} & \mathrm{Cl{=}Si{=}Cl}\\
| & | & | & | & \|\\
\mathrm{Cl} & \mathrm{Cl} & \mathrm{Cl} & \mathrm{Cl} & \mathrm{Cl}
\end{array}
$$

This last description of the molecule is the simplest one which represents it satisfactorily.

In the above discussion of the silicon-chlorine interatomic distance the possible direct effect of the ionic structure on the distance has been ignored.   This seems to be justified in practice—the carbon-fluorine bond in methyl fluoride, with about 43 percent ionic character, exhibits its normal distance—and, moreover, it can be justified to some extent by theoretical arguments also. The ionic radius (Chap. X) of an atom is a far more variable quantity than its covalent radius; it responds by large variations to change in coordination number, and it may be expected to leave to the more precise covalent radius the burden of determining the equilibrium distance for bonds of mixed type.

The amount of double-bond character of the M—X bonds in a molecule MX_n depends mainly on two factors: first, the tendency of the two atoms to form double bonds, and second, the tendency of one bond MX to become ionic and thus free an M orbital of the sp^3 type for use in forming a double bond with another X atom.   The first of these factors decreases from the first row to the second row and the lower rows of the periodic table; first row atoms form multiple bonds with ease, second row atoms occasionally, and the others rarely.   From the data collected in Table 29-1 it is seen that both of these factors are important. In the sequence Si, Ge, Sn, with decreasing electronegativity and hence increasing amount of ionic character of the bond formed with chlorine, the observed shortening of interatomic distance decreases, as a result of the operation of the first factor; whereas in a horizontal sequence, Si to P or Ge to As, with the first factor constant, the shortening decreases by virtue of the second factor, aided by decrease in the number of partially ionic M—X bonds which contribute.

An interesting test of the relative importance of the two factors may be made by considering the interatomic distances in a sequence of molecules such as $SiCl_4$, $SiHCl_3$, SiH_2Cl_2, and SiH_3Cl, in which the effect of the second factor decreases in the approximate ratios 3:2:1:0. The values reported for the Si-Cl distance in these substances[1,2] are 2.00 ± 0.02 Å for $SiCl_4$, 2.01 ± 0.03 Å for $SiHCl_3$, 2.02 ± 0.03 Å for SiH_2Cl_2, and 2.06 ± 0.05 Å for SiH_3Cl. These values indicate that the second factor is of somewhat smaller significance than the first factor in the chlorosilanes.

The very strongly electronegative first-row atom fluorine should be more effective than chlorine both in the formation of a double bond and in liberating a stable orbital on the central atom for use in forming a double bond with another halogen atom. The data in Table 29-2 show that this expectation is justified; the

TABLE 29-2.—INTERATOMIC DISTANCES IN FLUORIDE MOLECULES MF_n

Si—F	P—F
1.54 ± 0.02	1.52 ± 0.04 Å
1.81 1.61	*1.74 1.54*
-0.27	-0.22

As—F
1.72 ± 0.02
1.85
-0.13

shortening in fluorides is about 0.12 Å greater than in the corresponding chlorides. In silicon tetrafluoride and phosphorus trifluoride the interatomic distances fall somewhat below their double-bond values as given by the sum of the double-bond radii. This may be the result of the effect of electric charge (Sec. 21b).

[1] L. O. Brockway and J. Y. Beach, *J.A.C.S.* **60**, 1836 (1938).
[2] L. O. Brockway and I. E. Coop, *Trans. Faraday Soc.* **34**, 1429 (1938).

The Si—F and P—F bonds have a great deal of ionic character—over one-half—and structures of the type

$$\begin{matrix} \text{F} \\ | \\ \text{F—Si=F}^+ \\ \\ \text{F}^- \end{matrix}$$

are expected to be important. Here the charge correction of about -0.04 Å is operating, because of the positive fluorine atom, and the Si=F distance is reduced from 1.61 to 1.57 Å. A further decrease may be produced by other still more ionic structures; and it is also possible that in these very ionic molecules the ionic character of the bonds is playing some direct part in the determination of the interatomic distances. Structures with a silicon-fluorine triple bond, $\text{Si}\equiv\text{F:}^{++}$, are expected not to be very stable because they place a double positive charge on the fluorine atom; they may be of some significance, however, and some of the shortening may be due to partial triple-bond character of the silicon-fluorine bond.

The partial double-bond character of the bonds seems to have

TABLE 29-3.—INTERATOMIC DISTANCES IN HALIDES OF ELEMENTS OF THE FIFTH GROUP[1]

P—F	P—Cl	P—Br	P—I
1.52 ± 0.04	2.00 ± 0.02	2.23 ± 0.02	2.47 ± 0.05 Å
1.74	*2.09*	*2.24*	*2.43*
-0.22	-0.09	-0.01	$+0.04$

As—F	As—Cl	As—Br	As—I
1.72 ± 0.02	2.16 ± 0.03	2.33 ± 0.03	2.54 ± 0.04
1.85	*2.20*	*2.35*	*2.54*
-0.13	-0.04	-0.02	0.00

Sb—Cl	Sb—Br	Sb—I
2.37 ± 0.02	2.50 ± 0.02	2.71 ± 0.03
2.40	*2.55*	*2.74*
-0.03	-0.05	-0.03

[1] The observed values for PBr_3, PI_3, $AsBr_3$, AsI_3, $SbCl_3$, $SbBr_3$, and SbI_3 are averages of those reported by A. H. Gregg, G. C. Hampson, G. I. Jenkins, P. L. F. Jones, and L. E. Sutton, *Trans. Faraday Soc.* **33**, 852 (1937); O. Hassel and A. Sandbo, *Z. f. phys. Chem.* **B41**, 75 (1938); and D. P. Stevenson, V. Schomaker, and S. Swingle, unpublished work

little influence on the bond angles, which are observed to have the same values in the halides as in the methyl compounds of the elements of the fifth and sixth groups (Table 13-1).   It seems that a single covalent bond to each attached atom plays the deciding part in the determination of bond directions.

Recent investigations have provided data, given in Table 29-3, for a further test of the suggestion that the observed decrease in interatomic distance in the covalent halides is due to partial double-bond character of the bonds, and that this phenomenon is less significant for the heavier elements than for the lighter ones. It is seen that for the elements phosphorus and arsenic the amount of shortening decreases in the halogen sequence fluorine, chlorine, bromine, iodine.   The bromides and iodides show, indeed, no significant decrease below the single-bond value, suggesting that these elements have small power of double-bond formation. The results of different investigators are not in close agreement, and a careful reinvestigation must be made before more detailed conclusions are drawn.

29b. The Fluorochloromethanes.   The Effect of Bond Type on Chemical Reactivity.[1]—In a methyl halide molecule the double-bond structure $H_3C{=}X$ cannot occur because the carbon atom has only four orbitals available for bond formation.   If, however, two or more halogen atoms are introduced into the methane molecule, resonance with structures of the type

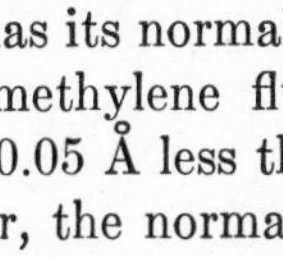

$$\begin{matrix} X^- \\ \\ H-C{=}X^+ \\ | \\ H \end{matrix}$$

might occur.   It was discovered by Brockway that, although the carbon-fluorine distance has its normal value in methyl fluoride, the values observed in methylene fluoride and carbon tetrafluoride (Table 29-4) are 0.05 Å less than the sum of the single-bond radii, and, moreover, the normal value is observed in the molecules CH_2FCl and $CHFCl_2$, containing only one fluorine atom, and the shorter distance in CHF_2Cl and CF_2Cl_2, containing two.   This mass of consistent evidence shows that in a molecule

---

[1] L. O. Brockway, *J. Phys. Chem.* **41**, 185 (1937)

TABLE 29-4.—INTERATOMIC DISTANCES IN THE FLUOROMETHANES,
CHLOROMETHANES, AND FLUOROCHLOROMETHANES[1]

Substance	C—F	C—Cl
CH_3F	1.42 ± 0.02 Å	
CH_2F_2	1.36 ± 0.02	
CF_4	1.36 ± 0.02	
CH_3Cl		1.77 ± 0.02 Å
CH_2Cl_2		1.77 ± 0.02
$CHCl_3$		1.77 ± 0.02
CCl_4		1.755 ± 0.005
CH_2FCl	1.40 ± 0.03	1.76 ± 0.02
$CHFCl_2$	1.41 ± 0.03	1.73 ± 0.04
$CFCl_3$	1.40 ± 0.03	1.76 ± 0.02
CHF_2Cl	1.36 ± 0.03	1.73 ± 0.03
CF_2Cl_2	1.35 ± 0.03	1.74 ± 0.03

[1] L. O. Brockway, *J. Phys. Chem.* **41**, 747 (1937).

with two fluorine atoms attached to the same carbon atom each
carbon-fluorine bond achieves about ten percent double-bond
character with the simultaneous assumption of ionic character by
the other bond.

Shortening of the carbon-chlorine distance by an amount as
large as 0.05 Å is not observed in the fluorochloromethanes. The
data for the five molecules, which, although unreliable individually, give mutual support in the aggregate, indicate that the
F^- $C{=}Cl^+$ interaction decreases the carbon-chlorine distance by
0.02 or 0.03 Å, corresponding to five percent double-bond character. From the comparison of this with the fluorine value it can
be deduced that chlorine has about one-half the power to form
double bonds that fluorine has. It would be interesting to have
similar structural information about the fluorobromomethanes
and fluoroiodomethanes.

We have seen (Sec. 26) that the partial double-bond character
of the carbon-chlorine bond in the chloroethylenes and chlorobenzenes provides an explanation of the great stability of these
substances relative to the chloroparaffins. The same explanation[1] applies to the fact[2] that although the substitution of one
fluorine atom in an aliphatic molecule gives an unstable product,
which easily loses hydrogen fluoride to form an olefine or hydro-
lyses to the alcohol, molecules containing two fluorine atoms at-

[1] L. O. Brockway, *loc. cit.*
[2] A. L. Henne and T. Midgley, Jr., *J.A.C.S.* **58**, 882 (1936).

tached to the same carbon atom are much more stable, the stability applying not only to the fluorine atoms but also to other halogen atoms on the same carbon atom.

29c. The Boron Halides.—In the boron trimethyl molecule (Sec. 21c) the boron atom is surrounded by only three pairs of valence electrons, which are involved in the formation of single covalent bonds to the three carbon atoms of the methyl groups. A similar structure, *A*,

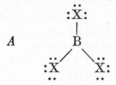

might be assigned to the halides of boron. The boron atom has, however, a fourth stable orbital which can be used for bond formation; and the three structures *B*, *C*, and *D* may be expected to be as stable as and perhaps more stable than *A*; they involve one more bond (that is, a double bond in place of one of the single

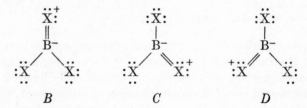

bonds), which stabilizes the molecule to an extent great enough to overcome the instability resulting from the unfavorable separation of charge. The boron halides are accordingly expected to resonate equally among the three equivalent structures *B*, *C*, and *D*, with some contribution by *A* also, and, indeed, with enough contribution by the various partially ionic structures, of the type of *E* and *F*, to overcome the

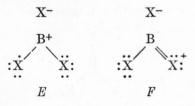

unfavorable distribution of charge and make the resultant average charge of the boron atom zero or slightly positive.

With such a resonating structure the boron halide molecules should be coplanar, with 120° bond angles, and with the predicted boron-halogen distances given in Table 29-5, corresponding to one-third double-bond and two-thirds single-bond character.

TABLE 29-5.—INTERATOMIC DISTANCES IN THE BORON
HALIDE MOLECULES

| | Boron-halogen distance | |
Molecule	Calculated for one-third double-bond character	Observed[1]
BF$_3$	1.39 Å	1.30 ± 0.02 Å
BCl$_3$	1.74	1.74 ± 0.02
BBr$_3$	1.89	1.87 ± 0.02
BI$_3$	2.08	

[1] Averages of the following reported values: B—F = 1.30 ± 0.02 Å, B—Cl = 1.72 ± 0.02 Å, B—Br = 1.87 ± 0.02 Å, H. Lévy and L. O. Brockway, *J.A.C.S.* **59**, 2085 (1937); B—Cl = 1.75 ± 0.03 Å, R. Wierl, *Ann. d. Phys.* **8**, 521 (1931); B—Cl = 1.76 ± 0.03 Å, A. H. Gregg, G. C. Hampson, G. I. Jenkins, P. L. F. Jones, and L. E. Sutton, *Trans. Faraday Soc.* **33**, 852 (1937); B—F = 1.31 ± 0.03 Å, H. Braune and P. Pinnow, *Z. f. phys. Chem.* **B35**, 239 (1937).

In these calculations no formal charge corrections have been made; if structures of type F are very important, a correction approaching −0.03 Å is indicated. On the other hand, a small increase would result from contribution of structure A, so that the values given may be expected to be valid to within about 0.03 A except for the fluoride, which is discussed below.

The symmetrical coplanar configuration has been verified by electron-diffraction investigation of the fluoride, chloride, and bromide and by the determination of the electric dipole moment of the chloride (found to have the value zero). The observed interatomic distances for the chloride and bromide agree satisfactorily with the calculated values, and the boron halides can accordingly be considered to have the valence-bond structure with two single bonds and one double bond resonating among the three positions; the bonds have some partial ionic character.

For the fluoride there is observed an additional decrease of 0.09 Å below the value expected for the boron-fluorine distance. This is attributed to the effect invoked in the discussion of the fluoromethanes in the preceding section; to wit, the contribution of structures such as

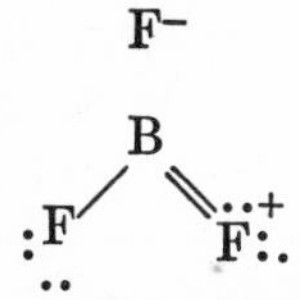

$$F^-$$

$$
\begin{array}{c}
B \\
\diagup \quad \diagdown\!\!\!\!\!= \\
:\!F \qquad \overset{..}{\underset{..}{F}}\!:.\!^+
\end{array}
$$

The greater decrease for boron trifluoride than for fluoroform (0.06 Å) is the result in part of the greater ionic character of the boron-fluorine bond and in part of the correction for incompletion of the valence shell for structures of the above types for BF_3.

30. THE OXIDES AND OXYGEN ACIDS OF THE HEAVIER ELEMENTS

The older conventional valence-bond formulas for an ion such as the sulfate ion,

$$
A \qquad
\begin{array}{c}
O^- \\
| \\
O\!\!=\!\!S\!\!-\!\!O^-, \\
\| \\
O
\end{array}
$$

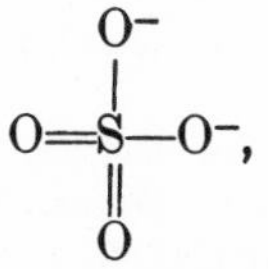

involving single and double covalent bonds from the central atom to the surrounding oxygen atoms in numbers determined by the position of the central atom in the periodic table, have now fallen into general disuse, in consequence of the suggestion, originally made by Lewis in his 1916 paper and accepted by most subsequent investigators, that the octet rule is to be applied to the sulfur atom and other second-row and heavier atoms, and that only four covalent bonds are to be represented in the electronic structures of the sulfate ion and similar ions:

$$
B \qquad
\begin{array}{c}
\overset{..}{:}\!\overset{..}{O}\!:^- \\
\overset{-\,..}{:}\!O\!:\!\overset{..+\,+\,..}{S}\ :\!O\!:^- \\
\overset{..}{:}\!\overset{..}{O}\!:_-
\end{array}
$$

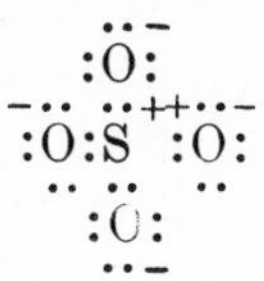

On considering the question of the structure of these ions from the resonance point of view, we see that structure B, although it makes some contribution, is not of overwhelming importance, that other structures involving double bonds between the central atom and oxygen are significant, and that the available evidence indicates that the older valence-bond formulas such as A, with the double bonds resonating among the oxygen atoms, making them equivalent, and with the bonds considered to have partial ionic character, represent the ions somewhat more satisfactorily than the extreme structures of the type of B.

The observed values of interatomic distances in the tetrahedral ions of the ortho oxygen acids of the second-row elements are given in Table 30-1.   They are about 0.20 A less than the sum of the single-bond covalent radii for the atoms; the octet-rule

TABLE 30-1.—INTERATOMIC DISTANCES IN TETRAHEDRAL IONS MO_4

	Si—O in SiO_4^{----}	P—O in PO_4^{---}	S—O in SO_4^{--}	Cl—O in ClO_4^{-}
Observed	1.60[a]	1.55[b]	1.51[c]	(1.48 Å[d])
Radius sum	*1.83*	*1.76*	*1.70*	*1.65*
Difference	−0.23	−0.21	−0.19	−0.17

[a] Values close to 1.60 Å for the Si—O distance have been reported for many silicates.

[b] The most reliable values for the P—O distance in the phosphate group are 1.56 Å in KH_2PO_4 (J. West, *Z. Krist.* **74**, 306 (1930)) and 1.54 Å in BPO_4 (G. E. R. Schulze, *Z. f. phys. Chem.* **B24**, 215 (1934)).

[c] The reliable value 1.51 Å in sulfohalite, $Na_6(SO_4)_2ClF$ (A. Pabst, *Z. Krist.* **89**, 514 (1934); T. Watanabe, *Proc. Imp. Acad. Tokyo* **10**, 575 (1934)), is supported by somewhat less accurate values close to this observed in more complex crystals.

[d] No accurate value of the Cl—O distance in a perchlorate has been reported.   The value chosen is close to several approximate values found in crystals of complicated structure.

structure B is accordingly shown to be unsatisfactory.   In view of the tendency for halogen atoms, usually considered to be unicovalent, to form double covalent bonds, we may well expect that the bivalent oxygen atom in these ions will strive still more strongly to share four valence electrons with the central atom, and that structures of the types C, D, E, and F will contribute largely to the normal state of the ion:

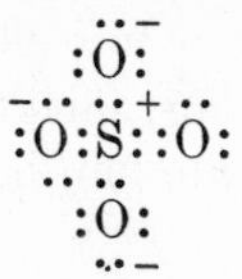

<pre>
                :Ö:⁻   :Ö:⁻
        ⁻:Ö:S::Ö:⁺   :Ö::S::Ö:
             :Ö: :Ö:
              ⁻   ⁻
              C   D

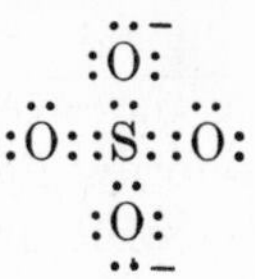

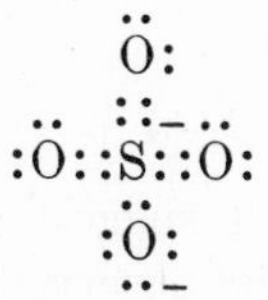

             Ö: Ö:
          :Ö::S::Ö: :Ö::S::Ö:
             :Ö: :Ö:
              ⁻
              E   F
</pre>

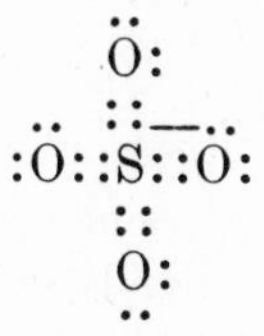

In addition to these structures, which make use of the relatively unstable $3d$ orbitals of the central atom, others of the types *G*, *H*, etc., involving a double ionic bond to one or more oxygen atoms, should be important. (The symbol O^{--} here represents oxygen with four unshared pairs of valence electrons.)

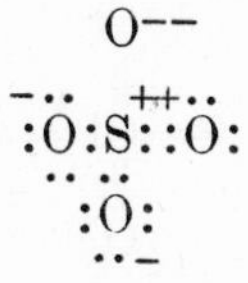

<pre>
           O⁻⁻   O⁻⁻
       ⁻:Ö:S::Ö:⁺⁺   :Ö::S::Ö:⁺⁺
          :Ö: O⁻⁻
           ⁻
           G   H
</pre>

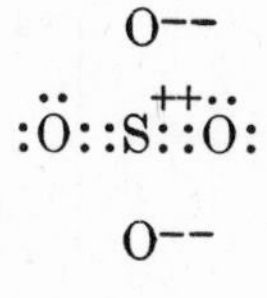

In these structures only the four stable $3s3p^3$ orbitals of sulfur are used, and the sulfur atom is given a double positive formal charge.

The observed shortening of the M—O distance of about 0.20 Å in these ions is greater than that calculated for partial double-bond character with neutral atoms, but it can be attributed to the large contribution of structures of the types *G* and *H*, for which a large formal charge correction is to be made.

The tetrahedral oxygen acids can accordingly be described as resonating among various structures in such a way as to give each bond the character in part of a double covalent bond. For the sulfate ion the old valence-bond structure A, with the bonds resonating among the several positions, might be considered to show this satisfactorily; for the silicate ion, however, the analogous valence-bond structure

$$-O-\underset{\underset{O_-}{|}}{\overset{\overset{O^-}{|}}{Si}}-O^-$$

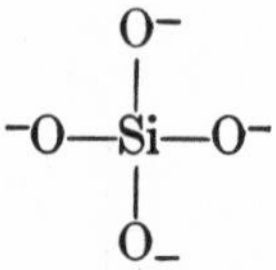

is not satisfactory, since it does not suggest any double-bond character for the bonds, whereas the observed shortening is in this ion even somewhat greater than for the sulfate ion. The valence-bond structures representing all four oxygen atoms as attached to the central atom by double bonds,

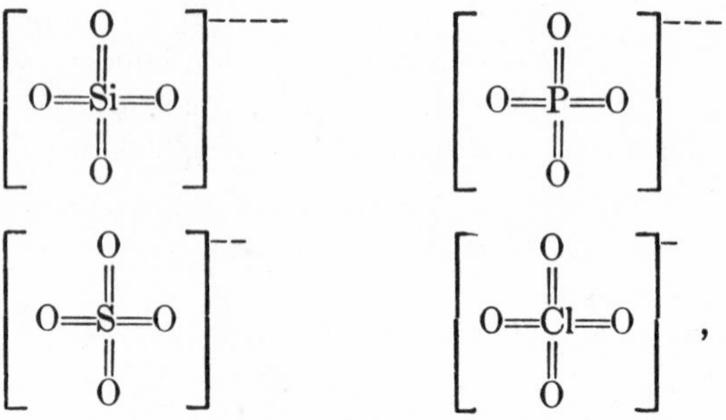

$$\left[O=\underset{\overset{\|}{O}}{\overset{\overset{O}{\|}}{Si}}=O \right]^{----} \qquad \left[O=\underset{\overset{\|}{O}}{\overset{\overset{O}{\|}}{P}}=O \right]^{---}$$

$$\left[O=\underset{\overset{\|}{O}}{\overset{\overset{O}{\|}}{S}}=O \right]^{--} \qquad \left[O=\underset{\overset{\|}{O}}{\overset{\overset{O}{\|}}{Cl}}=O \right]^{-} ,$$

might be conveniently used, each of the double bonds being considered (as in the ketones, for example) to correspond to resonance among the three electronic structures $M::\overset{..}{O}:$, $M^+:\overset{..}{O}:^-$, and $M^{++}O^{--}$, with the magnitude of the contributions of the ionic structures determined by the difference in electronegativity of the central atom and oxygen. These structures, however, do not correspond to the usual conventions regarding valence—they do not represent the chlorine atom, for example, as septivalent—and for this reason I believe that it is not wise to use them. In this case, as in many others, there is no one valence-bond formula which suitably represents the structure of the molecule. I suggest that the conventional valence-bond formulas be

$$
\left[\begin{array}{c} O^- \\ | \\ {}^-O-Si-O^- \\ | \\ O^- \end{array}\right]^{----}
\qquad
\left[\begin{array}{c} O^- \\ | \\ {}^-O-P=O \\ | \\ O^- \end{array}\right]^{---}
$$

$$
\left[\begin{array}{c} O^- \\ | \\ {}^-O-S=O \\ \| \\ O \end{array}\right]^{--}
\qquad
\left[\begin{array}{c} O \\ \| \\ {}^-O-Cl=O \\ \| \\ O \end{array}\right]^{-}
$$

used ordinarily, and that when a more precise description of the electronic structure is needed several of the resonating structures be enclosed in brackets, as in the following representation of the sulfate ion:

$$
\left\{
\begin{array}{ccc}
O^- & O^{--} & O^{--} \\
| & | & \\
{}^-O-\overset{++}{S}-O^{-}, & {}^-O-\overset{++}{S}=O, & O=\overset{++}{S}=O, \quad \text{etc.} \\
| & | & \\
O^- & O^- & O^{--}
\end{array}
\right\}
$$

In general a complex ion of this sort will retain its structure and dimensions essentially unchanged in different environments, since the forces acting upon it, due to the surrounding cations of small charge, are usually weaker than those acting within the complex. An exception seems to be provided by the phosphate group in silver phosphate, Ag_3PO_4. It was found by Helmholz[1] that the P—O distance in the phosphate group in this crystal is 1.61 ± 0.03 Å, rather than 1.55 Å as in other phosphates. The following reasonable explanation of the phenomenon can be given. In the crystal each oxygen atom is surrounded tetrahedrally by one phosphorus atom and three silver atoms. The bonds to the silver atoms have some covalent character. The oxygen atom can form only four covalent bonds, so that the covalent character of the oxygen-silver bonds inhibits in part the double-bond character of the phosphorus-oxygen bonds, leading to a larger phosphate group than in the more ionic phosphates.

The substitution of halogen for hydroxyl in these acids results in molecules in which the oxygen and halogen atoms are attached to the central atom by bonds similar in character to those in oxygen acids and the phosphorus halides. In the phosphorus

[1] L. Helmholz, *J. Chem. Phys.* **4**, 316 (1936).

oxyhalides[1] POF_3, POF_2Cl, $POFCl_2$, and $POCl_3$, the P—O distance is 1.55 ± 0.03 Å, as in the phosphate ion, the P—Cl distance is 2.02 ± 0.02 Å, which is practically the same as the value 2.00 ± 0.02 Å found in phosphorus trichloride, and the P—F distance is 1.51 ± 0.03 Å, as in phosphorus trifluoride. In $PSCl_3$ the P—Cl distance[2] is 2.02 ± 0.02 Å; the P—S distance, 1.94 ± 0.03 A, is close to the double-bond value, 1.95 Å, showing that for sulfur as well as oxygen the bonds with the central atom have a large amount of double-bond character. The P—S distance[3] in PSF_3 is 1.85 ± 0.02 Å; the additional shortening of this bond relative to that in $PSCl_3$ is presumably the result of triple-bond character made possible by the large amount of ionic character of the P—F bonds. The interatomic distances S—O $= 1.43 \pm 0.02$ Å, S—Cl $= 1.99 \pm 0.02$ Å, and S—F $= 1.56 \pm 0.02$ Å found in sulfuryl chloride,[4] SO_2Cl_2, and sulfuryl fluoride,[5] SO_2F_2, show that these molecules are similar in structure to those just discussed.

The pyro, meta, and other polyacids of the second-row atoms contain MO_4 tetrahedra condensed by sharing oxygen atoms. It might be thought that this would decrease the double-bond character of the bonds to the shared oxygen atoms and hence increase the M—O distance; this effect has, however, not been observed. The Si—O distance is reported to be close to 1.60 Å in the Si_2O_7, Si_3O_9, and Si_6O_{18} groups in many silicate crystals, and even in the various forms of silica itself, in which the condensation has continued to its limit, each oxygen atom being common to two SiO_4 tetrahedra.[5] The normal P—O distance of about 1.55 Å has been reported for the pyrophosphates[6] MP_2O_7, with M=Si, Ti, Zr, Sn, Hf, and U, and for the only metaphosphate of known structure, aluminum tetrametaphosphate,[7] $Al_4(P_4O_{12})_3$.

In potassium trithionate,[8] $K_2S_3O_6$, the $[S_3O_6]^{--}$ complex has the configuration of two tetrahedra with a common corner, the

[1] L. O. Brockway and J. Y. Beach, *J.A.C.S.* **60**, 1836 (1938).

[2] J. Y. Beach and D. P. Stevenson, *J. Chem. Phys.* **6**, 75 (1938).

[3] D. P. Stevenson and H. Russell, Jr., *J.A.C.S.* **61**, 3264 (1939).

[4] K. J. Palmer, *ibid.* **60**, 2360 (1938). .

[5] For references see Chapter X.

[6] G. R. Levi and G. Peyronel, *Z. Krist.* **92**, 190 (1935); G. Peyronel *ibid.* **94**, 511 (1936).

[7] L. Pauling and J. Sherman, *ibid.* **96**, 481 (1937).

[8] W. H. Zachariasen, *ibid.* **89**, 529 (1934).

common corner being a sulfur atom and the other six tetrahedron corners oxygen atoms:

$$
\begin{array}{ccc}
& \ddot{\text{O}}: & \ddot{\text{O}}: \\
& \| & \| \\
:\overset{..}{\underset{..}{\text{O}}}{}^{-}\!\!\!-\overset{..}{\underset{..}{\text{S}}}-\overset{..}{\underset{..}{\text{S}}}-\overset{..}{\underset{..}{\text{S}}}-\overset{..}{\underset{..}{\text{O}}}{}^{-}: \\
& \| & \| \\
& \underset{..}{\text{O}}: & \underset{..}{\text{O}}:
\end{array}
$$

The electronic structure is that indicated above, with resonance of the type discussed for the sulfate ion. The value 1.50 Å reported for the S—O distance indicates the same amount of double-bond character as in the sulfate ion. On the other hand, there seems to be in this complex ion little sulfur-sulfur double-bond character; the S—S distance reported, 2.16 Å, is slightly larger than twice the single-bond radius of sulfur.

The conventional electronic structure for the chlorate ion is

$$
\begin{array}{c}
:\overset{..}{\text{O}}:^{-} \\
| \\
:\overset{++}{\underset{|}{\text{Cl}}}-\overset{..}{\text{O}}:^{-} \\
| \\
:\underset{..}{\text{O}}:^{-}
\end{array}
$$

in which an unshared pair of electrons on the chlorine atom occupies one of its outer orbitals. The Cl—O distance observed in sodium chlorate[1] is 1.48 Å. This is very close to the value for the perchlorate ion; it shows that the Cl—O bond in the chlorate ion as well as in the perchlorate ion has a large amount of double-bond character. Crystal structure data are also available for the sulfite ion, the bromate ion, the chlorite ion, $[\text{ClO}_2]^-$, the dithionate ion, $[\text{S}_2\text{O}_6]^{--}$, the pyrosulfite ion, $[\text{S}_2\text{O}_5]^{--}$, and the hypophosphite ion, $[\text{H}_2\text{PO}_2]^-$, which show that the M—O bonds in these complexes have a large amount of double-bond character.

It is of interest to note that in these complexes, as in the case of the halogen compounds of the elements of the fifth and sixth groups, the bond angles have values close to those expected for single covalent bonds: 106° for the chlorate ion in sodium chlo-

[1] R. G. Dickinson and E. A. Goodhue, *J.A.C.S.* **43**, 2045 (1921); W. H. Zachariasen, *Z. Krist.* **71**, 517 (1929). The less reliable values 1.42 and 1.60 Å are reported for the more complex crystal potassium chlorate by W. H. Zachariasen, *Z. Krist.* **71**, 501 (1929).

rate and potassium chlorate, 103° for the sulfite ion in sodium sulfite, and 108° for the bromate ion in potassium bromate.

The O—Cl—O angle 114° and the Cl—O distance 1.59 Å reported for the chlorite ion[1] in NH_4ClO_2 agree with the values for the chlorate ion to within their rather large probable errors. For this ion the electronic structure

is to be written.

The configuration of the pyrosulfite ion,[2]

is similar to that of the dithionate ion,[3]

except that one oxygen atom is replaced by an unshared pair of electrons.

It is probable that in the oxyacids of the heavier atoms, such as H_2CrO_4, H_2MnO_4, $HMnO_4$, H_3AsO_4, etc., the M—O bonds have a large amount of double-bond character, and that the properties of the acids are influenced by this to some extent. Reliable interatomic-distance data are in general not available for these substances.

The value 1.93 ± 0.03 Å has been reported[4] for the I—O dis-

---

[1] G. R. Levi and A. Scherillo, *Z. Krist.* **76**, 431 (1930).

[2] W. H. Zachariasen, *Phys. Rev.* **40**, 923 (1932).

[3] M. L. Huggins and G. O. Frank, *Am. Mineral.* **16**, 580 (1931); G Hägg, *Z. Krist.* **83**, 265 (1932).

[4] L. Helmholz, *J.A.C.S.* **59**, 2036 (1937).

tance in the paraperiodate ion, $[IO_6]^{5-}$. Using 1.36 Å for the octahedral radius of iodine (six percent greater than the tetrahedral radius), the expected value for the single-bond I—O distance is 2.02 Å; the comparison of this with the observed value indicates that in the octahedral oxygen acids the bonds have some double-bond character, smaller in amount, however, than in the tetrahedral acids. The reliable value[1] 1.79 A for the I—O distance in the metaperiodate ion in $NaIO_4$ indicates that the bonds in this ion are essentially double bonds.

The structures of the oxides of the heavier non-metallic elements are similar to those of the oxygen acids. In sulfur dioxide the S—O distance is observed[2,3] to be 1.43 ± 0.01 Å, which is slightly less than that in the sulfate ion. The value of the O—S—O bond angle 121° ± 5°[3] lies close to that expected for

the structure $\left\{ \begin{array}{cc} S \nearrow^O \searrow_O \; , & S \searrow^O \nwarrow_O \end{array} \right\}$, 125°16'. The selenium dioxide

molecule has a similar structure,[4] with the Se—O distance 1.61 Å, which is approximately the value observed for the selenate ion. In crystals of selenium dioxide[5] there are chains

, the Se—O distance being 1.73 A

for the unshared oxygen atoms and 1.78 Å for the shared oxygen atoms. The difference in distance indicates a reasonable difference in amount of double-bond character of the bonds.

The molecules P_4O_6, P_4O_{10}, and As_4O_6 have interesting configurations.[6] In P_4O_6 and As_4O_6 the four phosphorus or arsenic atoms are at the corners of a tetrahedron, each bonded to three

[1] E. A. Hazlewood, *Z. Krist.* 98, 439 (1938).
[2] P. C. Cross and L. O. Brockway, *J. Chem. Phys.* 3, 821 (1935).
[3] V. Schomaker and D. P. Stevenson, unpublished research.
[4] K. J. Palmer and N. Elliott, *J.A.C.S.* 60, 1309 (1938).
[5] J. D. McCullough, *ibid.* 59, 789 (1937).
[6] L. R. Maxwell, S. B. Hendricks, and L. S. Deming, *J. Chem. Phys.* 5, 626 (1937); G. C. Hampson and A. J. Stosick, *J.A.C.S.* 60, 1814 (1938).

oxygen atoms along the tetrahedron edges (Figure 30-1). The values of the P—O and As—O distances, 1.64 and 1.80 Å, respectively, indicate a large amount of double-bond character for the bonds. This makes itself evident also in the values of about 126°

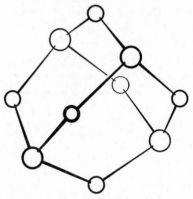

Fig. 30-1.—The structure of the molecules P_4O_6 and As_4O_6. Large circles represent phosphorus or arsenic atoms, small circles oxygen atoms.

observed for the P—O—P and As—O—As bond angles, 125°16′

being expected for $\overset{\diagdown\diagup}{O}$ and 109°28′ for $\overset{\diagdown\diagup}{O}$. The P_4O_{10} molecule is closely similar to the P_4O_6 molecule in structure, with the addition of an oxygen atom to each phosphorus atom, completing the PO_4 tetrahedra (Figure 30-2). These unshared oxygen atoms are at the surprisingly small distance 1.39 Å from the adjacent phosphorus atoms. In the $P_4O_6S_4$ molecule, which has a similar structure,[1] the P—S distance is also very short, having the value 1.85 Å.

There is an interesting change in structure of the As_4O_6 molecule on condensation to the cubic crystal arsenolite. In this crystal[2] the As—O—As bond angle is very close to 109°28′ and the As—O distance is increased to 2.00 Å. These changes indicate that the As—O bonds in the crystal are essentially single bonds. The loss of double-bond character can be attributed to the fact that near each oxygen atom there are two arsenic atoms of adjacent molecules, with which weak bonds are formed, with

[1] A. J. Stosick, *J.A.C.S.* **61**, 1130 (1939).
[2] R. M. Bozorth, *ibid.* **45**, 1621 (1923); D. Harker and J. Eskijian, unpublished research.

use of the electron pairs of the oxygen atom which might otherwise be used for double-bond formation with the arsenic atoms of the same molecule.

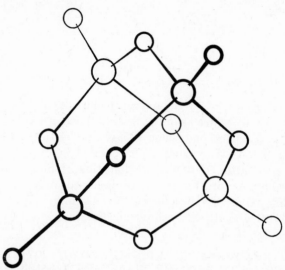

Fig. 30-2.—The structure of the molecules P_4O_{10} and $P_4O_6S_4$, showing the positions of attachment of the four oxygen or sulfur atoms to the P_4O_6 framework.

A careful study of the structure of valentinite, the orthorhombic modification of Sb_2O_3, made by Buerger and Hendricks,[1] has shown the presence in the crystal of infinite strings of atoms held together by covalent bonds, with the configuration

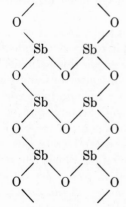

[1] M. J. Buerger and S. B. Hendricks, *Z. Krist.* **98**, 1 (1937).

The Sb—O bond distances have the value 2.00 Å, which is slightly less than the sum of the normal covalent radii, 2.07 Å, indicating a small amount of double bond character, of the type

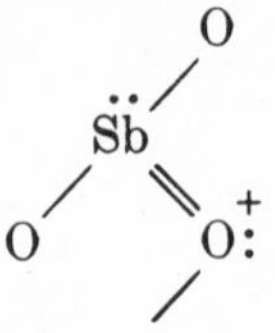

This is substantiated by the oxygen bond angles, <Sb—O—Sb = 132° and 116°, which lie in the neighborhood of the tetrahedral double bond-single bond value 125°16'. The three O—Sb—O bond angles have the values 81°, 93°, and 99°.

In senarmontite, the cubic modification of Sb_2O_3, there are molecules Sb_4O_6 with the structure discussed above for arsenolite.[1] The reported values for the Sb—O bond distance, 2.2 ± 0.1 Å, and the bond angles, all tetrahedral, indicate the presence of intermolecular bonds as in arsenolite.

31. THE STRUCTURE AND STABILITY OF COVALENT COMPLEXES OF THE TRANSITION ELEMENTS

The problem of the stability of the covalent complexes of the transition elements has in the past been a puzzling one. Questions such as the following have awaited answers: Why is the cyanide group so facile in the formation of complexes with these elements, whereas the carbon atom in other groups, such as the methyl group, does not form bonds with them? Why do the transition elements and not other metals (beryllium, aluminum, etc.) form cyanide complexes? In the covalent complex $[Fe(CN)_6]^{----}$, for example, the iron atom has a formal charge of 4−, assuming that it forms six covalent bonds with the six surrounding groups; how can this be made compatible with the tendency of metals to lose electrons and form positive ions?

As the result of a recent determination of the value of the Ni—C distance in nickel carbonyl and of its interpretation in terms of bond type, a new point of view has now been introduced which permits answers to be given to these and other questions. The fundamental innovation which has been made is the idea that *atoms of the transition groups are not restricted to the formation of single covalent bonds, but can form multiple covalent bonds*

[1] R. M. Bozorth, *J.A.C.S.* **45**, 1621 (1923).

with electron-accepting groups by making use of the electrons and orbitals of the shell within the valence shell. The application of this idea and of related ones in the discussion of the structure of complexes is given below.

31a. The Structure of the Metal Carbonyls and Related Compounds.—For nickel carbonyl we have discussed the structure in which the four carbonyl groups are attached to the nickel atom by four single covalent bonds, the nickel atom in this way acquiring the argon structure (Sec. 16d). An investigation of the atomic arrangement of this molecule by the electron-diffraction method, carried out by Brockway and Cross,[1] was found to lead to the expected tetrahedral configuration, with the Ni—C—O sequence linear and with the C—O distance equal to 1.15 Å, which is close to that in carbon monoxide itself, 1.13 Å. For the nickel-carbon distance, however, the surprising value 1.82 ± 0.03 Å was found. Now the octahedral radius of quadrivalent nickel is 1.21 Å and the square radius of bivalent nickel is 1.22 Å (Sec. 23); so for the tetrahedral radius of non-valent nickel a value close to 1.23 Å is expected. This corresponds to the interatomic distance 2.00 Å for a single covalent bond between nickel and carbon. The observed value is 0.18 Å less than this.

An explanation of part of the decrease might be found in the effect of incompletion of the valence shell of carbon. For the structure

$$A \quad —\overset{\displaystyle |}{\underset{\displaystyle |}{Ni}} : C ::: \overset{+}{O} :$$

the Ni—C distance would be equal to or a little greater than 2.00 Å, the formal charge on nickel having only a small effect. (The radii of the iron-group elements are nearly independent of atomic number.) For the structure

$$B \quad —\overset{\displaystyle |}{\underset{\displaystyle |}{Ni}} : \overset{+}{C} :: \overset{..}{O} :,$$

with only a sextet of electrons about the carbon atom, a decrease to about 1.90 Å is expected (Sec. 21).

---

[1] L. O. Brockway and P. C. Cross, *J. Chem. Phys.* **3**, 828 (1935). B. L. Crawford, Jr., and P. C. Cross, *J. Chem. Phys.* **6**, 525 (1938), have obtained spectroscopic evidence for this structure.

However, with this structure the carbon atom is left with an unused valence orbital, whereas there are in the nickel atom unshared $3d$ electron pairs which might be used in bond formation. We accordingly consider the structure

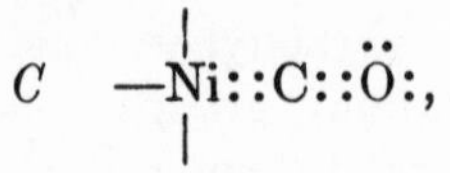

$$C \quad -\overset{\displaystyle |}{\underset{\displaystyle |}{Ni}}::C::\ddot{O}:,$$

which involves a *double bond from nickel to carbon*. This would lead to a nickel-carbon distance of about 1.79 Å; the observed value of the interatomic distance thus provides strong support for the suggestion that the nickel-carbon bonds have a large amount of double-bond character.

By using four of the $3d$ orbitals, with their electron pairs, as well as the $4s$ and $4p$ orbitals, the nickel atom can form four double bonds to carbon:

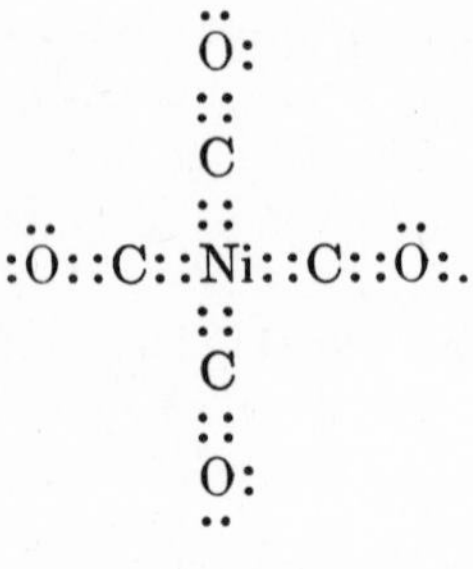

$$\ddot{O}:$$
$$::$$
$$C$$
$$::$$
$$:\ddot{O}::C::Ni::C::\ddot{O}:.$$
$$::$$
$$C$$
$$::$$
$$O:$$

This structure is more satisfying than the single-bonded structures for the following reason: it makes the nickel atom and the other atoms neutral, whereas the single-bonded structures place a four-fold negative charge on the nickel atom, which is in its general behavior electropositive rather than electronegative.

The nickel carbonyl molecule is seen not to be represented by the double-bonded structure alone, but to resonate between this structure and the single-bonded ones, from the fact that the observed C—O distance is 1.15 Å, showing that this bond has in part the character of a triple bond.[1]

The molecules $Co(CO)_3NO$ and $Fe(CO)_2(NO)_2$, which are isoelectronic with nickel tetracarbonyl, have structures of the same

---

[1] The partial ionic character of the single bonds (especially to C^+ of B) assists in neutralizing the negative charge of the central atom.

type, the interatomic distances being observed[1] to have the values
Co—C = 1.83, Fe—C = 1.84, Co—N = 1.76, Fe—N = 1.77,
C—O = 1.15, and N—O = 1.11 Å.   Similar tetrahedral structures have also been found[2] for the isoelectronic iron and cobalt
carbonyl hydrides $Fe(CO)_2(COH)_2$ and $Co(CO)_3COH$, with interatomic distances Fe—C = 1.79 and 1.84 Å, Co—C = 1.75 and
1.83 Å, and C—O = 1.15 Å.

For iron pentacarbonyl, $Fe(CO)_5$, a trigonal bipyramidal structure has been reported.[2]   The value found for the Fe—C distances, 1.84 A, shows that the bonds in this molecule also have
considerable double-bond character.

The electron-diffraction investigation of $Cr(CO)_6$, $Mo(CO)_6$,
and $W(CO)_6$ has been carried out by Brockway, Ewens, and
Lister.[3]   The molecules are regular octahedra, with Cr—C
= 1.92, Mo—C = 2.08, and W—C = 2.06 Å (all ±0.04 Å).
These values are about 0.10 Å less than those for single bonds,
indicating that the bonds have some double-bond character.

The discovery that the iron-group elements can form bonds
which have in part the character of multiple bonds by making
use of the orbitals and electrons of the $3d$ subshell, while surprising, need not be greeted with scepticism; the natural formula for a compound RCO is that with a double bond from R
to C, and the existence of the metal carbonyls might well have
been interpreted years ago as evidence for double-bond formation by metals.[4]

The single-bonded structures are not to be ignored; they seem
to play a determinative part with respect to the stereochemical
properties of the central atom, as discussed in Section 29a and
Chapter III.   Nickel tetracarbonyl and its isosteres, for example,
are tetrahedral in configuration, whereas the nickel cyanide complex ion $[Ni(CN)_4]^{--}$, in which the nickel-carbon bonds also
have some double-bond character, is square, this difference being
that predicted by discussion of the nature of the orbitals used
in the formation of single bonds.

[1] L. O. Brockway and J. S. Anderson, *Trans. Faraday Soc.* 33, 1233
(1937).

[2] R. V. G. Ewens and M. W. Lister, *ibid.* 35, 681 (1939).

[3] L. O. Brockway, R. V. G. Ewens, and M. W. Lister, *ibid.* 34, 1350
(1938).

[4] The nickel-carbon double bond was used in an otherwise unsatisfactory structural formula for nickel carbonyl by A. A. Blanchard and
W. I. Gilliland, *J.A.C.S.* 48, 872 (1926).

A very interesting discovery has been made by Powell and Ewens[1] who have determined the crystal structure of iron enneacarbonyl, $Fe_2(CO)_9$, finding the configuration of the molecule to be that shown in Figure 31-1, with a three-fold axis of symmetry. Six carbonyl groups are attached to one or the other of the iron atoms; the other three are bonded to both iron atoms, and thus have a structure similar to that in ketones. The iron atoms can be considered to be trivalent. The observed diamagnetism of the substance shows that the spins of the odd electrons of the two iron atoms are opposed; this suggests strongly that there is a covalent bond between the two iron atoms. The Fe—Fe distance, 2.46 Å, is compatible with this idea (see Chapter XI).

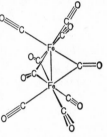

Fig. 31-1.

Hence in this substance each iron atom forms seven bonds (d^3sp^3), six with carbon atoms and one with the other iron atom; two unshared electron pairs occupy the two remaining $3d$ orbitals of each iron atom. The stabilizing effect of a metal-metal bond may well occur in other complexes, such as the brown binuclear tetra-ortho-phenanthroline-diol-diferric ion,[2] $[Fe_2(OH)_2(C_{12}H_8N_2)_4]^{++++}$.

31b. The Cyanide and Nitro Complexes of the Transition Elements.—The structural formula usually written for the ferrocyanide ion,

$$A \quad \begin{bmatrix} & N & \\ & C & CN \\ & | & \diagup \\ NC—Fe—CN \\ & \diagup & | \\ NC & C \\ & N & \end{bmatrix}^{----} ,$$

with single covalent bonds from the iron atom to each of the six carbon atoms, is seen to be especially surprising in that it places a charge of 4– on the iron atoms, whereas iron tends to assume a positive charge, as in the ferrous ion, and not a negative charge. Now the cyanide group is an electronegative group, and the Fe—C bonds accordingly have some ionic character, which,

[1] H. M. Powell and R. V. G. Ewens, *J. Chem. Soc.* **1939**, 286.

[2] A. Gaines, Jr., L. P. Hammett, and G. H. Walden, Jr., *J.A.C.S.* **58**, 1668 (1936).

however, can hardly be great enough to remove the negative charge completely from the iron atom. As suggested by the discussion of the metal carbonyls in the previous section, we assume that the cyanide group in this complex can function as an acceptor of electrons, and that the bonds resonate among the following types:

A Fe   (CN)⁻

B F̄e:C:::N:

C Fe::C::N̈:⁻

The first of these represents an electrostatic bond between the iron atom and the cyanide ion, the second a single covalent bond from iron to carbon, and the third a double covalent bond, with use of another $3d$ orbital of the iron atom, with its pair of electrons. The first and the third of these place a negative charge on the cyanide group, and the second leaves the group neutral. Resonance among these with the second structure contributing only about one-third would make the iron atom in the complex electrically neutral, the negative charge 4– being divided among the six cyanide groups. The magnitude of the contribution of the third structure could be found from the value of the Fe—C distance, which, however, has not been determined.

It is interesting to note that by using all of the $3d$, $4s$, and $4p$ orbitals of the iron atom the valence-bond structure B

B

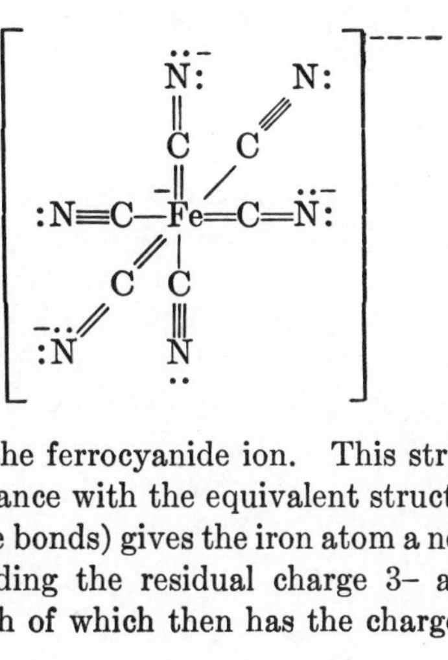

can be written for the ferrocyanide ion. This structure (which is of course in resonance with the equivalent structures obtained by redistributing the bonds) gives the iron atom a negative charge of only unity, dividing the residual charge 3– among the six nitrogen atoms, each of which then has the charge $\frac{1}{2}$–; and it is probable that the ionic character of the bonds is great enough to transfer further negative charge also to the nitrogen atoms, making the iron atom neutral or even positive. The structures of this type, involving some iron-carbon double bonds, are without doubt of greater significance to the normal state of the complex ion than the conventional structure *A* written at the beginning of this section; it may well be convenient, however, to continue to represent the complex ion by the conventional structure, just as for convenience the benzene molecule is often represented by a single Kekulé structure.

For other anionic cyanide complexes of the transition elements, such as $[Fe(CN)_6]^{---}$, $[Co(CN)_6]^{---}$, $[Mn(CN)_6]^{4-}$, $[Cr(CN)_6]^{4-}$, $[Ni(CN)_4]^{--}$, $[Zn(CN)_4]^{--}$, $[Cu(CN)_2]^{-}$, and the analogous complexes of the elements of the palladium and platinum groups, similar structures involving partial double-bond character of the metal-carbon bond can be written.

The nitrosyl group and the nitro group also are able to accept an additional pair of binding electrons, and the bonds in complexes such as $[Fe(CN)_5NO]^{--}$, $[Co(NH_3)_5NO]^{++}$, $[Co(NO_2)_6]^{---}$, etc., have to a considerable extent the character of the structures

$$M\equiv\overset{+}{N}\equiv\ddot{\overset{..}{O}}: \qquad \text{and} \qquad M=\overset{+}{N}\diagup\overset{\overset{..}{\overset{..}{O}}:}{}\diagdown\overset{}{\underset{..}{\ddot{O}}:} \; ,$$

For a complex such as $[Co(NH_3)_6]^{+++}$, containing six amino groups, structures involving double bonds cannot be formulated. The stability of such a complex is to be attributed to the electronegativity of the attached groups, which is large enough to remove most or all of the negative charge from the central atom and thus stabilize the complex without making the bonds so ionic as to cause transition from the essentially covalent structure indicated by the magnetic criterion for all cobalt ammines to an essentially ionic structure. The atoms and groups which occur in the octahedral complexes of cobalt are in the main strongly electronegative; they include NH_3, OH_2, $(OH)^-$, $(O_2)^{--}$ (peroxide), $H_2NCH_2CH_2NH_2$ (ethylenediamine), $(C_2O_4)^{--}$ (oxalate), $(NO_3)^-$, $(SO_4)^{--}$, etc. The atoms bonded to cobalt in all of these groups have about the same electronegativity (that of N^+ in $M—N^+H_3$, for example, being not much different from that of O in M—OH, etc.).   The somewhat less electronegative chlorine and bromine atoms can also be introduced, but to only a limited extent (occupying a maximum of two of the six positions), whereas the still less electronegative iodine atom cannot be introduced

To summarize: we attribute the stability of the octahedral complexes of cobalt to the removal of the negative charge assigned to the central atom on the basis of a normal covalent single-bonded structure from it to the surrounding electronegative groups; in the case of cyanide, nitrosyl, and nitro groups the transfer of charge is also accomplished in part by the formation of double bonds from the cobalt atom to the attached groups.

The iron-group elements are electropositive, tending to form positive ions; and this property is reflected in the nature of the complexes which they form. The metals of the palladium and platinum groups, on the other hand, have little tendency to form positive ions, but prefer to remain neutral or even become negative; this characteristic is indicated by their position (2.0–2.3) in the electronegativity scale.   In consequence these elements can form covalent octahedral complexes not only with cyanide, ammino, hydroxide, and related groups but also with chlorine, bromine, and even iodine atoms.   In the hexachloroplatinate ion, $[PtCl_6]^{--}$, the ionic character of the bonds may remove some of the negative charge from platinum to chlorine; but in the hexaiodo-osmiate ion $[OsI_6]^{----}$ the bonds to the weakly electronegative iodine atoms can have little ionic character and a good part of the negative charge must be left on the central atom.

Molybdenum and tungsten are classed with the elements of the palladium and platinum groups rather than with those of the iron group with respect to nobility, and they are to be similarly classed with respect to complex formation.   The stability of the complex ions $[Mo(CN)_8]^{---}$ and $[Mo(CN)_8]^{----}$ and their tungsten analogues cannot be attributed to double-bond formation, because of the small number of $3d$ electrons; these complexes presumably involve eight single covalent bonds with some ionic character, which transfer some of the negative charge from the central atom to the attached groups.   The fact that the large coordination number eight is shown in combination with cyanide and not with chloride has probably a steric explanation. In the cyanide groups with structure $M:C:::N:$ all of the carbon electrons are concentrated closely about the internuclear axis, and the only unshared pair projects toward the outside of the complex; hence there is little steric repulsion between eight cyanide groups attached to the same atom, whereas eight larger groups could not be fitted in.

CHAPTER VIII

THE ONE-ELECTRON BOND AND THE THREE-ELECTRON BOND

32. THE ONE-ELECTRON BOND. THE HYDRIDES OF BORON

The one-electron bond in the hydrogen molecule-ion is about half as strong as the electron-pair bond in the hydrogen molecule ($D_0 = 60.95$ kcal./mole for H_2^+, 102.62 kcal./mole for H_2, Secs. 4, 5); and since the same number of atomic orbitals is needed for a one-electron bond as for an electron-pair bond, it is to be expected that in general molecules containing one-electron bonds will be less stable than those in which all the stable bond orbitals are used in electron-pair-bond formation.   Moreover, there is a significant condition which must be satisfied in order that a stable one-electron bond be formed between two atoms; namely, that the two atoms be identical or closely similar (Sec. 4c).   For these reasons one-electron bonds are rare—much rarer, indeed, than three-electron bonds, to which similar restrictions apply. The only stable molecules for which the one-electron bond is of some significance are those of the boron hydrides.

Boron forms a series of hydrides of surprising composition.[1] The simple substance BH_3 has not been prepared; instead hydrides of various compositions occur, including B_2H_6, B_4H_{10}, B_5H_{11}, B_5H_9, B_6H_{10}, and $B_{10}H_{14}$.

The structural problem presented by these substances is not a simple one; the fundamental difficulty is that there are not enough valence electrons in the molecules to bind the atoms together with electron-pair bonds.   In B_2H_6, for example, there are twelve valence electrons; all twelve would be needed to hold the six hydrogen atoms to boron by covalent bonds, leaving none for the boron-boron bond.

It was suggested by Sidgwick[2] that electron pairs are used for the boron-boron bond and four of the boron-hydrogen bonds, and

---

[1] See, for a review of this subject, A. Stock, "Hydrides of Boron and Silicon," Cornell University Press, Ithaca, 1933.

[2] N. V. Sidgwick, "The Electronic Theory of Valency," 1927, p. 103.

that one-electron bonds are formed between boron atoms and the two remaining hydrogen atoms, the electronic structure being

$$
\begin{array}{cc}
\text{H} & \text{H} \\
\text{H}\!\cdot\!\ddot{\text{B}}\!:\!\ddot{\text{B}}\!\cdot\!\text{H}; \\
\ddot{\text{H}} & \ddot{\text{H}}
\end{array}
$$

and it was pointed out later[1] that the two elements boron and hydrogen (which are nearly equal in electronegativity) satisfy the condition for the formation of a stable one-electron bond, and that, moreover, the molecule would be further stabilized by the energy of resonance of the two one-electron bonds among the six positions.

Lewis[2] then suggested that the molecule might contain six electron-pair bonds resonating among seven positions, each of the seven bonds (one B—B and six B—H) having six-sevenths single-bond and one-seventh no-bond character; the resonance energy of the molecule among the seven structures

$$
\begin{array}{cccc}
\text{H} \quad \text{H} & & \text{H}^{+}\text{H} & \\
\text{H}\!:\!\ddot{\text{B}} \;\; \ddot{\text{B}}\!:\!\text{H}, & & \text{H}\!:\!\text{B}\!:\!\ddot{\text{B}}\!:\!\text{H}, & \text{etc.,} \\
\ddot{\text{H}} \quad \ddot{\text{H}} & & \ddot{\text{H}} \quad \ddot{\text{H}} &
\end{array}
$$

would then stabilize the substance.

Other suggestions have also been made, such as that the molecule, with the same number of valence electrons as ethylene, is similar to ethylene in structure, and contains a boron-boron double bond.[3]

The problem has been brought close to solution by the electron-diffraction investigation carried out by Bauer.[4] The diffraction photographs of diborane were found to be closely similar to those of ethane (with a change in scale), and dissimilar to those of ethylene. Their detailed analysis showed them to be incompatible with a structure for the molecule involving a double bond be-

---

[1] L. Pauling, *J.A.C.S.* **53**, 3225 (1931); see also R. S. Mulliken, *J. Chem. Phys.* **3**, 635 (1935).

[2] G. N. Lewis, *J. Chem. Phys.* **1**, 17 (1933).

[3] E. Wiberg, *Ber.* **69**, 2816 (1936), and earlier papers.

[4] S. H. Bauer, *J.A.C.S.* **59**, 1096 (1937); see also T. F. Anderson and A. B. Burg, *J. Chem. Phys.* **6**, 586 (1938).

tween the boron atoms, but to lead instead to an atomic configuration resembling that of ethane. The values found for the interatomic distances, B—B = 1.86 ± 0.04 Å and B—H = 1.27 ± 0.03 Å, are both significantly larger than the corresponding single-bond values, 1.76 Å and 1.18 A, showing that *the B—B bond, as well as the B—H bonds, is different from a single bond*. This is just what would be expected on the basis of Lewis's suggestion that each of the seven bonds has six-sevenths single-bond character.

However, it is now clear from theoretical considerations that the one-electron-bond structures are also of importance. The condition for resonance of B—H and B—B electron-pair bonds is the same as the condition for the formation of one-electron B—H bonds (and also for the one-electron B—B bond). With two one-electron bonds in the molecule, resonating among seven positions, the two electrons involved must have their spins either opposed or parallel. With their spins opposed the electrons are formally paired, and the corresponding structures can enter into resonance with structures of the Lewis type. The B_2H_6 molecule in its normal state thus resonates among the seven structures of the Lewis type,

$$\begin{matrix} H & H \\ \cdot\cdot & \cdot\cdot \\ H:B & B:H, \\ \cdot\cdot & \cdot\cdot \\ H & H \end{matrix} \qquad \begin{matrix} H^+H \\ \cdot\cdot\; \bar{} \\ H:B:B:H, \\ \cdot\cdot\;\cdot\cdot \\ H & H \end{matrix} \qquad \text{etc.,}$$

and also among the numerous structures involving one-electron bonds,

$$\begin{matrix} H & H \\ \cdot\cdot & \cdot\cdot \\ H\cdot B:B\cdot H, \\ \cdot\cdot & \cdot\cdot \\ H & H \end{matrix} \qquad \begin{matrix} H & H \\ \cdot\cdot & \cdot\cdot \\ H:B\cdot B\cdot H, \\ \cdot\cdot & \cdot\cdot \\ H & H \end{matrix} \qquad \text{etc.}$$

The substance in its normal state is diamagnetic; only by pairing the electrons in the one-electron-bond structures can resonance with the Lewis structures occur.

The atomic arrangements of B_4H_{10} and B_5H_{11} are similar[1] to those of *n*-butane and *n*-pentane, respectively, with one hydro-

---

[1] S. H. Bauer, *J.A.C.S.* 60, 805 (1938).

gen atom (presumably on the central boron atom) missing for the latter.

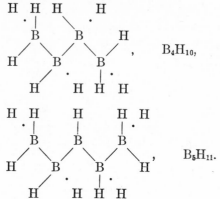

The average B—B distance is 1.84 Å for B_4H_{10} and 1.81 Å for B_5H_{11}, the B—H distance being close to 1.27 Å in each. Each of these molecules has four valence electrons less than needed to provide an electron pair for each bond; the assumption that the molecules involve resonance among structures with four one-electron bonds and those of the Lewis type with bonds missing is supported by the values of the interatomic distances.

The configuration found[1] for B_5H_9 is the following:

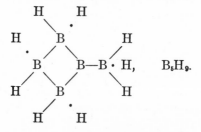

This molecule too involves four electrons less than the number required for a complete complement of electron-pair bonds. The average value of the B—B distances was found to be 1.76 Å; this small value may be due to the presence of a boron atom with a valence sextet, three of the five B—B bonds involving this atom.[2]

[1] S. H. Bauer and L. Pauling, *J.A.C.S.* **58**, 2403 (1936).
[2] The value 1.17 Å reported for the B—H distance is smaller than those found for the other boron hydrides, and may be in error.

The smaller B—B value in B_5H_{11} than in B_4H_{10} probably is due to the same cause.

It has been suggested[1] that B_6H_{10} and $B_{10}H_{14}$, which have not yet been subjected to studies leading to determination of their atomic arrangements, have the structures

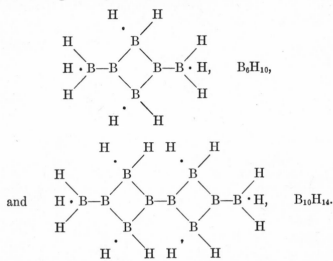

(In all of the foregoing structural formulas one-electron bonds have been indicated; it is to be understood that these structures resonate also with structures of the Lewis missing-bond type.) Some common features are to be seen for these structures; for example, there is in every case one electron less than the number needed for a complete set of electron-pair bonds for every BH_3 or BH_2 group in the molecule.

A similar structure,

can be written for B_2NH_7, which is observed[2] to have a propane-

[1] Bauer and Pauling, *loc. cit.*

[2] S. H. Bauer, *J.A.C.S.* **60**, 524 (1938).

like configuration. The observed B—N distance is 1.56 Å, which is close to the single-bond value, 1.59 Å.

Other compounds containing boron and hydrogen, together with other atoms, have normal structures. BH_3 combines with molecules with an available unshared electron pair to form substances such as borine trimethylammine, $H_3BN(CH_3)_3$, which is similar to neopentane in configuration[1] and has enough valence electrons for all the bonds, and borine carbonyl, H_3BCO, for which we may write the structures

$$\begin{matrix} \overset{..}{\overset{-}{H}} \\ H:\overset{..}{B}:C:::O: \\ \overset{..}{H} \end{matrix} \quad \text{and} \quad \begin{matrix} \overset{..}{\overset{-}{H}} \\ H:\overset{..}{B}:\overset{+}{C}::\overset{..}{O}:, \\ \overset{..}{H} \end{matrix}$$

between which resonance should occur. The observed inter-atomic distances,[1] B—H = 1.20 Å, B—C = 1.57 Å, and C—O = 1.13 Å, are compatible with this interpretation, the correction of −0.09 Å being made for the sextet carbon atom in the second structure.

33. THE THREE-ELECTRON BOND[2]

Lewis in his 1916 paper and in his book on valence emphasized the fact that there exist only a few stable molecules and complex ions (other than those containing atoms of the transition elements) for which the total number of electrons is odd. He pointed out that in general an "odd molecule," such as nitric oxide and nitrogen dioxide, would be expected to use its unpaired electron to form a bond with another such molecule, and that the monomeric substance should accordingly be very much less stable than its dimer; and he stated that the method by which the unpaired electron is firmly held in the stable odd molecule was at that time not understood. Since then the explanation of the phenomenon has been found, as the result of the application of quantum mechanics to the problem; the stability of odd molecules is the result of the power of certain pairs of atoms to form a new type of bond, the *three-electron bond*.

33a. The Conditions for Formation of a Stable Three-electron Bond.—Let us consider the normal state of a system of three electrons and two nuclei or kernels, A and B, each with one

---

[1] S. H. Bauer, *J.A.C.S.* 59, 1804 (1937).
[2] L. Pauling, *ibid.* 53, 3225 (1931).

stable bond orbital. There are only two essentially different ways of introducing the three electrons into the two available orbitals, I and II:

$$
\begin{array}{lll}
\text{I} & \text{A:} & \text{B} \\
\text{II} & \text{A·} & \text{:B}
\end{array}
$$

The exclusion principle permits only two electrons, which must have opposed spins, to occupy either one of the orbitals; the third electron must occupy the other orbital.[1]

It is found on carrying out the energy calculations that structure I alone does not correspond to the formation of a stable bond; it leads instead to repulsion or at the best only a very weak attraction between the atoms. Structure II alone also leads to a similar type of interaction. If, however, the atoms A and B are identical or are closely similar, so that the two structures have nearly the same energy, then there will occur resonance between them, which will stabilize the molecule, and lead to an interaction between the atoms corresponding to the formation of a stable bond.[2] This bond, corresponding to resonance of the type $\{A:\cdot B, A\cdot :B\}$, may be called the *three-electron bond*, and represented by the symbol $A \cdots B$. It is found by calculation and by experiment to be about one-half as strong as an electron-pair bond (that is, to have half as great a value of the bond energy). The system of two molecules $A \cdots B$, each containing a stable three-electron bond in addition to another bond between A and B, has accordingly about the same energy as $\ddot{A}$—B—B—$\ddot{A}$, involving an additional covalent bond; and we can expect that in some cases the heat of formation of the dimer will be positive and in others it will be negative, with corresponding differences in stability of the two forms. This is in accord with the results of observation: nitric oxide, to which we assign a structure involving a three-electron bond, does not form a stable dimer, whereas the similar substance nitrogen dioxide does form its dimer, nitrogen tetroxide.

---

[1] The spin of the unpaired electron can be either positive or negative. The structures with positive spin and those with negative spin have (with the very small spin-orbit interactions neglected) the same energy; together they correspond to a doublet state of the molecule.

[2] The reader will notice the close similarity of this argument to that given for the one-electron bond in Section 4.

In order that there be resonance between structures I and II and the formation of a stable three-electron bond the atoms A and B must be identical or similar; the conditions for formation of the bond are thus the same as those of the one-electron bond discussed in Section 4c, and the two bonds show the same dependence of bond energy on the energy difference of the resonating structures. It is found on examination of the energy quantities that a stable three-electron bond might be formed between unlike atoms which differ by not much more than 0.5 in electronegativity; that is, between oxygen and fluorine, nitrogen and oxygen, nitrogen and chlorine, chlorine and oxygen, etc. Three-electron bonds between oxygen and fluorine, oxygen and oxygen, nitrogen and oxygen, and chlorine and oxygen have been recognized in stable molecules, and others are indicated also by spectroscopic data.

It may be pointed out that the one-electron bond, the electron-pair bond, and the three-electron bond use one stable bond orbital of each of two atoms, and one, two, and three electrons, respectively.

33b. The Helium Molecule-ion.—The simplest molecule in which the three-electron bond can occur is the helium molecule-ion, He_2^+, consisting of two nuclei, each with one stable $1s$ orbital, and three electrons. The theoretical treatment[1] of this system has shown that the bond is strong, with bond energy about 55 kcal./mole and with equilibrium internuclear distance about 1.09 Å. The experimental values for these quantities, determined from spectroscopic data for excited states of the helium molecule, are about 58 kcal./mole and 1.09 Å, respectively, which agree well with the theoretical values. It is seen that the bond energy in He···He$^+$ is about the same as that in H·H$^+$, and a little more than half as great as that of the electron-pair bond in H:H.

34. THE OXIDES OF NITROGEN AND THEIR DERIVATIVES

Nitric oxide is the most stable of the odd molecules. For the first of the two structures I and II,

$$I \quad :\ddot{N}{=}\ddot{O}: \qquad II \quad \bar{:}\ddot{N}{=}\dot{O}\overset{+}{:},$$

[1] E. Majorana, *Nuovo Cim.* **8**, 22 (1931); L. Pauling, *J. Chem. Phys.* **1**, 56 (1933); S. Weinbaum, *ibid.* **3**, 547 (1935); L. Pauling and E. B. Wilson, Jr., "Introduction to Quantum Mechanics," p. 358.

we would expect great ease of polymerization to stable molecules of the type

$$:N\!=\!\overset{..}{O}:$$
$$|$$
$$:N\!=\!O:,$$

and structure II, because of its unfavorable charge distribution, should be somewhat less stable than I. But the difference in stability of I and II is small enough to permit nearly complete resonance between them, and we accordingly assign to the molecule the structure $:N\!\!\equiv\!\!O:$, involving a double bond and a three-electron bond between the two atoms. Of the four valence orbitals of each atom one is used for the unshared pair of electrons, two for the double bond, and the fourth for the three-electron bond.

The properties of the molecule are accounted for by this structure. The extra energy of the three-electron bond stabilizes the molecule relative to structure I to such extent that the heat of the reaction $2NO \rightarrow N_2O_2$ becomes negative, and the substance does not polymerize.[1]

The observed value of the internuclear distance, 1.14 Å, lies between the radius sums for double and triple bonds, 1.18 and 1.06 A, respectively.[2]

The electric dipole moment of the molecule is small, not over 0.2×10^{-18} e.s.u. In discussing this we must recall that structure I, $:N\!=\!O:$, itself corresponds to a large dipole moment, resulting from the partial ionic character of the double bond between unlike atoms (Sec. 12a), and that the structure $:N\!\!\equiv\!\!O:$ for the molecule really corresponds to resonance among the three structures $\{^+:N:O:^-, :N::O:, ^-:N::O:^+\}$, with perhaps some

---

[1] The values of the residual entropy of crystalline nitric oxide (H. L. Johnston and W. F. Giauque, *J.A.C.S.* **51**, 3194 (1929)) and of its paramagnetic susceptibility (E. Lips, *Helv. Phys. Acta* **8**, 247 (1935)) suggest that in the crystals the molecules are combined in pairs.

[2] It is of interest to note that resonance of the antibonding type between structures I and II should give rise to an excited state of the nitric oxide molecule, with the same term symbol ($^2\Pi$) as the normal state, in which the resonance energy exerts a destabilizing effect. A state of this type is known: $^2\Pi$ at 45486 cm^{-1}, with N—O distance 1.42 Å.

contribution of $:\overset{..}{N}:\overset{.}{\underset{..}{O}}:$ also; and that the two partially ionic structures, which correspond to opposed dipole moments, contribute about equally, causing the resultant dipole moment of the molecule in its normal state to be close to zero.

It is of interest that in several simple molecules, such as NO and N_2O, for which valence-bond structures can be written corresponding to a dipole moment vector in either direction along the internuclear axis, the resultant dipole moment is nearly zero; in other molecules, such as RNO_2, the only stable valence-bond structures are of such a type as to lead to a large resultant dipole moment.

Two excited states of the nitric oxide molecule are known ($^2\Sigma$ at 44199 cm^{-1} and $^2\Sigma$ at 52260 cm^{-1}) for which the values of the internuclear distance, 1.06 and 1.07 Å, show that the atoms are connected by a triple bond (sum of radii 1.06 Å). These states must be based on the structure $[:N\equiv O:]^+$ for the nitric oxide ion, with one electron occupying an outer unstable orbital. Indeed, when we consider that there is a gain in stability of the N—O bond (from a two-and-one-half bond to a triple bond) on removing one electron from NO to form NO$^+$, it need not surprise us that Klinkenberg and Ketelaar[1] have shown that NOClO$_4$, NOBF$_4$, and (NO)$_2$SnCl$_6$ (the last being usually written as 2NOCl·SnCl$_4$) are similar in structure to NH$_4$ClO$_4$, NH$_4$BF$_4$, and (NH$_4$)$_2$SnCl$_6$, and hence contain the nitrosyl cation, (NO)$^+$.

In NaNO, which is diamagnetic,[2] there probably exist (NO)$^-$ anions with the structure $[:\overset{..}{N}=\overset{..}{O}:]^-$. It is interesting that this anion, which is isoelectronic with molecular oxygen, does not have the same $^3\Sigma$ structure, which would lead to paramagnetism.

Nitrosyl chloride and bromide, ONCl and ONBr, have been studied by the electron-diffraction method.[3] Their configuration is the following:

[1] L. J. Klinkenberg, *Rec. Trav. Chim.* **56**, 749 (1937); L. J. Klinkenberg and J. A. A. Ketelaar, personal communication.

[2] J. H. Frazer and N. O. Long, *J. Chem. Phys.* **6**, 462 (1938).

[3] J. A. A. Ketelaar and K. J. Palmer, *J.A.C.S.* **59**, 2629 (1937). The thermodynamic constants of nitrosyl chloride have been discussed by C. M. Beeson and D. M. Yost. *J. Chem. Phys.* **7**, 44 (1939).

The N—O distance is about 1.12 Å. Although a reasonable electronic structure, I,

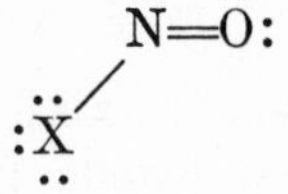

$$\ddot{N}{=}\ddot{O}:$$
$$/$$
$$:\ddot{X}$$

I

can be formulated for these molecules, this seems not to be correct, for the observed N—Cl and N—Br distances, 1.98 and 2.14 Å, are very much greater than the sums of the covalent radii, 1.69 and 1.84 Å, respectively. It seems probable that these molecules resonate between structure I and the ionic structure II,

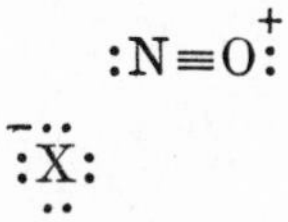

$$:N{\equiv}O\overset{+}{:}$$
$$\overset{-}{:}\overset{..}{X}:$$

II

and that the ionic N—X bond gives rise to the increase in the N—X distance.

The structure of the mixed metal nitrosyl-carbonyls has been mentioned in Section 31a, where it was pointed out that by use of two orbitals of the metal atom, and their associated electrons, the metal-nitrogen bond assumes a large amount of double-bond character, corresponding to the structures $M^-{::}N^+{::}\overset{..}{O}:$ and $M^+{::}\overset{..}{N}{:}\overset{..}{O}{:}^-$. Evidence regarding the nature of complex ions containing the nitroso group, for which no measurements of interatomic distances have been made, are provided by magnetic data. The observed magnetic moments of complexes of this type are the following:

$Na_2[Fe(CN)_5NO]\cdot 2H_2O$, μ = 0.00 Bohr magnetons
$[Ru(NH_3)_4NO\cdot H_2O]Cl_3$ 0.00
$[Ru(NH_3)_4NO\cdot Cl]Br_2$ 0.00
$[Co(NH_3)_5NO]Cl_2$ 2.81

The diamagnetism of the first three corresponds to structures of the octahedral covalent type. The observed moment of the fourth compound presents a problem. It has been suggested[1] that the nitroso group may assume a structure involving two three-electron bonds, $M:\overset{\cdot\cdot}{\underset{\cdot\cdot}{N}}:O:$ similar to that of the oxygen molecule (Sec. 35); the reason for this is not clear.

The organic nitroso compounds nitrosobenzene, C_6H_5NO, and p-nitrosodimethylaniline, $(CH_3)_2NC_6H_4NO$, as well as nitrosyl chloride, are diamagnetic,[2] corresponding to structures of the type $R—\overset{\cdot\cdot}{N}=\overset{\cdot\cdot}{O}:$.

To nitrogen dioxide we assign the resonating structure

in which one oxygen atom is held to nitrogen by a double bond and one by a single bond plus a three-electron bond. The configuration of this molecule is not known; we may predict the N—O distance to be about 1.18 Å and the O—N—O bond angle to be about 140°.[3]

---

[1] L. Pauling, *J.A.C.S.* **53**, 3225 (1931). Some doubt is thrown on the reported value of the magnetic moment by the work of Frazer and Long, *loc. cit.*

[2] E. B. Wilson, Jr., *ibid.* **56**, 747 (1934); C. M. Beeson and C. D. Coryell, *J. Chem. Phys.* **6**, 656 (1938).

[3] The prediction of about 140° for the O—N—O bond angle is based on the argument that the configuration $:\overset{\cdot\cdot}{O}—N\overset{\cdot\cdot}{\cdots}\overset{\cdot\cdot}{O}:$ is intermediate between $:\overset{\cdot\cdot}{O}=N^+=\overset{\cdot\cdot}{O}:$ and $:\overset{\cdot\cdot}{O}=\overset{\cdot\cdot}{N}—\overset{\cdot\cdot}{O}:^-$, with angles 180° and 125°16′, respectively, and that the angle should have an intermediate value. The N—O distance in the molecule should be slightly larger than the double-bond distance 1.16 Å; hence the value 1.18 Å is predicted. W. F. Giauque and J. D. Kemp, *J. Chem. Phys.* **6**, 40 (1938), have evaluated the product of the three principal moments of inertia of the molecule by entropy measurement; the value obtained corresponds to the distance N—O = 1.225 ± 0.010 Å for the assumed value 140° for the angle. The distance calculated from the entropy value changes rapidly with the assumed value of the angle; its values are 1.165 Å for 130° and 1.324 Å for 150°. Since the predicted value 1.18 Å for the N—O distance can be

The resonance energy of the three-electron bond stabilizes the molecule, but not enough to prevent polymerization to N_2O_4. The structure of the tetroxide is uncertain.   The symmetrical

structure 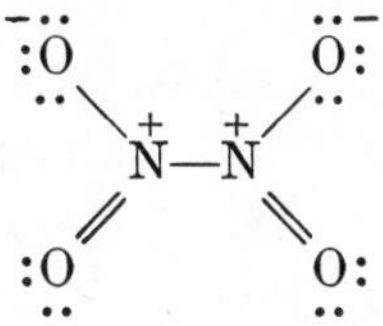 is indicated by x-ray data[1] and entropy

measurements,[2] whereas the adjacent charge rule suggests that it should be less stable than a structure such as

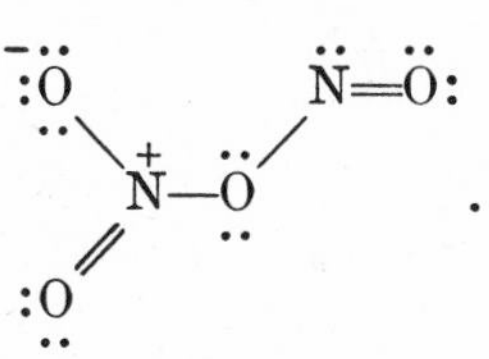

35. THE SUPEROXIDE ION AND THE OXYGEN MOLECULE

On oxidation the alkali metals are converted into oxides to which the formula R_2O_4 and the name alkali tetroxide were assigned until recently, in the belief that the substances were analogous to the tetrasulfides and contained the O_4^{--} anion with structure

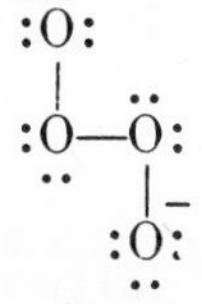

considered reliable to about 0.02 Å, the entropy measurements indicate 133° ± 5° for the O—N—O angle.

The electron-diffraction investigation of nitrogen dioxide (L. R. Maxwell, V. M. Mosley, and L. S. Deming, *J. Chem. Phys.* **2**, 331 (1934)) has given no reliable information about the configuration of the molecule. Band-spectroscopic data have been said to indicate a bond angle of about 120° (G. B. B. M. Sutherland and W. G. Penney, *Nature* **136**, 146 (1935)).

[1] S. B. Hendricks, *Z. f. Phys.* **70**, 699 (1931).

[2] W. F. Giauque and J. D. Kemp, *J. Chem. Phys.* **6**, 40 (1938).

With the discovery of the three-electron bond it was seen that these alkali oxides might contain the ion O_2^-, with the structure

$$[:\overset{..}{O}\overset{...}{}\overset{..}{O}:]^-,$$

involving a single bond and a three-electron bond between the two identical atoms. This suggestion was verified by the measurement of the magnetic susceptibility of the potassium compound.[1] The superoxide[2] ion O_2^- contains one unpaired electron, corresponding to the observed paramagnetism, which gives $\mu = 2.04$ Bohr magnetons, the theoretical value for the $^2\Pi$ state being about 1.85; whereas the O_4^{--} ion would be diamagnetic.

The existence of the superoxide ion in crystalline KO_2 has been verified also by x-ray examination.[3] The interatomic distance, reported as 1.28 ± 0.07 Å, is in satisfactory agreement with that expected for the single bond plus the three-electron bond, about 1.24 Å.

On heating rubidium superoxide it loses one-fourth of its oxygen, forming a substance with the stoichiometric formula Rb_2O_3. This, originally supposed to contain the ion O_3^{--}, with the structure

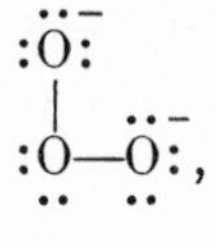

$$\begin{array}{c}:\overset{..}{O}:^- \\ | \\ :\overset{}{O}\!\!-\!\!\overset{..}{O}:^-, \\ {}^{..}\quad{}^{..}\end{array}$$

probably has the formula $Rb_2O_2 \cdot 2RbO_2$; that is, it contains both the peroxide ion, with structure $^-:\overset{..}{O}\!-\!\overset{..}{O}:^-$, and the superoxide ion.[4]

For the normal state of the oxygen molecule we would expect the structure

$$A \qquad :\overset{..}{O}\!\!=\!\!\overset{..}{O}:,$$

---

[1] E. W. Neuman, *J. Chem. Phys.* **2**, 31 (1934); W. Klemm and H. Sodomann, *Z. anorg. Chem.* **225**, 273 (1935).

[2] This name was suggested by Professors W. C. Bray and E. D. Eastman of the University of California.

[3] W. Kassatochkin and W. Kotow, *J. Chem. Phys.* **4**, 458 (1936).

[4] This has been verified by magnetic and x-ray data for both Rb_4O_6 and Cs_4O_6 by A. Helms and W. Klemm, *Z. anorg. Chem.* **242**, 201 (1939). The corresponding compound of potassium seems not to exist.

with a double bond. The normal molecule has, however, the term symbol $^3\Sigma$, showing it to contain two unpaired electrons; in consequence of this the substance is strongly paramagnetic. It seems probable[1] that the first excited state of the molecule, the $^1\Delta$ state, is represented by this double-bonded structure, and that the normal state, which is more stable by 22.4 kcal./mole, corresponds to a structure in which the two atoms are held together by a single bond and two three-electron bonds.[2] The numbers of electrons and orbitals are such as to permit this structure,

$$B \qquad :\!O\!\vdots\!\vdots\!\vdots\!O\!:,$$

to be formed, each oxygen atom using one of its four valence orbitals for an unshared pair, one for a single bond, and two for the two three-electron bonds.

Since the bond energy of a three-electron bond is about one-half that of a single bond, structure B would be expected to have about the same stability as structure A. There is another interaction to be considered, however; the coupling of the two three-electron bonds. Each of these involves one unpaired electron spin. The two unpaired spins can combine to give either a singlet state, by opposition, or a triplet state, by remaining parallel; one of these will be stabilized by the corresponding interaction energy, and the other destabilized. Theoretical arguments have been given[3] which lead to the conclusion that the triplet state should be the more stable, as observed. Strong support for these ideas is provided by the existence of a $^1\Sigma$ state 37.8 kcal./mole less stable than the normal state; this is to be identified as the state with structure B with unfavorable mutual interaction of the two three-electron bonds. The average energy of the normal state and this state is close to that of the double-bonded state.

It is probably the presence of unpaired electron spins in the normal oxygen molecules which gives rise to an interaction between them, somewhat stronger and more definitely directed than ordinary van der Waals forces, leading to the formation of O_4 (or $(O_2)_2$) molecules. These double molecules were discovered by Lewis,[4] by the analysis of the data on the magnetic suscepti-

[1] G. W. Wheland, *Trans. Faraday Soc.* 33, 1499 (1937).
[2] L. Pauling, *loc. cit.*
[3] G. W. Wheland, *loc. cit.*
[4] G. N. Lewis, *J.A.C.S.* 46, 2027 (1924).

bility of solutions of liquid oxygen in liquid nitrogen. The heat of the reaction $2O_2 \rightarrow O_4$ is very small, only about 130 cal./mole, so that the O_4 molecules exist in air only in very low concentration. This is, however, large enough to give rise to absorption spectra,[1] the analysis of which has verified the existence of the molecule.

The magnetic data show that the spins of two oxygen molecules combined in O_4 are paired together, to give a normal O_4 molecule containing no unpaired electrons. This does not have

the structure
$$\begin{array}{c} :\ddot{O}-\ddot{O}: \\ |\quad| \\ :\ddot{O}-\ddot{O}: \end{array}$$
(Sec. 10) but consists instead of two O_2

molecules, with nearly the same configuration and structure as when free, held together by bonds much weaker than ordinary covalent bonds. Whether the molecule has a coplanar rectangular configuration or that of a tetragonal bisphenoid is not known. It has been reported[2] that one form of crystalline oxygen contains rotating O_4 molecules in a cubic close-packed arrangement.

36. OTHER MOLECULES CONTAINING THE THREE-ELECTRON BOND

A few molecules in addition to those discussed in the preceding sections can be assigned structures involving one or two three-electron bonds. The normal states of the molecules SO and S_2 are $^3\Sigma$ states, like that of the normal oxygen molecule, and it is probable that the electronic structures $:\text{S}\vdots\vdots\text{O}:$ and $:\text{S}\vdots\vdots\text{S}:$ are satisfactory for these molecules. The observed values of interatomic distances, 1.49 and 1.93 Å, respectively, are about those expected for a single bond plus two three-electron bonds. Similar structures may also be assigned to Se_2 and Te_2.

It was reported some time ago[3] that the substance OF exists,

[1] O. R. Wulf, *Proc. Nat. Acad. Sci.* 14, 609 (1938); see also W. Finkelnburg and W. Steiner, *Z. f. Phys.* 79, 69 (1932); J. W. Ellis and H. O. Kneser, *ibid.* 86, 583 (1933); *Phys. Rev.* 44, 420 (1933); H. Salow and W. Steiner, *Z. f. Phys.* 99, 137 (1936).

[2] L. Vegard, *Nature* 136, 720 (1935).

[3] O. Ruff and W. Menzel, *Z. anorg. allgem. Chem.* 211, 204 (1933); 217, 85 (1934).

but evidence in support of this is very weak.[1] It might well be possible for the substance to be stable, however, and to be formed to some extent by the dissociation of O_2F_2, inasmuch as the conditions for resonance of the type $\{ :\ddot{O}\!-\!\ddot{F}:,\ :\ddot{O}\!-\!\ddot{F}: \}$, corresponding to the structure $:\ddot{O}\!\cdots\!\ddot{F}:$ with a single bond plus a three-electron bond, are satisfied for the atoms oxygen and fluorine, which differ in electronegativity by only 0.5. This structure for OF is closely similar to that of the NO molecule.

The Cl—O distance in the odd molecule ClO_2 has been found[2] to be 1.53 ± 0.03 Å. This value, which is somewhat less than the sum of the single-bond covalent radii, 1.65 Å, is compatible

with the structure $\left\{ \begin{array}{cc} \ddot{O}: & :\ddot{O} \\ :\ddot{Cl} & , \ :\ddot{Cl} \\ :\ddot{O}: & \ddot{O}: \end{array} \right\}$, involving resonance

of the three-electron bond between the two Cl—O positions. The O—Cl—O bond angle, which has not been evaluated experimentally, is probably about 125°.

No structural studies have as yet been made for other simple odd molecules (NO_3, ClO_4, IO_4), which may contain three-electron bonds. The nitrosodisulfonate ion, $[ON(SO_3)_2]^{-,-}$ which has been shown by magnetic measurements[3] of the potassium salt to be an odd ion, probably has the structure $:\ddot{O}\!\cdots\!N\!\!\!\begin{array}{c} {}^{SO_3^-} \\ \\ {}_{SO_3^-} \end{array}$.

To the tetra-p-tolylhydrazinium ion[3] we assign the structure $\left[\begin{array}{cc} CH_3C_6H_4 & C_6H_4CH_3 \\ & N\!\cdots\!N \\ CH_3C_6H_4 & C_6H_4CH_3 \end{array} \right]^+$, and to di-p-anisyl nitric oxide

[1] See P. Frisch and H. J. Schumacher, *ibid.* **229**, 423 (1936).
[2] L. O. Brockway, *Proc. Nat. Acad. Sci.* **19**, 303, 868 (1933).
[3] H. Katz, *Z. f. Phys.* **87**, 238 (1933).

the structure $\begin{array}{c} CH_3OC_6H_4 \\ \diagdown \\ \diagup \\ CH_3OC_6H_4 \end{array} N\mathbin{\cdot\cdot\cdot}\ddot{O}:.$ It is probable that in the

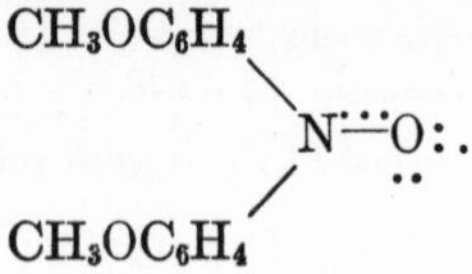

last compound there is also some resonance of the type described in the following section.

37. THE STRUCTURE OF THE SEMIQUINONES AND RELATED SUBSTANCES

The reduction of a quinone, such as p-benzoquinone, 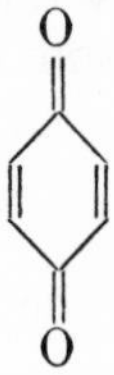 (I),

leads in general to the corresponding hydroquinone, 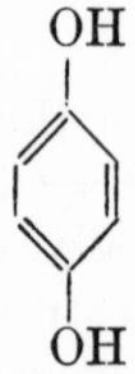 (II).

The molecule corresponding to the intermediate stage of reduc-

tion, (III), is not expected to be stable; although it is

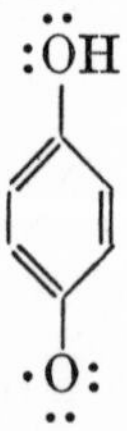

intermediate between I and II in regard to number of electrons, it is rendered unstable by the fact that the loss in bond energy from I with four double bonds to II with three occurs completely on the addition of the first hydrogen atom (at III). It is for this reason that odd molecules in general are of little importance.

There is, however, a way of stabilizing a semiquinone—the molecule intermediate between a quinone and a hydroquinone

In basic solution the semiquinone will exist as the ion,

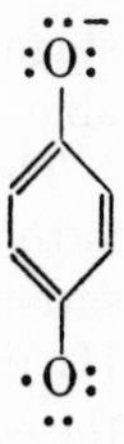

The structure written (with Kekulé resonance in the benzene ring, of course) is not the only one for the molecule; there is an equivalent structure obtained by interchanging the odd electron of the bottom oxygen atom with a pair of electrons of the other oxygen atom.   The semiquinone ion accordingly has the following resonating structure:

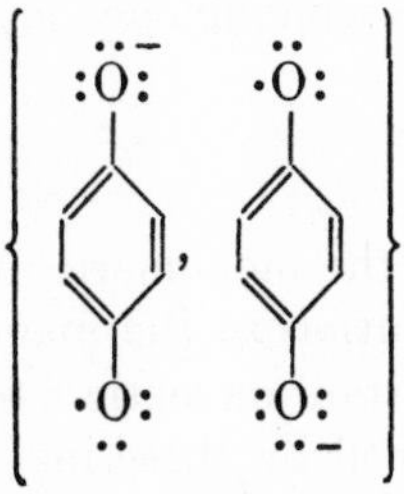

$$(IV),$$

with contributions also from the less important structures of the

type +

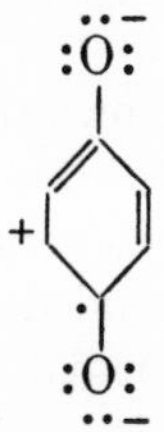

It is seen that the resonance indicated in IV is closely analogous to that of the three-electron bond; in each case there is interchange of a single electron and an electron pair.   In He_2^+, NO etc., this interchange takes place directly between adjacent atoms, whereas in the semiquinone ion it takes place by way of a conjugated system.   We may accordingly well expect the resonance energy of IV to be about one-half the energy of a single covalent bond; and this is just enough to permit the intermediate stage of reduction from quinone to hydroquinone to be observable.

The condition for stabilization of the semiquinone by resonance is that the two structures IV be equivalent. This condition is satisfied for the semiquinone anion, but not for the semiquinone III itself, in which the presence of the hydrogen atom destroys the equivalence of the two structures. We thus expect the semiquinone to be stable only in the form of the anion. This is verified by experiment. Michaelis and his collaborators[1] have shown that the semiquinone of phenanthrene-3-sulfonate is stable

in alkaline solution as the semiquinone ion,

proof of the existence of the monomeric ion by measurement of its paramagnetic contribution to the magnetic susceptibility of the solution (due to the spin magnetic moment of the unpaired electron) has been obtained by these investigators. The semiquinone ion is in equilibrium with a dimeric form, perhaps involving an O—O bond; and in acid solution only the dimer is present, in accordance with the above discussion of the expected instability of the unsymmetrical semiquinones.[2]

Many substances containing nitrogen have been shown to exist in intermediate reduction states corresponding to the semiquinone state; and for these substances it is found in general that the conditions are satisfied for resonance of the extended three-electron-bond type.[3] The tetramethyl-p-phenylenediaminium

[1] L. Michaelis and M. P. Schubert, *J. Biol. Chem.* **119**, 133 (1937); L. Michaelis and E. S. Fetcher, Jr., *J.A.C.S.* **59**, 2460 (1937); L. Michaelis, G. F. Boeker, and R. K. Reber, *ibid.* **60**, 202 (1938); L. Michaelis, R. K. Reber, and J. A. Kuck, *ibid.* **60**, 214 (1938); L. Michaelis, M. P. Schubert, R. K. Reber, J. A. Kuck, and S. Granick, *ibid.* **60**, 1678 (1938); G. Schwarzenbach and L. Michaelis, *ibid.* **60**, 1667 (1938).

[2] The green solid quinhydrone, with composition intermediate between quinone and hydroquinone, has been found to be diamagnetic (unpublished experiment performed by Dr. C. D. Coryell) and hence to contain no odd semiquinone molecules.

[3] For a review of the subject with an excellent discussion of potentio-

ion, shown by its paramagnetism to be monomeric,[1] resonates

$$CH_3—\overset{\cdot\,+}{N}—CH_3$$

between the two structures of the type 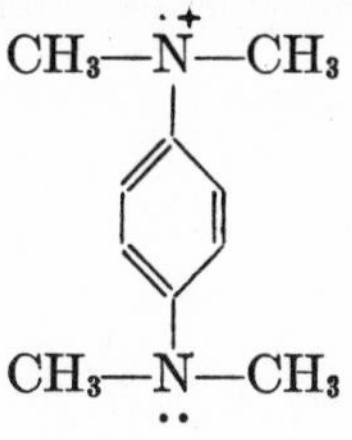   .   Similar

$$CH_3—\overset{\cdot\cdot}{N}—CH_3$$

resonance occurs for the semiquinone cations of p-naphthophenazine,

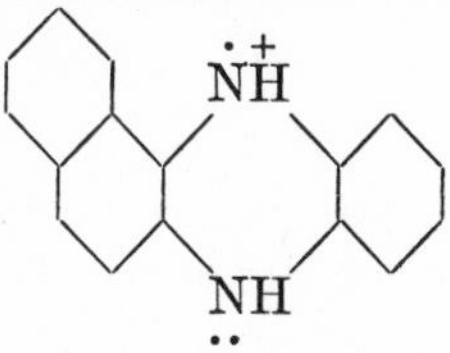

,   and of pyocyanine,[2]

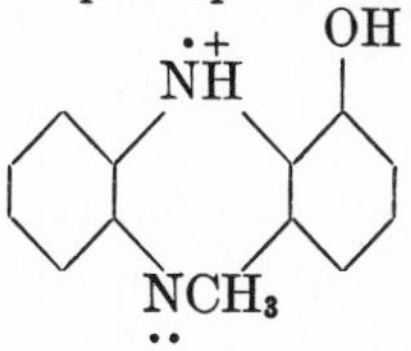

It is interesting to note that in the pyocyanine semiquinone the NH and NCH_3 groups are sufficiently alike to permit resonance complete enough to effect stabilization.

---

metric methods of investigating the existence of semiquinones see L. Michaelis, *Chem. Rev.* **16**, 243 (1935).

[1] H. Katz, *Z. f. Phys.* **87**, 238 (1933).   Katz reported values of about 1.6 Bohr magnetons (theoretical 1.73) for the perchlorates of this ion and the two mentioned in the following sentences.   The paramagnetism of the semiquinone of pyocyanine was also verified by R. Kuhn and K. Schön, *Ber.* **68B**, 1537 (1935).   Paramagnetism has also been shown for the semi-

quinones   as the chlorostannite and

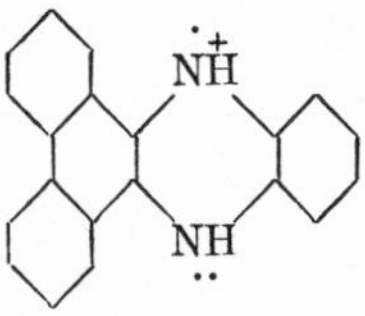

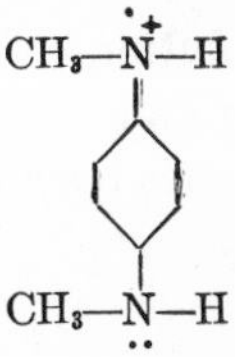

(Wurster's red), as the iodide (unpublished experiments by L. Pauling and J. H. Sturdivant, with preparations furnished by Dr. L. Michaelis).

[2] Pyocyanine itself, 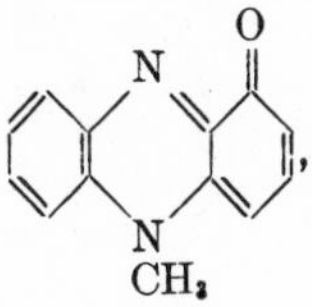 , is a blue pigment of an organism,

Bacillus pyocyaneus, encountered in purulent wounds.

Among the many other substances showing resonance of the semiquinone type mention may be made of those of the dipyridyl group.

On reduction of γ, γ'-dipyridyl, [structure], in acid solution there is

obtained a substance with a deep violet color, and similar violet substances are obtained by reduction of the biquaternary di-

pyridyl bases [structure] (called "viologens") in either acid or alkaline

solution.   The assignment of structure to these violet odd ions cannot be made with certainty.   By analogy with the semiqui-nones resonance of the type

[structure]

may be suggested, with contributions also from structures of the types

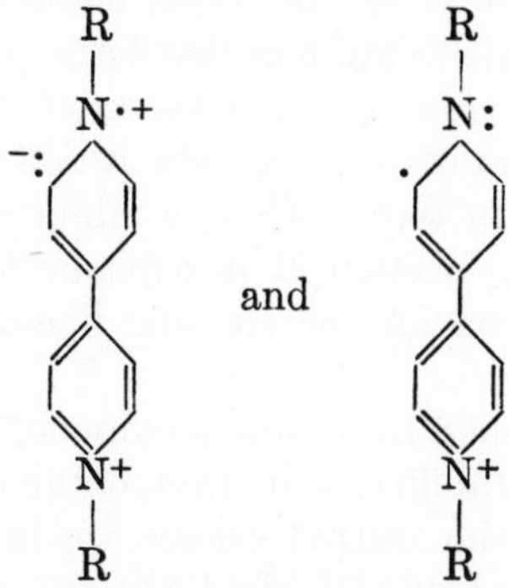

These violet substances, like semiquinones in general, are deeply colored. The color is correlated with resonance involving the transfer of electric charge from one end to another of a large molecule, as in the triphenylmethane dyes and other deeply colored substances. Although this correlation has a firm empirical foundation,[1] and has been shown to be reasonable by theoretical arguments,[2] a completely satisfactory theory of color has not yet been developed.

Some very interesting results have been obtained recently by Michaelis,[3] who has been studying the properties of the radicals

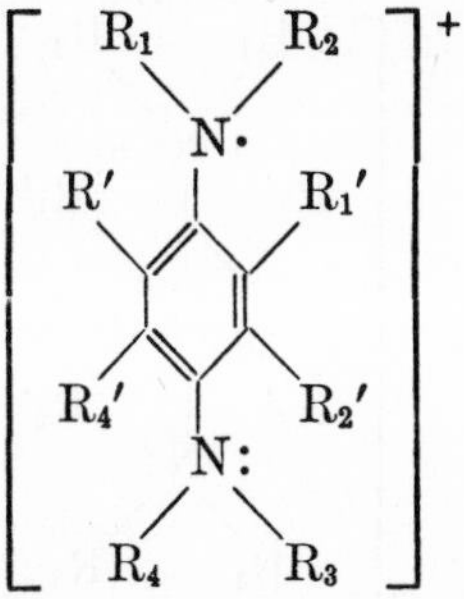

A

[1] C. R. Bury, *J.A.C.S.* **57**, 2115 (1935). Bury's treatment of color represents essentially the rephrasing in terms of resonance of the earlier suggestions of E. Q. Adams and L. Rosenstein, *ibid.* **36**, 1472 (1914) and A. Baeyer, *Ann.* **354**, 152 (1907).

[2] L. Pauling, p. 1888 of "Organic Chemistry," H. Gilman, Editor, John Wiley and Sons, Inc., New York, 1938; *Proc. Nat. Acad. Sci.* **25**, 577 (1939).

[3] L. Michaelis and collaborators, personal communication. I am indebted to Dr. Michaelis for information about this work and for permission to discuss it before publication.

of the general type A (Wurster's dyes). As mentioned above, the existence of radicals of this type, obtained by oxidation of substituted p-phenylenediamines, has been verified by magnetic measurements. It is found that the stability of the radicals is dependent on the nature of the groups R and R′, in a way which can be interpreted in terms of steric inhibition of resonance of the type adduced in Section 27 in explanation of the results of Birtles and Hampson on the electric dipole moments of substituted durenes.

The radical obtained from diaminodurene, $NH_2C_6(CH_3)_4NH_2$, is comparable in stability with that obtained from p-phenylenediamine; the ortho methyl groups apparently do not come into pronounced contact with the hydrogen atoms of the amino groups. (This conclusion is compatible with the values of the van der Waals radii of the groups.) On the other hand, although the phenylene radical with four methyl groups attached to nitrogen, $[(CH_3)_2NC_6H_4N(CH_3)_2]^+$, is stable, the corresponding durene radical $[(CH_3)_2NC_6(CH_3)_4N(CH_3)_2]^+$ is very unstable; no detectable concentration of it has ever been obtained. It is clear that this instability is the result of the action of steric repulsion between methyl groups. The coplanar configuration required for resonance with structures such as B

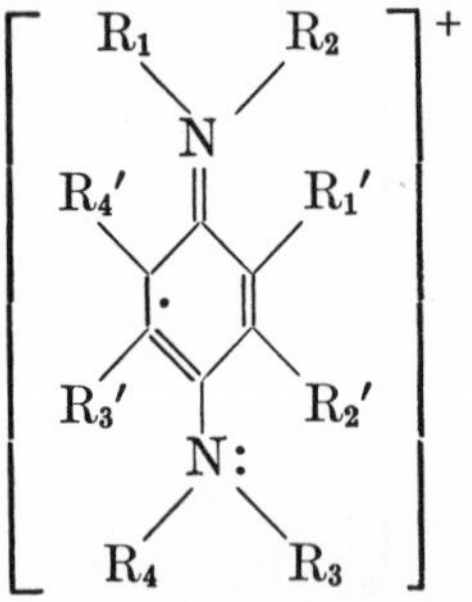

B

would place pairs of methyl groups such as R_2 and $R_1′$ only 2.4 Å apart; this configuration is very unstable, the distance for van der Waals contact being 4.0 Å. In consequence the molecule must assume a non-coplanar configuration, with inhibition of the resonance of this type and with decrease in stability of the radical by the amount of the corresponding resonance energy.

Semiquinone formation is undoubtedly of great significance

in physiological processes.   Thus it has been found[1] that whereas diaminodurene increases the respiration of erythrocytes to about the same extent as methylene blue, tetramethyldiaminodurene has no catalytic effect at all.

It is is of interest to note that odd ions of the type $H_2N^{\cdot+}$— $CH{=}CH{-}CH{=}CH{-}\overset{..}{N}H_2$ are stabilized by three-electron-bond resonance by way of the conjugated double bond system; the existence of substances of this type has, however, not been reported.

[1] S. Granick, L. Michaelis, and M. P. Schubert, *Science* 90, 422 (1939).

CHAPTER IX

THE HYDROGEN BOND

38. THE NATURE OF THE HYDROGEN BOND

It has been recognized in recent years that under certain conditions an atom of hydrogen is attracted by rather strong forces to two atoms, instead of only one, so that it may be considered to be acting as a bond between them. This is called the *hydrogen bond*.[1] The bond was for some time thought to result from the formation of two covalent bonds by the hydrogen atom, the hydrogen fluoride ion $[HF_2]^-$ being assigned the structure $[:\ddot{F}:H:\ddot{F}:]^-$. It is now recognized that the hydrogen atom, with only one stable orbital (the $1s$ orbital), can form only one covalent bond,[2] and that the hydrogen bond is largely ionic in character, and is formed only between the most electronegative atoms. A detailed discussion of its nature is given in the following sections.

Although the hydrogen bond is not a strong bond (its bond energy, that is, the energy of the reaction $XH + Y \rightarrow XHY$, being only about 5 kcal./mole), it has great significance in determining the properties of substances. Because of its small bond energy and the small activation energy involved in its formation and rupture, the hydrogen bond is especially suited to play a part in reactions occurring at normal temperatures. It has been

---

[1] Other names, such as "hydroxyl bond," "hydrogen bridge," etc., have also been used.

[2] It has been suggested by several authors that use may be made of an L orbital of hydrogen for formation of a second covalent bond. However, in case that a bond A—H with small ionic character is formed the proton is shielded almost completely by its half of the shared electron pair, and it has accordingly no power to attract an L electron. Only if the A—H bond were largely ionic would there occur appreciable attraction for an L electron, and under this circumstance the proton could use its $1s$ orbital for covalent bond formation with the atom B of the group A—H---B (during the ionic phases of the A—H bond), and so would not need to call on the unstable L orbital.

recognized that hydrogen bonds restrain protein molecules to their native configurations, and I believe that as the methods of structural chemistry are further applied to physiological problems it will be found that the significance of the hydrogen bond for physiology is greater than that of any other single structural feature.

The first mention of the hydrogen bond was made by Moore and Winmill,[1] who assigned to trimethylammonium hydroxide the structure

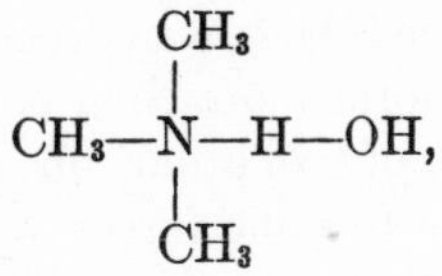

$$
\begin{array}{c}
CH_3 \\
| \\
CH_3-N-H-OH, \\
| \\
CH_3
\end{array}
$$

accounting in this way for the weakness of this substance as a base, as compared with tetramethylammonium hydroxide. Shortly thereafter Pfeiffer[2] introduced the bond into organic chemistry; to explain the fact that the combining power with amines and strong bases of hydroxyl ortho to carbonyl is less than that of hydroxyl meta to carbonyl, he wrote " . . . wir annehmen, dass das Wasserstoffatom des o-Hydroxyls koordinativ an ein Carbonylsauerstoffatom gebunden ist (innere Komplexsalzbildung):

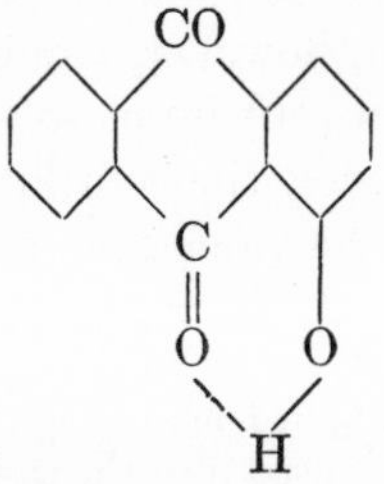

und dadurch in seiner Additionskraft für Amine und Metallhydroxyde geschwächt wird."

The recognition of the importance of the hydrogen bond and of its extensive occurrence was made by Latimer and Rodebush,[3]

[1] T. S. Moore and T. F. Winmill, *J. Chem. Soc.* **101**, 1635 (1912).

[2] P. Pfeiffer, *Ann.* **398**, 137 (1913).

[3] W. M. Latimer and W. H. Rodebush, *J.A.C.S.* **42**, 1419 (1920). Lewis ("Valence," p. 109) mentions that the idea was also used by Huggins in an unpublished work; see also M. L. Huggins, *Phys. Rev.* **18**, 333 (1921); **19**, 346 (1922).

who used this concept in the discussion of highly associated liquids, such as water and hydrogen fluoride, with their abnormally high dielectric constant values, of the small ionization of ammonium hydroxide, and of the formation of double molecules by acetic acid. The number of molecules recognized as containing hydrogen bonds has been greatly increased by spectroscopic and crystal-structure studies and by the analysis of physico-chemical data.[1]

With the development of the quantum-mechanical theory of valence it was recognized[2] that a hydrogen atom, with only one stable orbital, cannot form more than one pure covalent bond,[3] and that the attraction of two atoms observed in hydrogen-bond formation must be due to ionic forces. This conception of the hydrogen bond leads at once to the explanation of its important properties.

First, the hydrogen bond is a bond by hydrogen between *two* atoms; the coordination number of hydrogen does not exceed two.[4] The positive hydrogen ion is a bare proton, with no electron shell about it. This vanishingly small cation would attract one anion (which we idealize here as a rigid sphere of finite radius—see Chapter X) to the equilibrium internuclear distance equal to the anion radius, and could then similarly attract a second anion, as shown in Figure 38–1, to form a stable complex. A third anion, however, would be stopped by anion-anion contacts, which prevent its close approach to the proton. From the ionic point of view the coordination number of hydrogen is thus restricted to the value two, as is observed in general.[5]

Second, only the most electronegative atoms should form hy-

---

[1] This method has been applied mainly by Sidgwick, "The Electronic Theory of Valency," who has used it in the discussion of compounds such as the enolized β-diketones; see also E. N. Lassettre, *Chem. Rev.* **20**, 259 (1937).

[2] L. Pauling, *Proc. Nat. Acad. Sci.* **14**, 359 (1928).

[3] The bond-forming power of the outer orbitals of the hydrogen atom is negligibly small.

[4] In some circumstances a hydrogen atom with some residual positive charge, as in the ammonium ion, is attracted by the resultant electric field of two or more negative ions. The corresponding weak interactions, although similar in nature to those involved in hydrogen-bond formation, are not conveniently included in this category.

[5] It has been shown recently by G. A. Albrecht and R. B. Corey, *J.A.C.S.* **61**, 1087 (1939), that the crystal structure of glycine is such as to

drogen bonds, and the strength of the bond should increase with increase in the electronegativity of the two bonded atoms. Referring to the electronegativity scale, we might expect that fluorine, oxygen, nitrogen, and chlorine would possess this ability, to an extent decreasing in this order. It is found empirically that fluorine forms very strong hydrogen bonds, oxygen weaker ones, and nitrogen still weaker ones. Although it has the same electronegativity as nitrogen, chlorine has only a very small hydrogen-bond-forming power; this may be attributed to its large size (relative to nitrogen), which causes its electrostatic interactions to be weaker than those of nitrogen.

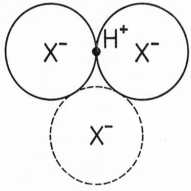

Fig. 38-1.

Increasing the electronegativity of an atom increases its power of forming hydrogen bonds. The ammonium ion and its derivatives, such as $[RNH_3]^+$, form stronger hydrogen bonds than ammonia or normal amines. The phenols form stronger hydrogen bonds than aliphatic alcohols because of the increase in electronegativity of the oxygen atom resulting from resonance with structures such as

$$:\langle\hspace{-6pt}\bigcirc\hspace{-6pt}\rangle\hspace{-2pt}=\overset{+}{O}H.$$

indicate strongly that one of the hydrogen atoms of the —NH₃⁺ group is attracted about equally by two oxygen atoms, forming a bifurcated hydro-

gen bond N—H $\begin{smallmatrix} O \\[2pt] \diagup \\[4pt] \diagdown \\[2pt] O \end{smallmatrix}$. Bonds of this type probably occur only rarely.

The hydrogen fluoride molecule resonates between the two structures H:F̈: and H⁺F⁻, with the second somewhat more important than the first, so that the bond has somewhat more than one-half ionic character. Similarly the complex ion $[HF_2]^-$ may be considered to resonate among the three structures A, B, and C:

$$A \qquad :\overset{..}{\underset{..}{F}}:H \ F^-$$

$$B \qquad F^- \ H^+ \ F^-$$

$$C \qquad F^- \ H:\overset{..}{\underset{..}{F}}:$$

If the equilibrium position of the proton were midway between the two fluorine nuclei the structures A and C would contribute equally to the normal state of the complex. If, however, the proton were closer to one nucleus than to the other nucleus the corresponding one of the covalent structures would be more important than the other one. Which of these configurations represents this complex has not yet been determined. In either case it is the ionic structure B which is of the greatest importance in leading to the formation of a hydrogen bond between the two fluorine atoms.

Crystalline ammonium fluoride differs from the other ammonium halides in its structure, which resembles that of wurtzite (Fig. 23–1). Each nitrogen atom is surrounded tetrahedrally by four fluorine atoms, with which it forms hydrogen bonds. In the ammonium ion the N—H bonds have only about 20 percent ionic character (Sec. 12), and these bonds will not be changed greatly in character by the presence of neighboring fluorine ions. The equilibrium positions of the four hydrogen atoms of an ammonium ion in the crystal are accordingly about 1.00 Å from the nitrogen atom, along the four lines directed towards the four surrounding fluorine ions. The N—F distance is 2.66 Å, so that the hydrogen atoms are about 1.66 Å from the fluorine ions. This distance is so much greater than the H—F covalent-bond distance (0.94 Å) that the corresponding structure is seen to have little significance; the N—H—F hydrogen bond hence corresponds to resonance between the structures N:H F⁻ and N⁻ H⁺ F⁻, with the second alone contributing the attractive force between the NH group and the fluoride ion. In this case the bond might be described as resulting from the interaction of the field of the fluoride ion and the N—H electric dipole moment,[1] and be represented by the symbol N—H---F.

Evidence is given in the following sections which shows that for the OHO hydrogen bonds which have been studied, with O—H—O distances between 2.5 and 2.9 Å, the equilibrium position of the hydrogen atom is about 1.00 Å from one of the two oxygen atoms and 1.5 to 1.9 Å from the other. In certain cases, such as the diaspore crystal (Sec. 40), the proton can be considered to be moving in the field of a potential function with two equivalent minima, each about 1.0 Å from one of the two oxygen atoms. The proton might then jump back and forth between these two equivalent positions, oscillating first about one and then about the other. The resonance of the proton between these two positions would not stabilize the molecule to an appreciable extent, however, because of the very low frequency of the nuclear motion.

There is evidence, discussed in later sections, that strong hydrogen bonds may involve an electron pair on each of the two bonded electronegative atoms; this is indicated, for example, by the tetrahedral coordination in ice. The two electron pairs are of course not used simultaneously in covalent-bond formation with the hydrogen atom; instead, the unshared electron pair of the atom more distant from the proton is probably directed toward the proton, with which it interacts electrostatically. In other cases, such as the ammonia and urea crystals, an electronegative atom forms hydrogen bonds to a number greater than the number of its available electron pairs, the electrostatic interactions then involving the atom as a whole rather than a particular electron pair.

[1] It has been suggested (C. P. Smyth, E. W. Engel, and E. B. Wilson, Jr., *J.A.C.S.* **51**, 1736 (1929)) that the association of water and similar substances is to be accounted for as resulting from strong electric dipole interactions rather than from hydrogen-bond formation. Recognizing the essentially ionic nature of the hydrogen bond, we see that there are no great differences between the two views, inasmuch as from both the interactions leading to attraction are electrostatic. The latter conception, which takes into account the finite separation of the charges contributing to the resultant dipole moment of a molecule, is somewhat less roughly approximative than the former, involving the idealization of mathematical dipoles.

39. THE EFFECT OF THE HYDROGEN BOND ON THE PHYSICAL PROPERTIES OF SUBSTANCES

It is the hydrogen bond which determines in the main the magnitude and nature of the mutual interactions of water molecules, and which is consequently responsible for the striking physical properties of this uniquely important substance. In this section we shall discuss the melting point, boiling point, and dielectric constant of water and related molecules; other properties of water are treated later.

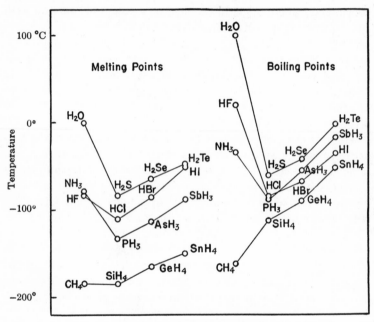

FIG. 39-1.—The melting points and boiling points of isoelectronic sequences of hydride molecules.

For the sequence of related substances H_2Te, H_2Se, H_2S the melting points and boiling points show the decreasing courses expected in view of the decreasing molecular weights and van der Waals forces[1] (Fig. 39-1). The continuation of the sequence in the way indicated by the values for the noble gases would lead to

---

[1] The van der Waals forces for these substances are due mainly to dispersion forces, which decrease with decrease in atomic number for atoms of similar structure. London's calculations (F. London, *Z. f. Phys.* 63,

the expectation of values of about $-100°C$ and $-80° C$, respectively, for the melting and boiling points of water. The observed values of these quantities are very much higher; this is the result of the formation of hydrogen bonds, which have the extraordinary effect of doubling the boiling point of the substance on the Kelvin scale.

The melting and boiling points of ammonia and hydrogen fluoride are also considerably higher than the values extrapolated from

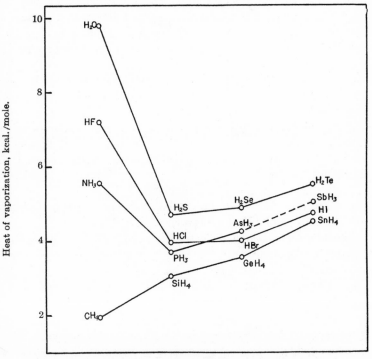

FIG. 39-2.—The heats of vaporization of isoelectronic sequences of hydride molecules.

the sequences of analogous compounds, the effects being, however, somewhat smaller than for water. This decrease for ammonia is due in part to the smaller electronegativity of nitrogen than of oxygen, and in part to the presence in the ammonia

---

245 (1930)) have shown the interaction of permanent dipoles to contribute only a small amount to the van der Waals forces for a substance such as hydrogen chloride.

molecule of only one unshared electron pair, which must serve as the source of attraction for the protons involved in all the hydrogen bonds formed with the N—H groups of other molecules. Hydrogen fluoride can form only one-half as many hydrogen bonds as water, and, although its F—H—F bonds are stronger than the O—H—O bonds in water and ice, the resultant effects are smaller for this substance than for water.

It is worthy of note that from the existence of both the melting point effect and the boiling point effect the deduction can be made that some of the hydrogen bonds existing in crystals of hydrogen fluoride, water, and ammonia are ruptured on fusion, and that others (more than one-half of the total) are retained in the liquid even at the boiling point, and are then ruptured on vaporization. Indeed, the very strong hydrogen bonds of hydrogen fluoride tend to hold the molecules together even in the vapor, which is partially polymerized.

Methane, with no power to form hydrogen bonds, shows the expected very low boiling point. Its melting point, however, lies about 20° higher than the expected value; the explanation of this is not known.

Properties which are related to melting point and boiling point also show the effect of hydrogen-bond formation; this is illustrated for the molal heat of vaporization in Figure 39-2.[1]

The abnormally high dielectric-constant values observed for certain liquid substances, such as water and ammonia, were attributed by Latimer and Rodebush to continued polymerization through hydrogen-bond formation, and this explanation has been supported also by other investigators.[2] In Figure 39-3 the comparison is made of the values of the dielectric constant of liquid substances, measured[3] at 20°C, and the values of the electric dipole moments of the molecules of the substances in the

---

[1] Figures similar to 39-1 and 39-2 were published by F. Paneth in his volume of George Fisher Baker Lectures, "Radio-Elements as Indicators," McGraw-Hill Book Company, Inc., New York, 1928.

[2] W. D. Kumler, *J.A.C.S.* **57**, 600 (1935).

[3] The value shown for the dielectric constant of liquid hydrogen fluoride at 20°C, 65, is extrapolated from measurements made at 0°C and lower temperatures; the value used for μ for this substance, 1.8×10^{-18} e.s.u., is an estimate suggested by the electronegativity scale. The value 87 for the dielectric constant of hydrogen peroxide is obtained by linear extrapolation of the value found for a 46% aqueous solution of the substance and that for pure water.

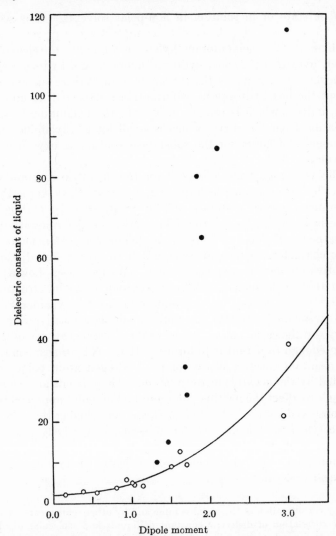

Fig. 39-3.—The dielectric constants of polar liquids plotted against the dipole moments of the gas molecules. From left to right the substances shown are: O, AsH₃, HI, PH₃, HBr, H₂S, CHCl₃, HCl, (C₂H₅)₂O, SOCl₂, SO₂, SO₂Cl₂, (CH₃)₂CO, CH₃NO₂; ●, CH₃NH₂, NH₃, CH₃OH, C₂H₅OH, H₂O, HF, H₂O₂, HCN.

gaseous state or in solution in non-polar solvents. It is seen that most of the points lie close to a simple curve, represented in the figure.[1] The points for methylamine, ammonia, the alcohols, water, hydrogen peroxide, hydrogen fluoride, and hydrogen cyanide, however, lie above the curve. For all of these substances except the last hydrogen-bond formation is expected, to an extent, indeed, which is roughly related to the magnitude of the deviation from the curve, which is small for methylamine and ammonia and larger for the substances containing oxygen and fluorine.

The very high value observed for the dielectric constant of liquid hydrogen cyanide is surprising, in that it shows that in this substance the carbon atom is able to use its attached hydrogen atom in hydrogen-bond formation. From the electronegativity scale the C—H bond would be attributed only a small amount of ionic character, insufficient to permit it to attract an adjacent negative atom with appreciable force. We have seen, however, from the dipole moment of the CN group that the structure R—$C^+::N:^-$ is of considerable importance for the cyanides (Sec. 12a); resonance with this structure, involving a positive formal charge on the carbon atom, increases the electronegativity of the atom enough to permit it to form C—H $\cdots$ N hydrogen bonds,[2] the resultant positive charge of the hydrogen atom being attracted by the negative nitrogen atom. These bonds are strong enough to affect the melting point and boiling point appreciably; the observed values, $-12°$ and $25°C$, are much higher than those of acetylene, which are $-81°$ and $-84°$, respectively. Their very large effect on the dielectric constant can be explained in the following way. Polymerization of hydrogen cyanide leads to linear molecules,

---

[1] By consideration of the molal volume and by other refinements a still closer correlation of dielectric constant of liquids and molecular dipole moments for substances which do not form hydrogen bonds might be achieved; the simple comparison made above is, however, suitable to our purpose. (See J. Wyman, Jr., *J.A.C.S.* **58**, 1482 (1936), L. Onsager, *ibid.* **58**, 1486 (1936), and J. N. Wilson, *Chem. Rev.* **25**, 377 (1939), for treatments of the dielectric constants of dipole liquids.)

[2] The symbol $\cdots$ used in this chapter to represent the longer interatomic separation in a hydrogen bond is not to be confused with the same symbol used for the three-electron bond.

H—C≡N···H—C≡N···H—C≡N···H—C≡N···H—C≡N,

with resultant dipole moments equal to about 3.00 $n \times 10^{-18}$ e.s.u. for polymers $(HCN)_n$ (the dipole moment of the simple molecule HCN being 3.00×10^{-18} e.s.u.). In the simple theory of the dielectric constant this quantity varies directly with the square of the dipole moment and with the first power of the number of molecules in unit volume; the observed value 116, which is about three times the value given by the curve for the monomeric substance, would accordingly result from an average degree of polymerization of three, which might well occur in the condensed system even with only weak hydrogen bonds.

It has been pointed out recently by Giauque and Ruehrwein[1] that data on the density of hydrogen cyanide gas show the presence of polymers $(HCN)_n$. The energy of the hydrogen bond in the dimer, H—C≡N···H—C≡N, was evaluated as 3.28 kcal./mole, and the sum of the energies of the two bonds in the trimer, H—C≡N···H—C≡N···H—C≡N, as 8.72 kcal./mole. The increase in hydrogen bond strength with increasing degree of polymerization is interesting, and can be given a simple interpretation in terms of resonance.[2]

Evidence of intermolecular association through weak hydrogen bond formation with use of a hydrogen atom attached to a carbon atom of a halogenated hydrocarbon molecule (chloroform and similar substances with ethers and glycols) has been reported recently.[3]

The degrees of polymerization of hydrogen fluoride, water, hydrogen peroxide, and the alcohols are without doubt very much greater than that of hydrogen cyanide. The dielectric constants of these substances remain smaller than that of hydrogen cyanide, however, because for them polymerization is not

---

[1] W. F. Giauque and R. A. Ruehrwein, *J.A.C.S.* **61**, 2626 (1939).

[2] It is interesting to note that the long polymers $(HCN)_n$ would not be expected to be able to change their orientation in the crystalline substance, and that in consequence solid hydrogen cyanide, unlike ice, would have a low dielectric constant. This has been found experimentally by C. P. Smyth and S. A. McNeight, *J.A.C.S.* **58**, 1723 (1936), who reported the value of the dielectric constant of the solid to be about 3.

[3] S. Glasstone, *Trans. Faraday Soc.* **33**, 200 (1937); D. B. McLeod and F. J. Wilson, *ibid.* **31**, 596 (1935); G. F. Zellhoefer, M. J. Copley, and C. S. Marvel, *J.A.C.S.* **60**, 1337 (1938); G. F. Zellhoefer and M. J. Copley, *ibid.* **60**, 1343 (1938).

accompanied by a linear increase in the magnitude of the resultant dipole moment of the molecule. Hydrogen fluoride, for example, tends to form hydrogen bonds at about 140° angles, and
a molecule $(HF)_n$, such as the following one,

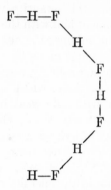

may have a very small resultant dipole moment; liquid hydrogen
fluoride probably also contains ring molecules with zero moment
in large numbers (Sec. 40a).

Hydrogen bond formation is of importance also for various
other properties of substances, such as the solubility of organic
liquids in water and other solvents,[1] melting points of substances
under water,[2] choice of crystal structure, cleavage and hardness
of crystals, infrared absorption spectra, etc. Some of these are
discussed in the following sections of this chapter.

40. THE STRUCTURE OF SIMPLE MOLECULES AND CRYSTALS CONTAINING HYDROGEN BONDS

40a. Hydrogen Fluoride and the Hydrogen Fluoride Ion.—
The size of the hydrogen fluoride ion, $[HF_2]^-$, which exists in
acid fluoride solutions and ionic crystals, is known from the
x-ray examination of crystals of sodium, potassium, and ammonium hydrogen fluoride, the following values having been
reported for the F—H—F distance:

[1] J. H. Hildebrand, *Science* **83**, 21 (1936); "Solubility," Reinhold Publishing Corporation, New York, **1936**, pp. 148, 166; N. V. Sidgwick,
"Electronic Theory of Valency," **1927**, p. 139.
[2] N. V. Sidgwick, W. J. Spurrll, and T. E. Davies, *J. Chem. Soc.* **107**,
1202 (1915).

	F—H—F distance	Reference
$NaHF_2$	$(2.5 \pm 0.2 \text{ Å})$	1
KHF_2	2.26 ± 0.01	2
NH_4HF_2	2.32 ± 0.02	3

There is no evidence as to whether the proton is midway between the two fluorine atoms or is closer to one than to the other. The H—F distance in the hydrogen fluoride molecule is 0.92 A. It is possible that the two potential functions with minima 0.92 A from the two fluorine nuclei combine to give a function with a single minimum 1.13 Å from each nucleus; if this does not occur, the potential hill between the two minima is expected to be small, so that the proton could move easily from one equilibrium position to the other.

Since the H—F bond in hydrogen fluoride is essentially ionic, its discussion from the extreme ionic point of view should lead to satisfactory results. With the assumption that the electron distribution in the fluorine ion is that given by the screening-constant treatment, and with the neglect of polarization, a calculation was made[4] of the equilibrium distance of the proton from the fluorine nucleus in hydrogen fluoride, leading to the value 0.91 Å, in excellent agreement with the observed value 0.92 Å. (Similar calculations for hydrogen chloride and hydrogen bromide gave very poor agreement, presumably because the bonds in these molecules are largely covalent rather than ionic in character.) An extension of this treatment can be applied to the [FHF]⁻ ion, the H—F interactions being calculated in the way described and the interaction energy of the two fluorine ions being given by an expression obtained from the alkali fluoride crystals (Chap. X). This treatment leads to a symmetrical linear equilibrium configuration of the three ions, with the F—H—F distance equal to 2.32 Å, which agrees closely with

[1] F. Rinne, H. Hentschel, and J. Leonhardt, *Z. Krist.* **58**, 629 (1923); C. Anderson and O. Hassel, *Z. f. phys. Chem.* **123**, 151 (1926). The value reported for the F—H—F distance in $NaHF_2$ is unreliable.

[2] R. M. Bozorth, *J.A.C.S.* **45**, 2128 (1923); the accurate value quoted is that obtained in a recent investigation by L. Helmholz and M. Rogers, *ibid.* **61**, 2590 (1939).

[3] L. Pauling, *Z. Krist.* **85**, 380 (1933); L. Helmholz and M. Rogers, unpublished investigation.

[4] L. Pauling, *Proc. Roy. Soc.* **A114**, 181 (1927).

the experimental value, 2.26 ± 0.01 Å. The fact that the extreme ionic concept of the hydrogen bond with fluorine leads to a satisfactory value of the F—H—F distance in the $[HF_2]^-$ ion provides further support for this view. It is expected that in the molecule H_6F_6, assumed to have the ring structure

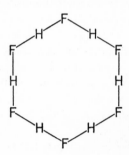

and in similar polymers the F—H—F distance would be somewhat larger; the experimental value[1] is 2.55 ± 0.05 Å.

The polymers $(HF)_n$ present in gaseous hydrogen fluoride consist in the main, according to Simons and Hildebrand,[2] of $(HF)_6$, with the ring structure discussed above. We would expect continued polymerization in this substance to give chains $(HF)_n$ with $n-1$ hydrogen bonds, H—F—H—F—H—F, and rings $(HF)_n$ with n hydrogen bonds. Calculations based on the ionic model show that for $n \geqq 6$ the polymer with the ring structure is more stable than its chain analogue, because of its additional bond, and that there is little difference in stability of rings with $n \geqq 6$. It is probable that the partial covalent character of the hydrogen bonds tends to stabilize bond angles of about 110° or 120° for fluorine,[3] and that in consequence the H_6F_6 ring is somewhat more stable than other polymers.

The results of an electron-diffraction investigation of gaseous hydrogen fluoride reported recently by S. H. Bauer, J. Y. Beach, and J. H. Simons, *loc. cit.*, indicate principally chain configura-

[1] S. H. Bauer, J. Y. Beach, and J. H. Simons, *J.A.C.S.* 61, 19 (1939).

[2] J. H. Simons and J. H. Hildebrand, *J.A.C.S.* 46, 2183 (1924).

[3] The crystal structure investigation of KH_2F_3, KH_3F_4, or KH_4F_5 (see G. H. Cady, *J.A.C.S.* 56, 1431 (1934)) would provide information regarding this bond angle.

tions for the polymers present in HF vapor, with the average value of the angles F—H$\cdots$F—H$\cdots$F about 140°.

The value of the heat of formation of H_6F_6 from 6HF found by Simons and Hildebrand is 40 kcal./mole, which corresponds to the value 6.7 kcal./mole for the energy of the F—H—F hydrogen bond in this substance. No value is available at present for the energy of the bond in the $[HF_2]^-$ ion.

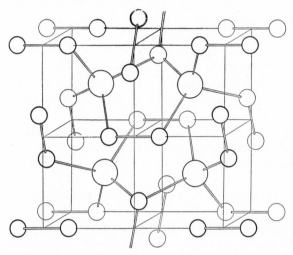

Fig. 40-1.—The atomic arrangement of the crystal NH$_4$HF$_2$. The large circles represent nitrogen atoms and the smaller circles fluorine atoms, with hydrogen bonds indicated by double lines.

40b. Ammonium Hydrogen Fluoride and Similar Crystals.— The crystal structure of NH_4HF_2 is of much interest, in that it is determined completely by hydrogen bonds. In KHF_2 each potassium ion has eight equidistant fluorine neighbors. The arrangement in NH_4HF_2 is similar, except that four of the eight fluorine ions, surrounding the nitrogen atom tetrahedrally, are drawn in to the distance 2.82 $\pm$ 0.02 Å through the formation of N—H$\cdots$F hydrogen bonds, the other four being at about 3.1 Å. The resulting structure is shown in Figure 40-1.

The same structure is found for ammonium azide,[1] the N—H$\cdots$N distances being about 2.98 Å and 3.20 Å.

[1] L. K. Frevel, *Z. Krist.* **94**, 197 (1936); E. W. Hughes, Dissertation, Cornell University, 1935.

In the ammonium fluoride crystal, NH_4F, with the wurtzite-like structure described above, each nitrogen atom is bonded by hydrogen bonds to four tetrahedrally-arranged fluorine ions, the $N-H \cdots F$ distance being 2.66 Å. The value of the energy of the $N-H \cdots F$ bond has been discussed by Sherman[1] by the comparison of the experimental value of the crystal energy of the substance with the value calculated for an ionic structure not involving hydrogen bonds, use being made of thermochemical data for the other ammonium halides. The added stability of the crystal due to hydrogen bond formation is 18.3 kcal./mole greater for ammonium fluoride than for ammonium iodide. If we assume the extra interaction energy of the ammonium ion with the surrounding iodide ions in the latter crystal[2] to be about 2 kcal./mole, the value 5 kcal./mole is obtained for the $N-H \cdots F$ bond energy in ammonium fluoride.

The great majority of ammonium salts are isomorphous with the corresponding potassium and rubidium salts, the effective ionic radius of the ammonium ion, about 1.48 Å, being nearly the same as that of rubidium ion (1.48 Å), and a little larger than that of potassium ion (1.33 Å). The exceptional substances NH_4F, NH_4HF_2, and NH_4N_3 contain hydrogen bonds from the ammonium ion to surrounding electronegative atoms. In other crystals containing such bonds a change in structure is not noted, but only a decrease in interatomic distances, the ammonium compound having a molecular volume much smaller than that of the rubidium compound. An example of this is provided by the fluoferriates, M_3FeF_6, for which the following values of the cubic unit of structure containing four stoichiometric molecules have been reported:[3]

[1] J. Sherman, *Chem. Rev.* **11**, 93 (1932).

[2] The data for ammonium chloride and bromide, treated similarly, lead to values of about 6–8 kcal./mole for the extra energy of interaction of the ammonium ion with the surrounding chloride and bromide ions. In these crystals each ammonium ion is surrounded by eight halide ions at cube corners. It can form hydrogen bonds with four, at tetrahedron corners, at a time. There is evidence that at room temperature the ammonium ion changes freely from one orientation to another.

[3] W. Minder, *Z. Krist.* **96**, 15 (1937); L. Pauling. *J.A.C.S.* **46**, 2738 (1924).

Li_3FeF_6	$a_0 = 8.88$ Å
$(NH_4)_3FeF_6$	9.17
Na_3FeF_6	9.26
K_3FeF_6	9.93
Rb_3FeF_6	10.23
Cs_3FeF_6	10.46

The value of a_0 for the ammonium compound is ten percent less than that of the rubidium compound, the molal volume being 26 percent less; other properties of the ammonium compound also differ somewhat from those of the alkali crystals.[1] These differences are attributed to N—H···F bond formation.

40c. Ice and Water.—The crystal structure of ice has been shown by x-ray investigation,[2] which has led to the assignment of the oxygen atoms to positions in the lattice, to be similar to that of wurtzite (Fig. 23-1), each oxygen atom being surrounded tetrahedrally by four other oxygen atoms, at the distance 2.76 Å. This is a very open structure, which causes ice to have a low density—hydrogen sulfide, for example, crystallizes in a closest-packed arrangement, each sulfur atom (hydrogen sulfide molecule) having twelve equidistant neighbors. The ice structure is, however, just that expected in case that O—H—O hydrogen bonds are formed, with each bond making greater or less use of one of the four valence electron pairs of each of the two bonded oxygen atoms.

The question now arises as to whether a given hydrogen atom is midway between the two oxygen atoms it connects or closer to one than to the other. The answer to this is that it is closer to one than to the other, and that (with few exceptions) each oxygen atom has two hydrogen atoms bonded to it by strong bonds. In the gas molecule the O—H distance is 0.96 Å, and the magnitudes of the changes in properties from steam to ice are not sufficiently great to permit us to assume that this distance is increased in ice to 1.38 Å. There is, for example, only a rather small difference in the frequencies of the vibrational motions of the molecule involving stretching the O—H bonds observed for ice and water vapor; this difference has been inter-

[1] The alkali crystals may be only pseudocubic in structure.
[2] D. M. Dennison, *Phys. Rev.* **17**, 20 (1921); W. H. Bragg, *Proc. Phys. Soc.* (*London*) **34**; 98 (1922); W. H. Barnes, *Proc. Roy. Soc.* **A125, 670** (1929).

preted[1] as corresponding to the value 0.99 Å for the O—H bond distance, 0.03 A greater than in the isolated molecule. (The same conclusion is reached by application of Badger's rule, Sec. 21d.)   An interesting verification of the existence of discrete water molecules in ice is provided by the discussion of its residual entropy, which moreover also gives definite information regarding the orientation of the water molecules in the crystal.[2]

It is found experimentally that ice[3] and heavy ice[4] retain at very low temperatures appreciable amounts of entropy. If each water molecule in the ice crystal were oriented in a definite way, permitting the assignment of a unique configuration to the crystal, such as that suggested by Bernal and Fowler,[5] the residual entropy would vanish. We accordingly assume that each water molecule is so oriented that its two hydrogen atoms are directed approximately toward two of the four surrounding oxygen atoms, that only one hydrogen atom lies along each oxygen-oxygen line, and that under ordinary conditions the interaction of non-adjacent molecules is such as not to stabilize appreciably any one of the many configurations satisfying these conditions with reference to the others.   Thus we assume that an ice crystal can exist in any one of a large number of configurations, each corresponding to certain orientations of the water molecules. It can change from one configuration to another by rotation of some of the molecules or by motion of some of the hydrogen nuclei, each moving 0.78 Å from a position 0.99 Å from one oxygen atom to the similar position near the other bonded atom.[6] It is probable that both processes occur. The fact that at temperatures above about 200° K the dielectric constant of ice is of the order of magnitude of that of water shows that the molecules can re-

[1] P. C. Cross, J. Burnham, and P. A. Leighton, *J.A.C.S.* 59, 1134 (1937).

[2] L. Pauling, *J.A.C.S.* 57, 2680 (1935).

[3] W. F. Giauque and M. Ashley, *Phys. Rev.* 43, 81 (1933); W. F. Giauque and J. W. Stout, *J.A.C.S.* 58, 1144 (1936).

[4] E. A. Long and J. D. Kemp, *ibid.* 58, 1829 (1936).

[5] J. D. Bernal and R. H. Fowler, *J. Chem. Phys.* 1, 515 (1933); these authors also suggested that at temperatures just below the melting point, but not at lower temperatures, the molecular arrangement might be partially or largely irregular.

[6] The protons will tend to jump in this way in groups, so as to leave each oxygen atom with two protons attached; ice is so similar to water that we are assured that the concentrations of $(OH)^-$ and $(H_2O)^+$ ions present in ice are very small.

orient themselves with considerable freedom, the crystal changing in the stabilizing presence of the electric field from unpolarized to polarized configurations satisfying the above conditions.[1]

On cooling a crystal of ice to very low temperatures it is caught in some one of the many possible configurations; but it does not assume (in a reasonable period of time) a uniquely determined configuration with no randomness of molecular orientation. It accordingly retains the residual entropy $k \ln W$, in which k is the Boltzmann constant and W is the number of configurations accessible to the crystal.

Let us now calculate W. In a mole of ice there are $2N$ hydrogen nuclei. If each had the choice of two positions along its O—O axis, one closer to one and the other closer to the second oxygen atom, there would be 2^{2N} configurations. However, many of these are ruled out by the condition that each oxygen atom have two attached hydrogen atoms. Let us consider a particular oxygen atom and the four surrounding hydrogen nuclei. There are sixteen arrangements of this OH_4 group; one with all four hydrogen nuclei close to the oxygen atom corresponding to the ion $(H_4O)^{++}$, four corresponding to $(H_3O)^{+}$, six to H_2O, four to $(OH)^{-}$, and one to O^{--}. The acceptable arrangements assigning two strongly bonded hydrogen nuclei to this oxygen atom accordingly comprise six-sixteenths or three-eighths of the total. Of these, only three-eighths are suitable with respect to the second oxygen atom, and so on; the number of configurations W is hence $2^{2N}(3/8)^N$ or $(3/2)^N$.

This leads to the theoretical value $k \ln (3/2)^N = R \ln 3/2 = 0.806$ cal./mole degree for the residual entropy of ice. The experimental values are 0.82 cal./mole degree for ordinary ice and 0.77 cal./mole degree for heavy ice; the agreement with the theoretical value provides strong support for the postulated structure involving hydrogen bonds with the hydrogen nucleus unsymmetrically placed between the two bonded oxygen atoms.[2]

---

[1] At the April, 1937, meeting of the American Chemical Society at Chapel Hill, North Carolina, L. Onsager reported that values of the dielectric constant calculated for this model agree approximately with experiment.

[2] It has been found by K. S. Pitzer and L. V. Coulter, *J.A.C.S.* **60,** 1310 (1938), that sodium sulfate decahydrate has a residual entropy of 1.7 cal./mole deg., corresponding to some randomness of orientation of water molecules.

By studying the Raman spectrum of ice and water it has been shown by Cross, Burnham, and Leighton[1] that at −183°C there is practically complete coordination (formation of four hydrogen bonds by each molecule) in ice, but that at the melting point there is an appreciable concentration of molecules which form only two or three bonds. On fusion and on further increase in temperature more bonds are broken; at 40°C the average number of hydrogen bonds per molecule is estimated to be somewhat greater than one-half of the maximum number possible.

The structure of water is in part similar to that of ice and in part based on closest packing, the maximum in density at 4°C resulting from the change in the equilibrium between these structural types.[2]

Of the heat of sublimation of ice, 12.2 kcal./mole, about one-fourth can be attributed to ordinary van der Waals forces (as estimated from values for other substances); the remainder, 9 kcal./mole, represents the rupture of hydrogen bonds, and leads to the value 4.5 kcal./mole for the energy of the O—H$\cdots$O bond in ice. The small value 1.44 kcal./mole of the heat of fusion of ice shows that on melting only about 15 percent of the hydrogen bonds present in ice are broken.

The heat of sublimation of hydrogen peroxide, 14.1 kcal./mole, leads, when corrected by subtraction of the estimated value 5 kcal./mole for the energy of the van der Waals attraction, to the same value for the O—H$\cdots$O bond energy in this substance as in water. The hydrogen bond formed by alcohols seems to be somewhat stronger. The heats of sublimation of methyl and ethyl alcohol are 9.8 and 11.2, respectively; when corrected by subtraction of the estimated values 3.5 and 5.0 for the van der Waals energy, these give about 6.2 kcal./mole. It is interesting to note that the O—H$\cdots$O distance in alcohols (see pentaerythritol, Sec. 40e) is correspondingly somewhat smaller (2.70 Å)[3] than that in water (2.76 Å).

[1] Loc. cit.

[2] For the discussion of x-ray and other data for water see Bernal and Fowler, loc. cit., S. Katzoff, J. Chem. Phys. 2, 841 (1934), and J. Morgan and B. E. Warren, ibid. 6, 666 (1938).

[3] W. H. Zachariasen, J. Chem. Phys. 3, 158 (1935), has reported the rough value 2.6 Å for liquid methyl alcohol. A recent investigation by G. G. Harvey, J. Chem. Phys. 6, 111 (1938), led to the value 2.7 Å.

In crystalline alcohols the molecules are combined by hydrogen bonds to polymers of the type

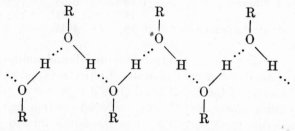

It is not necessary that many of these bonds be broken in order that the crystal melt to a liquid containing long chain[1] or ring polymers—indeed, if the liquid contained only ring polymers, such as $(ROH)_6$,

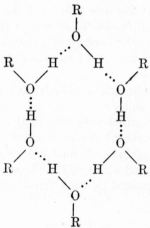

no loss of energy due to the rupture of hydrogen bonds would occur on fusion. It is for this reason that the heats of fusion and the melting points of alcohols are only slightly abnormal, whereas the heats of vaporization and boiling points show the effect of the hydrogen bonds strongly; and in consequence the liquid state is stable over a wide temperature range. It is instructive to compare ethyl alcohol with its isomer dimethyl ether; the respective values of some physical constants of these substances are the following:

---

[1] X-ray evidence for chain structures in liquid alcohols has been presented by W. C. Pierce and D. P. MacMillan, *J.A.C.S.* **60**, 779 (1938).

	C_2H_5OH	$(CH_3)_2O$	Difference
Melting point	−112°C	−138°C	26°C
Molal heat of fusion	1.15	0.95	0.20
Boiling point	78°	−24°	102°
Molal heat of vaporization	10.19	4.45	5.74

The hydrogen bonds in crystalline and liquid ammonia are weaker than those in ice and water for two reasons: the small ionic character of the N—H bond gives it only small hydrogen-bond-forming power, and the one unshared electron pair of the NH_3 molecule must serve for all of the bonds formed by the molecule with other N—H groups, whereas water has an electron pair for each hydrogen bond. In the ammonia crystal[1] each nitrogen atom has six neighbors[2] at 3.38 Å, this distance representing a weak N—H⋯N bond; the stronger N—H⋯N bonds in NH_4N_3 show the distance 2.94−2.99 Å. From the heat of sublimation, 6.5 kcal./mole, the energy of the N—H⋯N bond in ammonia can be calculated to be about 1.3 kcal./mole, with use of the estimated value 2.6 kcal./mole for the van der Waals energy.

40d. The Carboxylic Acids.—The hydrogen bonds formed by water are not sufficiently strong to lead to an appreciable concentration of polymerized molecules in the vapor phase. The oxygen atoms of carboxyl groups can, however, form stronger hydrogen bonds, leading to the formation of stable double molecules of formic acid and acetic acid. The structure of the formic acid dimer as determined by the electron-diffraction method[3] is the following:

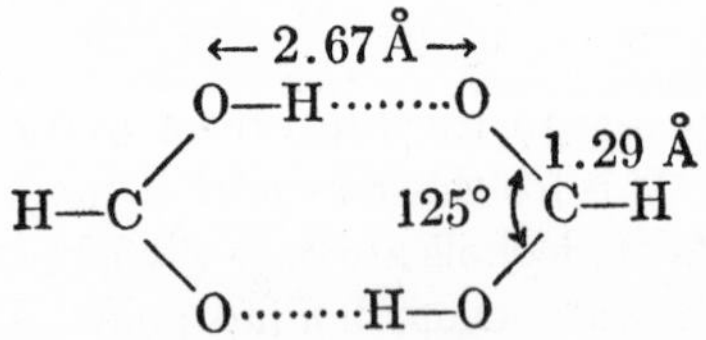

The value 2.67 Å for the O—H⋯O distance in this substance is smaller than that in ice, 2.76 Å, as expected for this stronger

[1] H. Mark and E. Pohland, *Z. Krist.* **61**, 532 (1925); J. de Smedt, *Bull. Ac. Roy. de Belgique* **10**, 655 (1925).

[2] The structure of the crystal represents a small distortion from cubic closest packing; the six next nearest neighbors are at 3.95 Å.

[3] L. Pauling and L. O. Brockway, *Proc. Nat. Acad. Sci.* **20**, 336 (1934).

bond. From the heat of dimerization,[1] 14.12 kcal./mole, the O—H$\cdots$O bond energy is found to have the value 7.06 kcal./mole. The value 8.2 kcal./mole is found for the hydrogen bond energy in acetic acid.[2] These values are about 50 percent greater than those for ice.

The distance from each hydrogen atom to the nearer of the two adjacent oxygen atoms in the dimer of acetic acid has been reported[3] to be 1.075 ± 0.015 Å; this is considerably greater than the value 0.99 Å reported by Cross, Burnham, and Leighton[4] for ice, as is to be expected in consequence of the increased strength of the hydrogen bond.

The increased strength of this hydrogen bond can be accounted for in the following way. The resonance of the molecule to the

structure $\text{H}—\text{C} \begin{array}{c} \overset{..}{\text{O}}\overset{+}{—}\text{H} \\ \diagup\diagup \\ \diagdown \\ \underset{..}{\overset{..}{\text{O}}}: \,^{-} \end{array}$ gives a resultant positive charge to the

oxygen atom which donates the proton in hydrogen bond formation, and thus increases the ionic character of the O—H bond and the positive charge of the hydrogen atom. It also gives to the other oxygen atom, the proton acceptor, an increased negative charge. Both of these effects operate to increase the strength of the O—H$\cdots$O bond.

It is interesting to note that in general the strength of an unsymmetrical hydrogen bond A—H$\cdots$B is increased by increasing the resultant positive charge of A and the negative charge of B.

Benzoic acid and other carboxylic acids have been shown to be associated to double molecules in solution in certain solvents,

[1] A. S. Coolidge, *J.A.C.S.* **50**, 2166 (1928).

[2] F. H. MacDougall, *ibid.* **58**, 2585 (1936).

[3] R. C. Herman and R. Hofstadter, *Phys. Rev.* **53**, 940 (1938); *J. Chem. Phys.* **6**, 534 (1938). This value is obtained by applying Badger's rule to frequencies observed in the infrared absorption spectra of light and heavy acetic acid (CH_3COOH and CH_3COOD). Spectroscopic work on carboxylic acids has been reported also by L. G. Bonner and R. Hofstadter, *J. Chem. Phys.* **6**, 531 (1938); R. Hofstadter, *ibid.* **6**, 540 (1938); M. M. Davies and G. B. B. M. Sutherland, *ibid.* **6**, 755, 767 (1938); A. M. Buswell, W. H. Rodebush, and M. F. Roy, *J.A.C.S.* **60**, 2239 (1938); F. T. Wall, *J. Chem. Phys.* **7**, 87 (1939); P. Koteswaram, *ibid.* **7**, 88 (1939).

[4] *Loc. cit.*

such as benzene, chloroform, carbon tetrachloride, and carbon disulfide.[1] The value 4.3 kcal./mole for the hydrogen bond energy has been found in this way for benzoic acid.

Benzoic acid exists in the monomeric form in solution in acetone, acetic acid, ethyl ether, ethyl alcohol, ethyl acetate, and phenol; in these solutions the single molecules are stabilized by hydrogen bond formation with the solvent.

Salicylic acid forms double molecules in solvents such as benzene and carbon tetrachloride.   It has, moreover, been shown by the spectroscopic method[2] that the double molecule contains no OH groups which are not involved in hydrogen bond formation.   This results from the assumption by the molecule of the following structure:

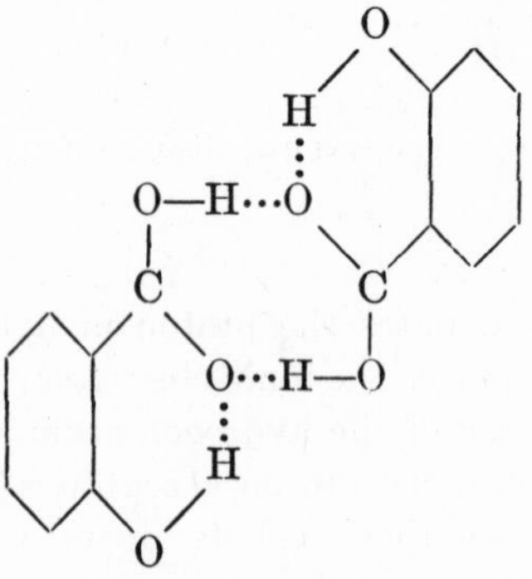

The two carboxyl groups are joined as in the dimer of formic acid, and in addition each hydroxyl group is bonded to an oxygen atom of the adjacent carboxyl group.   It has become customary to refer to this ring formation as *chelation* (from χηλή, a crab's claw) through hydrogen bond formation, the term being used also in a wider sense.[3]

The effect of chelation or internal hydrogen bond formation on the properties of salicylic acid is striking.   Branch and Yabroff[4]

[1] A discussion of the data on distribution ratios and the lowering of freezing points, with references to the original literature, is given by E. N. Lassettre, *Chem. Rev.* 20, 259 (1937); see also E. N. Lassettre and R. G. Dickinson, *J.A.C.S.* 61, 54 (1939).

[2] O. R. Wulf, unpublished investigation.

[3] G. T. Morgan and H. D. K. Drew, *J. Chem. Soc.* 117, 1457 (1920); see also N. V. Sidgwick, "The Electronic Theory of Valency," Chap. XIV.

[4] G. E. K. Branch and D. L. Yabroff, *J.A.C.S.* 56, 2568 (1934).

have pointed out that salicylic acid is a much stronger acid than its meta and para analogues, because of the effect of the hydrogen bond with the hydroxyl group in saturating in part the proton attraction of the carboxyl ion. The effect is still more pronounced in 2, 6-dihydroxybenzoic acid,[1] with the structure

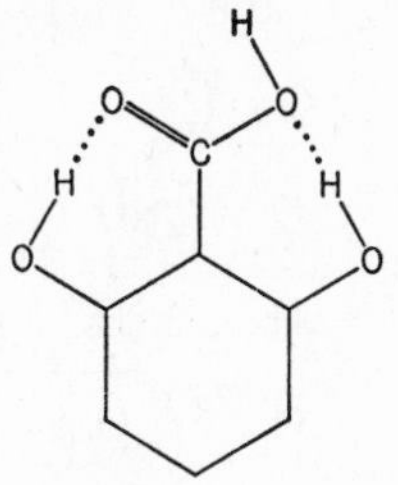

This substance is a very strong acid—stronger than phosphoric acid and sulfurous acid, its acid constant having the value 5×10^{-2}.

In crystals of *o, m,* and *p*-hydroxybenzoic acids hydrogen bonds are formed between molecules (and for the ortho compound within the molecule), whereas only the ortho compound can form the chelate bond in the single molecules of the vapor. The heat of vaporization is hence expected to be smaller for salicylic acid than for its analogues, and related properties should differ accordingly. This is observed to be the case; the vapor pressures of the substances at 100°C have the relative values 1320, 5, and 1. The quantities $RT \ln 1320/5$ and $RT \ln 1320/1$ have the values 4.16 and 5.36 kcal./mole, respectively; we deduce hence that the energy of the hydrogen bond in the *o*-hydroxybenzoic acid molecule is approximately 4.7 kcal./mole. In this argument the reasonable assumptions are made that the free energy values of the three crystals are the same and that the free energy values of the gases differ only by the hydrogen bond energy of the ortho compound.

The effect of hydrogen bonds on the physical properties of crystals is shown in a striking way by oxalic acid. This substance exists in two anhydrous crystal forms.[2] One of these, the α form, contains layers of molecules held together by hydrogen

---

[1] W. Baker, *Nature* 137, 236 (1936).
[2] S. B. Hendricks, *Z. Krist.* 91, 48 (1935).

bonds, the structure of a layer being represented schematically by the following diagram:

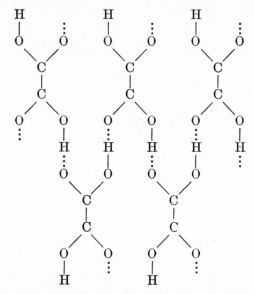

The crystal can correspondingly be easily cleaved into layers, this cleavage not breaking any of the hydrogen bonds. In the β form of the crystals there are long chains of molecules, with the structure

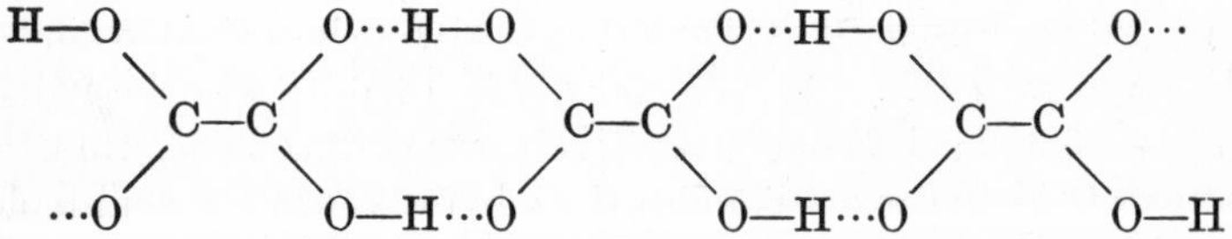

These crystals cleave along two planes parallel to the axis of these strings, breaking up into long laths. The O—H···O distances for both forms are about 2.6 Å.

40e. Other Crystals Containing Hydrogen Bonds.—Of the many crystals of known structure containing hydrogen bonds we shall mention a few, in addition to those referred to above, in order to indicate the stereochemical properties of this bond.

Boric acid[1] contains layers of $B(OH)_3$ molecules held together by hydrogen bonds as indicated in Figure 40-2, which represents a portion of one layer. The crystal cleaves easily along the layer

[1] W. H. Zachariasen, *Z. Krist.* **88,** 150 (1934).

plane. Each oxygen atom forms two hydrogen bonds, the O—H···O distance being 2.71 ± 0.05 Å. These bonds are coplanar with the BO_3 groups.

The substances ammonium trihydrogen paraperiodate, $(NH_4)_2$-H_3IO_6, and potassium dihydrogen phosphate, KH_2PO_4, contain one hydrogen atom for every two oxygen atoms. In their crystals hydrogen bonds are formed between oxygen atoms of ad-

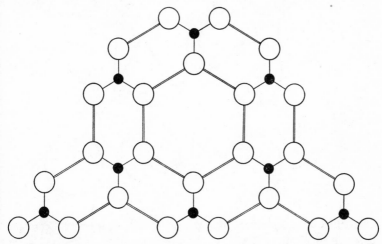

FIG. 40-2.—The arrangement of atoms in a layer of the boric acid crystal. Large circles represent oxygen atoms, small circles boron atoms, and double lines hydrogen bonds.

jacent complex anions, each oxygen atom forming one such bond. (It seems probable that the stability of the salts of paraperiodic acid with two of the five hydrogen atoms replaced by metals results from the achievement of the ratio H:O = 1:2.) The structure[1] of the hexagonal crystal $(NH_4)_2H_3IO_6$ is shown in Figure 40-3. The IO_6 groups, which lie on trigonal axes, are rotated about these axes in such a way as to bring each oxygen atom to the distance 2.60 ± 0.05 Å from an oxygen atom of an adjacent group, with which it forms a hydrogen bond. The structure[2] of the tetragonal crystal KH_2PO_4 is similar; the PO_4 groups rotate about the digonal axes on which they lie to give the O—H···O bond distance the value 2.54 ± 0.05 Å. This is the smallest O—H···O bond distance known.

[1] L. Helmholz, *J.A.C.S.* **59**, 2036 (1937).

[2] S. B. Hendricks, *Am. J. Sci.* **14**, 269 (1927); J. West, *Z. Krist.* **74**, 306 (1930).

Fig. 40-3.—The structure of the crystal $(NH_4)_2H_3IO_6$. Circles represent ammonium ions, octahedra $[IO_6]^{4-}$ ions, and double lines hydrogen bonds.

In diaspore, $AlHO_2$, with the structure[1] represented in Figure 40-4, the oxygen atoms occur in pairs connected by a hydrogen bond; the crystal accordingly contains the group O—H$\cdots$O. The O—H$\cdots$O distance is 2.71 $\pm$ 0.05 Å   The related crystal lepidocrocite,[2] $FeO(OH)$, contains oxygen atoms of two kinds (Fig. 40-5).   Those of the first kind are bonded to iron atoms only, whereas each of those of the second kind forms two hydrogen bonds, their configuration being similar to that for the

[1] F. J. Ewing, *J. Chem. Phys.* **3**, 203 (1935).
[2] F. J. Ewing, *ibid.* **3**, 420 (1935).

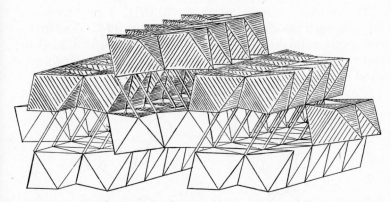

Fig. 40-4.—The structure of the diaspore crystal, AlHO₂ (after Ewing). Oxygen atoms are at the corners of the octahedra and aluminum atoms at their centers. Hydrogen bonds are indicated by tubes.

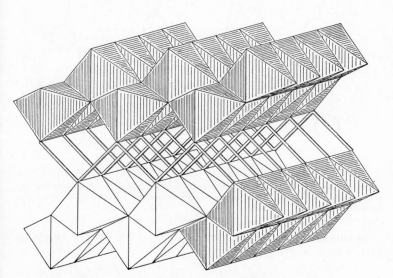

Fig. 40-5.—The structure of lepidocrocite, FeO(OH) (after Ewing)

alcohol polymers shown at the top of page 305.   The O—H···O
distance in this crystal is 2.70 ± 0.05 Å.

The alcohol pentaerythritol, $C(CH_2OH)_4$, forms tetragonal
crystals, with the structure[1] shown in Figure 40-6.   The hydrogen bonds, with the O—H···O distance 2.69 ± 0.03 Å, bind the
molecules into layers.   The crystal shows a correspondingly good
basal cleavage.

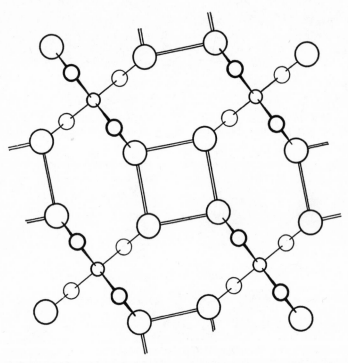

FIG. 40-6.—The structure of pentaerythritol, $C(CH_2OH)_4$. Small circles represent carbon atoms and large circles oxygen atoms. Hydrogen bonds are shown
by double lines.

In this alcohol the hydrogen bonds bind the oxygen atoms together into square groups:

[1] E. G. Cox, F. J. Llewellyn, and T. H. Goodwin, *J. Chem. Soc.* **1937**,
882; E. W. Hughes, unpublished investigation; I. Nitta and T. Watanabé,
Nature **140**, 365 (1937); *Sci. Papers Inst. Phys. Chem. Res. (Tokyo)* **34**,
1669 (1938). The intramolecular interatomic distances are C—C
= 1.53 Å, C—O = 1.45 Å.

```
     R              R
      \            /
       O—H···O
       :        |
       H        H
       |        :
       O···H—O
      /            \
     R              R
```

In resorcinol, *m*-dihydroxybenzene,[1] there are infinite ··OH-OHOH·· spirals (α modification) and staggered chains (β modification). The O—H···O distance is about 2.70 Å (the values 2.66, 2.70, and 2.75 Å being reported).

In urea,[2] $CO(NH_2)_2$, each oxygen atom serves as acceptor for four N—H···O bonds, with N—H···O distances 2.98 and 3.03 Å. The two shorter bonds are coplanar with the urea molecule containing the bonded oxygen atom, and the two longer bonds lie in the orthogonal plane; each of the bonds is coplanar with the molecule containing the bonded nitrogen atom, as expected in view of the partial double-bond character of the C—N bonds.

In diketopiperazine[3] the molecules are joined into infinite strings by hydrogen bonds:

```
···O    CH₂   H···O    CH₂   H···O    CH₂   H···
   \\   / \   / \\     / \   / \\     / \   /
    C      N     C       N     C       N
    |      |     |       |     |       |
    N      C     N       C     N       C
   /      / \\     / \     \\    / \     \\
···H    CH₂   O···H    CH₂   O···H    CH₂   O···
```

It is probable that the N—H··O bonds in this crystal, with distance 2.85 Å, are closely similar to those between the carbonyl and amino groups of polypeptide chains in proteins. The strongest bonds in glycine,[4] the only amino acid which has been thoroughly investigated with x-rays, have the distances 2.76 and 2.88 Å.

[1] J. M. Robertson, *Proc. Roy. Soc.* A157, 79 (1936); J. M. Robertson and A. R. Ubbelohde, *ibid.* A167, 122 (1938).
[2] R. W. G. Wyckoff and R. B. Corey, *Z. Krist.* 89, 462 (1934).
[3] R. B. Corey, *J.A.C.S.* 60, 1598 (1938).
[4] G. Albrecht and R. B. Corey, *ibid.* 61, 1087 (1939).

41. THE SPECTROSCOPIC STUDY OF THE HYDROGEN BOND

A most important method of studying the hydrogen bond has been developed by Wulf, Hendricks, Hilbert, and Liddell,[1] and applied by them in the study of a large number of compounds. Some of the results of this investigation are described below. The experimental method used is the study of the infrared absorption spectrum of substances in carbon tetrachloride solution, the spectral region of interest being that corresponding to the frequencies characteristic of the stretching of O—H or N—H bonds. Similar studies have been made for pure liquids by Errera and Mollet and for gases by Badger and Bauer, and other workers have also been active in this field in recent years.[2]

41a. Compounds Showing Strong Hydrogen Bond Formation.— The frequency of the vibration corresponding essentially to the stretching of the O—H bond in molecules containing this group lies in the neighborhood of 3500 cm^{-1} (in wave-number units), its first overtone being at about 7000 cm^{-1}. The absorption spectrum in this infrared region of a solution of methyl alcohol in carbon tetrachloride solution[3] is shown in Figure 41-1; it consists of a well-defined peak at about 7115 cm^{-1}. Other alcohols show a similar absorption spectrum; for triphenylcarbinol, for example, there is no noticeable difference from methyl alcohol except for a shift in frequency to 7050 cm^{-1}. The N—H group gives similar spectra, in the region near 6850 cm^{-1}, as is seen from

[1] U. Liddel and O. R. Wulf, *J.A.C.S.* 55, 3574 (1933); Wulf and Liddel, *ibid.* 57, 1464 (1935); G. E. Hilbert, O. R. Wulf, S. B. Hendricks, and U. Liddel, *Nature* 135, 147 (1935); *J.A.C.S.* 58, 548 (1936); Hendricks, Wulf, Hilbert, and Liddel, *ibid.* 58, 1991 (1936); Wulf, Liddel, and Hendricks, *ibid.* 58, 2287 (1936); O. R. Wulf and L. S. Deming, *J. Chem. Phys.* 6, 702 (1938).

[2] J. Errera and P. Mollet, *Journ. de Physique et le Radium* 6, 281 (1935); B. M. Bloch and J. Errera, *ibid.* 6, 154 (1935); R. M. Badger and S. H. Bauer, *J. Chem. Phys.* 4, 711 (1936); 5, 369 (1937); A. M. Buswell, V. Dietz, and W. H. Rodebush, *ibid.* 5, 501 (1937); P. Barchewitz and R. Freymann, *Compt. rend.* 204, 1729 (1937); S. Mizushima, Y. Uehara, and Y. Morino, *Bull. Chem. Soc. Japan* 12, 132 (1937); P. C. Cross, J. Burnham, and P. A. Leighton, *J.A.C.S.* 59, 1134 (1937); A. H. Blatt and L. A. Russell, *ibid.* 58, 1903 (1936); W. Gordy, *J. Chem. Phys.* 4, 749 (1936); 5, 202 (1937); E. L. Kinsey and J. W. Ellis, *ibid.* 5, 399 (1937); F. T. Wall and W. F. Claussen, *J.A.C.S.* 61, 2679, 2812 (1939); etc.

[3] Hilbert, Wulf, Hendricks, and Liddel, *loc. cit.*

the curve reproduced in Figure 41-1 for carbazole,

A more complex spectrum would be expected for the amino group, because of the presence of two interacting N—H bonds; the curve shown for aniline is characteristic of this group.

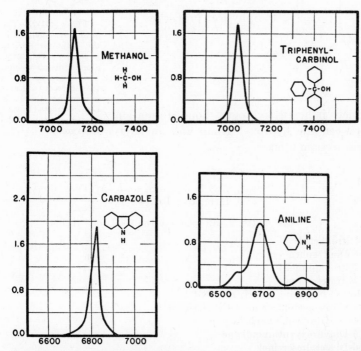

FIG. 41-1.—Infrared absorption spectra of methanol, triphenylcarbinol, carbazole, and aniline in carbon tetrachloride solution (Hilbert, Wulf, Hendricks, and Liddel). Ordinates represent the molal absorption coefficient, abscissas wave number.

The striking observation was made by Hilbert, Wulf, Hendricks, and Liddel that OH and NH groups which are involved in strong hydrogen bond formation do not absorb radiation in this way in the 7000 cm^{-1} region, nor in the region of the other overtones of the O—H and N—H oscillations. Instead of a sharp peak, the spectrum of these substances shows only a weak

and diffuse absorption band in these regions.[1]
This effect was observed for all the substances investigated which were known
from other evidence to contain hydrogen bonds, including, for example, *o*-nitro-
phenol (Fig. 41-2) and salicylaldehyde,

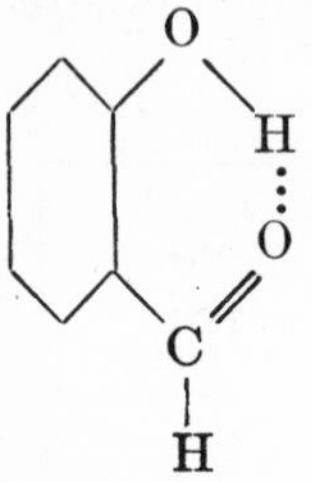

, the physical properties of

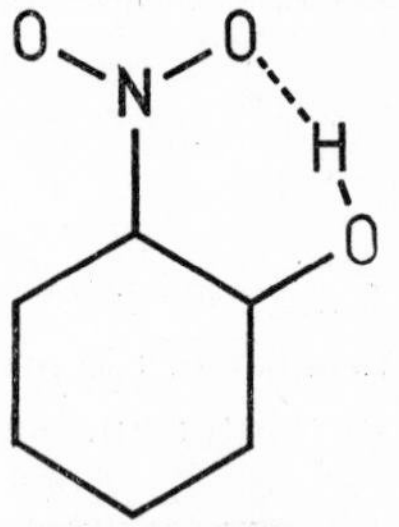

Fig. 41-2.—The
atomic arrangement in
the ortho-nitrophenol
molecule. The inter-
atomic distances and
bond angles are given
their correct values; it
is seen that the O—H
bond is directed toward
an oxygen atom of the
nitro group.

which indicate hydrogen bond formation
between the hydroxyl group and an adjacent oxygen atom.

TABLE 41-1.—SUBSTANCES FORMING STRONG INTRAMOLECULAR
HYDROGEN BONDS

(Absence of strong absorption in the 7000 cm^{-1} region)

o-Nitrophenol
2,6-Dinitrophenol
1-Nitronaphthol-2
2-Nitroresorcinol
Methyl salicylate, *o*-C$_6$H$_4$OHCOOCH$_3$
o-Hydroxyacetophenone, *o*-C$_6$H$_4$OHCOCH$_3$
1,4-Dihydroxy-5,8-naphthoquinone
1,5-Dihydroxyanthraquinone
4,6-Diacetylresorcinol
2,4-Dinitroresorcinol
4,6-Dinitroresorcinol
2,2'-Dihydroxybenzophenone
1,8-Dihydroxyanthraquinone
2,5-Dihydroxydiethylterephthalate

Acetylacetone,   CH$_3$—C=CH—C—CH$_3$
                         | ||
                         OH   O

[1] It is probable that there is strong absorption at lower frequencies due
to the O—H oscillation.

TABLE 41-1.—(Continued)

Salicylaldehyde,

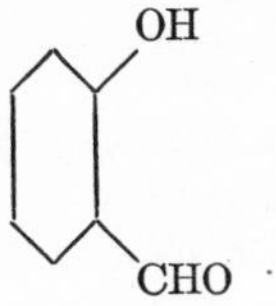

2,5-Dichlorobenzeneazo-1-naphthol-2
2,5-Dichloro-2'-hydroxy-4-methyl-5'-chloroazobenzene
Phenylazo-1-naphthol-2
Salicylaldehyde-anil, 2-OHC$_6$H$_4$CH=NC$_6$H$_5$
2-Hydroxy-5-methylbenzophenoneoxime acetate.

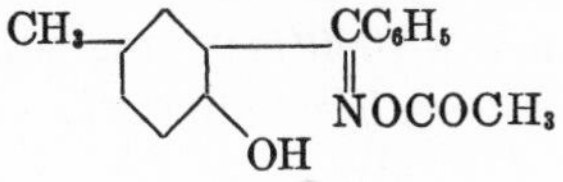

Salicylaldoxime acetate,

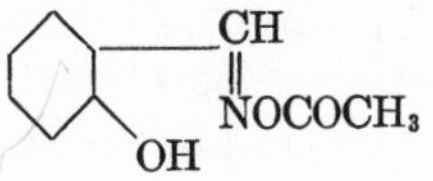

Salicylaldehyde-α-methyl-α-phenylhydrazone,

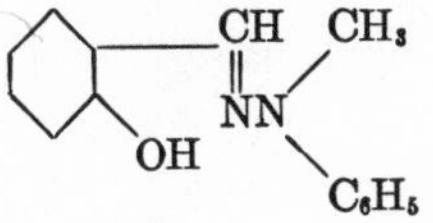

Salicylaldehydedimethylhydrazone,

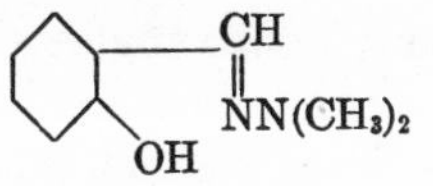

TABLE 41-2.—SUBSTANCES NOT FORMING STRONG INTRAMOLECULAR
HYDROGEN BONDS

(Presence of strong absorption in the 7000 cm^{-1} region)

m-Nitrophenol
p-Nitrophenol
o-Cresol, o-C$_6$H$_4$CH$_3$OH
o-Chlorophenol
Catechol, o-C$_6$H$_4$(OH)$_2$
Resorcinol, m-C$_6$H$_4$(OH)$_2$
Hydroquinone, p-C$_6$H$_4$(OH)$_2$
Benzoin, C$_6$H$_5$COCHOHC$_6$H$_5$
Ethyl lactate, CH$_3$CHOHCOOC$_2$H$_5$

TABLE 41-2.—(Continued)

o-Hydroxybenzonitrile
o-Phenylphenol
3,6-Dibromo-2,5-dihydroxydiethylterephthalate
m-Hydroxybenzaldehyde
p-Hydroxybenzaldehyde
p-Hydroxyazobenzene

This method of investigation, applied to nearly one hundred substances, has provided valuable information regarding the conditions which favor the formation of strong hydrogen bonds. In Table 41-1 a list is given of some of the substances found not to absorb strongly in the 7000 cm^{-1} region, and hence inferred to contain strong hydrogen bonds between the OH and NH and adjacent electronegative atoms in the molecule. A complementary list is given in Table 41-2 of molecules which do absorb strongly in this region; it is inferred that these substances do not form intramolecular hydrogen bonds at all or form only very weak bonds of the type discussed in Section 41b.

From these results it can be concluded that in o-nitrophenol and similar molecules the steric conditions for forming strong hydrogen bonds are satisfied, whereas in other molecules such as m-nitrophenol, o-hydroxybenzonitrile, etc., they are not. The evidence provided by this spectroscopic method agrees in general with that found in other ways, and the rules which can be deduced from it can be interpreted in a reasonable way in terms of interatomic distances and bond angles. These rules are summarized in Section 42.

41b. The Formation of Weak Intramolecular Hydrogen Bonds. —The spectra of many of the substances containing hydroxyl groups studied by Wulf and his co-workers consist of a single sharp peak in the neighborhood of 7050 cm $^{-1}$, as illustrated in Figure 41-1. Other substances which absorb strongly in this region (and are shown in this way not to be forming strong hydrogen bonds with use of the hydroxyl and amino groups) give curves of different types, involving pronounced frequency shifts and often splitting of the peak into two components, as shown in Figure 41-3. It has been suggested[1] that this complexity of the observed spectra is due to the presence in the solution of two or

---

[1] L. Pauling, *J.A.C.S.* **58**, 94 (1936).

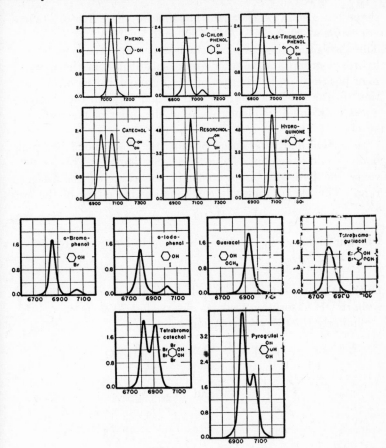

FIG 41-3.—Infrared absorption spectra of phenol and related substances in carbon tetrachloride solution (Wulf and collaborators).

more types of hydroxyl or amino groups with different characteristic frequencies—the groups of different type being either in different molecular species, as in the case of o-chlorophenol discussed below, or in the same molecule, as in catechol. This suggestion has received strong support through the experimental verification[1] of predictions based on it.

The substances resorcinol, hydroquinone, m-nitrophenol, and 2,6-dimethylphenol, as well as many others, show a single absorption peak resembling that of phenol very closely not only in

[1] O. R. Wulf, U. Liddel, and S. B. Hendricks, *J.A.C.S.* 58, 2287 (1936).

shape but also in position, the maxima for these five substances appearing at 7050, 7065, 7035, 7060, and 7050 cm^{-1}, respectively. This shows that there is very little interaction between a phenolic hydroxyl group and another group substituted in the meta or para position (or, in the case of alkyl groups, in the ortho position) in the benzene ring; the interaction through the ring produces only small frequency shifts of the order of magnitude of 20 cm^{-1}.

In phenol and substituted phenols the C—O bond has some double-bond character, as discussed in Section 19. This tends to cause the hydrogen atom to lie in the plane of the benzene ring. The phenol molecule can thus assume either of the two

configurations ⬡(O—H) and ⬡(H—O) , which, however, are equivalent, so that we expect for phenol only one molecular species and a sharp OH absorption peak, as observed at 7050 cm^{-1}.

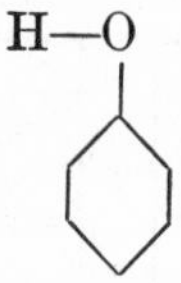

Similarly the two configurations

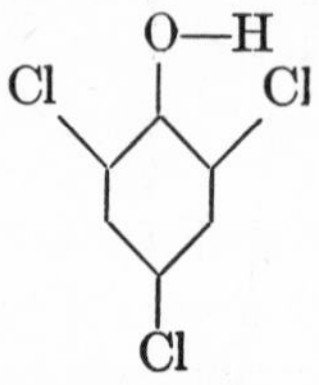

Cl ⬡(O—H) Cl / Cl   and   Cl ⬡(H—O) Cl / Cl

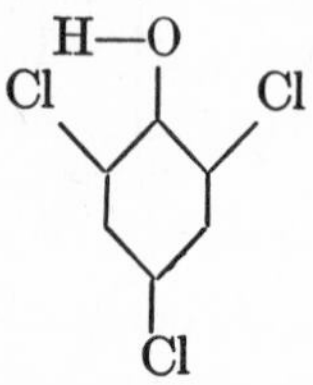

for 2,4,6-trichlorophenol are equivalent, and we expect a single peak for this substance also. However, we can predict that it will occur at a lower frequency than that for phenol, because of the attraction of the adjacent chlorine atom for the hydroxyl hydrogen. Both the carbon-chlorine and the oxygen-hydrogen bonds have an appreciable amount of ionic character, giving the chlorine atom a negative charge and the hydrogen atom a positive charge. The interaction of these causes the proton to be attracted by the chlorine atom and pulled a small distance away from the oxygen atom;[1] this leads, as shown by application of

---

[1] The equilibrium O—H distance is increased by about 0.01 Å by interaction with the chlorine atom.

Badger's rule (Sec. 21d), to a decrease in the OH frequency.   The decrease is observed; the spectrum of the substance is similar to that of phenol, but with a displacement of 160 cm^{-1}, to 6890 cm^{-1}.

For o-chlorophenol the two configurations (cis) and (trans) are not equivalent.   We expect these two molecular species to be present in solution with the cis form outnumbering the trans because of the stabilizing influence of the OH$\cdots$Cl interaction.   Hence the spectrum of the substance should show two peaks; one at about 7050 cm^{-1} (trans form, frequency as in phenol) and one at about 6890 cm^{-1} (cis form, frequency as in 2,4,6-trichlorophenol), with the 6890 cm^{-1} peak stronger than the other.   This is in fact observed; two peaks occur, at 7050 cm^{-1} and 6910 cm^{-1}, with the area of the 6910 cm^{-1} peak about ten times that of the 7050 cm^{-1} peak (Fig. 41-3).

The infrared absorption spectrum thus shows that o-chlorophenol in solution in carbon tetrachloride consists of about 91 percent cis and 9 percent trans molecules.   The cis molecules are more stable than the trans molecules by a free energy difference of about 1.4 kcal./mole (calculated from the ratio of the areas of the peaks).   This is presumably the difference in free energy of the cis molecule with its intramolecular hydrogen bond and the trans molecule with a weaker hydrogen bond with a solvent molecule (see footnote 2, next page).

The weak hydrogen bond in o-chlorophenol stabilizes the gas molecule relative to those of the meta and para isomers, whereas the crystalline and liquid phases of the three substances, in which hydrogen bonds can be formed between adjacent molecules, have about the same stability.   In consequence the boiling point of the ortho isomer, 176°C, is lower than those of the others, 214 and 217°C respectively.   The effect is shown also by the melting points, which have the values 7°, 0°, and −4° for three crystalline modifications of o-chlorophenol, 29° for m-chlorophenol, and 41° for p-chlorophenol.

An absorption peak at 6620 cm^{-1} has been observed for liquid
o-chlorophenol by Errera and Mollet.[1]   The further decrease in
frequency below the value 6910 cm^{-1} for the trans form of the
molecule can be explained by assuming that the liquid contains
double molecules with the structure

These double molecules would be stabilized by the energy of the
strong O—H$\cdots$O hydrogen bond.   The formation of the bond
would increase the electronegativity of the oxygen atom on the
right, causing its O—H bond to have increased ionic character;
this would increase the positive charge on the attached hydrogen
atom, and lead to a stronger O—H$\cdots$Cl hydrogen bond, with its
resultant decrease in OH vibrational frequency.

A spectrum of the same type as that of the solution has been
observed for the vapor of *o*-chlorophenol also.[2]

The absorption curves for *o*-bromophenol and *o*-iodophenol are
similar to those for *o*-chlorophenol, the shifted peaks lying at
6860 and 6800 cm^{-1}, respectively.   Guaiacol, *o*-methoxyphenol,
shows a single peak at 6930 cm^{-1}, corresponding to the cis con-

figuration ; there seems to be no appreciable

[1] *Loc. cit.*

[2] R. M. Badger and S. H. Bauer, *J. Chem. Phys.* **4**, 711 (1936).   The
effect of change in temperature in changing the relative amounts of the
two molecular forms has been studied by L. R. Zumwalt and R. M. Badger, *J. Chem. Phys.* **7**, 87 (1939), *J.A.C.S.* **62**, 305 (1940), who found for
the energy of the hydrogen bond in the gas molecule the value 3.9 ± 0.7
kcal./mole. and for the free energy of the bond 2.8 ± 0.5 kcal./mole.

amount of the trans form present. In this molecule the O—H$\cdots$O hydrogen bond which is formed is weak compared with other O—H$\cdots$O bonds because of the unfavorable steric conditions.

The broad peak observed for tetrabromoguaiacol has its maximum close to 6810 cm^{-1}, showing that the proton attraction of the O—H$\cdots$Br bond is greater than that of the O—H$\cdots$O bond under the steric conditions present in this molecule.

Catechol shows two nearly equal peaks, at 6970 and 7060 cm^{-1}. Of the three configurations

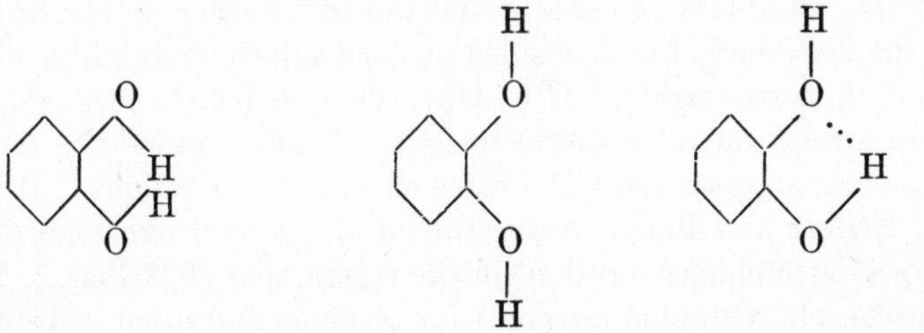

for this molecule, the third is the most stable, inasmuch as it is stabilized relative to the second by the O—H$\cdots$O interaction, and the first is made unstable by repulsion of the similarly charged hydrogen atoms. The third configuration accounts satisfactorily for the observed spectrum of two equal peaks.

The effect of the weak hydrogen bond on the boiling point of catechol is noticeable. The substance boils at 245°C, whereas the boiling point of resorcinol is 277° and that of hydroquinone 285°.

Pyrogallol shows a peak at 7050 cm^{-1} and another with doubled area at 6960 cm^{-1}; this spectrum corresponds to the structure

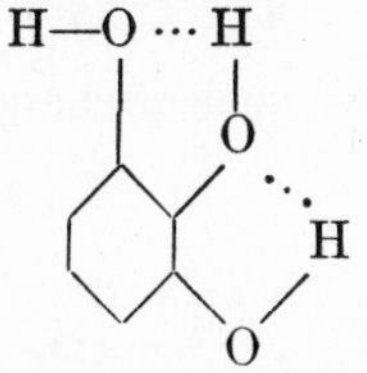

The two equal peaks observed for tetrabromocatechol at 6820 and 6920 cm^{-1} similarly correspond to the structure.

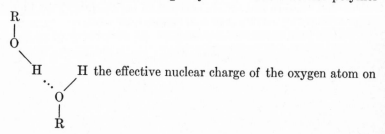

The weak hydrogen bonds shown by this spectroscopic method to be present in the molecules discussed above and in many others are not of great significance in affecting the melting and boiling points and other physical properties of substances, nor do they lead to isomeric forms of substances of sufficient stability to permit their separation. It is, however, possible that these bonds are strong enough to influence the chemical properties of substances, and especially the rates of chemical reactions.

Badger and Bauer[1] have studied the second overtone of the O—H stretching vibration (in the region near 10,000 cm^{-1}, lying in the photographic infrared) for alcohols and other substances as gases, liquids, and in solution in carbon disulfide and carbon tetrachloride, and have obtained interesting information regarding the nature of the polymers. On increasing the concentration of methyl alcohol in solution in carbon tetrachloride the intensity of the sharp band at 10,440 cm^{-1} decreases, and the intensities of the adjacent broad bands increase. The broad band of lower frequency, about 10,000 cm^{-1}, is attributed to the vibration of hydrogen atoms involved in hydrogen bond formation. The broad band of higher frequency, about 10,900 cm^{-1}, can be accounted for in the following way. In a linear alcohol polymer

H the effective nuclear charge of the oxygen atom on

[1] R. M. Badger and S. H. Bauer, *J. Chem. Phys.* **5**, 839 (1937); **4**, 469, 711 (1936). Additional work on alcohols has been reported by A. Borden and E. F. Barker, *J. Chem. Phys.* **6**, 553 (1938); E. F. Barker and G.

the right is increased by the attraction of an electron pair by the hydrogen atom involved in hydrogen bond formation; in consequence the O—H bond is strengthened and its vibrational frequency is increased.

The amyl alcohols, unlike the lighter alcohols, show in the liquid state appreciable absorption characteristic of the monomer, in addition to the broad polymer bands. The amount of monomer absorption increases in the order primary, secondary, tertiary amyl alcohol. Badger and Bauer have attributed this failure to achieve complete hydrogen bond formation to steric effects, and have shown that the monomer spectrum is absent for a mixture of tertiary amyl alcohol with methyl alcohol, for which the steric inhibition of hydrogen bond formation is expected to be less than for pure amyl alcohol.

The presence of molecules $CH_3O—H\cdots OC(CH_3)_2$ in appreciable concentration in a solution of methyl alcohol and acetone in carbon tetrachloride and in an alcohol-acetone mixture was verified by these investigators, who also found that diacetone alcohol in 18 mole percent solution in carbon tetrachloride consists of about 75 percent of molecules containing internal hydrogen

$$H_3C \qquad CH_2$$

bonds, with the structure $H_3C—C \qquad C—CH_3$, and of about 25

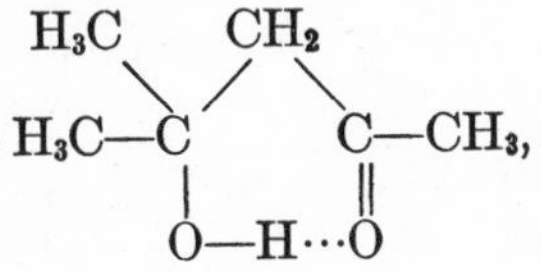

$$O—H\cdots O$$

percent of molecules not containing these bonds.

42. A SUMMARY OF THE CONDITIONS FOR THE FORMATION AND THE PROPERTIES OF THE HYDROGEN BOND

It is seen by reference to Tables 41-1 and 41-2 that a phenolic hydroxyl group forms a strong hydrogen bond with an oxygen atom of an adjacent nitro group. The conditions here are favorable to the formation of this bond. The conjugation of the groups with the benzene ring causes the coplanar configuration

---

Bosschieter, *ibid.* **6**, 563 (1938); M. M. Davies, *ibid.* **6**, 770 (1938); and L. R. Zumwalt and R. M. Badger, *ibid.* **7**, 87 (1939); *J.A.C.S.* **62**, 305 (1940).

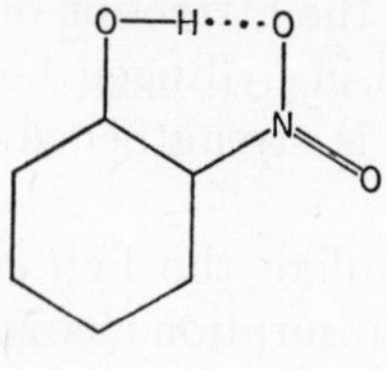

to be stable. This places the hydroxyl oxygen atom 2.6 A from a nitro oxygen atom, with the hydrogen atom directed approximately toward it (Fig. 41-2).

The nitro group is able to form hydrogen bonds with two hydroxyl groups, as in 2-nitroresorcinol, with the structure

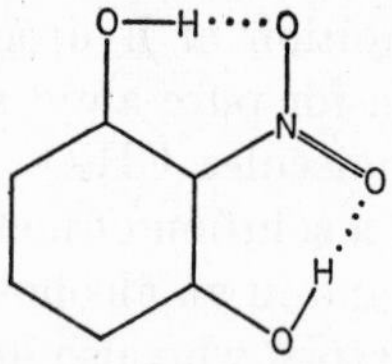

Carboxyl oxygen is also effective in hydrogen bond formation, as in methyl salicylate,

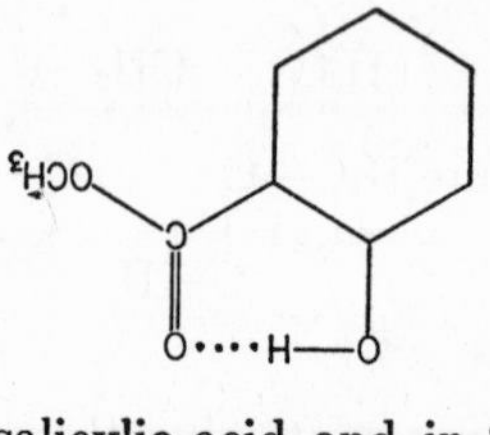

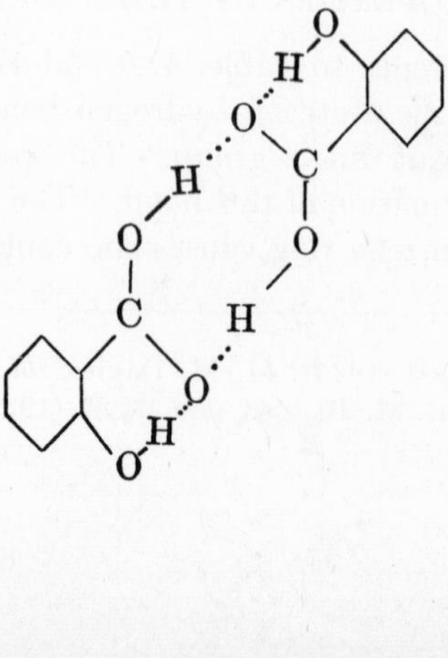

and in the dimer of salicylic acid and in 2,6-dihydroxybenzoic acid, mentioned in Section 40d.   In the dimer of salicylic acid, with the structure as mentioned in the earlier section, one of the oxygen atoms of the carboxyl group forms one hydrogen bond and the other forms two; the presumption exists that the latter acts as receptor, the hydrogen atoms being relatively weakly attracted to this atom and strongly held to the others as indicated by the full and dotted lines.

In 1,8-dihydroxyanthraquinone, with the structure

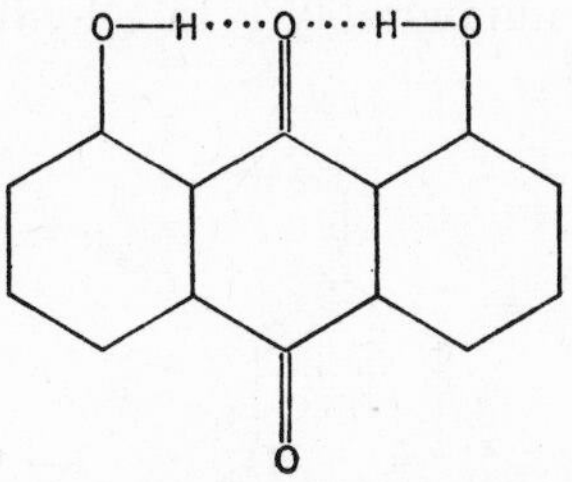

the carbonyl oxygen similarly acts as receptor for two hydrogen bonds. This is observed also for 2,2'-dihydroxybenzophenone,

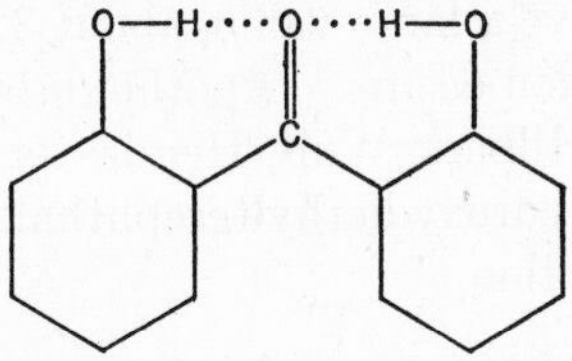

In most of these substances hydrogen bond formation involves closing a six-membered ring (counting the hydrogen atom), the values of interatomic distances and bond angles being such as to favor the formation of a strong hydrogen bond. On the other hand, a strong hydrogen bond is not formed with completion of a five-membered ring, the conditions being unfavorable   Ethyl lactate, for which the structure

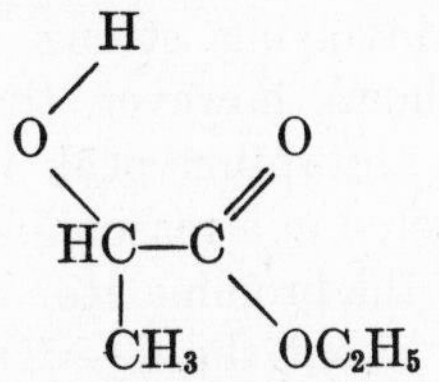

can be written, shows a large infrared absorption peak at 6900 cm^{-1}, representing a weak hydrogen bond, and a small peak at 7050 cm^{-1}, corresponding to a small number of molecules with configurations which do not permit this weak bond to be formed. The bond is weak in this substance for two reasons; the oxygen-oxygen distance is large (about 3.0 Å), and the hydrogen atom of the hydroxyl group is not well directed toward the carbonyl oxygen atom.

The possibility of forming a six-membered ring does not insure that a strong hydrogen bond will be formed, for other steric effects may operate unfavorably. In *o*-hydroxybenzonitrile, for which the structure

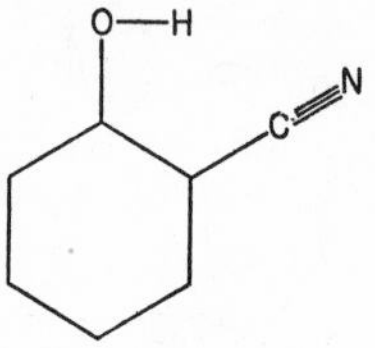

can be written, the 180° C—C≡N bond angle causes the O—H ···N distance to have a large value, about 3.5 Å; in consequence only a weak attraction occurs. Another interesting example has been discussed by Hilbert, Wulf, Hendricks, and Liddel, that of 3,6-dibromo-2,5-dihydroxydiethylterephthalate. For this substance the configuration

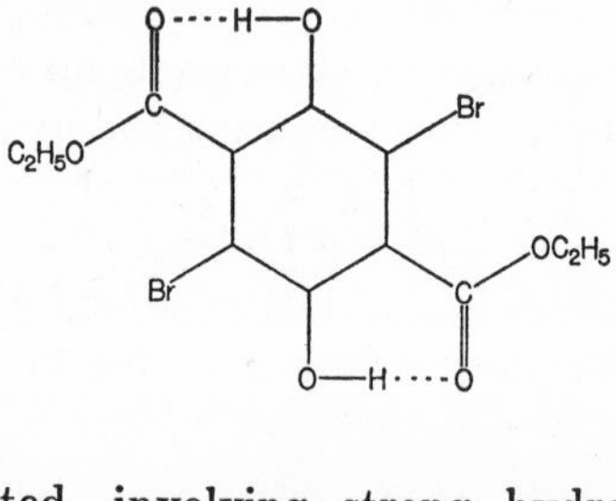

might be expected involving strong hydrogen bonds. The spectroscopic study shows, however, that the hydrogen bonds formed are weak, an absorption peak being observed at 6810 cm^{-1}. This is interpreted in a reasonable way as resulting from the steric repulsion of the bromine atoms for the ethoxy groups, which causes rotation about the C—$COOC_2H_5$ bonds and thus increases the O—H···O distance by several tenths of an Ångström. The effect is shown to be due to the bromine atoms by the fact that 2,5-dihydroxydiethylterephthalate contains strong hydrogen bonds, as shown by absence of infrared absorption in the 7000 cm^{-1} region.[1]

Evidence which need not be discussed in detail has been obtained showing that the conditions for forming other hydrogen bonds such as O—H$\cdots$N and N—H$\cdots$O are similar to those for the O—H$\cdots$O bond.

In general the usual rules of stereochemistry (coplanarity for conjugated systems, tetrahedral values of bond angles) apply to both of the atoms connected by hydrogen bonds. Many examples have been quoted of coplanar aggregates involving hydrogen bonds (boric acid, oxalic acid, etc.) and approximately tetrahedral bond angles for the hydrogen-bonded atoms. As mentioned earlier, it is not surprising that these rules apply with smaller force to the atom B than to the atom A of a group A—H$\cdots$B, as illustrated by the urea crystal.

A very interesting difference of behavior in regard to the formation of hydrogen bonds by closely related substances has been discovered and discussed by Baker and his collaborators.[2] It would be expected that 2,4-diacetylresorcinol (A) and 4,6-diacetylresorcinol (B) would have

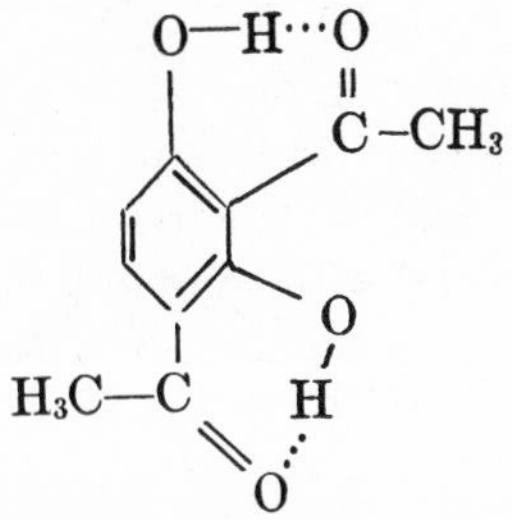

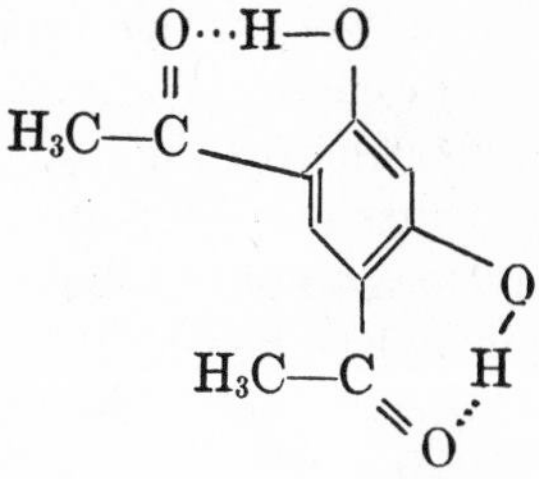

the same tendency to form internal hydrogen bonds. Baker pointed out that they actually exhibit pronounced differences in physical properties which indicate that hydrogen bond forma-

---

[1] There may be some decrease in strength of the hydrogen bonds in both of the substances as the result of the Baker resonance effect discussed later in this section. This effect is, however, not pronounced enough in the dihydroxydiethylterephthalate to be evident in the spectroscopic test.

[2] W. Baker, *J. Chem. Soc.* **1934**, 1684; W. Baker and O. M. Lothian, *ibid.* **1935**, 628; **1936**, 274; W. Baker and A. R. Smith, *ibid.* **1936**, 346

tion is much more nearly complete for the 2,4 compound than
for its isomer, as shown in the following table:

	2,4-Diacetylresorcinol	4,6-Diacetylresorcinol
Melting point	89°	182°
Boiling point at 10 mm	168–9°	188–9°
Solubility in benzene at 15°	10%	1%
Solubility in petroleum ether	Soluble	Almost insoluble
Volatility in steam	Easily volatile	Almost non-volatile
Lowering of melting point by water	5°	23°

He interpreted this as resulting from the possibility of the fixation of one of the two Kekulé structures for the benzene ring in
such a way as to favor double chelation for 2,4-diacetylresorcinol
but not for the 4,6 isomer.

It has been mentioned above that a conjugated system such
as shown in A increases the strength of the hydrogen bond which
is formed, by increasing the ionic character of the O—H bond and
also increasing the resultant negative charge of the oxygen atom
which is the more distant from the proton. It is seen that in
2,4-diacetylresorcinol the fixation of one Kekulé structure as
shown in A would lead to a conjugated system of this type for
each of the two chelate rings, whereas for 4,6-diacetylresorcinol
(B) only one of the rings can be thus favored.

The energy of a hydrogen bond is, however, only about 7 kcal./
mole, whereas the resonance energy of the two Kekulé structures
of benzene is about 36 kcal./mole; accordingly the resonance can
not be completely inhibited by chelation, with complete fixation
of one Kekulé structure. It is instead possible that the chelation-
conjugation effect increases somewhat (by 10 percent, say) the
contribution of one Kekulé structure to the normal state of the
molecule, and decreases that of the other. This partial fixation
of one Kekulé structure would have the same qualitative effects
as the complete fixation suggested by Baker (see the discussion
of the Mills-Nixon effect, Sec. 19).

It should be mentioned again that hydrogen bond formation
is possible in the absence as well as the presence of a conjugated
system; the bonds are stronger, however, with conjugation than
without it. The spectroscopic test shows the presence of two
strong hydrogen bonds in 2,5-dihydroxydiethylterephthalate,
although fixation of one Kekulé structure would favor the formation of only one.

Baker and Lothian[1] have discovered some interesting chemical

[1] *Loc. cit.*

effects of hydrogen bond formation and the resultant partial fixation of one Kekulé structure. The compound 4-O-allyl-resacetophenone (C), which on thermal rearrangement might be expected to give either 3-allylresacetophenone (D) or 5-allyl-resacetophenone, was found to give exclusively the first of these,

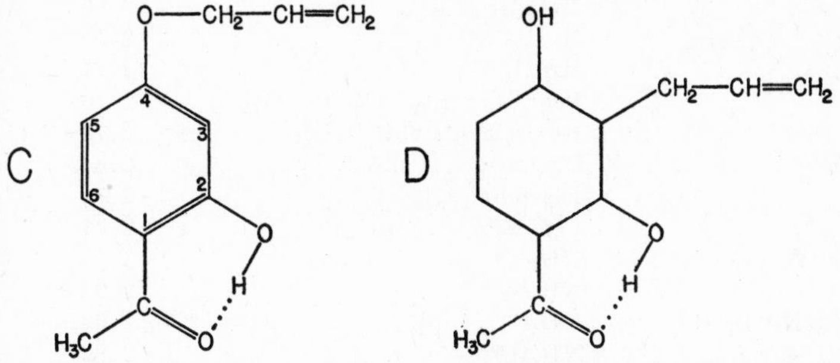

indicating a larger amount of double-bond character for the 3,4 bond in the benzene ring than for the 4,5 bond; whereas 2-O-methyl-4-O-allylresacetophenone, which contains no hydrogen bond, rearranges to 2-O-methyl-5-allylresacetophenone. The same phenomenon has also been observed for *o*-hydroxypropio-phenones and *o*-hydroxyaldehydes.

A summary of hydrogen bond energy values is given in Table 42-1. It is seen that except for the weak N—H⋯N bond in crystalline ammonia the bond energy lies in the range 4 to 8 kcal./mole. Interatomic distance values are summarized in Table 42-2. It is noteworthy that, as expected, there is an inverse cor-relation (for bonds of the same type) between bond energy and interatomic distance, the sequences 4.5, 6.2, 7.1 kcal./mole and

TABLE 42-1.—HYDROGEN BOND ENERGY VALUES

Bond	Substance	Bond energy
F—H—F	H_6F_6	6.7 kcal./mole
O—H⋯O	H_2O(ice), H_2O_2	4.5
	CH_3OH, C_2H_5OH	6.2
	$(HCOOH)_2$	7.06
	$(CH_3COOH)_2$	8.2
C—H⋯N	$(HCN)_2$	3.28
	$(HCN)_3$	4.36
N—H⋯N	NH_3	1.3
N—H⋯F	NH_4F	5
O—H⋯Cl	$o\text{-}C_6H_4OHCl$(g)	3.9

TABLE 42-2.—A—H···B INTERATOMIC DISTANCE VALUES

Bond	Substance	Observed A—H···B distance[1]
F—H—F	KHF_2	2.26 Å
O—H···O	H_2O	2.76
	$(HCOOH)_2$	2.67
	KH_2PO_4	2.54
	$(NH_4)_2H_3IO_6$	2.60
	$NaHCO_3$	2.55
	H_3BO_3	2.71
	Pentaerythritol, $C(CH_2OH)_4$	2.70
	Resorcinol, o-$C_6H_4(OH)_2$	2.70
	Oxalic acid, α and β	2.6
	Diaspore, $AlHO_2$	2.70
	Lepidocrocite, $FeO(OH)$	2.71
N—H···N	NH_3	3.38
	NH_4N_3	2.98
N—H···F	NH_4F	2.63
	NH_4HF_2	2.82
N—H···O	Urea, $CO(NH_2)_2$	2.98, 3.03
	Diketopiperazine	2.85
	Glycine	2.76, 2.88

[1] These values are reliable in general to about 0.05 Å; those quoted to only one decimal place are less reliable.

2.76, 2.70, 2.67 Å being observed for ice, alcohol, and formic acid.

It has been pointed out by Badger and Bauer[1] that the decrease in frequency of the O—H stretching vibration on the formation of a hydrogen bond is approximately proportional to the energy of the hydrogen bond, being for the fundamental about 35 cm^{-1} and for the second overtone about 70 cm^{-1} for each kcal. /mole of bond energy.

Further detailed evidence regarding the occurrence and properties of hydrogen bonds has been summarized by several authors.[2]

[1] R. M. Badger and S. H. Bauer, *J. Chem. Phys.* **5**, 839 (1937).
[2] N. V. Sidgwick, "The Electronic Theory of Valency"; E. N. Lassettre, *Chem. Rev.* **20**, 259 (1937); M. L. Huggins, *J. Org. Chem.* **1**, 407 (1936).

CHAPTER X

THE SIZES OF IONS AND THE STRUCTURE OF IONIC CRYSTALS

Of all of the different types of atomic aggregates, ionic crystals have been found to be most suited to simple theoretical treatment. The theory of the structure of ionic crystals described briefly in the following sections was developed about twenty years ago by Born, Haber, Landé, Madelung, Ewald, Fajans, and other investigators.[1] The simplicity of the theory is due in part to the importance in the interionic interactions of the well-understood Coulomb terms, and in part to the spherical symmetry of the electron distributions of the ions with noble-gas or eighteen-shell configurations.

43. INTERIONIC FORCES AND CRYSTAL ENERGY

The electron distribution function, as given by quantum mechanical calculations, for an ion with the electronic configuration of a noble gas or with a completed eighteen shell (such as Zn^{++}, with eighteen outer electrons occupying the $3s$ orbital, the three $3p$ orbitals, and the five $3d$ orbitals in pairs) is spherically symmetrical,[2] showing that the interaction of the ion with other ions is independent of direction. The nature of the electron distribution functions for the alkali and halide ions is indicated by the drawings in Figure 43-1, which represent the results of theoretical calculations.[3] It is seen that the successive K, L, M, etc. shells of electrons in an ion become evident as successive regions

---

[1] For a summary of this work see J. Sherman, *Chem. Rev.* **11**, 93 (1932). Very simple methods of evaluating Madelung constants have been proposed by H. M. Evjen, *Phys. Rev.* **39**, 680 (1932), and K. Højendahl, *Det Kgl. Danske Vid. Selsk.* **16**, 135 (1938).

[2] A. Unsöld, *Ann. d. Phys.* **82**, 355 (1927).

[3] These drawings are based on the application of the screening constant method, the results of which approximate closely those of Hartree's method of the self-consistent field.

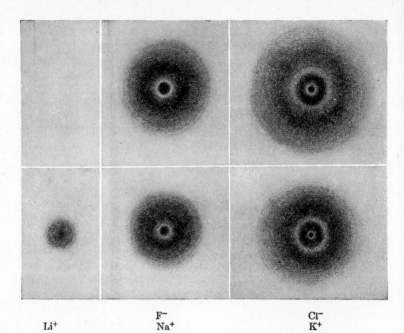

Li+

F⁻
Na+

Cl⁻
K+

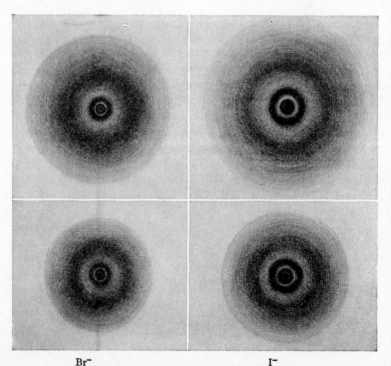

Br⁻
Rb+

I⁻
Cs+

FIG. 43-1.—Drawings showing the distribution of electrons in the alkali and halide ions.

of large electron density. The electron distributions of iso-electronic ions, such as F^- and Na^+, are similar, and show the operation of increased effective nuclear charge from halide ion to the corresponding alkali ion in holding the electrons closer to the nucleus.

The interaction of two ions i and j with electric charges $z_i e$ and $z_j e$ can be described in the following way. At large distances the ions attract or repel one another by Coulomb interaction of their charges, the potential function for this interaction being $z_i z_j e^2 / r_{ij}$, with r_{ij} the distance between the ions. In addition there occurs some attraction resulting from the polarization of each ion in the field of the other; we shall neglect this attraction, which except at very small distances is negligible in comparison with the Coulomb attraction or repulsion. As the ions are brought closer together, so that their outer electron shells begin to overlap, an additional characteristic repulsive force becomes operative, resulting from the overlapping of the ions. It is this repulsive force which opposes the Coulomb attractive force between a positive and a negative ion and causes them to come to equilibrium at a finite value of the internuclear distance.[1]

The characteristic repulsive potential falls off very rapidly in value with increase in r_{ij}. It was suggested by Born that it be approximated by an inverse power of r_{ij}, so that the mutual potential energy of two ions would be written as

$$V_{ij} = \frac{z_i z_j e^2}{r_{ij}} + \frac{b_{ij} e^2}{r_{ij}{}^n} . \qquad (43\text{-}1)$$

The total potential energy of an ionic crystal MX with the sodium chloride arrangement can be obtained by summing the terms V_{ij} over all the pairs of ions in the crystal, and the quotient of this quantity by the number of stoichiometric molecules MX in the crystal is the potential energy of the crystal per molecule MX. Since in the crystal all of the interionic distances are related to the smallest interionic distance R by geometrical factors, the potential energy of the crystal can be written as

---

[1] In addition to these interactions there are to be considered the van der Waals interactions (dispersion forces) between the ions in an ionic molecule or crystal; this effect has been discussed by M. Born and J. E. Mayer, *Z. f. Phys.* **75**, 1 (1932), and J. E. Mayer, *J. Chem. Phys.* **1**, 270 (1933).

$$V = -\frac{Ae^2z^2}{R} + \frac{Be^2}{R^n} \cdot \qquad (43\text{-}2)$$

The constant A in this expression is called the *Madelung constant*. It can be evaluated by straightforward mathematical methods developed by Riemann and Appell, Madelung, Ewald, Born, and Emersleben.[1] Values of A for the more important ionic crystals are given in Table 43-1, which is taken from Sherman's review. The magnitudes of the A values are seen to be reasonable on comparison with those for finite molecules; A for an isolated molecule Na^+Cl^- is 1, the Coulomb energy being $-1 \cdot e^2/R_0$, whereas for a sodium chloride crystal with the same interionic distance the crystal energy is about 75% greater in magnitude, the value of A_{R_0} being 1.747558.

TABLE 43-1.—VALUES OF MADELUNG CONSTANTS*

Structure	A_{R_0}	A_{δ_0}	A_{a_0}
Sodium chloride, M^+X^-	1.747558	2.201785	3.495115
Cesium chloride, M^+X^-	1.762670	2.035356	2.035356
Sphalerite, M^+X^-	1.63806	2.38309	3.78292
Wurtzite, M^+X^-	1.641	2.386	
Fluorite, $M^{++}X_2^-$	5.03878	7.33058	11.63656
Cuprite, $M_2^+X^{--}$	4.11552	6.54364	9.50438
Rutile, $M^{++}X_2^-$	4.816	7.70	
Anatase, $M^{++}X_2^-$	4.800	8.04	
CdI$_2$(Bozorth), $M^{++}X_2^-$	4.71	6.21	
β-Quartz, $M^{++}X_2^-$	4.4394	9.5915	
Corundum, $M_2^{+++}X_3^{--}$	25.0312	45.825	
Perovskite, $M^+M^{++}X_3^-$		12.37744	12.37744

* Values of A_{R_0} are such that the Coulomb energy per stoichiometric molecule is $-A_{R_0}e^2/R_0$, with R_0 the smallest anion-cation distance; those for A_{δ_0} and A_{a_0} have similar meanings, with δ_0 the cube root of the molecular volume and a_0 the edge of the cubic unit of structure (for cubic crystals). The parameter values used for structures containing parameters are those found experimentally.

The factor z^2 is introduced in the Coulomb term to permit the application of the equation to crystals containing multivalent

[1] P. Appell, *Acta Math.* **4**, 313 (1884); E. Madelung, *Phys. Z.* **19**, 524 (1918); P. P. Ewald, *Ann. d. Phys.* **64**, 253 (1921); M. Born, *Z. f. Phys.* **7**, 124 (1921); O. Emersleben, *Phys. Z.* **24**, 73, 79 (1923). For a brief description of these methods see J. Sherman, *loc. cit.*

ions; with $z = 1$ it applies to substances Na^+Cl^-, $Mg^{++}F_2^-$, etc., and with $z = 2$ to $Mg^{++}O^{--}$, $Ti^{++++}O_2^{--}$, etc.

At equilibrium the attractive forces and the repulsive forces are balanced. The value of $R(= R_0)$ at which this occurs can be found by differentiating V of Equation 43-2 with respect to R, equating to zero, and solving for R_0:

$$\frac{dV}{dR} = \frac{Ae^2z^2}{R^2} - \frac{nBe^2}{R^{n+1}}$$

$$\frac{Ae^2z^2}{R_0^2} - \frac{nBe^2}{R_0^{n+1}} = 0$$

$$R_0 = \left(\frac{nB}{Az^2}\right)^{1/(n-1)}. \tag{43-3}$$

With B and n known, this equation can be used to calculate R_0. Actually it is R_0 which can be easily determined experimentally; from its value the repulsive coefficient B can then be found by the equation

$$B = \frac{R_0^{n-1}Az^2}{n}, \tag{43-4}$$

provided that the value of n is known.

The Born exponent n can be evaluated from the results of experimental measurements of the compressibility of the crystal, which depends on the second derivative d^2V/dR^2. It is found that for all crystals n lies in the neighborhood of 9. A somewhat better approximation to the experimental values is shown in Table 43-2; for a crystal of mixed ion type an average of values of this table is to be used (6 for LiF, for example).

TABLE 43-2.—VALUES OF THE BORN EXPONENT n

Ion Type	n
He	5
Ne	7
Ar, Cu^+	9
Kr, Ag^+	10
Xe, Au^+	12

It is convenient to introduce the symbol $U_0 = -NV_0$ (with N Avogadro's number) to represent the *crystal energy*. U_0 is a positive quantity, representing the heat of formation per mole of MX (crystal) from M^+ (gas) and X^- (gas).

The substitution in Equation 43-2 of the expression 43-4 for B leads to the following equation for the crystal energy U_0:

$$U_0 = \frac{NAe^2z^2}{R_0}\left(1 - \frac{1}{n}\right). \qquad (43\text{-}5)$$

It is seen that the crystal energy is smaller in magnitude than the Coulomb energy (with changed sign) by the fractional amount $1/n$, which is approximately ten percent. With $R_0 = 2.814$ Å for sodium chloride and $n = 8$, U_0 is given the value 179.2 kcal./mole by this equation. This value, representing the heat of formation of NaCl(c) from $Na^+(g)+Cl^-(g)$, may be considered to be uncertain by about two percent, that is, about 4 kcal./mole, because of uncertainty in the form of the energy function V. A more refined treatment,[1] involving consideration of van der Waals forces and use of an exponential repulsive potential, has been found to give the value 183.1 kcal./mole, and a direct thermochemical measurement, mentioned below,[2] has provided the value 181.3 kcal./mole, substantiating the estimate of two percent as the order of reliability of the Born expression.

43a. The Born-Haber Thermochemical Cycle.—The following cycle was devised by Born and Haber[3] to relate the crystal energy to other thermochemical quantities:

$$
\begin{array}{ccc}
\text{MX(c)} & \xrightarrow{\;\;U_0\;\;} & M^+(g) + X^-(g) \\
{\scriptstyle -Q}\uparrow & & \downarrow{\scriptstyle -I+E} \\
M(c) + \tfrac{1}{2}X_2(g) & \xleftarrow{\;-S-\frac{1}{2}D\;} & M(g) + X(g)
\end{array}
$$

(For convenience the cycle is given for the special case of an alkali halide.) Here U_0 is the crystal energy, I the ionization energy of the metal $M(g)$, E the electron affinity of $X(g)$, S the heat of sublimation of the metal, D the heat of dissociation of the halogen molecule, and Q the heat of formation of MX(c) from

---

[1] M. Born and J. E. Mayer, *Z. f. Phys.* **75**, 1 (1932); J. E. Mayer and L. Helmholz, *ibid.* **75**, 19 (1932).

[2] L. Helmholz and J. E. Mayer, *J. Chem. Phys.* **2**, 245 (1934).

[3] M. Born, *Verhandl. deut. physik. Ges.* **21**, 13 (1919); F. Haber *ibid.* **21**, 750 (1919).

the elements M(c) and $\frac{1}{2}X_2(g)$. All of the quantities except I and E represent changes in heat content, ΔH, for the corresponding reactions at 25°C; it is convenient to define I and E as giving the change in energy at 0°K. The condition that the total change in heat content for the cycle is zero leads to the equation

$$U_0 = Q + S + I + \tfrac{1}{2}D - E. \qquad (43\text{-}6)$$

A few years ago experimental values were available for Q, S, I, and D, but not for E; the procedure adopted in testing the equation was to use the equation with calculated values of U_0 (Equation 43-5) to find E, and as a test of the method examine the constancy of E for a series of alkali halides containing the same halogen. The results of this treatment are given in Table 43-3, taken from Sherman's paper written in 1932 (*loc. cit.*). It is seen that the maximum deviation of individual values from the means is 2.7 kcal./mole.

TABLE 43-3.—ELECTRON AFFINITIES OF THE HALOGENS
CALCULATED BY THE BORN-HABER CYCLE

Crystal	a_0	n	U_0	U	Q	I	S	$\frac{1}{2}D$	E
LiF	4.02	6.0	238.9	240.1	144.7	123.8	38.3	32.2	98.9
NaF	4.619	7.0	213.8	215.0	136.6	118.0	26.0	32.2	97.8
KF	5.33	8.0	189.2	190.4	134.5	99.6	21.7	32.2	97.6
RbF	5.63	8.5	180.6	181.8	132.8	95.9	19.9	32.2	99.0
CsF	6.008	9.5	171.6	172.8	131.5	89.4	19.1	32.2	99.4
								mean =	98.5
LiCl	5.143	7.0	192.1	193.3	97.5	123.8	38.3	28.9	95.2
NaCl	5.628	8.0	179.2	180.4	98.2	118.0	26.0	28.9	90.7
KCl	6.277	9.0	163.2	164.4	104.9	99.6	21.7	28.9	90.7
RbCl	6.54	9.5	157.7	158.9	104.9	95.9	19.9	28.9	90.7
CsCl	4.110	10.5	147.7	148.9	106.6	89.4	19.1	28.9	95.1
								mean =	92.5
LiBr	5.490	7.5	181.9	183.1	83.7	123.8	38.3	26.9	89.6
NaBr	5.962	8.5	170.5	171.7	86.3	118.0	26.0	26.9	85.6
KBr	6.586	9.5	156.6	157.8	94.2	99.6	21.7	26.9	84.6
RbBr	6.854	10.0	151.3	152.5	96.1	95.9	19.9	26.9	86.3
CsBr	4.287	11.0	142.3	143.5	97.5	89.4	19.1	26.9	89.4
								mean =	87.1
LiI	6.000	8.5	169.5	170.7	65.0	123.8	38.3	25.4	81.8
NaI	6.462	9.5	159.6	160.8	69.5	118.0	26.0	25.4	78.1
KI	7.052	10.5	147.8	149.0	78.9	99.6	21.7	25.4	76.6
RbI	7.325	11.0	143.0	144.2	80.8	95.9	19.9	25.4	77.8
CsI	4.56	12.0	134.9	136.1	83.9	89.4	19.1	25.4	81.7
								mean =	79.2

A method of measuring directly the heat of ionic dissociation of an alkali halide gas molecule has been developed by Mayer.[1] This can be combined with the known value for the heat of sublimation of the alkali halide and other thermochemical data to give the crystal energy U_0. The values found for U_0 by Mayer, with the Born values from Table 43-3 given in parentheses for comparison, are 148.6 $\pm$ 4 (147.8) for KI and 131 $\pm$ 4 (134.9) for CsI. Helmholz and Mayer[2] have applied the method to NaCl and RbBr, obtaining 181.3 $\pm$ 3 (179.2) and 151.3 $\pm$ 3 (151.3), respectively.[3]

Another interesting test of the crystal energy equation has been made by Sutton and Mayer[4] by the direct evaluation of the electron affinity of iodine by the measurement of the equilibrium between $I^-(g)$, $I(g)$, and $E^-(g)$. The value found, 72.4 $\pm$ 1.5 kcal./mole, is somewhat lower than that given in Table 43-3 (79.2). It seems not unlikely that the electron affinity values 95.3 for F, 86.5 for Cl, 81.5 for Br, and 74.2 for I found by a refinement of the Born-Haber calculation by Mayer and Helmholz[5] are somewhat more reliable than those in Table 43-3.

A few results of measurements of electron affinities of halogen atoms by other methods, agreeing reasonably well with the crystal-energy values, have been reported. These include the values 74.6 for I and 88 for Br obtained by Glockler and Calvin[6] by a space-charge method, and 87.6 $\pm$ 4 for Br obtained by a mass-spectrographic method by Blewett.[7]

In general the results of recent investigations support the thesis that the forces operative in ionic crystals are those described above which underlie the Born equation for the crystal energy; and we may feel justified in investigating the further consequences of this postulate. The question of the sizes of ions is studied from this point of view in the following section.

[1] J. E. Mayer, *Z. f. Phys.* **61**, 798 (1930).
[2] *Loc. cit.*
[3] The results 176.3 (170.5) for NaBr and 159.7 (156.6) for KBr by the Mayer method have been reported by A. N. Tandon, *Indian J. Phys.* **11**, 99 (1937).
[4] P. P. Sutton and J. E. Mayer, *J. Chem. Phys.* **3**, 20 (1935).
[5] *Loc. cit.*
[6] G. Glockler and M. Calvin, *J. Chem. Phys.* **3**, 771 (1935); **4**, 492 (1936).
[7] J. P. Blewett, *Phys. Rev.* **49**, 900 (1936).

44. THE SIZES OF IONS.   UNIVALENT RADII AND CRYSTAL RADII[1]

It is possible to make an approximate quantum-mechanical calculation of the forces operating between ions in a crystal, and to predict values for the equilibrium interionic distance, the crystal energy, the compressibility, and other properties of the crystal.   This calculation has been made in a straightforward manner for lithium hydride (Li+H−, with the sodium chloride structure) by Hylleraas, with results in good agreement with experiment.[2]   Similar calculations have also been made for other ionic molecules and crystals by several investigators.[3]   The values for interionic distances obtained in this way are unreliable, however, and for chemical considerations it is desirable to have a set of empirical or semi-empirical values of ionic radii which reproduce experimental lattice constants to within one or two percent.

It has been found possible to formulate a semi-empirical set of ionic radii by using as the starting point only five experimental values of interionic distances; namely, the observed cation-anion distances in NaF, KCl, RbBr, CsI, and Li_2O.   The way in which this was done is described below.

Since the electron distribution function for an ion extends indefinitely, it is evident that no single characteristic size can be assigned to it.   Instead the apparent ionic radius will depend upon the physical property under discussion, and will differ for different properties.   We are interested in ionic radii such that the sum of two radii (with certain corrections when necessary) is equal to the equilibrium distance between the corresponding ions in contact in a crystal.   It will be shown later that the

---

[1] The treatment given in this section and in some later sections of the chapter was published in 1927 (L. Pauling, *J.A.C.S.* **49**, 765 (1927)).

[2] E. A. Hylleraas, *Z. f. Phys.* **63**, 771 (1930).   The calculated value of the crystal energy is 219 kcal./mole, and the Born-Haber cycle value is 218 kcal./mole, using for the electron affinity of hydrogen the reliable quantum-mechanical value 16.480 kcal./mole (see "Introduction to Quantum Mechanics," Sec. 29c).   The calculated value for the lattice constant a_0, 4.42 Å, is less reliable than the value for the energy, and the poor agreement with the experimental value 4.08 Å is not significant.

[3] L. Pauling, *Proc. Roy. Soc.* **A114**, 181 (1927); H. Brück, *Z. f. Phys.* **51**, 707 (1928); W. E. Bleick and J. E. Mayer, *J. Chem. Phys.* **2**, 252 (1934); J. A. Wasastjerna, *Soc. Sci. Fenn. Comm. Phys. Math.* **VI**, 22 (1932); B. O. Grönblom, *ibid.* **VIII**, 13 (1935).

equilibrium interionic distance for two ions is determined not only by the nature of the electron distributions for the ions, as shown in Figure 43-1, but also by the structure of the crystal and the ratio of radii of cation and anion. We take as our standard crystals those with the sodium chloride arrangement, with the ratio of radii of cation and anion about 0.75, and with the amount of ionic character of the bonds about the same as in the alkali halides, and calculate crystal radii of ions such that the sum of two radii gives the equilibrium interionic distance in a standard crystal.

The crystals NaF, KCl, RbBr, and CsI, with observed interionic distances 2.31, 3.14, 3.43, and 3.85 Å respectively, are standard crystals—it will be seen later that their radius ratios are about 0.75. (The value 3.85 Å for the Cs⁺—I⁻ distance in the as yet unobserved modification of cesium iodide with the sodium chloride arrangement is obtained by subtracting 2.7% from the observed value for the crystal with the cesium chloride arrangement; the justification for this will be given later.) Now the size of an ion is determined by the distribution of the outermost electrons, which varies in a simple way for isoelectronic ions, being inversely proportional to the effective nuclear charge operative on these electrons. The effective nuclear charge is equal to the actual nuclear charge Ze minus the screening effect Se of the other electrons in the ion; and we write for a sequence of isoelectronic ions the equation

$$R_1 = \frac{C_n}{Z - S}, \qquad (44\text{-}1)$$

in which C_n is a constant determined by the total quantum number of the outermost electrons in the ions. A complete set of values of the screening constant S has been obtained, partially by theoretical calculation[1] and partially by the interpretation of observed values of mole refraction[1] and x-ray term values[2] of atoms. For ions with the neon structure, for example, S for the outermost electrons has the value 4.52, and the effective nuclear charges for Na⁺ and F⁻ are thus 6.48 e and 4.48 e, respectively. By dividing the Na⁺—F⁻ distance 2.31 Å in the inverse ratio of

[1] L. Pauling, *Proc. Roy. Soc.* **A114**, 181 (1927).
[2] L. Pauling and J. Sherman, *Z. Krist.* **81**, 1 (1932).

these values for the effective nuclear charge we obtain the values 0.95 Å for the crystal radius of sodium ion and 1.36 Å for that of fluorine ion.

In a similar way there are obtained the values K^+ 1.33, Cl^- 1.81, Rb^+ 1.48, Br^- 1.95, Cs^+ 1.69, and I^- 2.16 Å. The value 0.60 Å is selected for Li^+ in order to give agreement, when combined with the oxygen radius 1.40 Å discussed below, with the observed Li^+ O^{--} distance 2.00 Å in Li_2O.

For the alkali and halogen ions these radii represent the relative extension in space of the outer electron shells,[1] that is, they may be considered to be a measure of the relative sizes of the ions; and in addition they have such absolute values as to cause their sums to be equal to interionic distances in standard crystals. We may continue to apply Equation 44-1, using the values for the constants C_n given by the alkali and halogen ions. In this way radii can be obtained for all ions with the helium, neon, argon, krypton, and xenon structures. These radii represent correctly the relative sizes of the outer electron shells of the ions, compared with those for the alkali and halogen ions; *they do not, however, have absolute values such that their sums are equal to equilibrium interionic distances.* The significance of the radii is the following: if the Coulomb attractive and repulsive forces in a standard crystal (with the sodium chloride arrangement) containing one of these cations, with charge $+ze$, and one of these anions, with charge $-ze$, were to have the magnitude corresponding to charges $+e$ and $-e$, respectively (as though the ions were univalent), and the characteristic repulsive forces were to retain their actual magnitude, the equilibrium interionic distance would be equal to the sum of these radii. That is, these radii are the radii the multivalent ions would possess if they were to retain their electron distributions but enter into Coulomb interaction as if they were univalent. These radii are called the *univalent radii* of the ions. Values of univalent radii are given in parentheses in Table 44-1.

The *crystal radii* of multivalent ions, such that the sum of two crystal radii is equal to the actual equilibrium interionic distance in a crystal containing the ions, can be calculated from their uni-

---

[1] The relation between ionic radius and electron distribution has been discussed by J. A. Wasastjerna, *Soc. Sci. Fenn. Comm. Phys. Math.* VI, 21 (1932).

Univalent Radii in Parenthes (handwritten)

TABLE 44-1.—CRYSTAL RADII AND UNIVALENT CRYSTAL RADII OF IONS

Noble	1+	2+	3+	4+	4-	5+	3-	6+	2-	7+	1-
He (0.93)											H- 2.08 (2.08)
Ne (1.12)	Li+ 0.60 (0.60)	Be++ 0.31 (0.44)	B3+ 0.20 (0.35)	C4+ 0.15 (0.29)	C4- 2.60 (4.14)	N5+ 0.11 (0.25)	N3- 1.71 (2.47)	O6+ 0.09 (0.22)	O-- 1.40 (1.76)	F7+ 0.07 (0.19)	F- 1.36 (1.36)
Ar (1.54)	Na+ 0.95 (0.95)	Mg++ 0.65 (0.82)	Al3+ 0.50 (0.72)	Si4+ 0.41 (0.65)	Si4- 2.71 (3.84)	P5+ 0.34 (0.59)	P3- 2.12 (2.79)	S6+ 0.29 (0.53)	S-- 1.84 (2.19)	Cl7+ 0.26 (0.49)	Cl- 1.81 (1.81)
Kr (1.69)	K+ 1.33 (1.33)	Ca++ 0.99 (1.18)	Sc3+ 0.81 (1.06)	Ti4+ 0.68 (0.96)		V5+ 0.59 (0.88)		Cr6+ 0.52 (0.81)		Mn7+ 0.46 (0.75)	
	Cu+ 0.96 (0.96)	Zn++ 0.74 (0.88)	Ga3+ 0.62 (0.81)	Ge4+ 0.53 (0.76)	Ge4- 2.72 (3.71)	As5+ 0.47 (0.71)	As3- 2.22 (2.85)	Se6+ 0.42 (0.66)	Se-- 1.98 (2.32)	Br7+ 0.39 (0.62)	Br- 1.95 (1.95)
Xe (1.90)	Rb+ 1.48 (1.48)	Sr++ 1.13 (1.32)	Y3+ 0.93 (1.20)	Zr4+ 0.80 (1.09)		Cb5+ 0.70 (1.00)		Mo6+ 0.62 (0.93)			
	Ag+ 1.26 (1.26)	Cd++ 0.97 (1.14)	In3+ 0.81 (1.04)	Sn4+ 0.71 (0.96)	Sn4- 2.94 (3.70)	Sb5+ 0.62 (0.89)	Sb3- 2.45 (2.95)	Te6+ 0.56 (0.82)	Te-- 2.21 (2.50)	I7+ 0.50 (0.77)	I- 2.16 (2.16)
	Cs+ 1.69 (1.69)	Ba++ 1.35 (1.53)	La3+ 1.15 (1.39)	Ce4+ 1.01 (1.27)							
	Au+ 1.37 (1.37)	Hg++ 1.10 (1.25)	Tl3+ 0.95 (1.15)	Pb4+ 0.84 (1.06)		Bi5+ 0.74 (0.98)					

valent radii by multiplication by a factor obtained from consideration of Equation 43-3. From this equation it is seen that the equilibrium interionic distance in a crystal containing ions with valence z is

$$R_z = \left(\frac{nB}{Az^2}\right)^{1/(n-1)}.$$

If the Coulomb forces were to correspond to $z = 1$ (univalent ions), with the characteristic repulsive coefficient B unchanged, the equilibrium interionic distance would be

$$R_1 = \left(\frac{nB}{A}\right)^{1/(n-1)}.$$

From these expressions it is seen that crystal radii R_z and univalent radii R_1 are related by the equation

$$R_z = R_1 z^{-2/(n-1)}. \tag{44-2}$$

This equation, with the values of n given by Table 43-2, has been used in calculating the values of the crystal radii given in Table 44-1.

Values are given in the table for univalent and crystal radii of ions with outer eighteen-shells (Cu^+, Ag^+, Au^+, etc.) also. These were calculated by using the same values for C_n as for argon, krypton, and xenon-like ions, respectively, with the appropriate screening constants. It might seem at first that the eighteen-shell radii should be larger than the values calculated in this way, since there are ten electrons in the outermost subshell (nd), and only six (np) for the noble-gas type ions. However, the nd orbitals have their maxima somewhat nearer the nucleus (for given effective nuclear charge) than the corresponding np orbitals; in consequence the density of the ten d electrons is, in the outer part of the ion, about equal to that for six p electrons, and this effect permits the simple calculation to be made without correction.

Univalent radii and crystal radii are represented graphically in Figure 44-1 as functions of the atomic number Z, and crystal radii are shown also in Figure 44-2. It is seen that there is great regularity in the univalent radii sequences. The crystal radii

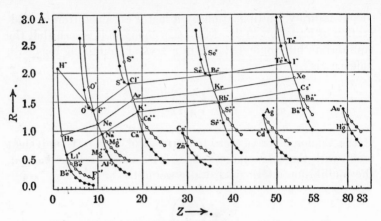

Fig. 44-1.—The crystal radii (solid circles) and univalent radii (open circles) of ions.

deviate from the univalent radii in an understandable way, which, however, introduces such apparent lack of system in the crystal radii as to have prevented an early satisfactory interpretation of the empirical information on interionic distances.

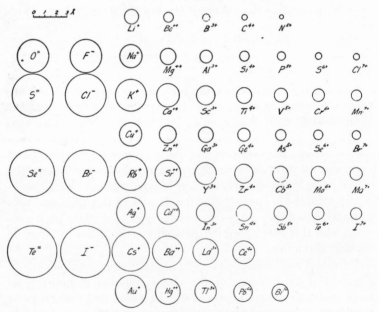

Fig. 44-2.—The crystal radii of ions.

This valence effect shows up strikingly in the comparison of interatomic distances for isoelectronic sequences. In crystals containing covalent bonds the interatomic distance remains almost constant through an isoelectronic sequence, such as Ge—Ge, 2.44; Ga—As, 2.44; Zn—Se, 2.45; Cu—Br, 2.46Å. Here the effect of decrease in nuclear charge of one atom is balanced by that of increase for the other. In ionic crystals, however, there is observed uniformly a decrease of about ten percent for the change from a crystal M^+X^- to its isoelectronic $M^{++}X^{--}$, as in the examples K^+—Br^-, 3.29; Ca^{++}—Se^{--}, 2.96 Å; and Na^+—Cl^-, 2.81; Mg^{++}—S^{--}, 2.54 Å. This decrease is not due to lack of compensation of the changes in the electron distributions (the univalent radius sums remain nearly constant), but results instead from the effect of doubling the electric charges on the ions.

There are corresponding great increases in hardness, melting point, and other properties of ionic crystals of an isoelectronic sequence with increase in valence.

The comparison of the radii with experimental values of interionic distances and the discussion of various corrections are treated in the following sections.

The first roughly correct values assigned to ionic radii were those obtained by A. Landé (*Z. f. Phys.* **1**, 191 (1920)) from the assumption that in the lithium halide crystals the halogen ions are in mutual contact (see Section 45). More accurate values were then given in 1923 by J. A. Wasastjerna (*Soc. Sci. Fenn. Comm. Phys. Math.* **38**, 1 (1923)), who divided the observed interionic distances in crystals in ratios determined by the mole refraction values of the ions, the mole refraction being roughly proportional to ionic volume. The following values were given by Wasastjerna:

O^{--}	1.32 Å	F^-	1.33 Å	Na^+	1.01 Å	Mg^{++}	0.75 Å
S^{--}	1.69	Cl^-	1.72	K^+	1.30	Ca^{++}	1.02
Se^{--}	1.77	Br^-	1.92	Rb^+	1.50	Sr^{++}	1.20
Te^{--}	1.91	I^-	2.19	Cs^+	1.75	Ba^{++}	1.40

It is seen that these agree with the values of Table 44-1 to within about 0.10 Å in general.

Wasastjerna's table of radii was then revised and greatly extended by Goldschmidt, with use of empirical data (V. M. Goldschmidt, "Geochemische Verteilungsgesetze der Elemente," *Skrifter det Norske Videnskaps-Akad. Oslo I. Matem.-Naturvid Klasse*, **1926**). Goldschmidt based his values on Wasastjerna's values 1.33 Å for F^- and 1.32 Å for O^{--}, and, using data obtained from crystals which he considered to be essentially ionic in nature, he deduced from this starting point empirical values of the crystal radius for over eighty ions. His values (indicated by G) are compared with those from Table 44-1 in the following table.

TABLE 44-2.—COMPARISON OF CRYSTAL RADII FROM TABLE 44-1
WITH GOLDSCHMIDT'S VALUES

		Li	Be^{++}		
		0.60	0.31		
	G	.78	.34		

	O^{--}	F$^-$	Na$^+$	Mg^{++}	Al^{3+}	Si^{4+}
	1.40	1.36	0.95	0.65	0.50	0.41
G	1.32	1.33	.98	.78	.57	.39

	S^{--}	Cl$^-$	K$^+$	Ca^{++}	Sc^{3+}	Ti^{4+}
	1.84	1.81	1.33	0.99	0.81	0.68
G	1.74	1.81	1.33	1.06	.83	.64

	Se^{--}	Br$^-$	Rb$^+$	Sr^{++}	Y^{3+}	Zr^{4+}
	1.98	1.95	1.48	1.13	0.93	0.80
G	1.91	1.96	1.49	1.27	1.06	.87

	Te^{--}	I$^-$	Cs$^+$	Ba^{++}	La^{3+}	Ce^{4+}
	2.21	2.16	1.69	1.35	1.15	1.01
G	2.11	2.20	1.65	1.43	1.22	1.02

The agreement is good in general, and would be better in case that Goldschmidt had selected 1.40 Å instead of 1.32 Å for O^{--} as the basis for the values for bivalent ions. W. L. Bragg in his early important investigations[1] on the structure of silicates and related crystals selected 1.35 Å for the radius of O^{--} as well as F$^-$, this value having been indicated by the average O—O distance 2.7 Å observed in crystals showing anion contact (Sec. 47).

[1] W. L. Bragg and J. West, *Proc. Roy. Soc.* A114, 450 (1927).

Empirical crystal radius values, based on O^{--} = 1.40 Å and designed for application to the same standard crystals, are given in Table 44-3. These are in part obtained from Goldschmidt's set with suitable small corrections.

TABLE 44-3.—EMPIRICAL CRYSTAL RADII

NH$_4^+$	1.48 Å	Mn^{++}	0.80 Å	Ti^{3+}	0.69 Å
Tl$^+$	1.44	Fe^{++}	.75	V^{3+}	.66
		Co^{++}	.72	Cr^{3+}	.64
		Ni^{++}	.70	Mn^{3+}	.62
				Fe^{3+}	.60

Trivalent rare earth ions 0.90 ± 0.05 Å

45. THE ALKALI HALIDE CRYSTALS

The alkali halides all crystallize with the sodium chloride arrangement (Fig. 2-1) except cesium chloride, bromide, and iodide, which have the cesium chloride arrangement, shown in Figure 45-1. (The chloride, bromide, and iodide of rubidium have also been found to assume this structure under high pressure,[1] the transitions occurring at about 5000 kg./cm^2; and cesium chloride has a high-temperature modification with the sodium chloride arrangement, stable above 460°C.[2]) The observed values of interionic distances for the crystals with the sodium chloride structure are compared with the radius sums in Table

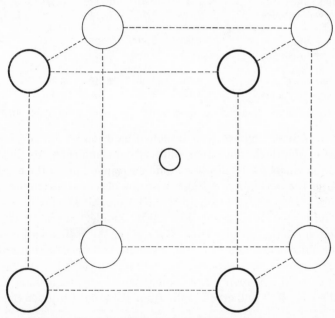

Fig. 45-1.—The cesium chloride structure.

45-1. It is seen that the agreement is not very good in general, the lithium salts showing especially large deviations, and that no set of ionic radii could reproduce the experimental values

[1] J. C. Slater, *Phys. Rev.* **23**, 488 (1924); P. W. Bridgman, *Z. Krist.* **67**, 363 (1927); L. Pauling, *ibid.* **69**, 35 (1928); R. B. Jacobs, *Phys Rev.* **53**, 930 (1938); **54**, 468 (1938). The potassium halides other than the fluoride are reported to show similar transitions at about 20000 kg/cm.^{2}; see also P. W. Bridgman, *ibid.* **57**, 237 (1940).

[2] C. D. West, *Z. Krist.* **88**, 94 (1934).

satisfactorily, since these values do not satisfy the criterion of additivity. The difference between the observed values for Li^+—I^- and Li^+—F^- is 1.01 Å, and that between Rb^+—I^- and Rb^+—F^- is only 0.84 Å; these quantities, representing the difference in radius of I^- and F^-, should be equal.

TABLE 45-1.—INTERIONIC DISTANCES FOR ALKALI HALIDE CRYSTALS
WITH THE SODIUM CHLORIDE STRUCTURE

		Li^+	Na^+	K^+	Rb^+	Cs^+
Radius sum	F^-	1.96 Å	(2.31 Å)	2.69 Å	2.84 Å	3.05 Å
Observed distance		2.01	2.31	2.67	2.82	3.01
Radius sum	Cl^-	2.41	2.76	(3.14)	3.29	3.50
Observed distance		2.57	2.81	3.14	3.29	3.45*
Radius sum	Br^-	2.55	2.90	3.28	(3.43)	
Observed distance		2.75	2.98	3.29	3.43	
Radius sum	I^-	2.76	3.11	3.49	3.64	
Observed distance		3.02	3.23	3.53	3.66	

* Extrapolated from the value at 500°C; see footnote to Table 45-4.

45a. Anion Contact and Double Repulsion.[1]—The explanations of the deviations from additivity are indicated by Figure 45-2, in which the circles have radii corresponding to the crystal radii of the ions and are drawn with the observed interionic distances. It is seen that for LiCl, LiBr, and LiI *the anions are in mutual contact*, as suggested in 1920 by Landé. A simple calculation shows that if the ratio $\rho = R_+/R_-$ of the radii of cation and anion falls below $\sqrt{2} - 1 = 0.414$ there will occur anion-anion contact rather than cation-anion contact (the ions being considered as rigid spheres). The comparison of apparent anion radii in these crystals and crystal radii from Table 44–1 is given below.

TABLE 45-2.—HALIDE ION RADII IN THE LITHIUM HALIDES

	Apparent radius in Li^+X^-	Crystal radius
Cl^-	1.82 Å	1.81 Å
Br^-	1.95	1.95
I^-	2.12	2.16

The radius ratio for lithium fluoride is 0.44. In this crystal each anion is approaching contact not only with the surrounding cations but also with other anions. In consequence the repul-

[1] L. Pauling, *J.A.C.S.* **49**, 765 (1927).

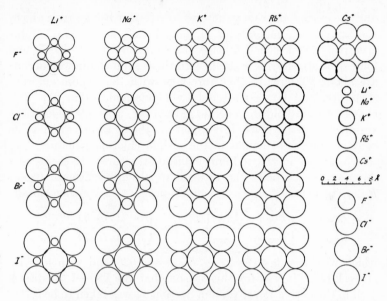

FIG. 45-2.—The arrangement of ions in cube-face layers of alkali halide crystals with the sodium chloride structure.

sive forces are larger than they would be for either anion-cation or anion-anion contact alone, and equilibrium with the attractive Coulomb forces is reached with a lattice constant such that the cation-anion distance is larger than the sum of the radii and the anion-anion distance is also larger than twice the anion radius. This phenomenon of *double repulsion* is shown also by sodium iodide, bromide, and chloride.

It is seen that the *radius ratio* is an important quantity in influencing the properties of ionic crystals. Its significance in the chemistry of ionic substances was first pointed out by Magnus,[1] and was emphasized by Goldschmidt[2] in the field of crystal chemistry. The effect of the radius ratio on the properties of ionic substances is discussed below in connection with a more refined treatment of the phenomena of anion contact and double repulsion.

45b. The Cesium Chloride Arrangement.—Ammonium chloride, bromide, and iodide crystallize with both the sodium chloride

[1] A. Magnus, *Z. anorg. allgem. Chem.* **124**, 288 (1922).
[2] V. M. Goldschmidt, "Geochemische Verteilungsgesetze der Elemente."

and the cesium chloride structures, the former being stable above the transition temperatures (184.3°, 137.8°, and −17.6°C., respectively), and the latter below these temperatures.[1]   The interionic distances for the crystals with the cesium chloride structure are about 3% greater than for those with the sodium chloride structure, and it was inferred by Goldschmidt that this 3% change should hold in general.   Moreover, a simple theoretical argument can be given in support of this.   Each cation is in contact with eight anions in the cesium chloride structure, but with only six in the sodium chloride structure.   It seems not unreasonable to place the ratio of repulsive coefficients B_{CsCl}/B_{NaCl} equal to 8/6; with use of Equation 43-3 we then obtain

$$\frac{R_{CsCl}}{R_{NaCl}} = \left\{ \frac{B_{CsCl}}{B_{NaCl}} \cdot \frac{A_{NaCl}}{A_{CsCl}} \right\}^{1/(n-1)} = \left\{ \frac{8}{6} \cdot \frac{1.7476}{1.7627} \right\}^{1/(n-1)} ,$$

which with $n = 9$ gives $R_{CsCl}/R_{NaCl} = 1.036$ and with $n = 12$ gives 1.027.   It was for this reason that the Cs^{+}—I^{-} distance used in the derivation of radii in Section 44 was taken to be 2.7% less than the observed value.[2]

The observed interionic distances for the cesium and rubidium halides (the latter being at high pressure) with the cesium chloride structure are compared with the crystal radius sums in Table 45-3.

TABLE 45-3.—INTERIONIC DISTANCES FOR CRYSTALS WITH THE
CESIUM CHLORIDE STRUCTURE

	Observed distance	Radius sum	Ratio
CsCl	3.56 Å	3.50 Å	(1.027)
CsBr	3.72	3.64	1.022
CsI	3.96	3.85	1.029
RbCl	3.41*	3.29	1.036
RbBr	3.56*	3.43	1.037
RbI	3.75†	3.64	1.030

* Calculated from the density changes reported by Bridgman to accompany the transitions.   These values are probably a little too large.

† R. B. Jacobs, *Phys. Rev.* 54, 468 (1938).

[1] At still lower temperature the substances undergo further transitions to forms characterized by decreased freedom of rotational motion of the ammonium ions.

[2] A more detailed discussion of the change in interionic distance accompanying this transition for the cesium and rubidium halides has been published: L. Pauling, *Z. Krist.* 69, 35 (1928).

The increase in interionic distance of approximately 3% is of especial interest in relation to the question of the relative thermodynamic stability of the two structures. It is seen from Equation 43-5 that if the Born postulate were valid the cesium chloride and sodium chloride modifications of a substance would have the same energy (and presumably nearly the same free energy) when the equilibrium interionic distances have the same ratio as the Madelung constants; that is, at the value $R_{CsCl}/R_{NaCl} = A_{CsCl}/A_{NaCl} = 1.0135$. Actually the transition occurs at about 1.030 to 1.035 for the rubidium halides, and the stability of the cesium chloride modification of the cesium halides shows that the equilibrium ratio is greater than 1.022 to 1.029 for them also. This requires that the crystal energy for the cesium chloride structure be greater than that given by the Born equation (relative to that for the sodium chloride structure) by about two percent, which is about 3 kcal./mole. Various suggestions have been made as to the source of this extra stability (van der Waals forces,[1] multipolar deformation,[2] etc.), but the question must be considered as still unsettled.

45c. A Detailed Discussion of the Effect of Relative Ionic Sizes on the Properties of the Alkali Halides.—It has been found possible to formulate a simple detailed representation of interionic forces in terms of ionic radii which leads to complete agreement with the observed values of interionic distances for alkali halide crystals, and provides a quantitative theory of the anion-contact and double-repulsion effects.[3]

Let us assume that the mutual potential energy of two ions A and B at the distance r_{AB} can be expressed approximately by the equation

$$u_{AB} = \frac{z_A z_B e^2}{r_{AB}} + \beta_{AB} B_0 e^2 \frac{(r_A + r_B)^{n-1}}{r_{AB}{}^n}, \qquad (45\text{-}1)$$

in which $z_A e$ and $z_B e$ are the electric charges of the ions, r_A and r_B are constants representing their radii (which we shall call *standard radii*), B_0 is a characteristic repulsive coefficient, and β_{AB} is a constant with the value 1 for univalent cation-anion interaction, 1.25 for cation-cation interaction, and 0.75 for

[1] M. Born and J. E. Mayer, *Z. f. Phys.* **75**, 1 (1932).
[2] H. Lévy, Dissertation, California Institute of Technology, **1938**.
[3] L. Pauling, *J.A.C.S.* **50**, 1036 (1928); *Z. Krist.* **67**, 377 (1928).

anion-anion interaction.[1]   This form for the repulsive term, with inclusion of the factor $(r_A + r_B)^{n-1}$, is reasonable in that it makes the repulsive forces increase in magnitude with increase in the sizes of the ions.

For a crystal with the sodium chloride structure containing univalent cations and anions with radii r_+ and r_- respectively the total energy per molecule then becomes

$$V = -\frac{Ae^2}{R} + 6B_0e^2\frac{(r_+ + r_-)^{n-1}}{R^n} + 6 \cdot 1.25B_0e^2\frac{(2r_+)^{n-1}}{(\sqrt{2}\,R)^n}$$
$$+ 6 \cdot 0.75B_0e^2\frac{(2r_-)^{n-1}}{(\sqrt{2}\,R)^n}, \tag{45-2}$$

in which the first term on the right, containing the Madelung constant, results from summing the Coulomb terms (the first term of 45-1), R being the minimum cation-anion distance in the crystal, the second term represents the repulsion between each cation and its six anion neighbors, the third term the repulsion of each cation and its nearest cation neighbors, at the distance $\sqrt{2}\,R$, and the fourth term the repulsion of anion-anion neighbors at the distance $\sqrt{2}\,R$.   The repulsions of more distant ions are neglected.   This equation can be rewritten in the form

$$V = -\frac{Ae^2}{R} + \frac{6B_0e^2}{R^n}\left\{(r_+ + r_-)^{n-1} + \frac{1.25(2r_+)^{n-1}}{(\sqrt{2})^n}\right.$$
$$\left. + 0.75\frac{(2r_-)^{n-1}}{(\sqrt{2})^n}\right\}, \tag{45-3}$$

which is analogous to Equation 43-2; the equilibrium value of R is accordingly found from Equation 43-3 to be

$$R_0 = (r_+ + r_-)F(\rho), \tag{45-4}$$

in which $F(\rho)$ is a function of the radius ratio, with the form

---

[1] The values for β_{AB} are obtained from a quantum-mechanical discussion: L. Pauling, *Z. Krist.* **67**, 377 (1928).   Equation 45-1 and the following equations differ slightly from those originally published, in that $(r_A + r_B)^{n-1}$ replaces $(r_A + r_B)^n$.   I am indebted to Professor J. E. Lennard-Jones of Cambridge University for suggesting this change, and to Dr. F. J. Ewing for assistance with the revised calculations.

$$F(\rho) = \left(\frac{6nB_0}{A}\right)^{1/(n-1)} \left\{ 1 + \frac{1.25}{(\sqrt{2})^n}\left(\frac{2\rho}{\rho+1}\right)^{n-1} \right.$$

$$\left. + \frac{0.75}{(\sqrt{2})^n}\left(\frac{2}{\rho+1}\right)^{n-1} \right\}^{1/(n-1)}. \quad (45\text{-}5)$$

It is convenient to give B_0 a value such as to make $F(\rho)$ equal to unity for $\rho = 0.75$; this causes R_0 to be equal to the sum of the

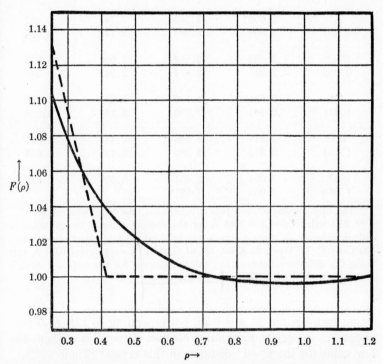

Fig. 45-3.—The function $F(\rho)$ showing the effect of radius ratio on equilibrium interionic distance of crystals with the sodium chloride arrangement.

standard radii of cation and anion for crystals with this radius ratio, which was selected as standard in Section 44 because it is approximated by isoelectronic alkali and halogen ion pairs. Moreover, the exponent n is assumed to have the value 9 for all the alkali halides, for the sake of simplicity.

The form of the correction factor $F(\rho)$ as a function of ρ is shown in Figure 45-3. The broken line represents the same function for rigid spheres ($n = \infty$). It is seen that for ρ less than about 0.35 anion contact is effective in determining the equilibrium interionic distances, and between 0.35 and 0.60 the curve for $n = 9$ rises above the rigid sphere curve because of the

TABLE 45-4.—CALCULATED AND OBSERVED INTERIONIC DISTANCES
IN ALKALI HALIDE CRYSTALS

	F⁻ $r_- = 1.341$	Cl⁻ 1.806	Br⁻ 1.951	I⁻ 2.168
Li⁺ $r_+ = 0.607$	2.009* 2.009	2.566 2.566	2.747 2.747	3.022 3.025
Na⁺ 0.958	2.303 2.307	2.814 2.814	2.980 2.981	3.233 3.231
K⁺ 1.331	2.664 2.664	3.139 3.139	3.293 3.293	3.529 3.526
Rb⁺ 1.484	2.817 2.815	3.283 3.285	3.434 3.434	3.664 3.663
Cs⁺ 1.656	3.005 3.005	3.451 3.45**	3.598	3.823

* The upper value of each pair is calculated, the lower observed.
** The value Cs—Cl = 3.45 Å for the sodium chloride modification of cesium chloride at room temperature is obtained from that observed at 500°C by C. D. West, Z. Krist. **88**, 94 (1934), by subtracting 0.09 Å, this being the difference between the values observed for the ordinary modification at 460°C and at room temperature.

operation of the phenomenon of double repulsion. It is interesting to note that at $\rho = 0.28$, corresponding to LiI, $F(\rho)$ falls about 1% below the rigid anion contact curve; this explains the low value for the I⁻—I⁻ distance in this crystal (Table 45-2).

It is possible by assigning suitable values to r_+ and r_- for the nine alkali and halogen ions to calculate with use of Equations 45-4 and 45-5 values of R_0 for the seventeen alkali halides with the sodium chloride structure at room temperature which agree with the experimental values to within 0.001 Å on the average. The comparison of calculated and observed values is given in Table 45-4. The agreement is striking, especially when it is considered that the radius ratio effect amounts for lithium iodide to 0.247 Å, nearly ten percent of R_0, and there is accordingly little doubt that the deviations from additivity in the interionic distances in the alkali halide crystals are to be attributed to this effect.[1] The standard radii r_+ and r_- for the ions have the same values as the corresponding crystal radii (to within 0.008 Å) except for F^- and Cs^+, which show somewhat larger deviations, -0.019 and -0.034 Å respectively. It is possible that these deviations are to be attributed to the use of the constant value 9 for n.

The deviations in additivity of interionic distances in the alkali halides resulting from the radius ratio effect may be expected to be associated with irregularities in other properties of the substances. For some properties the radius ratio is unimportant; thus the interatomic distance in a gaseous diatomic salt molecule is not a function of it (for only the radius sum enters in the equation expressing the potential energy of two ions), nor is the energy of formation of such a molecule from free ions. In order to separate the effect of the radius ratio from other effects let us define for each substance a corresponding hypothetical standard substance; namely, one with the same radius sum $r_+ + r_-$, and the same ionic properties otherwise, but with the standard radius ratio $\rho = 0.75$. The properties attributed to this hypothetical substance will be designated as corrected for the radius ratio effect, or, briefly, corrected.

The properties to be expected for the hypothetical alkali halides with $\rho = 0.75$ are the following. The equilibrium interionic distances would be additive, being equal to $r_+ + r_-$. The crystal energy, which is inversely proportional to the interionic distances, would show a corresponding regularity. A large number of properties of salts depend essentially on the crystal

---

[1] Similar calculations with use of an exponential form for the repulsive potential have been made recently by M. L. Huggins and J. E. Mayer *J. Chem. Phys.* **1**, 643 (1933), and M. L. Huggins, *ibid.* **5**, 143 (1937). The problem has been treated also by Jarl A. Wasastjerna, *Soc. Sci. Fenn. Comm. Phys. Math.* **VIII**, 21 (1935).

It is possible to extend the treatment of this section, based on Equation 45-1, to crystals other than the alkali halides, with suitable choice of standard radii. It is found that the standard radii differ somewhat in general from the univalent radii of Table 44-1, because of the different choice of values of n. An approximate value for the standard radius of a multivalent ion can be obtained by multiplying its crystal radius by $z^{1/4}$, z being the magnitude of the valence of the ion; this is the correction factor from crystal radius to univalent radius corresponding to $n = 9$.

energy—the heat of fusion, heat of sublimation, melting point, boiling point, solubility, etc. All of these properties would exhibit for the hypothetical alkali halides a regular dependence on the interionic distance, and hence the values of any one of these properties should vary monotonically for a sequence LiX, NaX, KX, RbX, CsX, or MF, MCl, MBr, MI. The properties of the actual alkali halides deviate very much from this expected regularity, as is seen from Figures 45-4 and 45-5, in which there

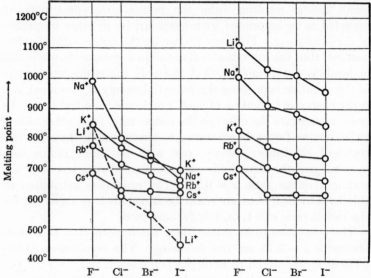

Fig. 45-4.—The observed melting points of the alkali halides (left) and values corrected for the radius ratio effect (right).

are shown on the left the experimental values of their melting points and boiling points.

The explanation of these irregularities is given by the radius ratio effect. The crystal energy of the corrected and that of the actual alkali halide crystal can be calculated with Equation 43-5. Values of the difference ΔU_O between the corrected and the actual crystal energy obtained in this way are given in Table 45-5. This energy quantity is required to correct the heat of sublimation, as the energy of a gaseous molecule is not a function of the radius ratio.

The heat of sublimation at room temperature is equal to the sum of the heat of fusion at the melting point, the heat of vaporization at the boiling point, and the difference between the heat capacity of the solid and liquid and that of the vapor, integrated from room temperature to the boiling point; so that the energy correction ΔU_0 is to be divided among these quantities. For potassium chloride the heat of fusion amounts to 10% of the heat of sublimation, the integrated heat capacity difference to 30%, and the heat of vaporization to 60%. It might be reasonable to apportion the correction ΔU_0 in these ratios; however, it

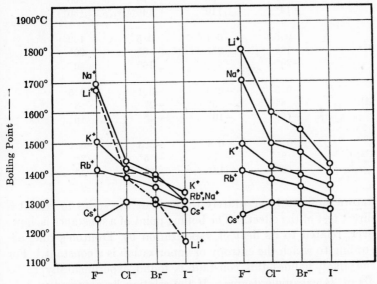

FIG. 45-5.—The observed boiling points of the alkali halides (left) and values corrected for the radius ratio effect (right).

is to be expected that the transition from crystal to liquid would destroy in some part the octahedral coordination of the ionic aggregate, causing the heat of fusion to assume a larger share of the radius ratio correction, and that furthermore the coordination surviving in the liquid would decrease rapidly with increasing temperature, causing the heat content of the liquid also to assume more than its proportionate share of ΔU_0. The following calculations were made by apportioning 20% of ΔU_0 to the heat of fusion and 40% to the heat of vaporization, these proportions being chosen partially so as to give satisfactory results in the consideration below of melting points and boiling points.

The heat of sublimation and related heat quantities are not

TABLE 45-5.—THE EFFECT OF RADIUS RATIO ON CRYSTAL ENERGY, BOILING POINTS, AND MELTING POINTS OF THE ALKALI HALIDES

		F⁻	Cl⁻	Br⁻	I⁻
Li⁺	$\Delta U_0 =$	7.9	12.7	13.8	15.1 kcal./mole
	$\Delta T_{BP} =$	132°	212°	230°	252°
	$\Delta T_{MP} =$	264°	424°	460°	504°
Na⁺		0.4	3.3	4.2	5.4
		7°	55°	70°	90°
		14°	110°	140°	180°
K⁺		−0.6	0.1	0.5	1.2
		−10°	2°	8°	20°
		−20°	4°	16°	40°
Rb⁺		−0.5	−0.3	−0.1	0.5
		− 8°	− 5°	−2°	8°
		−16°	−10°	−4°	16°
Cs⁺		0.5	−0.4	−0.3	−0.1
		8°	− 7°	− 5°	−2°
		16°	−13°	−10°	−4°

known sufficiently accurately throughout the series to permit a direct test of the effect. The boiling point of a substance is, however, related to its heat of vaporization by Trouton's rule, according to which the entropy of vaporization is a constant. For the alkali halides this constant is found experimentally to be about 24 cal./mole degree. If the relation be assumed to hold for the corrected alkali halides the boiling point correction, in degrees, is $\Delta T_{BP} = 0.40 \ \Delta U_0/0.024$. If we similarly assume the entropy of fusion to be constant (Richard's rule) with the value 6.0 cal./mole degree the melting point correction is $\Delta T_{MP} = 0.20 \ \Delta U_0/0.0060$. The values calculated for ΔT_{BP} and ΔT_{MP} are included in Table 45-5.

The observed melting points and boiling points of the alkali halides (Figs. 45-4 and 45-5, left side) show large irregularities; thus the boiling points and melting points of all the lithium salts lie below those of the corresponding sodium salts. It has been suggested[1] that these irregularities are due to deformation of the ions. Our calculations show, however, that they result mainly

[1] K. Fajans, *Z. Krist.* 61, 18 (1925).

from the radius ratio effect. The corrected melting points and boiling points vary in a regular manner throughout each sequence and correspond closely in qualitative behavior to the interionic distances, except for a small deviation shown by the cesium salts.

46. THE STRUCTURE OF OTHER SIMPLE IONIC CRYSTALS

46a. The Alkaline Earth Oxides, Sulfides, Selenides, and Tellurides.—All of the alkaline-earth compounds with oxygen, sulfur, selenium, and tellurium crystallize with the sodium chloride arrangement except beryllium oxide and magnesium telluride, with the wurtzite structure, and beryllium sulfide, selenide, and telluride, with the sphalerite structure. The comparison of observed interionic distances with the sums of the crystal radii, shown in Table 36-1, leads to excellent agreement except for the magnesium compounds, and provides a striking verification of the arguments used in the derivation of the table of crystal radii, inasmuch as the experimental values for these substances were in no way involved in the formulation of the table.

TABLE 46-1.—INTERIONIC DISTANCES IN CRYSTALS $M^{++}X^{--}$ WITH THE SODIUM CHLORIDE ARRANGEMENT

		Mg^{++}	Ca^{++}	Sr^{++}	Ba^{++}
Radius sum	O^{--}	2.05 Å	2.39 Å	2.53 Å	2.75 Å
Observed distance		2.10	2.40	2.54	2.75
Radius sum	S^{--}	2.49	2.83	2.97	3.19
Observed distance		2.54	2.83	3.00	3.18
Radius sum	Se^{--}	2.63	2.97	3.11	3.33
Observed distance		2.72	2.96	3.11	3.31
Radius sum	Te^{--}		3.20	3.34	3.56
Observed distance			3.17	3.33	3.50

In magnesium sulfide and selenide the anions are in contact; the radii deduced on this assumption (1.80 Å for S^{--}, 1.93 Å for Se^{--}) are slightly smaller than the crystal radii. The ratio $R_{Mg}{}^{++}/R_{O}{}^{--}$ is 0.46, which lies in the region in which double repulsion is operative; this accounts for the high value observed for magnesium oxide.

46b. Crystals with the Rutile and the Fluorite Structures. Interionic Distances for Substances of Unsymmetrical Valence

Type.—In a crystal of a substance of unsymmetrical valence type, such as fluorite, CaF_2 (Fig. 46-1), the equilibrium cation-anion interionic distance cannot be expected without detailed consideration to be given by the sum of the crystal radii of the bivalent calcium ion and the univalent fluoride ion. The sum of the univalent radii of calcium and fluorine, 2.54 Å, would give

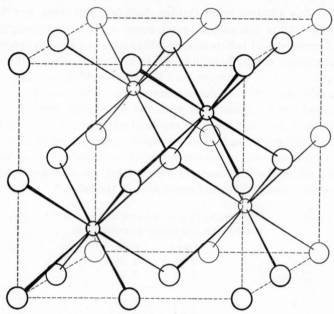

Fig. 46-1.—The structure of fluorite, CaF_2. Small circles represent calcium ions and large circles fluoride ions.

the equilibrium interionic distance in a hypothetical crystal with attractive and repulsive forces corresponding to the sodium chloride arrangement. This can now be corrected for the valence effect in the following way.[1]

According to Equation 43-3 the ratio of equilibrium distances for the two structures is

$$\frac{R_{CaF_2}}{R_{NaCl}} = \left\{ \frac{B_{CaF_2}}{B_{NaCl}} \cdot \frac{A_{NaCl}}{A_{CaF_2}} \right\}^{1/(n-1)}.$$

[1] L. Pauling, *J.A.C.S.* **49**, 765 (1927); a more detailed discussion of methods of calculating interionic distances from univalent radii has been given by W. H. Zachariasen, *Z. Krist.* **80**, 137 (1931).

Now in fluorite there are eight cation-anion contacts per stoichiometric molecule, and in NaCl six; we accordingly assume the ratio B_{CaF_2}/B_{NaCl} to have the value 8/6. Introducing this and the values of A_{NaCl} (1.7476) and A_{CaF_2} (5.0388) in this equation, and placing n equal to 8 (the mean of the values for Ca^{++} and F^-), we obtain $R_{CaF_2}/R_{NaCl} = 0.894$, which on multiplication by the sum of the univalent radii gives for R_{CaF_2} the value 2.27 Å. This value is somewhat smaller than the observed Ca^{++}—F^- distance for fluorite, 2.36 Å. It is probable that the anion-anion contacts in fluorite make the ratio B_{CaF_2}/B_{NaCl} somewhat greater than 8/6, perhaps about 9/6 (that is, proportional to the number of ions); this leads to a calculated value of 2.32 Å.

It is found empirically, indeed, that these complicated and unreliable calculations need not be made; in general even for substances of unsymmetrical valence type the interionic distances are very closely approximated by the sum of the crystal radii. For fluorite this sum is 2.35 A, which agrees very well with the observed value. The reason for this is apparent; in the crystal radius of Ca^{++} a correction for bivalence of cation and anion is made, and this has nearly the same magnitude as

TABLE 46-2.—INTERIONIC DISTANCES FOR SUBSTANCES OF
UNSYMMETRICAL VALENCE TYPE

Crystals with the fluorite structure

	Radius sum	Observed distance		Radius sum	Observed distance
CaF₂	2.35 Å	2.36 Å	Li₂O	2.00 Å	2.00 Å
SrF₂	2.49	2.50	Li₂S	2.44	2.47
SrCl₂	2.94	3.02	Li₂Se	2.58	2.59
BaF₂	2.71	2.68	Li₂Te	2.81	2.82
CdF₂	2.33	2.34	Na₂O	2.35	2.40
HgF₂	2.46	2.40	Na₂S	2.79	2.83
ZrO₂	2.20	2.20	Na₂Se	2.93	2.95
CeO₂	2.36	2.34	Na₂Te	3.16	3.17
			K₂O	2.69	2.79
			K₂S	3.17	3.20
			K₂Se	3.31	3.33
			K₂Te	3.54	3.53

Crystals with the rutile structure

	Radius sum	Observed distance		Radius sum	Observed distance
MgF₂	2.01	2.00	GeO₂	1.93	1.89
ZnF₂	2.10	2.05	SnO₂	2.11	2.05
TiO₂	2.04	1.96	PbO₂	2.24	2.16

the correction for bivalence of cation alone made for the sum of the univalent radii of calcium and fluorine.

A comparison of observed interionic distances and crystal radius sums for some crystals with the fluorite structure and the rutile structure is given in Table 46-2. It is seen that in general the agreement is excellent. Similarly good agreement is found for other ionic crystals of unsymmetrical valence type, the available data being so extensive as to prevent their reproduction here. For these crystals, as for those of symmetrical valence type also, greater refinement can be attained in the discussion of interionic distances by considering the effect of change of coordination number. This question is treated in the following section.

It is of interest in connection with the theory of interionic forces discussed in Section 45c to consider the rutile crystal in somewhat greater detail. The structure of this crystal, aside from the absolute dimensions, depends on two parameters, the axial ratio c_0/a_0 and another parameter determining the positions of the oxygen atoms (Fig. 7-2). This parameter can be given a value, for any value of c_0/a_0, such as to make the distances from the cation to the six surrounding anions equal, as is reasonable for an ionic crystal. The Madelung constant is then found on calculation to be given by the expression

$$A_{R_0} = 4.816 - 4.11\left(0.721 - \frac{c_0}{a_0}\right)^2. \qquad (46\text{-}1)$$

It is seen that A has its maximum value, corresponding to maximum stability of the crystal, if R_0 is constant, at $c_0/a_0 = 0.721$. This is greater than the values observed, which lie near 0.66 (0.660 for MgF_2, 0.644 for TiO_2, etc.). The explanation of this is seen when the $F^- - F^-$ and $O^{--} - O^{--}$ distances are considered; the axial ratio 0.721 corresponds to a very small value of the minimum anion-anion distance—about 2.40 Å, as compared with 2.72 and 2.80 Å, twice the crystal radius of F^- and O^{--}, respectively. It is accordingly anion-anion repulsion which increases the value of a_0 for rutile-type crystals. A quantitative treatment[1] with use of the potential function of Section 45c leads to $c_0/a_0 \cong 0.66$, in agreement with experiment. The $F^- - F^-$ and $O^{--} - O^{--}$ distances are then about 2.50 Å; this value is less than twice the crystal radii of the anions, showing that a

[1] L. Pauling, Z. Krist. **67**, 377 (1928).

compromise is reached in the attempt of the anion-anion repulsion to decrease the axial ratio and that of the Madelung constant to increase it.

The same phenomenon is shown also by anatase and brookite, two additional crystal modifications of titanium dioxide. In these crystals also the minimum $O^{--} - O^{--}$ distances have the low value 2.50 Å. A theoretical treatment like that described above has been carried out for anatase, with results in good agreement with experiment.

46c. The Effect of Coordination Number on Interionic Distance.—It was pointed out in Section 45b that an approximate value for the ratio of interionic distances for two modifications of a substance can be obtained by use of the equation

$$\frac{R_{II}}{R_I} = \left\{\frac{A_I B_{II}}{A_{II} B_I}\right\}^{1/(n-1)}, \tag{46-2}$$

in which the repulsive coefficients B_I and B_{II} are assumed to be proportional to the numbers of cation-anion contacts for the two structures. With $B_{CsCl}/B_{NaCl} = 8/6$, this equation leads to $R_{CsCl}/R_{NaCl} = 1.036$ for $n = 9$, in approximate agreement with the experimental results.

Goldschmidt[1] emphasized the necessity of making corrections of this type for the effect of coordination number, and suggested the factor 1.03 for changing from coordination number 6 to 8, and 0.93 to 0.95 for changing from 6 to 4.

We see from application of Equation 46-2 that the correction depends in the main on the coordination number of the cation; that is, the number of anions grouped about each cation. With $n = 9$ Equation 46-2 leads to the following ratios:
Coordination numbers

$6 \to 8$: $\dfrac{R_{CsCl}}{R_{NaCl}} = 1.036$, $\dfrac{R_{fluorite}}{R_{rutile}} = 1.031$, $\left(\dfrac{8}{6}\right)^{1/8} = 1.036$;

$6 \to 4$: $\dfrac{R_{sphalerite\ or\ wurtzite}}{R_{NaCl}} = 0.957$, $\dfrac{R_{\beta\text{-quartz}}}{R_{rutile}} = 0.960$

$\left(\dfrac{4}{6}\right)^{1/8} = 0.950.$

[1] V. M. Goldschmidt, "Geochemische Verteilungsgesetze der Elemente" 8, 69 (1926).

It is seen that the changes from the standard sodium chloride and rutile arrangements, with coordination number 6, to cesium chloride and fluorite, respectively, with coordination number 8, are nearly the same, as are also those to sphalerite or wurtzite and β-quartz, respectively, with coordination number 4. Moreover, the values are nearly the same as those calculated by ignoring the differences in Madelung constants; that is, by placing $A_{II}/A_{I} = 1$.

Values of the ratio $\{B_{II}/B_{I}\}^{1/n-1}$ with B_{I} equal to 6 (coordination number 6 having been chosen as the standard in the derivation of the table of ionic radii) and with B_{II} equal to the coordination number for the second structure are given in Table 46-3 for various values of the exponent n.

As an example of the application of this table we may consider the Al—O distances for octahedral and tetrahedral coordination of oxygen ions about aluminum. In corundum ($\alpha - Al_2O_3$), topaz ($Al_2SiO_4F_2$) diaspore (AlOOH, Fig. 40-4), and many other crystals with aluminum octahedra the observed values for the Al—O distances lie close to 1.90 Å, the sum of the crystal radii of the ions. The values observed for tetrahedral cordination, in crystals such as $\beta - Al_2O_3$, sillimanite (Al_2SiO_5), sodalite ($NaAl_3-Si_3O_{12}Cl$), and other aluminosilicates, lie between 1.66 and 1.76 Å.

TABLE 46-3.—CORRECTION FACTOR FOR CHANGE OF COORDINATION NUMBER FROM THE STANDARD VALUE 6

$n =$	6	7	8	9	10	11	12
Coordination number							
12	1.149	1.122	1.104	1.091	1.080	1.072	1.065
9	1.085	1.070	1.060	1.052	1.046	1.041	1.038
8	1.059	1.049	1.042	1.037	1.032	1.029	1.026
7	1.031	1.026	1.022	1.019	1.017	1.016	1.014
6	1.000	1.000	1.000	1.000	1.000	1.000	1.000
5	0.964	0.970	0.974	0.978	0.980	0.982	0.984
4	0.922	0.935	0.944	0.951	0.956	0.960	0.964

The sum of the radii corrected by the appropriate factor from the table is 1.78 Å, somewhat larger than the average of these experimental values. It seems likely that in AlO_4 tetrahedra the bonds have considerable covalent character, and that the interatomic distances are influenced by this. The same comment applies also to the Si—O distance for the SiO_4 tetrahedron, for which the observed value, 1.59 Å, lies below the corrected ionic radius sum, 1.69 Å. (See the discussion in Section 30.)

In cubic crystals M_2RX_6, such as potassium fluosilicate, with the structure shown in Figure 46-2, each ion M is surrounded by twelve X ions. Many of these compounds have been studied, the observed values for M—X being given in Table 46-4. It is

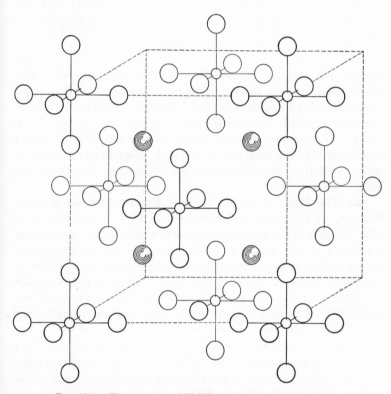

Fɪɢ. 46-2.—The structure of K_2SiF_6 and related cubic crystals.

seen that in general these agree well with the radius sums corrected to coordination number twelve. It is interesting to point out that this agreement is found even though in many of the substances (M_2SeCl_6, M_2PtCl_6, etc.) the R—X bonds are essentially covalent; this reflects the fact that van der Waals radii and ionic radii are nearly equal (Sec. 24).

It is to be emphasized that equilibrium interionic distances are much less well defined than covalent bond distances; their values

TABLE 46-4.—INTERATOMIC DISTANCES M—X FOR COORDINATION
NUMBER TWELVE

	Crystal radius sum	Corrected sum	Observed distance
K—F	2.69 Å	2.97 Å	2.90 Å
Rb—F	2.84	3.12	3.01
Cs—F	3.05	3.31	3.18
K—Cl	3.14	3.43	3.44–3.50
Rb—Cl	3.29	3.57	3.50–3.60
Cs—Cl	3.50	3.77	3.60–3.70
K—Br	3.28	3.56	3.65

depend not only on coordination number, but also on radius ratio (anion contact, double repulsion), amount of covalent bond character, and other factors, and a simple discussion of all the corrections which have been suggested and applied cannot be given. On the other hand, we have a reliable picture of the forces operating between ions, and it is usually possible to make a reliable prediction regarding interionic distances for particular structures.

46d. The Effect of Radius Ratio in Determining the Relative Stability of Different Structures.—It is seen from Table 46-3 that the transition from the rutile structure, with coordination number 6 for the cations, to the fluorite structure, with coordination number 8, is accompanied by an increase in equilibrium interionic distance R_0 of about 3.7%, for $n = 9$. Now the Madelung constant A has for the two structures the values 4.816 and 5.039, respectively, with ratio 1.046, and accordingly (Eq. 43-5) the fluorite structure will be the more stable of the two so long as the increase in R_0 from rutile to fluorite remains less than 4.6%. The discussion of the radius ratio effect in Section 45c indicates the conditions under which the rutile structure becomes stable. Let us consider a cation M^{++} in the center of a cube of anions X^- in the fluorite structure (Fig. 46-1). If the repulsive forces from cations to anions are stronger than those between anions they will determine the equilibrium cation-anion interionic distance, which will be equal to the sum of the crystal radii with correction for coordination number, whereas if the anion-anion forces are the larger (anion contact) or of about the same magnitude (double repulsion) the value of R_0 will be larger than the corrected crystal radius sum, and in consequence the structure will be unstable relative to the rutile structure. The value of the radius ratio ρ at which this effect sets in can be calculated in the following way. If r_+ and r_- represent the univalent radii of the ions (the use of univalent radii is pertinent here because the discussion depends on the relative magnitudes of cation-anion and anion-anion repulsions), double repulsion will be effective when $2r_-$ and $r_+ + r_-$ are in the ratio $1:\sqrt{3}/2$; that is, the ratio of edge and half body diagonal of a cube. From the equation $(r_+ + r_-)/2r_- = \sqrt{3}/2$ we obtain

$$\rho = \sqrt{3} - 1 = 0.732 \qquad (46\text{-}3)$$

as the limiting radius ratio for stability of the fluorite structure, or in general for structures with cubic coordination; for values of ρ less than 0.732 the rutile structure is expected to occur for ionic crystals MX_2.

TABLE 46-5.—RADIUS RATIO VALUES FOR CRYSTALS WITH
RUTILE AND FLUORITE STRUCTURES

Rutile Structure	ρ	Fluorite Structure	ρ
MgF_2	0.60	CaF_2	0.87
ZnF_2	.65	SrF_2	.97
TiO_2	.55	BaF_2	1.12
GeO_2	.43	CdF_2	0.84
SnO_2	.55	HgF_2	.92
PbO_2	.60	$SrCl_2$	.73
		ZrO_2	.62
		CeO_2	.72

The comparison with experiment is shown in Table 46-5; it is seen that with two exceptions (ZrO_2 and CeO_2) the conditions $\rho < 0.73$ and $\rho > 0.73$ for stability of the rutile and fluorite structures respectively are satisfied.[1]

TABLE 46-6.—RADIUS RATIO VALUES FOR CRYSTALS WITH OCTAHEDRAL
AND TETRAHEDRAL COORDINATION

Octahedral coordination	ρ	Tetrahedral coordination	ρ
PbO_2	0.60	GeO_2	0.43
SnO_2	.55	SiO_2	.37
GeO_2	.43		
MgF_2	.60	BeF_2	.32

[1] The radius ratio effect is not of great importance for the transition from the sodium chloride to the cesium chloride structure.

A similar calculation leads to the limiting value $\rho = \sqrt{2} - 1$ = 0.414 for transition from octahedral to tetrahedral coordination. The extent to which this is verified by experiment is shown in Table 46-6.

It is interesting that GeO_2, with $\rho = 0.43$, crystallizes with both the rutile and the quartz structure.

The discussion of the relation between radius ratio and coordination number is continued in Section 48.

47. THE CLOSEST PACKING OF SPHERES

It is not surprising that in general a crystalline substance is a rather closely packed aggregate of atoms or ions, since the van der Waals interactions, Coulomb interactions, and other interatomic interactions tend to stabilize structures in which the interatomic distances are as small as possible. It has been found that the structures of many crystals can be profitably discussed in terms of the packing of spheres, to which we now direct our attention.

47a. Cubic and Hexagonal Closest Packing of Equivalent Spheres.—The problem of packing spheres in the ways which leave the minimum of interstitial space has interested many investigators. It was discovered fifty-five years ago by W. Barlow[1] that there are two ways of arranging equivalent spheres in closest packing, one with cubic and one with hexagonal symmetry.

There is only one way of arranging spheres in a single closest-packed layer. This is the familiar arrangement in which each sphere is in contact with six others, as in the bottom layer of

---

[1] W. Barlow, *Nature* **29**, 186, 205, 404 (1883); *Z. Krist.* **23**, 1 (1894); **29**, 433 (1898). In the first of these papers Barlow suggested five "very symmetrical" structures, the sodium chloride, cesium chloride, and nickel arsenide arrangements, and cubic and hexagonal closest packing. L. Sohncke, *Nature* **29**, 383 (1883), criticized his selection as arbitrary, and also said that an alkali halide such as NaCl could not have the sodium chloride arrangement, because it does not show the existence of discrete molecules! Lord Kelvin, *Proc. Roy. Soc. Edinburgh* **16**, 693 (1889), in discussing the packing of spheres, required that they be not only equivalent but also oriented similarly, and showed that cubic closest packing is the only closest-packed structure satisfying this condition. His additional requirement has no physical significance; hexagonal closest packing is as important an arrangement as cubic closest packing.

Figure 47-1. A second similar layer can be superimposed on this layer in such a way that each sphere is in contact with three spheres of the adjacent layer, as shown in the figure. A third layer can then be added in either one of two possible positions,

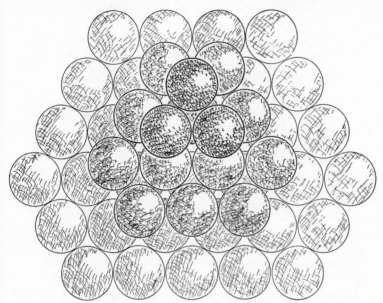

FIG. 47-1.—The arrangement of spheres in hexagonal closest packing.

with its spheres either directly above those of the first layer, as in Figure 47-1, or over the holes in the first layer not occupied by the second layer. Once either choice is made, the structure is determined, if all of the spheres are to be equivalent. The first structure, with hexagonal symmetry, is shown in Figure 47-1 and at the left in Figure 47-2; it is called *hexagonal closest packing*. The second structure, called *cubic closest packing*, is shown in Figures 47-2 (at the right) and 47-3, the latter being taken from one of Barlow's papers.

A convenient description of these structures utilizes the symbols A, B, and C for the three layers of close-packed spheres differing from one another in position. Hexagonal closest packing corresponds to the sequence of layers ABABAB··· (or BCBC··· or ACAC···), and cubic closest packing to ABCABCABC···. The structure repeats itself after two layers in hexagonal closest packing and after three layers in cubic closest packing.

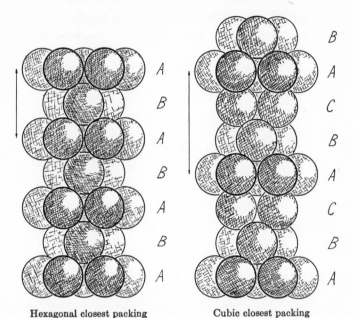

Hexagonal closest packing   Cubic closest packing

FIG. 47-2.—The modes of superposition of closest-packed layers of spheres in hexagonal closest packing (left) and cubic closest packing (right).

In each of the closest-packed structures each sphere is in contact with twelve others, a hexagon of six in the same plane and two triangles of three above and below. In hexagonal closest packing the upper triangle has the same orientation as the lower triangle and in cubic closest packing it is rotated through 60°.

The suggestion that in metal crystals the atoms are arranged in closest packing was made before the development of the x-ray technique, in order to account for the observations that many

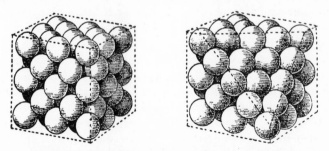

FIG. 47-3.—Cubic closest packing of spheres (after Barlow).

metals crystallize with cubic or hexagonal symmetry, and that in the latter case many of the observed values of the axial ratio lie near the ideal value $2\sqrt{2}/\sqrt{3} = 1.633$ for hexagonal closest packing. The structure of metal crystals is discussed in detail in Chapter XI.

For crystals involving spherical or nearly spherical molecules which are attracted to one another by van der Waals forces closest-packed structures, giving the maximum number of intermolecular contacts, can be expected to be stable. It has been shown that all the noble gases (He, Ne, Ar, Kr, and Xe) crystallize in cubic closest packing. Moreover, it has been found that in many molecular crystals of simple gases the molecules are rotating with considerable freedom, permitting them to simulate spheres in their interactions with neighboring molecules;[1] these crystals are usually closest-packed. Thus crystals of molecular hydrogen consist of rotating H_2 molecules in hexagonal closest packing, and in crystalline HCl, HBr, HI, H_2S, H_2Se, CH_4, and SiH_4 the molecules are arranged in cubic closest packing.[2]

47b. The Closest Packing of Large Ions in Ionic Crystals.— In several of the simple structures which can be assumed by crystals of simple ionic substances it can be considered that the large ions (usually the anions) are arranged in closest packing. As pointed out by Landé in 1920, this is true for the sodium chloride structure; in the lithium halides it is the closest-packed anion lattices which essentially determine the values of the lattice constant. This observation regarding the sodium chloride arrangement should, indeed, be attributed to Barlow, who in 1898, in discussing this structure for spheres with radius ratio 0.414, as shown in Figure 2-1 (taken from his paper), pointed out that the large spheres are in cubic closest packing.

The sphalerite, wurtzite, antifluorite (Li_2S), cadmium iodide, cadmium chloride, and many other arrangements also involve closest packing of the large ions.

It was pointed out by Bragg and West[3] in 1927 that in many silicate crystals and other minerals the volume per oxygen atom lies between 14 and 20 $\mathring{A}^3$, indicating that in these crystals oxygen

---

[1] L. Pauling, *Phys. Rev.* **36**, 430 (1930).

[2] Some of these substances have low-temperature modifications in which the molecules do not rotate freely.

[3] W. L. Bragg and J. West, *Proc. Roy. Soc.* **A114**, 450 (1927).

ions (with volume per ion 15.5 Å³ for crystal radius 1.40 Å) are in closest packing, the small metal ions being inserted in the interstices. This idea was of great use to Bragg and his coworkers in their successful attack on the structures of many silicate minerals.

It often occurs in crystals containing the larger cations (K⁺, Rb⁺, Cs⁺, Ba⁺⁺, NH₄⁺, etc.) that these large cations and the

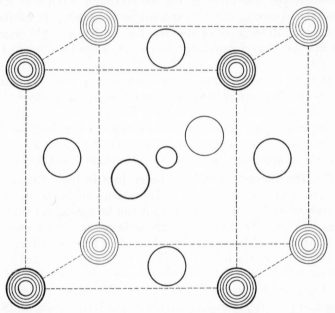

Fig. 47-4.—The perovskite structure (KMgF₃, etc.). The small circle represents Mg⁺⁺, the large shaded circles K⁺, and the large open circles F⁻.

anions together form a closest-packed array. An example of this is the KMgF₃ arrangement (the so-called perovskite structure), shown in Figure 47-4. It is seen that K⁺, with radius 1.33 Å, and 3F⁻, with radius 1.36 Å, together are in cubic closest packing, with the small ions Mg⁺⁺ in the centers of fluorine octahedra. A similar arrangement of alkali and halogen ions is also shown by the potassium chlorostannate structure, Figure 46-2, and by the structures reported for Cs₃Tl₂Cl₉, Cs₃As₂Cl₉, and similar substances.[1]

[1] J. L. Hoard and L. Goldstein, *J. Chem. Phys.* **3**, 117, 199 (1935).

47c. Closest-packed Structures Containing Non-equivalent Spheres.—Although the cubic and hexagonal arrangements described above are the only closest-packed arrangements of equivalent spheres, there is an infinite number of other arrangements which do not differ greatly from them. These are the closest-packed arrangements of spheres of the same size which, however, are not all crystallographically equivalent. Any sequence of closest packed layers, such as ABCBACBC···, is just as close packed as these two; each sphere is in contact with twelve others, which are arranged about it either as in cubic or as in hexagonal closest packing. These arrangements, which differ so little from the other two, are found to have some importance.

In Figure 47-5 there are shown the four possible ways of superimposing closest-packed layers so that only two kinds of non-equivalent layers are present. The simplest of these, called double-hexagonal closest packing, corresponds to the sequence ABACABAC···, repeating after four layers. It involves alternation of layers (A) with adjacent layers arranged as in cubic closest packing and of layers (B and C) with adjacent layers arranged as in hexagonal closest packing.[1] This type of closest packing was first found[2] for the oxygen ions in brookite, the orthorhombic form of titanium dioxide, and for the oxygen and fluorine ions in topaz,[3] $Al_2SiO_4F_2$. It has since been reported for the halogens in one modification of cadmium iodide,[4] in mercuric bromide,[5] and in mercuric chloride,[6] and for chlorine and hydroxyl in CdOHCl.[7] It has been found, moreover, that modifications of cadmium bromide and nickel bromide exist for which the sequence of layers A, B, and C of bromine atoms is largely a random one.[8]

[1] The structure can accordingly be described by the sequence $c\, h\, c\, h$···, indicating alternation of cubic and hexagonal closest packing. The three other structures have the similar sequences $h\, c\, c\, h\, c\, c$···, $h\, h\, c\, h\, h\, c$···, and $h\, h\, c\, c\, h\, h\, c\, c$···.

[2] L. Pauling and J. H. Sturdivant, Z. Krist. **68**, 239 (1928).

[3] L. Pauling, Proc. Nat. Acad. Sci. **14**, 603 (1928).

[4] O. Hassel, Z. f. phys. Chem. **B22**, 333 (1933).

[5] H. J. Verweel and J. M. Bijvoet, Z. Krist. **77**, 122 (1931).

[6] H. Braekken and L. Harang, ibid. **68**, 123 (1928).

[7] J. L. Hoard and J. D. Grenko, ibid. **87**, 110 (1934).

[8] J. M. Bijvoet and W. Nieuwenkamp, ibid. **86**, 466 (1933); J. A. A. Ketelaar, ibid. **88**, 26 (1934).

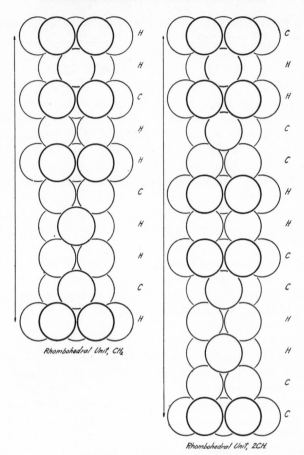

Rhombohedral Unit, CH₄

Rhombohedral Unit, 2CH

Fig. 47-5.—The four closest-packed structures involving

48. THE PRINCIPLES DETERMINING THE STRUCTURE OF COMPLEX IONIC CRYSTALS

Simple ionic substances, such as the alkali halides, have little choice of structure; there exist only a very few relatively stable ionic arrangements corresponding to the formula M^+X^-, and the various factors which influence the stability of the crystal are pitted against one another, with no one factor finding clear expression in the final decision between the sodium chloride and the cesium chloride arrangement. For a complex substance, such as mica, $KAl_3Si_3O_{10}(OH)_2$, or zunyite, $Al_{13}Si_5O_{20}(OH)_{18}Cl$, on the

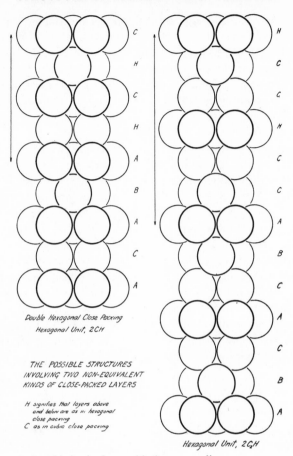

Double Hexagonal Close Packing
Hexagonal Unit, 2CH

THE POSSIBLE STRUCTURES
INVOLVING TWO NON-EQUIVALENT
KINDS OF CLOSE-PACKED LAYERS

H signifies that layers above
and below are as in hexagonal
close packing
C as in cubic close packing

Hexagonal Unit, 2C₂H

two non-equivalent kinds of spheres with the same radius.

other hand, very many conceivable structures differing only slightly in nature and stability can be suggested, and it might be expected that the most stable of these possible structures, the one actually assumed by the substance, will reflect in its various features the various factors which are of significance in determining the structure of ionic crystals. It has been found possible to formulate a set of rules relating to the stability of complex ionic crystals, described in the following paragraphs. These rules were obtained[1] in part by induction from the structures

[1] L. Pauling, "Sommerfeld Festschrift," S. Hirzel, Leipzig, 1928; *J.A.C.S.* 51, 1010 (1929).

known in 1928 and in part by deduction from the equations for the crystal energy. They are not rigorous in their derivation or universal in their application, but they have been found useful as a criterion for the probable correctness of reported structures for complex crystals and as an aid in the x-ray investigation of crystals by making possible the suggestion of reasonable structures for experimental test. The rules are, moreover, of some significance also for molecules and complex ions.

The substances to which the rules apply are those in which the bonds are essentially ionic in character rather than essentially covalent, and in which all or most of the cations are small (with radius less than 0.8 Å) and multivalent, the anions being large (greater than 1.35 Å in radius) and univalent or bivalent. The anions which are most important are oxygen and fluorine.

The differentiation between cations and anions in regard to size and charge is reflected in the rules; markedly different roles are attributed to cations and anions in a crystal. The rules are based upon the concept of the coordination of anions at the corners of a tetrahedron, octahedron, or other polyhedron about each cation, as assumed in the early work of W. L. Bragg on the silicate minerals, and they relate to the nature and interrelations of these polyhedra.

48a. The Nature of the Coordinated Polyhedra.—The first rule, relating to the nature of the coordinated polyhedron of anions about a cation, is the following: *a coordinated polyhedron of anions is formed about each cation, the cation-anion distance being determined by the radius sum and the coordination number of the cation by the radius ratio.*

In crystals containing highly charged cations the most important terms in the expression for the crystal energy are those representing the interaction of each cation and the adjacent anions. The negative Coulomb energy of the cation-anion interactions causes each cation to attract a number of anions, which approach to the equilibrium distance from it. This distance is given with some accuracy by the sum of the crystal radii of cation and anion, as discussed in earlier sections.

If too many anions are grouped around one cation, the anion-anion repulsion becomes strong enough to prevent the anions from approaching this closely to the cation. The increase in Coulomb energy resulting from increase in the cation-anion distance then makes the structure less stable than another structure with fewer anions about each cation.   This phenomenon has been discussed in Section 46d, where it was shown that the transition from cubic to octahedral coordination would occur at about the value 0.732 for ρ, the ratio of univalent radii of anion and cation, and that the transition from octahedral to tetrahedral coordination would occur at about $\rho = 0.414$.   It may be men-

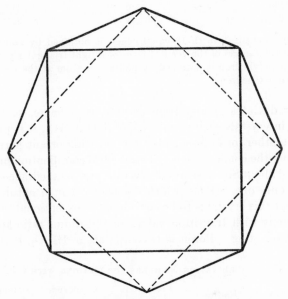

Fig. 48-1.—The square Archimedean antiprism.

tioned also that the square Archimedean antiprism, the polyhedron with sixteen equal edges shown in Figure 48-1, is a more satisfactory ionic coordination polyhedron than the cube, and that the transition from the antiprism to the octahedron would occur at about $\rho = 0.645$.

Values of the radius ratio for various cations relative to oxygen are given in Table 48-2, together with the predicted coordination numbers.   The observed coordination numbers which are given in the fourth column of the table are seen to lie close to the predicted values.   The values in bold-face type are those usually found for the cation.   The other values are observed only in a few crystals.   In the cases where the observed coordination

TABLE 48-1.—VALUES OF THE MINIMUM RADIUS RATIO FOR STABILITY
OF VARIOUS COORDINATION POLYHEDRA

Polyhedron	Coordination number	Minimum radius ratio
Cubo-octahedron	12	1.000
	9*	0.732
Cube	8	.732
Square antiprism	8	.645
	7**	.592
Octahedron	6	.414
Tetrahedron	4	.225

* This polyhedron, with 18 equal edges, is obtained by adding three atoms at the centers of the vertical faces of a right triangular prism.

** This polyhedron is obtained by adding an atom at the center of a face of an octahedron.

number deviates greatly from the expected value, such as 12 for K^+ in crystals such as mica, $KAl_3Si_3O_{10}(OH)_2$, it is probable that the other ions present play the most important part in determining the configuration. Tetrahedral coordination has been observed about Si^{4+} in scores of crystals, and octahedral coordination in only one, SiP_2O_7 (which does not occur in nature); it is clear that this crystal is to be considered as exceptional.

The ions with transition values of the radius ratio are especially interesting. Boron is tricoordinate in H_3BO_3, Be_2BO_3OH

TABLE 48-2.—COORDINATION NUMBERS FOR CATIONS WITH OXYGEN ION

Ion	Radius ratio	Predicted coordination number	Observed coordination number	Strength of electrostatic bond
B^{3+}	0.20	3 or 4	3, 4	1 or $\frac{3}{4}$
Be^{++}	.25	4	4	$\frac{1}{2}$
Li^+	.34	4	4	$\frac{1}{4}$
Si^{4+}	.37	4	4, 6	1
Al^{3+}	.41	4 or 6	4, 5, 6	$\frac{3}{4}$ or $\frac{1}{2}$
Ge^{4+}	.43	4 or 6	4, 6	1 or $\frac{2}{3}$
Mg^{++}	.47	6	6	$\frac{1}{3}$
Na^+	.54	6	6, 8	$\frac{1}{6}$
Ti^{4+}	.55	6	6	$\frac{2}{3}$
Sc^{3+}	.60	6	6	$\frac{1}{2}$
Zr^{4+}	.62	6 or 8	6, 8	$\frac{2}{3}$ or $\frac{1}{2}$
Ca^{++}	.67	8	7, 8, 9	$\frac{1}{4}$
Ce^{4+}	.72	8	8	$\frac{1}{2}$
K^+	.75	9	6, 7, 8, 9, 10, 12	$\frac{1}{9}$
Cs^+	.96	12	12	$\frac{1}{12}$

(hambergite), CaB_2O_4, and many other crystals, and tetracoordinate in $CaB_2Si_2O_8$ (danburite) and duodecitungstoboric acid; in $KH_8B_5O_{12}$ one boron atom is tetracoordinate and four are tricoordinate. Aluminum ion forms oxygen tetrahedra in many aluminosilicates and octahedra in others; it has the coordination numbers 4 and 6 in sillimanite, 5 and 6 in andalusite, and 6 alone in cyanite, all three stable minerals having the composition Al_2SiO_5. Germanium dioxide is dimorphous, showing both a quartz-like and a rutile-like modification. Zirconium is octahedrally coordinated in several crystals, but has coordination number 8 in zircon, $ZrSiO_4$.[1]

The calcite-aragonite transition may be discussed as an illustration of the significance of the radius ratio in determining the choice among alternative structures for a substance.[2] Calcium carbonate crystallizes with the well-known rhombohedral calcite structure, in which calcium has the coordination number six, and the pseudo-hexagonal orthorhombic aragonite structure, in which calcium has the coordination number nine. The choice of these structures by univalent nitrates, bivalent carbonates, and trivalent borates is shown in the following table, together with the ratios of univalent radii of the cations and oxygen:

	ρ		ρ		ρ	
Calcite structure	LiNO$_3$	0.34	MgCO$_3$	0.47	ScBO$_3$	0.60
	NaNO$_3$	.54	ZnCO$_3$	.50	InBO$_3$	.59
			CdCO$_3$	.65	YBO$_3$	.68
			CaCO$_3$	.67		
Aragonite structure	KNO$_3$	0.76	CaCO$_3$	0.67	LaBO$_3$	0.79
			SrCO$_3$	.75		
			BaCO$_3$	.87		
RbNO$_3$ structures	RbNO$_3$	0.84				
	CsNO$_3$	.96				

It is seen that the transition occurs at about $\rho = 0.67$, and that this is the value of ρ for the dimorphous substance calcium car-

---

[1] The relation of radius ratio to the formulas of oxygen acids has been discussed by L. Pauling, *J.A.C.S.* **55**, 1895 (1933); see also E. Zintl and W. Morawietz, *Z. anorg. allgem. Chem.* **236**, 372 (1938).

[2] V. M. Goldschmidt, "Geochemische Verteilungsgesetze der Elemente," VII; V. M. Goldschmidt and H. Hauptmann, *Nach. Ges. Wiss. Göttingen*, **1932**, 53.

bonate.   At $\rho \cong 0.85$ transition occurs to other structures, shown
by rubidium nitrate and cesium nitrate, in which the univalent
cation probably has the coordination number twelve.

**48b. The Number of Polyhedra with a Common Corner.   The
Electrostatic Valence Rule.**—In silica crystals, SiO_2, each silicon
ion is surrounded by four oxygen ions[1] at tetrahedron corners.
In order that the stoichiometric ratio 1 Si:2 O be retained it is
accordingly necessary that each oxygen ion act as a corner of two
tetrahedra on the average.   This might be achieved by having
alternate oxygen ions serve as corners of one tetrahedron and
three tetrahedra, or in other such ways; the following *electrostatic valence rule* requires, however, that each oxygen ion serve
as a corner of two tetrahedra: Let ze be the electric charge of a
cation and ν its coordination number; we then define the *strength
of the electrostatic bond* to each coordinated anion as

$$s = \frac{z}{\nu}$$

and make the postulate that *in a stable ionic structure the valence
of each anion, with changed sign, is exactly or nearly equal to the
sum of the strengths of the electrostatic bonds to it from the adjacent
cations;* that is, that

$$\zeta = \sum_i s_i = \sum_i \frac{z_i}{\nu_i}, \qquad (48\text{-}1)$$

in which $- \zeta e$ is the electric charge of the anion and the summation is taken over the cations at the centers of all the polyhedra
of which the anion forms a corner.

In justification of the rule it may be pointed out that it leads
to stability of the crystal by placing the anions with large negative charges in positions with large positive potentials, inasmuch
as the bond strength for a cation is an approximate measure of
the contribution of the cation to the positive potential at the
polyhedron corner (the factor $1/\nu$ corresponding to the larger
cation-anion distance and the greater number of adjacent anions
in the case of cations with larger coordination number).   It has

---

[1] Here, as elsewhere in this chapter, the use of the word ion is to be
interpreted as meaning that the bonds are largely ionic but not necessarily
of the extreme ionic type.

been shown by Professor W. L. Bragg[1] that the rule can be given a simple interpretation and justification in terms of lines of force. Lines of force start from cations in numbers proportional to their valence, and end on anions. We divide these lines of force for each cation equally among the bonds to the corners of its coordinated polyhedron; the rule than states that each anion receives from the cations to which it is coordinated enough lines of force to satisfy its valence. It is not necessary for lines of force to connect distant ions, and in consequence the crystal is stable.

This simple rule restricts greatly the acceptable structures for a substance, and it has been found useful in the determination of the structures of complex ionic crystals, including especially the silicate minerals. The rule is satisfied nearly completely by most of the structures which have been reported for the silicate minerals, deviations by as much as $\pm 1/6$ being rare. Somewhat larger deviations from the rule are occasionally found for substances prepared in the laboratory, for which as great stability as for minerals is not expected.

Values of electrostatic bond strengths are given in Table 48-2. It is seen that an oxygen ion ($\zeta = 2$) may be satisfied by two silicon bonds, one silicon bond plus two octahedral aluminum bonds, one silicon bond plus three octahedral magnesium bonds, four octahedral aluminum bonds, three titanium bonds, and in various other ways. These are exemplified by many crystals:[2] 2 Si in the various forms of silica and in the disilicates, metasilicates, and other silicates in which silicon tetrahedra share corners; $Si + 2Al(6)$ in topaz ($Al_2SiO_4F_2$), muscovite ($KAl_3Si_3O_{10}(OH)_2$), cyanite (Al_2SiO_5), etc.; $Si + 3Mg$ in phlogopite ($KMg_3AlSi_3O_{10}$- $(OH)_2$), olivine (Mg_2SiO_4), etc.; $4Al(6)$ in corundum (Al_2O_3), cyanite etc.; $3Ti$ in rutile, anatase, and brookite (TiO_2); $Si + 2Be$ in phenacite (Be_2SiO_4); $Si + Al(6) + 2Ca(8)$ in garnet (Ca_3Al_2- Si_3O_{12}); $Si + 2Zr(8)$ in zircon ($ZrSiO_4$); $Si + Al(6) + Be(4)$ in beryl ($Be_3Al_2Si_6O_{18}$).

Fluorine and hydroxyl ions are saturated by bonds of total strength 1. This is achieved by two aluminum octahedral bonds, as in hydrargillite ($Al(OH)_3$), with the structure shown in Figure 48-6, topaz ($Al_2SiO_4F_2$), zunyite, described below, and many

---

[1] W. L. Bragg, *Z. Krist.* 74, 237 (1930); "Atomic Structure of Minerals," Cornell University Press, 1937, p. 35.

[2] See W. L. Bragg's "Atomic Structure of Minerals."

other crystals, and also by three magnesium octahedra in brucite, $Mg(OH)_2$, and other crystals.

Many aluminosilicates are based on a complete framework of linked tetrahedra similar to those of the various forms of silica, but involving aluminum ions with coordination number four as well as silicon ions. The oxygen ions common to an aluminum and a silicon tetrahedron are then reached by bonds of total strength 7/4, and require a bond of strength 1/4 for saturation. Such a bond is not provided by a cation with large charge and small radius; it is hence necessary that there be present large univalent or bivalent cations, namely, alkali or alkaline earth ions, to the extent of one alkali ion or one-half an alkaline earth ion for every quadricoordinate aluminum ion. This requirement of the electrostatic valence rule is thoroughly substantiated by the formulas of the zeolites, feldspars, and other aluminosilicates with tetrahedral frameworks, as is shown by the following small list:

Orthoclase, $KAlSi_3O_8$	Heulandite, $CaAl_2Si_7O_{18} \cdot 6H_2O$
Celsian, $BaAl_2Si_2O_8$	Chabazite, $NaAlSi_2O_6 \cdot 3H_2O$
Albite, $NaAlSi_3O_8$	Marialite, $Na_4Al_3Si_9O_{24}Cl$
Anorthite, $CaAl_2Si_2O_8$	Meionite, $Ca_4Al_6Si_6O_{24}(SO_4, CO_3)$
Analcite, $NaAlSi_2O_6 \cdot H_2O$	Nepheline, $NaAlSiO_4$
Natrolite, $Na_2Al_2Si_3O_{10} \cdot 2H_2O$	Kaliophilite, $KAlSiO_4$
Scolecite, $CaAl_2Si_3O_{10} \cdot 3H_2O$	Leucite, $KAlSi_2O_6$
Thomsonite, $NaCa_2Al_5Si_5O_{20} \cdot 6H_2O$	Sodalite, $Na_4Al_3Si_3O_{12}Cl$
Edingtonite, $BaAl_2Si_3O_{10} \cdot 4H_2O$	

It is seen that in all of these crystals the ratio of number of oxygen atoms to number of aluminum atoms and silicon atoms is 2:1, as required for a complete tetrahedral framework, and that the number of alkali and alkaline earth atoms is that required by the argument given above. (In a few cases, such as sodalite, described below, more alkali ion is present, balanced by halogen ion or a similar anion.)

The tetrahedral framework crystals have interesting properties. It is sometimes possible for the alkali and alkaline earth ions to be interchanged with others in solution; this property permits the zeolites to be used for softening water. The water molecules also can be removed and replaced by other molecules without the destruction of the crystal. The presence of definite available positions for occupancy by large cations or water molecules is clearly indicated by the formulas of such isomorphous pairs as natrolite and scolecite, differing in the replacement of $2Na^+ + 2H_2O$ by $Ca^{++} + 3H_2O$.

The structure of sodalite, $Na_4Al_3Si_3O_{12}Cl$, a representative

Fig. 48-2.—A model showing the structure of sodalite, $Na_4Al_3Si_3O_{12}Cl$. SiO_4 and AlO_4 tetrahedra alternate, with shared corners. The large spheres represent chloride ions. The sodium ions are not shown.

crystal of the framework class, is shown in Figure 48-2. It is interesting that the same framework is present in ultramarine (lapis lazuli).[1] In the ultramarines there are present in place of

[1] F. M. Jaeger, Baker Lectures, McGraw-Hill Book Co., New York, 1930

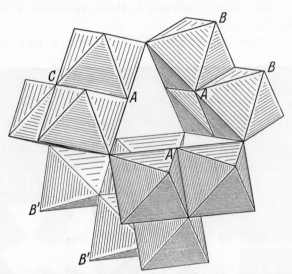

FIG. 48-3.—The group of twelve aluminum octahedra in zunyite. Groups of this type are attached to one another by corners B and B', to silicon tetrahedra by corners A, and to the aluminum tetrahedron by the shared corner C.

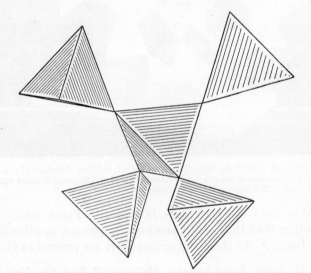

FIG. 48-4.—The group of five silicon tetrahedra in zunyite.

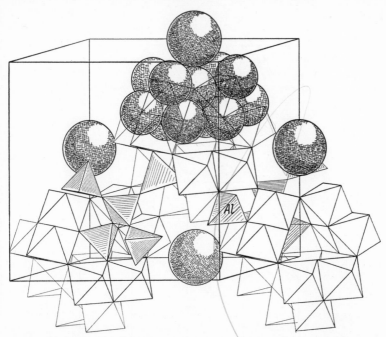

FIG. 48-5.—The structure of the cubic crystal zunyite, Al₁₃Si₅O₂₀(OH)₁₈Cl, show-ing the arrangement of aluminum octahedra and aluminum and silicon tetrahedra. The large spheres represent the chloride ions.

FIG. 48-6.—Layers of aluminum octahedra with shared edges as in hydrargillite, Al(OH)₃.

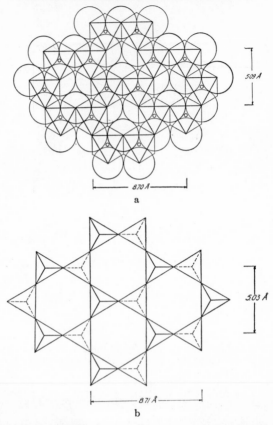

FIG. 48-7.—The fundamental layers of the clays, micas, and chlorites.   a. A hydrargillite layer of octahedra.   The light circles indicate oxygen ions, the heavier ones hydroxyl ions in mica.   b. A tetrahedral layer from β-cristobalite or β-tridymite.   A silicon ion is located at the center of each tetrahedron, and an oxygen ion at each corner.

chlorine sulfur complexes, S_x^{--}, to which the blue color is attributed.   The selenium and tellurium analogues are blood-red and yellow, respectively.

The mineral zunyite, $Al_{13}Si_5O_{20}(OH)_{18}Cl$, may be described as an example of a complex silicate.   Of the thirteen aluminum ions twelve show octahedral coordination, the twelve octahedra forming the group shown in Figure 48-3.   The five silicon ions are present as the tetrahedral complex Si_5O_{16} (Fig. 48-4).   These two complexes are combined together, along with an aluminum tetrahedron, in the way shown in Figure 48-5.   Of the anions in

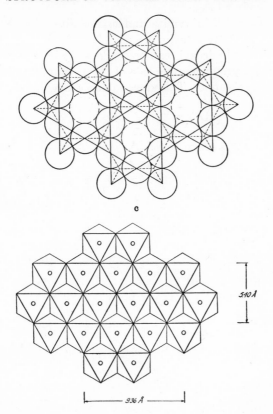

FIG. 48-7.—c. A tetrahedral layer in which all the tetrahedra point in the same direction.   d. A complete layer of octahedra (brucite layer).

the formula $4\ O^{--}$ are held by two silicon tetrahedra, $12\ O^{--}$ by a silicon tetrahedron and two aluminum octahedra, and $18\ OH^{-}$ by two aluminum octahedra; these all satisfy the electrostatic valence rule.   The four remaining oxygen ions are common to an aluminum tetrahedron and three aluminum octahedra, with total bond strength $2\frac{1}{4}$.   It is to balance this excess of bond strength that the chloride ion is introduced.

The clay minerals, micas, and chlorites make an interesting group.[1]   In hydrargillite, $Al(OH)_3$, there are pseudo-hexagonal layers of octahedra as shown in Figure 48-6, and linked tetrahedral layers with almost the same dimensions occur as part of

---

[1] L. Pauling, *Proc. Nat. Acad. Sci.* **16**, 123, 578 (1930).

the framework of tridymite and cristobalite (Fig. 48–7). By turning all of the tetrahedra of such a layer in the same direction, their unshared hydroxyls can be condensed with three-fourths of the hydroxyl groups on one side of the hydrargillite layer, with elimination of water. This gives a double layer, as shown on the

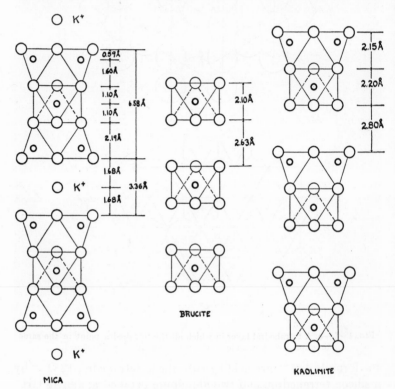

FIG. 48-8.—The structures of mica, brucite, and kaolinite, showing the sequence of layers normal to the cleavage planes. Large circles represent O^- or OH^- (or K^+ when so marked), small ones Si^{4+} or Al^{3+} at tetrahedron centers and Mg^{++} or Al^{3+} at octahedron centers.

right of Figure 48-8; it represents a layer of kaolin, with formula $Al_2Si_2O_5(OH)_4$. The complete crystal contains these neutral layers loosely piled together; the layers are easily separated, making the substance soft and giving it pronounced basal cleavage. (The three modifications of kaolin, kaolinite, dickite, and nacrite, differ in the way in which the layers are superimposed.[1])

[1] J. W. Gruner, *Z. Krist.* **83**, 75, 394 (1932); **85**, 345 (1933).

If layers of silicon tetrahedra are condensed on both sides of a hydrargillite layer there is obtained a substance of composition $Al_2Si_4O_{10}(OH)_2$. This is the clay mineral pyrophyllite. The substance $Mg_3Si_4O_{10}(OH)_2$ obtained similarly from a brucite layer (Fig. 48-9) is the mineral talc. Both of these substances, involving the loose superposition of neutral layers, are very soft, with extreme basal cleavage.[1]

Fig. 48-9.—Layers of magnesium octahedra in brucite, $Mg(OH)_2$.

By the replacement of one-fourth of the silicon ions in a talc or pyrophyllite layer by aluminum ions there is obtained a layer with a negative electric charge, corresponding to the composition $[Mg_3AlSi_3O_{10}(OH)_2]^-$ or $[Al_2AlSi_3O_{10}(OH)_2]^-$. A neutral crystal can be built up by alternating these layers with layers of potassium ions or other alkali ions, which fit into the pockets formed by rings of six oxygen ions of each of the adjacent layers (Figs. 48-7 and 48-8). The mica crystals obtained in this way have the composition $KMg_3AlSi_3O_{10}(OH)_2$ (phlogopite) and $KAl_2AlSi_3O_{10}(OH)_2$

---

[1] The structures have been described in detail by J. W. Gruner, *Z. Krist.* **88**, 412 (1934); see also S. B. Hendricks, *ibid.* **99**, 264 (1938), who has reported that there is some randomness of superposition of the layers.

(muscovite). The general formula of the mica minerals can be written as (K, Na) $X_nAlSi_3O_{10}(OH, F)_2$, with $X = Al^{3+}$, Mg^{++}, Fe^{3+}, Fe^{++}, Mn^{3+}, Mn^{++}, Ti^{4+}, Li^+ (ions with coordination number 6), and n lying between 2 and 3. It is interesting that in lithium micas (lepidolite, zinnwaldite) the lithium ions are in the octahedral layers and not in the positions occupied by potassium ion.

In the margarites or brittle micas the potassium ions are largely replaced by calcium ions, the ideal composition of margarite being $CaX_nAl_2Si_2O_{10}(OH)_2$. In talc and pyrophyllite the layers are electrically neutral, and are held together only by van der Waals forces; these crystals are accordingly very soft, and feel soapy to the touch as do graphite crystals. To separate the layers in mica it is necessary to break the electrostatic bonds of the univalent potassium ions, so that the micas are not so soft, and thin plates are sufficiently elastic to straighten out after being bent. Separation of layers in the brittle micas involves breaking bonds of bivalent calcium ions; these minerals are hence harder and are brittle, but still show perfect basal cleavage. The sequence of hardness of the minerals on the Mohs scale is the following: talc and pyrophyllite, 1–2; the micas, 2–3, the brittle micas, $3\frac{1}{2}$ – 5.

By replacing one-third of the magnesium ions in a brucite layer by aluminum ions a positively charged octahedral layer of composition $[Mg_2Al(OH)_6]^+$ is obtained. Layers of this type can be alternated with negatively charged mica layers to give substances with the structure shown in Figure 48-10. Their general formula is $X_mY_4O_{10}(OH)_8$, with m between 4 and 6; X represents cations with octahedral coordination and Y cations (Al^{3+} and Si^{4+}) with tetrahedral coordination. These are called the chlorite minerals[1] (chlorite, penninite, clinochlore, amesite, etc.).

There are many ways in which the electrostatic valence rule can be used other than those relating directly to the structure of crystals. Some of these are discussed in the following paragraphs.

[1] L. Pauling, *Proc. Nat. Acad. Sci.* 16, 578 (1930). The methods of superposition of layers in the micas and chlorites have been discussed by W. W. Jackson and J. West, *Z. Krist.* 76, 211 (1931), and R. C. McMurchy, *ibid.* 88, 420 (1934).

Although the metasilicates, disilicates, and other silicates in which tetrahedron corners are shared are very stable, the corresponding compounds of phosphorus and sulfur are unstable. The explanation of this is the following: an oxygen ion shared by two silicon tetrahedra satisfies the electrostatic valence rule, whereas there is an infraction by $\frac{1}{2}$ for the common corner of two phosphorus tetrahedra and by 1 for two sulfur tetrahedra. In consequence the pyrophosphates and metaphosphates are unstable—they do not occur at all as minerals and in solution they hydrolyze easily to orthophosphates—and the pyrosulfates are exceedingly unstable. It is for the same reason that silicon dioxide is stable but phosphorus pentoxide and sulfur trioxide combine with water with great avidity.

The electrostatic valence rule can be satisfied for sulfuric acid by the formation of OHO hydrogen bonds between molecules, the strength of the electrostatic bond of a shared proton being taken as $\frac{1}{2}$. This situation occurs in many crystals, in which for each of two adjacent oxygen ions, presumably bonded together by a proton, the sum of bond strengths from other cations is 3/2. Examples of this are diaspore (Fig. 40-4), KH_2PO_4, and $(NH_4)_2H_3IO_6$ (Fig. 40-3). It has been mentioned in Chapter IX that the proton between two oxygen ions is closer to one than to the other; it seems wise[1] in some cases to divide

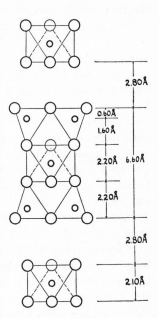

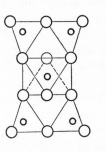

CHLORITE

FIG. 48-10.—The sequence of layers normal to the cleavage plane of the chlorite minerals, showing the alternation of mica layers such as $[Mg_3AlSi_3O_{10}(OH)_2]^-$ with charged brucite-like layers $[Mg_3Al(OH)_6]^+$.

[1] C. A. Beevers and C. M. Schwartz, Z. Krist. 91, 157 (1935).

the total bond strength unequally, in about the ratio 3/4:1/4.
The acid strengths in the sequence $Si(OH)_4$, $PO(OH)_3$,
$SO_2(OH)_2$, $ClO_3(OH)$ can be discussed qualitatively in a simple
way. The bonds from the central atoms have the strengths 1
5/4, 3/2, and 7/4, respectively, leaving each oxygen atom with
further bonding power of 1, 3/4, 1/2, and 1/4, respectively, for
hydrogen. In consequence silicic acid is a very weak acid, phosphoric acid is a weak acid, sulfuric acid is a strong acid, and
perchloric acid is a very strong acid.[1] (This argument is valid
even for molecules containing single and double covalent bonds
provided that there is nearly complete resonance of the covalent
bonds among all the coordinated oxygen atoms; it is not valid
for acids of such atoms as molybdenum, which are able to form
double covalent bonds with some of the adjacent oxygen atoms
and single bonds with others.[2])

In hydrargillite and similar structures involving aluminum octahedra with shared hydroxyl ions the electrostatic valence rule
is satisfied as for silicic acid; $Al(OH)_3$ is hence expected to be
about as strong an acid as $Si(OH)_4$. An aluminum tetrahedron
with corners shared with silicon tetrahedra is, however, similar
to the perchlorate ion, and the acid obtained by replacing the
potassium ion of mica by hydrogen ion should be very strong.
This has been verified by experiment for the acid obtained from
clays by replacement of their alkali ions by hydrogen ion.[3] The
alkali aluminates $MAlO_2$ are salts of acids obtained by the polymerization of tetrahedral $Al(OH)_4$ groups.[4]

48c. The Sharing of Polyhedron Corners, Edges, and Faces.—
Characteristic features of the structure of complex ionic crystals
other than those included within the field of application of the
electrostatic valence rule can be summarized in further rules dealing with the sharing of polyhedron corners, edges, and faces.
The electrostatic valence rule indicates the number of polyhedra

---

[1] See A. Kossiakoff and D. Harker, *J.A.C.S.* **60**, 2047 (1938).

[2] The infractions of the electrostatic valence rule observed for the
heteropoly acids of tungsten and molybdenum (J. F. Keggin, *Proc. Roy.
Soc.* A144, 75 (1934); J. A. Santos, *ibid.* A150, 309 (1935); A. J. Bradley
and J. W. Illingworth, *ibid.* A157, 113 (1936)) are indicated by the values
of interatomic distances to be due to this phenomenon.

[3] Personal communication from Professor Richard Bradfield of Cornell
University.

[4] T. F. W. Barth, *J. Chem. Phys.* **3**, 323 (1935).

with a common corner but makes no prediction as to the number of corners common to two polyhedra; that is, as to whether they share one corner only, two corners defining an edge, or three or more corners defining a face.   In rutile, brookite, and anatase, for example, each oxygen ion is common to three titanium octahedra, but the number of edges shared by each octahedron with adjoining octahedra is two in rutile, three in brookite, and four in anatase.   The significance of this difference in structure is contained in the following rule: *the presence of shared edges and especially of shared faces in a coordinated structure decreases its stability; this effect is large for cations with large valence and small coordination number.*

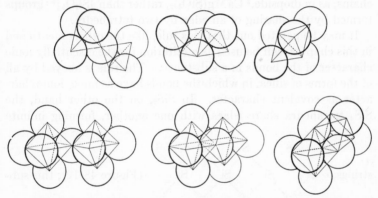

Fig. 48-11.—The sharing of a corner, an edge, and a face by a pair of tetrahedra and by a pair of octahedra.

The decrease in stability arises from the cation-cation Coulomb terms.   The sharing of an edge between two regular tetrahedra brings the cations at their centers to a distance from each other only 0.58 times that obtaining in case the tetrahedra share a corner only; and the sharing of a face decreases this distance to 0.33 times that for a shared corner (Fig. 48-11).   The corresponding positive Coulomb terms cause a large increase in crystal energy and decrease in stability of the crystal to accompany the sharing of edges and faces, especially for highly charged cations. The effect is less for octahedra than for tetrahedra, the interatomic-distance ratios[1] being 0.71 and 0.58 in place of 0.58 and 0.33.

[1] These values are for undistorted polyhedra.   Some compensating distortion always occurs, as discussed in a later paragraph.

In agreement with this rule, it is observed that silicon tetrahedra tend to share only corners with other silicon tetrahedra or other polyhedra.   No crystal is known in which two silicon tetrahedra share an edge or a face, and in most of the silicate structures only corners are shared between silicate tetrahedra and other polyhedra also.   This rule leads to the formation of framework structures such as that shown in Figure 48-2, rather than the more compact structures which could be built by the sharing of edges and faces.   It requires that metasilicates (and also metaphosphates and related substances) contain rings of three or more tetrahedra with shared corners ($[Si_3O_9]^{6-}$ in benitoite,[1] $BaTiSi_3O_9$, $[Si_6O_{18}]^{12-}$ in beryl,[2] $Be_3Al_2Si_6O_{18}$, etc.) or infinite chains, as in diopside,[3] $CaMg(SiO_3)_2$, rather than $[Si_2O_6]^{4-}$ groups formed by the sharing of an edge by two tetrahedra.

It may be pointed out that this rule, like the others mentioned in this chapter, can be used as a criterion for the essentially ionic character of the bonds in a substance.   The rule is obeyed by all of the forms of silica, in which the bonds have as much ionic character as covalent character.   In SiS_2, on the other hand, the SiS_4 tetrahedra share edges with one another, forming infinite

$$\text{strings, }\cdots Si \begin{smallmatrix} S & & S & & S & & S \\ \diagup & \diagdown \diagup & & \diagdown \diagup & & \diagdown \diagup & \\ & Si & & Si & & Si & \\ \diagdown \diagup & & \diagdown \diagup & & \diagdown \diagup & & \diagdown \\ S & & S & & S & & S \end{smallmatrix} \cdots \text{(Figure 48-12); this sub-}$$

stantiates the idea that the Si—S bonds are essentially covalent (Sec. 12).

It is interesting that rutile, with only two shared edges per octahedron, is reported to be more stable than brookite and anatase, and, moreover, that many substances MX_2 have the rutile structure, whereas only titanium dioxide has been reported to have the brookite and anatase structures.

Another rule relating to the sharing of corners, edges, and faces is the following: *in a crystal containing different cations those with large valence and small coordination number tend not to share polyhedron elements with each other.*   This rule expresses the fact that

[1] W. H. Zachariasen, *Z. Krist.* **74**, 139 (1930).
[2] W. L. Bragg and J. West, *Proc. Roy. Soc.* **A111**, 691 (1926).
[3] B. E. Warren and W. L. Bragg, *Z. Krist.* **69**, 168 (1928).

cations with large electric charges tend to be as far apart from each other as possible, in order to reduce their contribution to the Coulomb energy of the crystal.

The rule requires that in silicates the silicon tetrahedra share no elements with each other if the oxygen-silicon ratio be equal

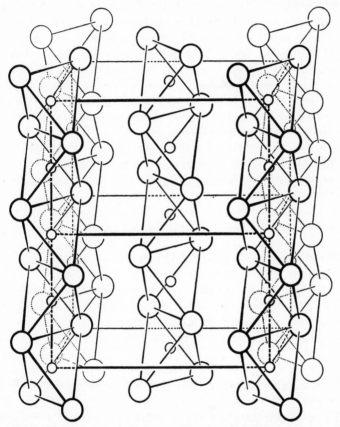

FIG. 48-12.—The structure of the crystal SiS₂; the small circles represent silicon atoms, the larger ones sulfur atoms (Strukturbericht).

to or greater than four. This is found to be true in general (topaz, zircon, olivine, other orthosilicates). Most of the few exceptional substances now known contain extra oxygen atoms in the form of hydroxyl ions. These include the clay minerals, micas, and chlorites, discussed above, and also the mineral hemimorphite, $Zn_4Si_2O_7(OH)_2 \cdot H_2O$, in which there is a disilicate group.[1]

[1] T. Ito and J. West, *Z. Krist.* **83**, 1 (1932).

There is one crystal, danburite, $CaB_2Si_2O_8$, which has been reported[1] to contain a framework of silicon and boron tetrahedra in which the silicon tetrahedra do not alternate with the boron tetrahedra, as indicated by the rule, but instead occur in Si_2O_7 pairs.

When coordinated polyhedra about cations with large charge do share edges or faces with one another it is to be expected that the repulsion of the cations will lead to deformation of the polyhedra such as to increase the cation-cation distance. This can occur without change in cation-anion distance by decrease in length of the shared edges. It will continue until the effect of the cation-cation repulsion is balanced by the characteristic repulsion of the anions defining the shared edges. Theoretical calculations for rutile and anatase, described in Section 46b, have shown that this effect for edges shared between titanium octahedra leads to an oxygen-oxygen distance of 2.50 Å, in place of the normal distance 2.80 Å. The edges bounding the face shared between two aluminum octahedra in corundum, Al_2O_3, are also 2.50 Å long, and the same edge length has been found for edges shared by aluminum octahedra in other crystals (diaspore, hydrargillite) and for edges shared by other polyhedra.

The shortening of shared edges can be used as another test of the amount of ionic character of the bonds in a substance. In essentially covalent crystals such as niccolite, $NiAs$, and marcasite, FeS_2, there occur MX_6 octahedra which share faces; the edges bounding these faces are, however, longer than unshared edges, instead of shorter, as required by the rule for essentially ionic crystals. In the gas molecules Al_2Cl_6, Al_2Br_6, and Al_2I_6 the edge shared by the two AlX_4 tetrahedra is shorter than the other edges;[2] this shows that the Al—X bonds have appreciable ionic character.

The silicate minerals, many of which have been thoroughly investigated by x-ray methods, provide excellent illustrations for the rules given in the preceding paragraphs. The structures of these minerals have been described by W. L. Bragg in his recent book[3] "Atomic Structure of Minerals," to which the attention of the reader is directed.

[1] C. Dunbar and F. Machatschki, *ibid.* **76**, 133 (1930).
[2] K. J. Palmer and N. Elliott, *J.A.C.S.* **60**, 1852 (1938).
[3] Cornell University Press, 1937.

CHAPTER XI

THE METALLIC BOND

49. THE PROPERTIES OF METALS

The elements which are classed as metals display to a larger or smaller extent certain characteristic properties, including high thermal and electrical conductivity, metallic luster, ductility and malleability, power to replace hydrogen in acids, etc. These properties are shown most strikingly by the elements in the lower left region of the periodic table; in fact, metallic character is closely associated with electropositive character, and in general a small value of the electronegativity of an element, as given by the bond-energy method, the electromotive force series, or any similar treatment, corresponds to pronounced metallic properties.

Lorentz[1] advanced a theory of metals which accounts in a qualitative way for some of their characteristic properties, and which has been extensively developed in recent years by application of the quantum mechanics. He thought of a metal as a crystalline arrangement of hard spheres (the metal cations), with free electrons moving in the interstices. This free-electron theory provides a simple explanation of metallic luster and other optical properties, of high thermal and electrical conductivity, of high values of heat capacity and entropy, and of certain other properties.

One of the most interesting of these properties is the small temperature-independent paramagnetism shown by many metals, including the alkali metals. It was the discussion of this phenomenon by Pauli[2] in 1927 which initiated the development of the modern electronic theory of metals. The fundamental concept is that there exists in a metal a continuous or partially continuous set of energy levels for the "free" electrons. At the absolute zero the electrons (N in number) would occupy the $N/2$ most stable levels in pairs, and, as required by the Pauli

[1] H. A. Lorentz, "The Theory of Electrons," Teubner, 1916.
[2] W. Pauli, Z. f. Phys. **41**, 81 (1927).

401

exclusion principle, the spins of the electrons of each pair would be opposed, so that the spin magnetic moments of the electrons would not be available for orientation in an applied magnetic field. At higher temperatures some of these pairs are broken, as one of the electrons of a pair is raised to a higher energy level, and the spin moments of these unpaired electrons then make a contribution to the paramagnetic susceptibility of the metal. The number of unpaired electrons increases with increasing temperature; the contribution of one unpaired electron spin to the paramagnetic susceptibility decreases with increasing temperature, however (Sec. 16a), and the two effects are found on quantitative discussion to lead to an approximately temperature-independent paramagnetic susceptibility of the observed order of magnitude.

The quantum-mechanical theory of metals has been extensively developed by Sommerfeld and many other investigators.[1] Its discussion is beyond the scope of this book, however, and we shall instead consider the problem of the structure of metals from a more chemical point of view. The treatment given in the following sections is not to be interpreted as being a rival of the quantum-mechanical theory, but rather as offering an alternative avenue of approach toward the same goal as that of the theoretical physicists.

50. THE NATURE OF THE METALLIC BOND

Let us consider the lithium crystal. It consists of an arrangement of lithium atoms at the points of a body-centered cubic lattice, as shown in Figure 50-1. Each atom has about it as nearest neighbors eight atoms, arranged at the corners of a cube. The distance to each of these neighbors is 3.04 Å. The approximation of this distance to that expected for a one-electron bond or an electron-pair bond between two lithium atoms is of great interest.

[1] A. Sommerfeld, W. V. Houston, and C. Eckart, Z. f. Phys. 47, 1 (1928); J. Frenkel, ibid. 47, 819 (1928); W. V. Houston, ibid. 48, 449 (1928); F. Bloch, ibid. 52, 555 (1928); etc. For summarizing discussions and further references see A. Sommerfeld and N. H. Frank, Rev. Modern Phys. 3, 1 (1931); A. Sommerfeld and H. Bethe, Handbuch der Physik, Vol. 24, 2nd edition; J. C. Slater, Rev. Modern Phys. 6, 209 (1934); N. F. Mott and H. Jones, "The Theory of the Properties of Metals and Alloys," Oxford University Press, 1936; A. H. Wilson, "The Theory of Metals," Cambridge University Press, 1936; H. Fröhlich, "Elektronentheorie der Metalle," J. Springer, Berlin, 1937.

The lithium-lithium one-electron bond distance has been estimated at 3.02 Å by quantum-mechanical methods,[1] and, moreover, the position of the maximum in the electron distribution
function for the free lithium atom, at 1.6 A from the nucleus,[2]
suggests a similar value of about 3.2 Å, since the H—H distance
in the hydrogen molecule-ion is just twice the distance from the
nucleus to the electron distribution maximum in the hydrogen

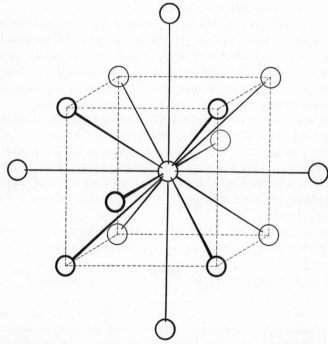

Fig. 50-1.—The cubic body-centered atomic arrangement shown
by lithium and other metal crystals.

atom.   Since the conditions for a one-electron bond are satisfied,
we may picture the lithium crystal as involving bonds of this
type, as well as electron-pair bonds.   These bonds are not fixed,
however, but resonate among the various pairs of atoms.   The

[1] L. Pauling and J. Sherman, *J.A.C.S.* **59**, 1450 (1937); see also H. M.
James, *J. Chem. Phys.* **3**, 9 (1935).
[2] J. Hargreaves, *Proc. Cambridge Phil. Soc.* **25**, 75 (1929); E. B. Wilson,
Jr., *J. Chem. Phys.* **1**, 210 (1933).

structure of the lithium crystal is thus considered to be somewhat similar to that of diborane (Sec. 32), with one-electron bonds and electron-pair bonds in resonance.

It will be observed that in addition to the eight nearest neighbors at 3.04 Å each lithium atom has six neighbors at 3.51 Å, only 15% farther away, and that bonds may be formed to some extent with these atoms also. The body-centered arrangement of a metal crystal may well be considered as involving coordination with fourteen neighbors instead of eight.

The picture of a metal as a structure in which one-electron bonds and electron-pair bonds resonate among several positions suggests that maximum stability will be associated in general with maximum coordination number, since with increase in the number of positions among which the bonds can resonate there will be an increase in the resonance energy stabilizing the system. This conclusion is in agreement with experiment; the characteristic metal structures are the two types of closest packing of spheres, with coordination number twelve, and the body-centered arrangement, with coordination number approaching fourteen. In intermetallic compounds, containing atoms of different sizes, still closer packing, with larger coordination numbers, is sometimes achieved.

Atomic arrangements, interatomic distances, and other topics are discussed in the following sections from the point of view just developed.

It may be mentioned that the postulate that an atom in a metal shows great versatility in the formation of bonds, and that there is little difference in stability of structures involving varied types of coordination, leads to an explanation of the characteristic metallic properties of malleability and ductility. During deformation of a crystal some of the atoms are moved from their stable positions relative to adjacent atoms. In general this displacement leads to great decrease in strength of the interatomic bonds, because of the unfavorable configurations produced by the deformation, and the crystal is fractured. In a metal, however, an atom is not greatly restricted in regard to the number and direction of the bonds which it can form with adjacent atoms, and in consequence it can form bonds after deformation of the original structure which are approximately as strong as the original bonds.

This gives to a metal its characteristic ability to heal itself after deformation.

51. THE ATOMIC ARRANGEMENT IN CRYSTALS OF METALLIC ELEMENTS

51a. Closest-packed Structures.—If stability of a metal crystal were determined by the number of bonds formed at a minimum interatomic distance, with no contribution of longer bonds, the structures with closest packing would be the most stable. These structures, which have been described in Section 47, involve contact between each atom and twelve nearest neighbors. (The next interatomic distances are 41% larger, and presumably have little significance.) It is noteworthy that of the fifty-one metallic elements listed in Table 51-1 thirty crystallize with either the cubic closest-packed or the hexagonal closest-packed arrangement or with both. The close approximation of metal atoms in these crystals to mutually attractive spheres is further shown by the values observed for the axial ratio c/a of the hexagonal closest-packed structures, as tabulated below.

Be	1.585	La	1.615	Ti	1.601	Ru	1.583
Mg	1.624	Ce	1.62	Zr	1.589	Os	1.579
Ca	1.64	Pr	1.620	Hf	1.587	Co	1.624
Y	1.587	Nd	1.608	Cr	1.626	Ni	1.64
Tl	1.600	Er	1.63	Re	1.615	Zn	1.856
						Cd	1.886

Of the twenty-one values nineteen lie within four percent of the theoretical value $2\sqrt{2}/\sqrt{3} = 1.633$ which makes the twelve smallest interatomic distances equal; the two exceptional substances, zinc and cadmium, are discussed below, together with several other metals which crystallize with structures obtained from closest-packed arrangements by a deformation which shortens some of the twelve small interatomic distances at the expense of others.[1]

The small difference in nature of the cubic and hexagonal closest-packed arrangements is verified by the approximate equality

---

[1] It is interesting to note (M. L. Fuller, *Phys. Rev.* **54**, 388 (1938)) that zinc in η brass acts like a prolate spheroid and in ϵ brass like an oblate spheroid, and that there is no intermediate phase.

of interatomic distances for the two structures of metals which exist in the corresponding allotropic forms, as shown in the following table:

| | Interatomic distances for | |
Metal	cubic closest packing (A1)	hexagonal closest packing (A3)
Ca	3.932 Å	3.940, 3.955 Å
Co	2.506	2.499, 2.507
Ni	2.487	2.490, 2.490
La	3.754	3.727, 3.754
Ce	3.637	3.630, 3.650
Tl	3.423	3.404, 3.450

51b. Interatomic Distances and Metallic Radii.—In the cubic body-centered structure, observed for fifteen metals, each atom forms eight strong bonds and six weak ones, the former corresponding to the smallest interatomic distance in the crystal and the latter to a distance 15% greater. It seems probable that this structure becomes more stable than the closest-packed structures for certain metals because the eight strong bonds and six weak ones represent a greater total bond energy than the twelve equivalent bonds of the closest-packed structures; and the general observation that increasing strength of bond is accompanied by decreasing interatomic distance suggests that the radius of a metal atom for coordination number twelve should be somewhat greater than that for coordination number eight. The difference is found empirically to amount to about 3%, which is 0.04 to 0.06 Å for most metals. In Figure 51-1 there are represented graphically the observed atomic radii (one-half the interatomic distances) for coordination number twelve[1] (circles) and for coordination number eight, in the cubic body-centered structure (squares). It is seen that for each sequence of atoms a smooth curve can be drawn representing the radii for coordination number twelve, and that the points for coordination number eight fall on the average about 3% below these curves.

The metallic radii of the elements of the third long period are only slightly larger (about 0.02 Å) than those of the corresponding elements of the second long period, and these are 0.10 to 0.15

---

[1] The values for Mn, Zn, Cd, Hg, and In are averages of the radii for the deformed structures which correspond to the twelve contacts of closest packing.

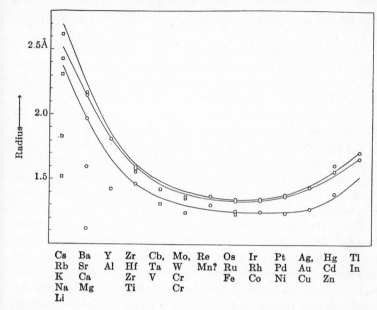

Cs	Ba	Y	Zr	Cb,	Mo,	Re	Os	Ir	Pt	Ag,	Hg	Tl
Rb	Sr	Al	Hf	Ta	W	Mn?	Ru	Rh	Pd	Au	Cd	In
K	Ca		Zr	V	Cr		Fe	Co	Ni	Cu	Zn	
Na	Mg		Ti		Cr							
Li												

FIG. 51-1.—Observed values of metallic radii. The circles correspond to co-ordination number twelve and the squares to coordination number eight (cubic body-centered structure) for the metals listed below the figure.

Å larger than those for the first long period. It is interesting to note that the minimum in the curve for each period falls at about the ninth element in the period, and the following explanation of this can be given. The orbitals which are available for bond formation by the transition elements are the outermost d, s, and p orbitals ($3d$, $4s$, and $4p$ for the iron group elements, etc.), which are nine in number; and with nine electrons available per atom the maximum number of bonds can be formed, since with fewer electrons there is a deficiency of bond electrons and with more a deficiency of bond orbitals, some of the nine orbitals being necessarily occupied by unshared pairs.

It is, in fact, to be observed that the interatomic distance, after falling rapidly in value from the first to the sixth element in each long period, remains nearly constant from the sixth to the tenth, and then begins to increase rapidly. This indicates that the number of valence bonds resonating among the available positions first increases from one to six with increase in the number of outer electrons, but then remains constant at about six. This can be explained[1] on the assumption that of the five d orbitals only about 2.5 are available for bond formation (by hybridization with s and p orbitals). This theory is strongly supported by observed values of the saturation magnetic moments of ferromagnetic metals, and it leads moreover to a reasonable explanation of the phenomenon of ferromagnetism itself.[2]

There are collected in Table 51-2 values of metallic radii for coordination number twelve and eight as given by smooth curves of the type shown in Figure 51-1. (The observed values for some metals correspond to small deviations from these smoothed values, the detailed explanation of which is not known.) It is of great interest that the metallic radii of the transition elements and other metals are very nearly equal in value to the covalent radii for these atoms, as is seen by comparing the values given in Table 51-2 with the corresponding values for octahedral covalent radii (Tables 23-2, 23-4). The octahedral covalent radii are in general slightly smaller than the metallic radii for coordination number eight, as would indeed be expected as a result of the decrease in coordination number. This striking relation between metallic and covalent radii provides very strong support for the idea that metallic bonds are essentially resonating covalent bonds.

Table 51-2 is closely similar to the table of metallic radii published in 1929 by Goldschmidt.[3] It is significant that Goldschmidt originally collected[4] a set of values of "atomic radii" for use in non-ionic crystals without distinguishing between metals and other non-ionic crystals such as diamond, sphalerite, pyrite, etc.; and only later was a distinction made between metallic radii and covalent radii.

51c. Metal Structures Related to Closest-packed Structures. —Zinc and cadmium crystallize with a structure which is identical with hexagonal closest packing except for extension in the direction of the hexagonal axis, the axial ratio c/a having the values 1.856 and 1.886 respectively, which are about fifteen percent greater than the value for closest packing of spheres. In consequence the interatomic distances for the six contacts be-

---

[1] L. Pauling, *Phys. Rev.* **54**, 899 (1938).

[2] L. Pauling, *loc. cit.*, p. 904.

[3] V. M. Goldschmidt, *Trans. Faraday Soc.* **25**, 253 (1929).

[4] V. M. Goldschmidt, "Geochemische Verteilungsgesetze der Elemente," VII, Oslo, 1926.

TABLE 51-1*—THE STRUCTURE OF CRYSTALS OF METALLIC ELEMENTS

Li 3	Be 4												Al 13				
A2 3.04(8)	A3 2.224(6) 2.268(6)												A1 2.858(12)				

Na 11	Mg 12	Al 13
A2 3.72(8)	A3 3.190(6) 3.202(6)	A1 2.858(12)

K 19	Ca 20	Sc 21
A2 4.618(8)	A1 3.932(12) / A3 3.940(6) 3.955(6)	

Ti 22	V 23	Cr 24	Mn 25	Fe 26	Co 27	Ni 28	Cu 29	Zn 30	Ga 31	Ge 32
A3 2.915(6) 2.953(6)	A2 2.627(8)	A2 2.493(8) / A3 2.709(6) 2.717(6) / A12	A6 2.582(8) 2.669(4) / A12 / A13	A1 2.520(12) / A2 2.478(8)	A1 2.506(12) / A3 2.499(6) 2.507(6)	A1 2.487(12) / A3 2.49(6) 2.49(6)	A1 2.551(12)	A3 2.660(6) 2.907(6)	A11 2.437(1) 2.706(2) 2.736(2) 2.795(2)	A4 2.445(4)

Rb 37	Sr 38	Y 39	Zr 40	Cb 41	Mo 42	Ma 43	Ru 44	Rh 45	Pd 46	Ag 47	Cd 48	In 49	Sn 50
A2 4.87(8)	A1 4.296(12)	A3 3.595(6) 3.663(6)	A2 3.13(8) / A3 3.166(6) 3.223(6)	A2 2.853(8)	A2 2.720(8)		A3 2.645(6) 2.699(6)	A1 2.684(12)	A1 2.745(12)	A1 2.884(12)	A3 2.973(6) 3.287(6)	A6 3.242(4) 3.370(8)	A4 2.80(4) / A5 3.016(4) 3.175(2)

Cs 55	Ba 56	Rare Earths 57–71 See below	Hf 72	Ta 73	W 74	Re 75	Os 76	Ir 77	Pt 78	Au 79	Hg 80	Tl 81	Pb 82
A2 5.24(8)	A2 4.343(8)		A3 3.139(6) 3.200(6)	A2 2.854(8)	A2 2.735(8) / A15 2.816(12) 2.519(2) 2.816(4) 3.085(8)	A3 2.735(6) 2.755(6)	A3 2.670(6) 2.730(6)	A1 2.709(12)	A1 2.769(12)	A1 2.878(12)	A10 2.999(6) 3.463(6)	A1 3.423(12) / A3 3.404(6) 3.450(6)	A1 3.492(12)

Th 90	U 92
A1 3.590(12)	A2 2.97(8) / α 2.75(2) 2.84(2) 3.25(4) 3.34(4)

RARE EARTHS

La 57	Ce 58	Pr 59	Nd 60	Er 68
A1 3.754(12) / A3 3.727(6) 3.754(6)	A1 3.637(12) / A3 3.63(6) 3.65(6)	A3 3.638(6) 3.657(6)	A3 3.620(6) 3.657(6)	A3 3.73(6) 3.74(6)

* This table is taken in the main from the summary by M. C. Neuburger, Z. Krist. 93, 1 (1936). The symbols A1 (cubic closest-packed arrangement), A2 (cubic body-centered arrangement), A3 (hexagonal closest-packed arrangement), A4 (diamond arrangement), etc., are those used in the Strukturbericht. The numbers below these symbols are the smallest interatomic distances (in A), followed by the number of corresponding neighboring atoms in parentheses.

TABLE 51-2.—METALLIC RADII

Coordination number		
	Li	Be
12	1.58	1.12
8	1.52	1.07

Coordination number			
	Na	Mg	Al
12	1.92	1.60	1.43
8	1.86	1.55	1.39

Coordination number	K	Ca	Sc	Ti	V	Cr	Mn	Fe	Co	Ni	Cu	Zn	Ga
12	2.38	1.97	1.66	1.47	1.36	1.30	1.27	1.26	1.25	1.25	1.28	1.37	1.53
8	2.31	1.91	1.60	1.42	1.31	1.26	1.24	1.23	1.22	1.22	1.24	1.32	1.48

Coordination number	Rb	Sr	Y	Zr	Cb	Mo	Ma	Ru	Rh	Pd	Ag	Cd	In
12	2.53	2.15	1.82	1.60	1.47	1.39	1.35	1.34	1.34	1.37	1.44	1.54	1.67
8	2.43	2.07	1.76	1.54	1.43	1.36	1.32	1.31	1.31	1.34	1.40	1.49	1.62

Coordination number	Cs	Ba	Rare earths	Hf	Ta	W	Re	Os	Ir	Pt	Au	Hg	Tl
12	2.72	2.24	1.86	1.62	1.49	1.41	1.37	1.35	1.36	1.39	1.46	1.57	1.71
8	2.62	2.17	1.80	1.57	1.44	1.37	1.33	1.31	1.32	1.35	1.42	1.52	1.66

tween each atom and its nearest neighbors in the basal plane are appreciably smaller than those for the other six significant contacts, with three atoms in the plane above and three atoms in the plane below. The interatomic distances are 2.660 and 2.907 Å for zinc and 2.973 and 3.287 Å for cadmium. The expected values for coordination number twelve lie between these values for each element.

From the interatomic distances the conclusion is to be drawn that the bonds in the hexagonal layers of atoms in these metals are stronger than those between layers. This conclusion is substantiated by the properties of the crystals, which show basal cleavage and have larger values of the compressibility, coefficient of thermal expansion, and electrical resistance in the direction perpendicular to the basal plane than in this plane. Moreover, measurements of the intensities of x-ray reflections have shown that the restoring forces of oscillation of the atoms in the basal plane are greater than those for oscillation out of this plane.[1]

The structure of mercury (A10) is closely related to that of zinc and cadmium; it is obtained from cubic closest packing by compression along one of the three-fold axes of the cube, the hexagonal layers of atoms thus being brought closer to one another than in a closest-packed structure. Each mercury atom has three neighbors in the layer above and three in the layer below at the interatomic distance 2.999 Å, and six in the same layer at the somewhat larger distance 3.463 Å. Thus mercury, like zinc and cadmium, forms six strong bonds and six weaker bonds, but it differs from its congeners in the directions of the bonds.

The structures of selenium and tellurium, of arsenic, antimony, and bismuth, and of silicon, germanium, and grey tin involve two, three, and four nearest neighbors, respectively. These structures are interpreted reasonably as involving covalent bonds between each atom and its nearest neighbors. These bonds are formed to the number indicated by the usual valence of the element and also by the octet rule. It was suggested by Hume-Rothery[2] that the sequence of number of nearest neighbors could

---

[1] G. W. Brindley, *Nature* **137**, 315 (1936); *Phil. Mag.* **21**, 790 (1936); C. Zener, *Phys. Rev.* **49**, 122 (1936); G. W. Brindley and P. Ridley, *Nature* **140**, 461 (1937); G. E. M. Jauncey and W. A. Bruce, *Phys. Rev.* **51**, 1062, 1067 (1937); W. A. Bruce and E. M. McNatt, *ibid.* **51**, 1065 (1937).

[2] W. Hume-Rothery, *Phil. Mag.* **9**, 65 (1930); **11**, 649 (1931).

be continued further to the left in the periodic table, leading to the expected values five for gallium, indium, and thallium (and perhaps boron and aluminum), six for zinc, cadmium, and mercury, seven for copper, silver, and gold, and so on. The rule does not have general validity, but it is given significance by its compatibility with the zinc-cadmium and mercury structures.

A quantitative theoretical treatment of the rule has not been reported. The application of the usual valence theory to zinc, cadmium, and mercury leads to the expectation of the formation of two bonds by each atom; ten of the twelve outermost electrons may be considered to occupy the five $3d$, $4d$, or $5d$ orbitals, as in the bivalent ions, leaving two electrons for bond formation. There is, however, the alternative possibility that the atoms in the metals make the maximum use of the stable orbitals for forming bonds. There are nine of these orbitals; for zinc these are the five $3d$, one $4s$, and three $4p$ orbitals, and for cadmium and mercury the corresponding orbitals with increased total quantum number. Twelve electrons can be placed in these orbitals by pairing six and leaving six unpaired electrons occupying six orbitals, and each atom can then form six covalent bonds with its neighbors, corresponding to the Hume-Rothery rule.

It is not possible to predict that the six bonds will tend to stay localized rather than to resonate among twelve positions of a closest-packed structure. (In zinc and its congeners the covalent bonds are not completely localized, but tend to occupy the positions toward the nearest neighbors to a greater extent than those toward the others.) It seems probable that the decision regarding localization of bonds is determined in large part by the topological properties of the structure with localized bonds. The zinc-cadmium and mercury structures, with six strong bonds, are simple and stable; on the other hand, it is difficult to construct an atomic arrangement in which each atom forms seven strong bonds and five weak bonds, as indicated for copper, silver, and gold by the Hume-Rothery rule; and it may be for this reason that these metals crystallize with a closest-packed structure, with seven covalent bonds resonating among twelve positions.

The prediction that five strong bonds should be evident for gallium, indium, and thallium is not verified. In gallium each atom has one nearest neighbor at 2.447 Å, and two each at 2.706, 2.736, and 2.795 Å, with others at 3.73 Å and larger distances.

It might be suggested tentatively that of the many electronic structures contributing by resonance to the normal state of the metal the one corresponding to occupancy of six orbitals (such as five $3d$ and one $4s$) by electron pairs, leaving only one unpaired electron for the formation of one covalent bond, plays an important part. Indium crystallizes with a tetragonal structure corresponding to a cubic closest-packed arrangement elongated by seven percent in the direction of one of its four-fold axes. This gives rise to four nearest neighbors of each atom, at 3.242 Å, with eight at the larger distance 3.370 A; the structure may result from an attempt to approximate a structure with five localized strong bonds. Thallium assumes both the cubic and the hexagonal closest-packed arrangement.

Uranium exists in two known modifications, one with the cubic closest-packed structure and the second with a unique structure,[1] with orthorhombic symmetry, which is obtained from hexagonal closest packing by a deformation which gives each atom four nearest neighbors, at 2.80 Å. The tendency of the uranium atom in the metal crystal to form four strong bonds may be explained by assuming that two of the six valence electrons occupy the stable $7s$ orbital, leaving four electrons for bond formation. It is of interest to note that the four nearest neighbors of each atom are at four of the five corners of a trigonal bipyramid; the fifth corner may be considered to be occupied by the unshared electron pair, and the configuration then becomes analogous to that of the molecules PF_5, PF_3Cl_2, and PCl_5.

51d. Other Metal Structures.—In silicon, germanium, and grey tin, which crystallize with the diamond arrangement, each atom has four nearest neighbors which surround it tetrahedrally; in these substances, as in arsenic, antimony, bismuth, selenium, and tellurium, the covalent bonds are restricted to definite positions.

White tin crystallizes with a tetragonal structure (A5) which can be described as obtained from the diamond arrangement by great shortening of one of the cube edges. The tetrahedron of four atoms about each atom, at the Sn—Sn distance 3.016 Å, is very flat, the four bonds being nearly coplanar; in addition there

[1] C. W. Jacob and B. E. Warren, *J.A.C.S.* 59, 2588 (1937); A. H. Cash unpublished investigation.

are two neighbors which are nearly as close, at 3.175 Å, one above and one below the median plane of the flattened tetrahedron. A recently discovered modification of tungsten crystallizes with the unique cubic A15 arrangement. The tungsten atoms in this crystal are of two kinds; those of the first kind have twelve nearest neighbors, at 2.816 Å, and those of the second kind two neighbors at 2.519, four at 2.816, and eight at 3.085 Å, giving an effective coordination number of fourteen. This structure can accordingly be considered as representing a transition between cubic closest packing, with coordination number twelve, and the cubic body-centered arrangement, with effective coordination number fourteen.

Manganese is an unconventional metal; it crystallizes in three modifications, each with an unusual structure. In the α modification, with the A12 arrangement, there are four kinds of manganese atoms, each having from twelve to sixteen neighbors at distances between 2.24 and 2.96 Å, and in the β modification (A13) there are two kinds of atoms, each with twelve neighbors at distances between 2.36 and 2.67 Å. The structure of γ-manganese is obtained from cubic closest packing by shortening one edge of the unit cube; each atom has eight neighbors at 2.582 Å and four at 2.669 Å. Chromium has also been reported to have a modification with the A12 structure, in addition to those with the A2 and A3 structures. The explanation of the stability of these modifications of manganese and chromium is not known.

52. THE METALLIC BOND AND THE PROPERTIES OF METALS

We have seen that the metallic radii for each of the three sequences of transition elements have their minima between the sixth and the tenth atoms of the sequence, and we have interpreted this as resulting from the presence of metallic bonds of the maximum strength possible with the available valence orbitals. As the number of electrons per atom increases from one to six there is a corresponding increase in the number of electron pairs effective in binding the atoms together in the metal; with further increase in the number of electrons per atom, however, the number of bond electrons first remains constant at about six, and then becomes smaller, through operation of the exclusion principle, as discussed above. The increase in bond strength to a maximum makes itself evident not only in the interatomic distance but also in many other properties. The closely related properties density and atomic volume show maxima and minima, respectively, at nickel, ruthenium, and osmium. The compressibility for the elements of the first transition group has a minimum at nickel, its values (x 10^7) at 20° being K 31.7, Ca 5.7, Cr 0.9, Mn 0.84, Fe 0.63, Ni 0.40, Cu 0.75, Zn 1.7, Ga 2.1. The yield point, tensile strength, and hardness all have their maximum values in the region between the sixth and tenth elements in each sequence. The melting points of the elements similarly indicate maximum bond strength in this region.[1]

On first consideration it seems surprising that six outer electrons of the iron atom, for example, are involved in bond formation in the metal, since iron is ordinarily bivalent or trivalent, and is hence usually considered to have only two or three valence electrons. However, it has been shown in Section 31 that there is evidence that in the carbonyl, cyanide, and nitrite complexes of the transition elements all of the outer electrons and orbitals of the metal atom are involved in bond formation, so that our new picture of the structure of metals is supported by the new picture of the structure of these complexes.

It is interesting to note that in Figure 51-1 the observed radius for manganese lies above the curve for the other elements of the series. This corresponds to similarly anomalous values of the density, atomic volume, compressibility, melting point, and other properties of the element. The explanation of this behavior of manganese is not known, but it may well be related to the anomalous manganese radius observed for the compounds MnS_2, $MnSe_2$, and $MnTe_2$, discussed in Section 23d, and to the tendency of the element to crystallize with unusual atomic arrangements, involving a wide range of interatomic distances.

53. INTERMETALLIC COMPOUNDS

In the last fifteen years the structures of crystals of many intermetallic compounds have been determined, and there has been

---

[1] The existence of extrema for several properties of the transition elements in the region of the ninth atom of each sequence was discussed by J. D. Bernal (*Trans. Faraday Soc.* **25**, 367 (1929)) in connection with the nature of the metallic bond. Bernal concluded, however, that the interactions involved in the metallic bond are essentially different from those involved in the covalent bond, whereas we have concluded that they are essentially the same.

some progress made in the attack on the difficult problem of the stability of these compounds. The composition of intermetallic compounds, such as Sb_2Tl_7, $PtCu_3$, $MgZn_2$, Cu_5Zn_8, KCd_{13}, etc., bears in general little relation to the customary valences of the metals, and the factors which are significant (relative values of metallic radii, ratio of valence electrons to atomic nuclei, etc.) are at present only partially understood. In the following paragraphs some of the simple structures are described and discussed.

It is interesting to note that many alloys which on first formation involve a random distribution of metal atoms of two or more kinds among the atomic positions provided by the structure assume an ordered arrangement on annealing. This phenomenon has been extensively investigated both experimentally and theoretically during recent years.[1]

53a. Structures Based on the Simple Elementary Structures.— Many intermetallic compounds have structures which involve the regular distribution of metal atoms of two or more kinds among the atomic positions for cubic or hexagonal closest packing or for the cubic body-centered structure. Among the substances with structures of this type based on cubic closest packing are the following: AuCu, PtCu, $AuCu_3$, $PdCu_3$, $PtCu_3$, $CaPb_3$, $CaTl_3$, $CaSn_3$, $CePb_3$, $CeSn_3$, $LaPb_3$, $LaSn_3$, $PrPb_3$, $PrSn_3$. In general there is small difference in radius of the atoms in a compound of this type.

Among the intermetallic compounds which crystallize with structures based on the cubic body-centered structure A2 are the binary compounds CuPd, CuBe, CuZn, AgMg, FeAl, AgZn, AgCd, AuZn, AuCd, NiAl, and NdAl, with the cesium chloride structure. In these crystals each atom has as nearest neighbors, at the corners of a cube about it, eight unlike atoms, whereas in NaTl, LiZn, LiCd, LiGa, LiIn, NaIn, and LiAl, which represent another type of structure based on A2 (B32, Strukturbericht III, p. 19), each atom has as nearest neighbors four like atoms and

---

[1] Representative papers in this field are the following: G. Tammann, "Lehrbuch der Metallographie" L. Voss, Leipzig, 1921, G. Tammann and O. Heusler, *Z. anorg. Chem.* 158, 349 (1926); U. Dehlinger and L. Graf, *Z. f. Phys.* 64, 359 (1930); A. J. Bradley and A. H. Jay, *Proc. Roy. Soc.* A136, 210 (1932); W. L. Bragg and E. J. Williams, *ibid.* 145A, 699 (1934); A151, 540 (1935); H. A. Bethe, *ibid.* 150A, 552 (1935); R. Peierls, *ibid.* A154, 207 (1936). For a summary and additional references see F. C. Nix and W. Shockley, *Rev. Modern Phys.* 10, 1 (1938).

four unlike atoms.   Other compounds with structures related to
A2 are LaMg$_3$, CeMg$_3$, PrMg$_3$, Fe$_3$Al, Fe$_3$Si, Sb$_2$Tl$_7$, Cu$_2$AlMn,
Cu$_3$Al, Cu$_5$Sn, and the γ-alloys, discussed below.

**53b. The β-Alloys and γ-Alloys. The Significance of the Va-
lence Electron-Atom Ratio.**—It was pointed out by Hume-
Rothery[1] in 1926 that certain intermetallic compounds with
closely related structures but apparently unrelated stoichiometric
composition can be considered to have the same ratio of number
of valence electrons to number of atoms.   For example, the β
phases of the systems Cu—Zn, Cu—Al, and Cu—Sn are analogous in structure, all being based on the A2 arrangement; their
compositions correspond closely to the formulas CuZn, Cu$_3$Al,
and Cu$_5$Sn.   Considering copper to be univalent, zinc bivalent,
aluminum trivalent, and tin quadrivalent, we see that the ratio
of valence electrons to atoms has the value 3/2 for each of these
compounds:

CuZn: $(1 + 2)/2 = 3/2$;
Cu$_3$Al: $(3 + 3)/4 = 3/2$;
Cu$_5$Sn: $(5 + 4)/6 = 3/2$.

Other alloys which may be placed in this class are CuBe, AgZn,
AgCd, AgMg, AuZn, and Ag$_3$Al.

A more striking example is provided by the γ-alloys, the principal representatives of which are Cu$_5$Zn$_8$, Cu$_9$Al$_4$, Cu$_{31}$Sn$_8$, and
Fe$_5$Zn$_{21}$.   The corresponding phases of several other systems are
also known, with ideal compositions Cu$_5$Cd$_8$, Ag$_5$Zn$_8$, Ag$_5$Cd$_8$,
Au$_5$Zn$_8$, Ag$_9$Al$_4$, Cu$_9$Ga$_4$, Ag$_{31}$Sn$_8$, Co$_5$Zn$_{21}$, Ni$_5$Zn$_{21}$, Rh$_5$Zn$_{21}$,
Pd$_5$Zn$_{21}$, Pt$_5$Zn$_{21}$, etc.; in some of these systems the γ phase shows
a wide range of composition about the ideal value.   These crys-
tals are cubic, with fifty-two atoms in the unit of structure
(27×52 for Cu$_{31}$Sn$_8$, corresponding to tripling the value of a_0).
The structure is obtained from the body-centered structure A2
by taking a cube, with edge three times that of the unit for A2,
which contains $3^3 \times 2 = 54$ atoms, removing two atoms, and
displacing the others by small amounts.   The atoms of different
kinds are distributed among the atomic positions in different ways

[1] W. Hume-Rothery, *J. Inst. Metals* **35**, 295 (1926); see also A. F.
Westgren and G. Phragmen, *Z. Metallkunde* **18**, 279 (1926); *Metall-
wirtschaft* **7**, 700 (1928), *Trans. Faraday Soc.* **25**, 379 (1929); W. Hume-
Rothery, "The Metallic State," Oxford, 1931.

for the different stoichiometric compositions given above (see Strukturbericht I, p. 497, III, p. 57).

For the γ-alloys the ratio of valence electrons to atoms has the surprising value 21/13:

Cu_5Zn_8: $(5 + 16)/13 = 21/13$;
Cu_9Al_4: $(9 + 12)/13 = 21/13$;
$Cu_{31}Sn_8$: $(31 + 32)/39 = 21/13$;
Fe_5Zn_{21}: $(0 + 42)/26 = 21/13$.

It is to be noted that Fe, Co, Ni, Rh, Pd, and Pt are assigned zero valence electrons in order that the ratio retain its value.

An interesting theoretical treatment of the stability of the γ-alloys has been carried out by Jones,[1] who has shown that the number of stable orbitals for the γ atomic arrangement is just great enough to accommodate 21/13 valence electrons per atom, with an electron pair occupying each stable orbital. It is significant, as pointed out by Bernal,[2] that the three γ-alloys of ideal composition Cu_5Zn_8, Cu_9Al_4, and $Cu_{31}Sn_8$ are diamagnetic (corresponding to complete pairing of electrons), whereas metals in general show a weak paramagnetism, as discussed above.

53c. Structures Involving Packing of Atoms of Different Sizes. —Several structures reported for intermetallic compounds can be considered to result from the effort to pack together as closely as possible spherical atoms of different sizes, and in this way introduce as many effective metallic bonds as possible.[3] A crystal of this type is $MgZn_2$ (type C14, Strukturbericht I, p. 180), in which zinc has coordination number twelve and magnesium sixteen. The observed interatomic distances are close to those given by Table 51-2; they are Zn—Zn = 2.66 (2.74), Zn—Mg = 3.02 (3.07), and Mg—Mg = 3.17 Å (3.20 Å), the radius sums being given in parentheses. In Al_4Ba (type $D1_3$, Strukturbericht III, p. 45) barium has coordination number twenty, having sixteen aluminum neighbors at 3.47–3.59 Å (3.67 A) and four barium neighbors at 4.53 A (4.48 Å).

Other compounds of metal atoms of different sizes which represent close packing of unlike spheres include MgZn, $MgZn_5$, Cu_2Mg, Au_2Pb, Au_2Bi, $CuAl_2$, and ZrW_2. In general the inter-

---

[1] H. Jones, *Proc. Roy. Soc.* A144, 225 (1934).
[2] J. D. Bernal, *Trans. Faraday Soc.* 25, 367 (1929).
[3] This was pointed out to me some years ago by Dr. J. L. Hoard.

atomic distances in these crystals are close to the corresponding radius sums of Table 51-2, and the bonds may be considered to be normal metallic bonds.

53d. Other Metallic Structures.—Through the efforts of many investigators, including in particular Bradley, Westgren, and Phragmen, many structures of intermetallic compounds other than those described above have been determined by x-ray investigation during the last fifteen years. Some of these are simple; Mg_2Sn, for example, has the fluorite arrangement (CaF_2, C1, Strukturbericht I, p. 148), and SnSb the sodium chloride arrangement. Others are complex, such as $Cu_{15}Si_4$, with sixty copper atoms and sixteen silicon atoms in a cubic unit 9.69 Å on edge ($D8_6$, Strukturbericht III, p. 62). The general principles determining the choice of alternative structures by intermetallic compounds have not yet been formulated. A little progress in systematizing and clarifying the problem has been made, as described above, but the metallic bond remains at present the least satisfactorily understood of the important types of chemical bonds.

54. COMPOUNDS OF METALS WITH BORON, CARBON, AND NITROGEN

Some of the compounds of the metals with boron, carbon, and nitrogen have structures which can be described in a simple way as involving the arrangement of the metal atoms in closest packing or in some other simple structure and the insertion of the small non-metal atoms into interstices of the lattice of metal atoms.[1] AlN, with the wurtzite structure, can be described in this way, the aluminum atoms having a hexagonal closest-packed arrangement with the nitrogen atoms in tetrahedral positions; this crystal can be described as involving covalent bonds between the nitrogen atom and its four aluminum neighbors. ScN, TiN, ZrN, VN, CbN, TiC, ZrC, VC, CbC, and TaC, which have the sodium chloride structure, contain metal atoms in cubic closest packing with nitrogen or carbon atoms in octahedral positions. Since these first-row atoms are restricted to a maximum of four covalent bonds, it is probable that the octahedral coordination of six metal atoms about each light atom involves resonance of covalent bonds among the six positions. The structure of Fe_4N is similar in nature; the iron atoms are in cubic closest packing,

[1] G. Hägg, *Z. f. phys. Chem.* **B6**, 221 (1929); **B12**, 33 (1931).

with nitrogen atoms at the centers of octahedra of six iron atoms (cubic unit, 4Fe at 000, $\frac{1}{2}\frac{1}{2}0$, $\frac{1}{2}0\frac{1}{2}$, $0\frac{1}{2}\frac{1}{2}$; N at $\frac{1}{2}\frac{1}{2}\frac{1}{2}$).

Cementite, Fe_3C, has an interesting structure, involving both octahedral and trigonal-prismatic arrangements of six iron atoms about a carbon atom (Strukturbericht II, p. 33). The iron boride FeB (Strukturbericht III, p. 12) contains trigonal prisms of iron atoms about the boron atoms, the Fe—B distance being about 2.15 Å, which is approximately equal to the sum of the covalent radii. However, each boron atom also has two boron atoms close to it, at 1.77 Å, so that B—B covalent bonds are present in the structure.

The process of forming boron—boron bonds is carried on further in aluminum boride, AlB_2, which has a very simple hexagonal structure, consisting of hexagonal layers of boron atoms,

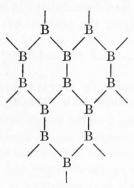

exactly like the layers of carbon atoms in graphite, with aluminum atoms interspersed between the layers.[1] The boron—boron distance is 1.73 Å (Strukturbericht III, p. 28). A structure involving a three-dimensional framework of boron atoms, each with five boron neighbors at 1.72 Å, is shown by CaB_6, LaB_6, and other borides MB_6 (Strukturbericht II, pp. 37, 308; III, p. 334).

---

[1] It is interesting that atoms of alkali metals can be introduced in a similar way between the layers of carbon atoms in graphite to give compounds such as KC_8 and KC_{16}: K. Fredenhagen and G. Cadenbach, *Z. anorg. allgem. Chem.* **158**, 249 (1926); K. Fredenhagen and K. Suck, *ibid.* **178**, 353 (1929); A. Schleede and M. Wellman, *Z. f. phys. Chem.* **B18**, 1 (1932). It has also been reported by W. Rüdorff and U. Hofmann, *Z. anorg. allgem. Chem.* **238**, 1 (1938), that graphite forms compounds such as $C_{24}HSO_4 \cdot 2H_2SO_4$ with sulfuric acid and other acids (perchloric, nitric, selenic, and phosphoric).

55. THE TRANSITION FROM METALLIC TO COVALENT BOND TYPE. THE SYSTEMATIZATION OF SUBSTANCES ON THE BASIS OF STRUCTURE

There are many sequences of related substances which illustrate the transition between bonds of the extreme metallic and the extreme covalent type. In the sequence C(diamond), CSi, Si, Ge, Sn(grey), for example, all with tetrahedral structures, the metallic properties become first noticeable at carborundum and then increase rapidly in significance. Many compounds of the transition metals with non-metallic elements or metalloids, such as pyrite, FeS_2, arsenopyrite, FeAsS, skutterudite, Co_3As_4, etc., to which electronic structures with localized covalent bonds can be assigned, show metallic luster, electronic conductance, and other metallic properties, usually to an extent increasing with increase in the metallic or electropositive character of the constituent elements.

It is of interest that there is little evidence for a direct transition from the extreme ionic type of bond to the metallic type; in every sequence of substances which suggests itself transition from ionic to covalent bond type first occurs, followed by further transition to the metallic type.[1] This provides further support for the concept of the metallic bond as similar in nature to the covalent bond, with added freedom of motion of the electrons. A linear arrangement of substances on the basis of bond type, from extreme ionic through covalent to extreme metallic, might be attempted.[2]

The complete systematization of substances on the basis of bond type is difficult because of the complexity of the problem; it is necessary to describe the bonds of various types which may be present in the structure of a substance, and also their relations to one another, including especially the type of atomic aggregates

---

[1] Silver subfluoride, Ag_2F, may be considered to be a substance intermediate between a salt and a metal. This bright yellow, electrically conducting crystal consists of close packed layers in the sequence ···Ag Ag F Ag Ag F Ag···. The bonds between silver layers are essentially metallic, and those between silver and fluorine layers are ionic-covalent bonds (Strukturbericht I, p. 784; II, p. 276).

[2] Systems of similar type have been suggested, such as that of H. G. Grimm, *Die Naturwiss.* **17**, 535 (1929); *Angew. Chem.* **47**, 53 (1934); etc. Although Grimm's system provides place for substances intermediate between salts and metals, no examples of this type are given.

which result from the action of the bonds.   The number of structures which are possible is very great, and attempts at complete systematization tend to fail because the system becomes so complex as to make it a burden rather than an aid to the student.

It is nevertheless possible to discuss the structure of any substance which has been thoroughly investigated by describing the types and interrelations of its bonds, and in this way to account for its characteristic properties.   As more and more information about the structure of molecules and crystals is gathered, by the application of the available methods of investigation and by the development of new and more powerful methods, we may expect that new structural principles will be discovered and that further progress will be made in the attack on the great problem of bringing order into the field of structural chemistry.

CHAPTER XII

A SUMMARIZING DISCUSSION OF RESONANCE AND ITS SIGNIFICANCE FOR CHEMISTRY

56. THE NATURE OF RESONANCE

Now that we have considered some of the ways in which the idea of resonance has brought clarity and unity into modern structural chemistry, has led to the solution of many problems of valence theory, and has assisted in the correlation of the chemical properties of substances with the information obtained about the structure of their molecules by physical methods, we may well inquire again into the nature of the phenomenon of resonance.[1]

The goal of the structural investigation of a system is the description of the system in terms of simpler entities. This description may be divided into two parts, the first relating to the material particles or bodies of which the system is considered to be composed, and the second to the ways in which these particles or bodies are interrelated; that is, to their interactions and interconnections. In describing a system it is usually convenient to resolve it first into the next simpler parts, rather than into its ultimate constituents, and then to carry the resolution farther and farther in steps. We are thoroughly accustomed to this way of describing the material constitution of substances. The use of the concept of resonance permits the extension of the procedure to include the discussion not only of the next simpler constituent bodies but also of their interactions. Thus the material description of the benzene molecule as containing carbon and hydrogen atoms, which themselves contain electrons and nuclei, is amplified with use of the resonance concept in the following way: the structure of the normal benzene molecule corresponds to resonance

---

[1] An interesting discussion of resonance is given in the introduction of "The Organic Chemistry of Nitrogen," N. V. Sidgwick, T. W. J. Taylor, and W. Baker, Oxford, 1937. The concept of resonance is extensively used in this book, which gives a modern and thorough treatment of an important branch of organic chemistry.

between the two Kekulé structures, with smaller contributions by other valence-bond structures, and the molecule is stabilized and its other properties are changed somewhat by this resonance from those expected for either Kekulé structure alone; each Kekulé structure consists of a certain distribution of single and double bonds, with essentially the properties associated with these bonds in other molecules; each bond represents a type of interaction between atoms which can be discussed in terms of the resonance between structures differing in the interchange of electrons between atomic orbitals.

It was pointed out in Chapter I that the selection of the primary structures for the discussion of any particular case of quantum-mechanical resonance is arbitrary, but that this arbitrariness (which has an analogue in the classical resonance phenomenon) does not impair the value of the concept of resonance.

57. THE RELATION BETWEEN RESONANCE AND TAUTOMERISM

There is no sharp distinction which can be made between tautomerism and resonance; but it is convenient in practice to make a distinction between the two which is applicable to all except the border-line cases.

Tautomers are defined as isomers which are readily interconvertible. It is clear that the distinction between tautomerism and ordinary isomerism is very vague indeed, and that it depends on the interpretation of the adverb "readily." It is customary to designate as tautomers those isomers whose half-lives (with respect to interconversion) are under ordinary circumstances less than the times required for laboratory operations to be carried out (some minutes or hours), so that the separation of the isomers from the equilibrium mixtures is difficult. The distinction between tautomers and ordinary isomers has no molecular significance whatever, since it is dependent on the accidental ordinary rate of human activity.

It is possible, on the other hand, to define tautomerism and electronic resonance in a way which gives structural significance to them individually.

Let us consider as a definite example a benzene molecule, which may have different substituent groups in the 1, 2, ⋯ , 6 positions. The nuclei of the molecule vibrate relative to one another in a way which is determined by the electronic energy function for nuclear configurations.[1] For most molecules this electronic energy function is such that there is one most stable nuclear configuration, about which the nuclei carry out small vibrations, with amplitudes of about 0.1 Å. If the molecule can be assigned a single valence-bond structure, the nature of this equilibrium configuration can be predicted by the rules of stereochemistry. Thus for tetramethylethylene the expected configuration is

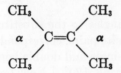

with the angle α equal to about 110° (close to the tetrahedral angle 109°28′). This has been verified experimentally. In benzene, however, there is resonance between the two valence-bond structures ⬡ ‖ (I) and ⬡ ‖ (II). This resonance is so rapid that its frequency (the resonance energy divided by Planck's constant h) is a thousand-fold greater than the frequency of nuclear vibration, so that resonance between the Kekulé structures occurs in the time required for the nuclei to move an inappreciable distance (0.0001 Å). Hence the effective electronic energy function determining the nuclear configuration is not that for either Kekulé structure, but instead that corresponding to the Kekulé resonance. Since the predicted stable configurations for the two Kekulé structures do not differ greatly, there is an intermediate configuration which is the stable equilibrium configuration for the actual resonating molecule. This is the hexagonal coplanar configuration with 120° bond angles.

Now the magnitude of the resonance integral, which determines the resonance energy and the resonance frequency, depends on the nature of the structures involved. In benzene it is large (about 36 kcal./mole); but it might have been much smaller. Let us consider what the benzene molecule would be like if the value of the resonance integral were very small, so that the resonance frequency were less than the frequency of nuclear

---

[1] "Introduction to Quantum Mechanics," Chap. X.

oscillation. For each nuclear configuration there would be more or less electronic resonance of the Kekulé type. We may discuss three nuclear configurations, *a*, *b*, and *c*.

a   *b*   *c*

In *a* and *c* the bond angles to the substituent groups approach 110° and 125° in alternate pairs, corresponding to the tetrahedral model for alternating single and double bonds in the ring, and in *b* the bond angles are all 120°. Now for configuration *a* the valence-bond structure I is stable, whereas structure II is unstable because of the strain involved in the bond angles. Since the resonance integral is assumed to be small in value, this energy difference would cause structure II to be unimportant. The normal electronic state of the molecule would be represented for this nuclear configuration essentially by Kekulé structure I alone, with only a negligible amount of resonance with structure II.

Similarly for configuration *c* structure II alone would be of significance.

The intermediate configuration *b* would involve complete resonance between I and II. Since the resonance energy is assumed to be very small, and this configuration corresponds to bond-angle strain for both I and II, the configuration would be less stable than *a* or *c*.

This hypothetical benzene molecule would accordingly oscillate for some time about the configuration *a*, with essentially the valence-bond structure I; it might then pass through the configuration *b*, with resonance to structure II becoming complete, and then oscillate for some time about configuration *c*, with essentially the valence-bond structure II.

The chemical properties of this hypothetical benzene would be just those expected for the valence-bond structures I and II, and, indeed, the substance would be correctly described as **a** mixture of these two isomers or tautomers.

It is evident that we may define tautomerism and resonance in the following reasonable way: *When the magnitudes of the electronic resonance integral (or integrals) and of the other factors determining the electronic energy function of a molecule are such that there are two or more well-defined stable nuclear equilibrium configurations, we refer to the molecule as capable of existing in tautomeric forms; when there is only one well-defined stable nuclear equilibrium configuration, and the electronic state is not satisfactorily represented by a single valence-bond structure, we refer to the molecule as a resonating molecule.*

This may be expressed somewhat more loosely by saying that, whereas a tautomeric substance is a mixture of two types of molecules, differing in configuration, in general the molecules of a substance showing electronic resonance are all alike in configuration and structure.

Each of the tautomeric forms of a substance may show electronic resonance; tautomerism and resonance are not mutually exclusive. Let us discuss 5-methylpyrazole as an example. This substance exists in two tautomeric forms, A and B, differing in the position of the N-hydrogen atom.

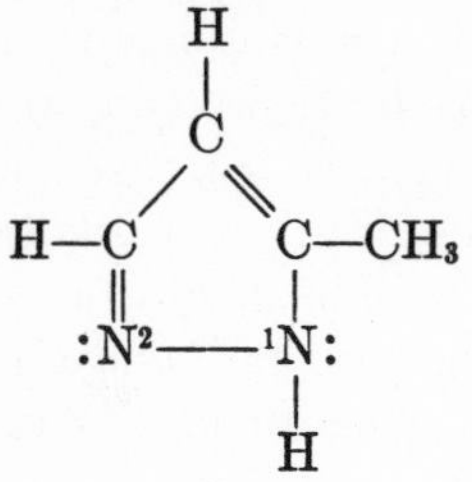

A 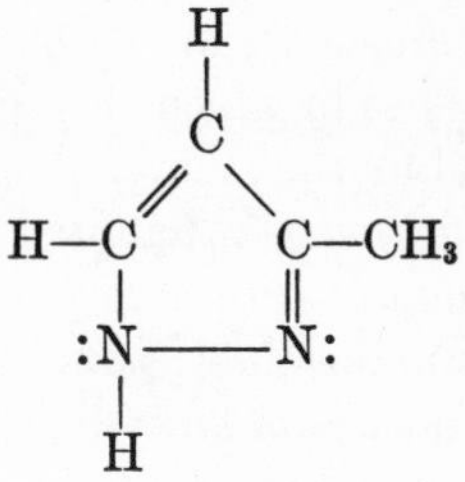   B

Each of these tautomers in its normal state is represented not by the conventional valence-bond structure shown above, but by a resonance hybrid of this structure and others. For tautomer A, with the hydrogen atom attached to the nitrogen atom 1, the principal resonance is between structures A I and A II, with A I the more important; smaller contributions are made also by other structures such as A III. Similar resonance occurs for tautomer B. Thus for both tautomers the principal resonance

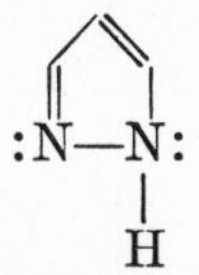

A I 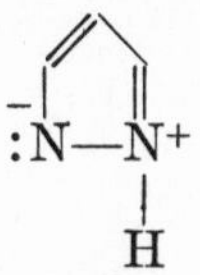   A II 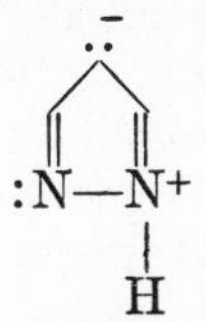   A III is between valence-bond structures I ⌂ . and II . ⌂ ,

with I the more important for A and II for B; but it is not correct (according to our conventional nomenclature regarding electronic resonance) to say that methylpyrazole resonates between the structures

$$\begin{array}{ccc} & CH & \\ CH & & CCH_3 \\ N & \!\!\!\!\!\!\!\! & NH \end{array} \qquad \text{and} \qquad \begin{array}{ccc} & CH & \\ CH & & CCH_3 \\ HN & \!\!\!\!\!\!\!\! & N \end{array}.$$

58. THE REALITY OF THE CONSTITUENT STRUCTURES OF A RESONATING SYSTEM

It is often asked whether or not the constituent structures of a resonating system, such as the Kekulé structures for the benzene molecule, are to be considered as having reality. There is one sense in which this question may be answered in the affirmative; but the answer is definitely negative if the usual chemical significance is attributed to the structures. *A substance showing resonance between two or more valence-bond structures does not contain molecules with the configurations and properties usually associated with these structures.* The constituent structures of the resonance hybrid do not have reality in this sense.

The question may also be discussed in a different way. The stable equilibrium configuration of the nuclei of a benzene molecule is not that appropriate to either of the two Kekulé structures, but is the intermediate hexagonal configuration. The valence-bond structures I and II are hence to be interpreted as being

somewhat different from those for non-resonating molecules; they mean that the electronic motion is that corresponding to alternating single and double bonds, but with the equilibrium internuclear distances constant (1.39 Å), rather than alternating between 1.54 Å and 1.33 Å. The electronic wave function for the normal benzene molecule can be composed of terms corresponding to the Kekulé structures I and II, plus some additional terms; hence, according to the fundamental ideas of quantum mechanics, *if it were possible to carry out an experimental test of the electronic structure which would identify structure I or structure II, each structure would be found for the molecule to the extent determined by the wave function.* The difficulty for benzene and for other molecules showing electronic resonance is to devise an experimental test which could be carried out quickly enough and which would distinguish among the structures under discussion. In benzene the frequency of Kekulé resonance is only a little less than the frequency of the bonding resonance of electron pairs, so that the time required for the experiment is closely limited.

Most methods of testing bond type involve the motion of nuclei. The chemical method, such as substitution at positions adjacent to a hydroxyl group in testing for double-bond character, as used in the Mills-Nixon studies, is one of these. This method gives only the resultant bond type over the period required for the reaction to take place. Since this period is much longer than that of ordinary electronic resonance, the chemical method cannot be used in general to identify the constituent structures of a resonating molecule. Only in case that the resonance frequency is very small (less than the frequencies of nuclear vibration) can the usual methods be applied to identify the constituent structures; and in this case the boundary between resonance and tautomerism is approached or passed.

The foregoing statement is not to be construed as meaning that chemical methods, as well as physical methods, cannot be used as the basis for inference regarding the nature of resonating structures. This inference is based on the resultant bond type, and not on the direct identification of individual structures.

59. THE FUTURE DEVELOPMENT AND APPLICATION OF THE CONCEPT OF RESONANCE

When we compare our present knowledge of structural chemistry with that of ten years ago and become cognizant of the extent to which clarity has been brought into this field of knowledge by the extensive application of the concept of resonance we are tempted to speculate about the future development of this concept and the nature of the further applications of it which may be made.

The applications of the idea of resonance which have been made during the last decade are in the main qualitative in nature. This represents only the first step, which should be followed by more refined treatments with quantitative significance. Some rough quantitative considerations, such as those regarding interatomic distances, the partial ionic character of bonds, and the energy of resonance of molecules among several valence-bond structures, have been described in the preceding chapters of this book; these, however, deal with only small portions of the broad field of structural chemistry. The ultimate goal, a theory permitting the quantitative prediction of the structure and properties of molecules, is still very far away.

In this book the discussion has been restricted to the structure of the normal states of molecules, with little reference to the great part of chemistry dealing with the mechanisms and rates of chemical reactions. It seems probable that the concept of resonance can be applied very effectively in this field. The "activated complexes" which represent intermediate stages in chemical reactions are, almost without exception, unstable molecules which resonate among several valence-bond structures. Thus, according to the theory of Lewis, Olson, and Polanyi, Walden inversion occurs in the hydrolysis of an alkyl halide by the following mechanism:

$$\text{HO}^- + \text{R}_1\overset{\displaystyle\text{H}}{-}\text{C}-\text{I} \qquad \text{HO}--\overset{\displaystyle\text{H}}{\text{C}}--\text{I} \qquad \text{HO}-\overset{\displaystyle\text{H}}{\text{C}}-\text{R}_1 + \text{I}^-.$$

The activated complex can be described as involving resonance of the fourth bond of carbon between the hydroxyl and iodine ions. Some very interesting rough quantum-mechanical calculations bearing on the theory of chemical reactions have been made of Eyring and Polanyi and their collaborators. It is to be hoped that the quantitative treatments can be made more precise and more reliable; but before this can be done effectively there must take place the extensive development of the qualitative theory of chemical reactions, probably in terms of resonance.

So far only a start has been made (mainly by G. E. K. Branch and G. Schwarzenbach) on the problem of correlating the acidity or basicity of a substance with its resonating electronic structure.

It should be possible to develop the theory of molecular structure to such an extent as to permit the reliable prediction of the behavior of substances with respect to this property and other physical and chemical properties.

The color of organic dyes is obviously closely connected with resonance.[1] Recent experimental work, especially that of Schwarzenbach and Michaelis, shows more and more clearly how close this connection is; and, although there exists now no real theory of color, we may look forward to seeing the development of one on the basis of resonance, probably during the next decade.

Among the most interesting problems of science are those of the structure and properties of substances of biological importance. I have little doubt that in this field resonance and the hydrogen bond are of great significance, and that these two structural features will be found to play an important part in such physiological phenomena as the contraction of muscle and the transmission of impulses along nerves and in the brain. A conjugated system provides the only way of transmitting an effect from one end to another of a long molecule; and the hydrogen bond is the only strong and directed intermolecular interaction which can come into operation quickly. It will be many years before our understanding of molecular structure becomes great enough to encompass in detail such substances as the proteins, with highly specific properties (such as those shown by antibodies) which must be attributed to their possession of well-defined and complex molecular structures; but the attack on these substances by the methods of modern structural chemistry can be begun now, and it is my belief that this attack will ultimately be successful.

[1] C. R. Bury, *J.A.C.S.* 57, 2115 (1935); L. Pauling, Chapter 22 of Gilman's "Organic Chemistry," John Wiley and Sons, New York, 1938. Significant progress in the attack on this problem has been made during 1939: L. Pauling, *Proc. Nat. Acad. Sci.* 25, 577 (1939); G. N. Lewis and M. Calvin, *Chem. Rev.* 25, 273 (1939); T. Förster, *Angew. Chem.* 52, 223 (1939) An interesting discussion of the effect of resonance on the ultraviolet absorption spectra of substituted benzenes has been given by A. L. Sklar, *J. Chem. Phys.* 7, 984 (1939).

INDEX OF NAMES

INDEX OF NAMES

INDEX OF SUBJECTS

INDEX OF SUBJECTS

effect of resonance on, 171ff, 195f
of hydrogen, 166, 168
of manganese, 186f
for multiple bonds, 168f
observed values of, 161ff, 165f,
  167f, 181, 183ff, 187
octahedral, 1, 181f, 184
relation to atomic number, 166f
square, 185f
tables of, 164, 179, 182, 184
tetrahedral, 178ff
Covalent nitrates, 209f
Crystal ionic radii, 343ff
and atomic number, 347f
effect of coordination number,
  367ff
observed values of, 350, 352, 354,
  358, 365, 370
tables of, 346, 350
Crystal potential energy, 337ff, 340
of alkali halides, 341, 362
and radius ratio, 362
Crystal structure, of metals, 409
relation to radius ratio, 370ff, 383
Cubic closest packing, 372f
Curie constant, 113
Cyameluric acid, 224ff
Cyanide complexes, 254f
Cyanides, 75, 198f, 294
Cyanogen, 223
Cyanuric derivatives, 224f
Cyclopentadiene, 218

Danburite, 400
Deformation, of electron shells, 22f
of ions, 362
Diacetone alcohol, 327
Diacetylene, 223
2,4-Diacetylresorcinol, 331f
4,6-Diacetylresorcinol, 331f
Dialkyl carbonates, 138
Diamagnetism, 112f
Di-p-anisyl nitric oxide, 275f
Diaspore, crystal structure of, 312f
Dibenzyl, 218
Diborane, 259f
3,6-Dibromo-2,5-dihydroxydiethyl-
  terephthalate, 330f
Dielectric constant, of ice, 302
relation to hydrogen bond, 292ff
1,8-Dihydroxyanthraquinone, 329
2,6-Dihydroxybenzoic acid, 309,
  328
2,2'-Dihydroxybenzophenone, 329
Diketopiperazine, crystal structure
  of, 190, 193, 315
o-Diphenylbenzene, 219
p-Diphenylbenzene, 218f
1,2-Diphenylethane, 155f
Dipole moment, electric, of alkyl
  derivatives, 153f

of aryl derivatives, 153f
effect of resonance on, 127, 153f
and electronegativity, 67ff
and hydrogen bond, 292ff
of hydrogen halides, 46
and inhibited resonance, 221f
of multiple bonds, 75
and partial ionic character, 46,
  69, 75
Dipole moment, magnetic, 21, 112f
of ions of the iron-group, 113ff
of hydrocarbon free radicals, 156f
of manganese, 186
of octahedral complexes, 115ff
of oxygen, 273
of palladium-group complexes,
  116
of platinum-group complexes,
  116
relation to unpaired electrons, 21,
  113
of square complexes, 118ff
of tetrahedral complexes, 118ff
Dipyridyl group, 280f
Dithionate ion, 246
Double hexagonal closest packing
  377ff
Double repulsion, 352f
effect on crystal properties, 359ff
quantitative treatment of, 355ff

Electric dipole moment, see dipole
  moment, electric
Electron affinities, of the halogens,
  341f
relation to electronegativity, 66f
Electron shells, 24ff
Electron spin, 21
pairing of, 21
Electronegativity, of atoms, 58ff
and dipole moments of bonds, 68
effect of electric charge on, 65
and hydrogen bond formation,
  287f
and metallic character, 69
and partial ionic bonds, 69ff
relation to other properties, 66ff
tables of, 60, 64f
thermochemical interpretation of,
  61f
Electronic distribution, in atoms,
  12
in hydrogen atom, 13
in hydrogen molecule-ion, 17
in ions, 335f
in rubidium ion, 29f
Electrostatic bond, 3f
Electrostatic valence rule, 384ff
and acid strengths 395
and stability of shared polyhedra,
  395